How life of author D to story
Personal experience to experience
of Peasant. Marcy
Comparision of Plate of
Youth vs age
3 generation conflict
Intellect outcast
Reuneal of forgotten heroes
Humanity in penal Institutions
Jody Peasant marcy
developement of understanding

Read Clay
Write Theme

32

Stan
Fa 7 2275

Gail
Fa 7 2346

Elenor
P 4 5558

english
exam

Phil
Sp 6 4119

403

SHORT STORIES FOR STUDY

SHORT STORIES
for STUDY

AN ANTHOLOGY

by RAYMOND W. SHORT

Hofstra College

and RICHARD B. SEWALL

Yale University

THIRD EDITION

HENRY HOLT AND COMPANY New York

CONTENTS

ACKNOWLEDGMENTS

The editors are grateful to authors and publishers for permission to include in this volume the following stories:

Stella Benson, "Story Coldly Told," from *Collected Short Stories,* 1936, copyright, Curtis Brown, Ltd.

Erskine Caldwell, "Daughter," from *Jackpot,* copyright, 1940, by Erskine Caldwell; by permission of Duell, Sloan & Pearce, Inc.

Anton Chekhov, "Gooseberries," from *A Treasury of Great Russian Short Stories,* edited by Avrahm Yarmolinsky; copyright, 1944, by The Macmillan Company and used with their permission.

Samuel Langhorne Clemens (Mark Twain), "The Man That Corrupted Hadleyburg," from *The Man That Corrupted Hadleyburg and Other Stories,* copyright 1900, by Olivia L. Clemens; copyright 1928, by Clara Clemens Gabrilowitsch. By permission of Harper and Brothers.

Joseph Conrad, "Heart of Darkness," from *Youth and Two Other Stories,* copyright 1903 and 1925, by Doubleday, Doran and Company, Inc.

Fyodor Dostoevsky, "The Peasant Marey," from *A Treasury of Great Russian Short Stories,* edited by Avrahm Yarmolinsky; copyright, 1944, by The Macmillan Company and used with their permission.

William Fain, "Harmony." Reprinted by permission. Copyright 1955 The New Yorker Magazine, Inc.

William Faulkner, "The Bear," copyright, 1942, by Curtis Publishing Company. Reprinted by permission of Harold Ober Associates.

Jean Giono, "The Corn Dies," from *Modern French Stories,* edited by John Lehmann and published by New Directions.

Thomas Hardy, "The Three Strangers," from *Wessex Tales,* copyright by Harper and Brothers.

Nathaniel Hawthorne, "Mr. Higginbotham's Catastrophe," from *Twice-Told Tales,* used by permission of Houghton Mifflin.

Ernest Hemingway, "In Another Country," from *The Fifth Column, and the First Forty-nine Stories,* copyright, 1938, by Charles Scribner's Sons; used by permission of the publishers.

Henry James, "The Pupil," reprinted from Volume II of The New York Edition of *The Novels and Tales of Henry James;* copyright, 1908, by Charles Scribner's Sons; 1936 by Henry James; used by permission of the publishers.

James Joyce, "Clay," from *Dubliners,* by permission of The Viking Press, Inc.

Franz Kafka, "The Great Wall of China," from *The Great Wall of China: Stories and Reflections,* copyright, 1946, Schocken Books Inc.

Thomas Mann, "Mario and the Magician," from *Stories of Three Decades,* copyright, 1936, Alfred A. Knopf, Inc.

Katherine Mansfield, "A Dill Pickle," from *The Short Stories of Katherine Mansfield,* copyright, 1937, Alfred A. Knopf, Inc.

Frank O'Connor, "Mac's Masterpiece," from *The London Mercury,* 1938.

Allan Seager, "This Town and Salamanca," from *Story Magazine,* copyright, 1934, by Story Magazine.

John Steinbeck, "The Leader of the People," from *The Long Valley,* copyright, 1938, by John Steinbeck; by permission of The Viking Press, Inc.

Dylan Thomas, "A Story," from *Quite Early One Morning,* copyright 1954 by New Directions.

INTRODUCTION

To be beautiful, a living organism, or any other individual thing made up of parts, must possess not only an orderly arrangement of these parts, but also a proper magnitude; for beauty depends upon these two qualities, size and order. Hence an extremely minute creature cannot be beautiful to us; for we see the whole in an almost infinitesimal moment of time, and lose the pleasure that comes from a distinct perception of order in the parts. Nor could a creature of vast dimensions be beautiful to us—a beast, say, one thousand miles in length; for in that case the eye could not take all of the object in at once—we should see the parts, but not the unity of the whole.—Aristotle.

THE STORIES in this volume have been chosen by the editors because each of them represents a serious artistic achievement. Arranged roughly in order of length and complexity, they lend themselves, we believe, to a singularly fruitful method of teaching literature. This method may be described in terms of Aristotle's interlocking principles of size and order.

A work of art is an ordered structure, appealing strongly to the same instinct in us that delights in other intricate but well-composed structures, when we find them in nature or in systems of abstract values. Into this structure the various parts are introduced with a due sense of their relation to the whole; and it is by this means that the matters to be transmitted become significant and impressive. A work of art, it is true, may be more than framework; or to put it differently, a work of art may involve in its framework materials of greater value than those involved in other systems; but an ill-formed work of art, however noble or exquisite its individual members may be, generally lacks not only the intellectual but the emotional effectiveness of a work of surer design.

This structural quality in art is especially important to the teacher of literature, who must always be asking himself this question: for how much of a given literary experience can I successfully act as agent? Aristotle's statement suggests a reassuring approach to this question. A full comprehension of the whole work must include a perception of the order in its parts. The relations of parts to a whole can be explored by the teacher of English as well as by the teacher of geometry, and with as much profit to the student, even though the parts of literature may be less conveniently isolated than the parts in a geometrical proposition.

Such an approach to teaching must not be regarded as a surrender to mere mechanical exercises, for it is anything but that. Words, metaphors, images, and narrative devices may seem to invite a purely technical investigation, for such matters are obviously among the parts of a literary whole. But no less so are human emotions, attitudes, morals, and ideas. These matters, even more than the others, must be dealt with in their relation to their context, if we believe that one important obligation of the teacher or critic of literature is to deal with the organic nature of his subject. Certainly the "technical" parts must be studied with painstaking care, but for this reason and from this point of view, that each part, every image, minor character, or sentence of description, embodies some purpose bearing upon the rest of the organism.

Such a way of discussing literature with students is not the easiest teaching procedure. Obviously it produces few neat outlines or diagrams to be transferred from blackboard to notebook. The teacher finds he has little time on his hands to devote to such subjects as "Samuel Langhorne Clemens and American Realism" or "Ernest Hemingway and the Lost Generation." And he will find it easier to frame examination questions about the lives of authors than about their works, or about their works as moral, social, or historical essays, than about their works as works of art, objectified whole experiences. Yet the approach of which we are speaking has a value to the student that outweighs the difficulties it imposes upon the teacher. It furnishes a direct method of assisting students toward a successful reading of more difficult texts than they have yet mastered.

When we come actually to apply Aristotle's concept of the organic nature of art to the formation of a course in literature, we recognize the importance of his emphasis upon magnitude, since successful reading requires that the mind apprehend not only the parts but the wholeness of the work of art. Nor is it a question of size alone, for the "distinct perception of order in the parts" depends also upon the intricacy of the whole. A whole of many parts, intricately patterned, requires more effort in return for its promise of pleasure than does a simpler structure, even though they may be the same in size. Though about the same in length, "The Bear" by William Faulkner is more difficult to apprehend than "The Three Strangers" by Thomas Hardy.

Neither magnitude nor complexity, however, can be measured by a constant standard. In practice, readers differ greatly in their ability to perceive order in the minute and unity in the vast. One's progress in successful reading starts with small, simple units and embraces increasingly more difficult forms. A person tackling literature much beyond his ability to grasp does not read it, in the sense of which we have been talking, but rather makes excerpts from it. Parts and groups of parts register on his mind, but not the whole. These parts may register with great clarity, so that in any discussion confined to them the reader will seem to have mastered the work; events of plot and vigorously drawn characters are usually thus grasped. Only a very bad reader will fail to get a sharp impression of the blinding of Gloucester, Father Mapple's sermon in *Moby Dick,* or of Polonius, little Pearl, and Caliban; but only a very good one will have sensed their full importance to the works in which they occur. Commonly the unprepared reader reduces a difficult text to shorthand notes, which he may attempt to connect or summarize in some trite, inadequate axiom, often of an ethical kind. Perhaps it is partly to overcome the feeling of frustration caused by incomplete reading that so many readers cast about for some ready summary of a difficult text. These summaries seem to grow shorter as the works themselves become more complex. The parts of *Lear,* for example, are made to equal "filial ingratitude," and *Hamlet* becomes a "study of procrastination."

The short story is an admirable form to present to students early in a course aiming to increase the power of reading. It is of a magnitude convenient to this purpose. Most short stories can be read at a sitting, and the carefully restricted number of parts retained in the mind with the clarity necessary for an apprehension of their function in the whole. Though the organization of a good short story is relatively simple, as compared with the organization of some even shorter forms, such as the lyric, it is necessarily efficient and economical. The temptation to make excerpts, to reduce to a précis, to extract adages, may easily be overcome. One can demonstrate how hard, how nearly impossible, it is to say in other words what James Joyce's "Clay," for example, is about. Such statements as "Maria's kindliness is loved by everyone," or "Kindliness like Maria's is a wonderful quality," are quite inadequate; it can quickly be shown that they ignore the function in the whole of such details as brother Alphy, Maria's blunders, and the incident of the clay. Poorly read,

"Clay" gives the effect of confused sentimental tenderness; successfully read, it also creates an effect of tenderness, but tenderness of a clear, searching, and anything but sentimental kind. By perceiving the relevancy of all the parts, and by realizing that Joyce intended all that he said (Joe is not *either* soft or hard, but *both* soft and hard), one can advance from an acceptance of the first, incomplete effect to an enjoyment of the second, full effect.

Successful reading is an experience very like many of the experiences we derive from life. It has a fullness of meaning that may defy a quick summary or paraphrase; a moral may be involved that is too intricate to express in simple tags of good and bad; attitudes may be expressed that modify or extend the attitudes we already harbor. Such reading sharpens the mind, but perhaps more important than that, it refines the sensibilities and enlarges the domain in which they are at home. A course in reading should aim to secure an efficient response to books concerned with increasingly subtler ideas, wider moral problems, and richer human associations.

These are the considerations that have dictated the choice of stories and their arrangement in this volume. The contents range from relatively short, simple stories to stories of considerable difficulty, not in any rigidly controlled progression, for that would be impossible. Difficulty may arise from diction, from proportions of implicit to explicit, and from the level of profundity or complexity at which the subjects are presented. A story like "Harmony" is among the simplest in diction, but nevertheless somewhat difficult because all of its goals are implicit. The same reader may o'erperch "The Great Wall of China" with a bound, but puzzle long and hard over Joyce's little cameo, "Clay." Yet, all aware of these considerations, the editors have tried to order the contents in a general march from simple to complex, from brief to extensive.

SHORT STORIES FOR STUDY

THE LEADER OF THE PEOPLE

by JOHN STEINBECK

ON SATURDAY afternoon Billy Buck, the ranch-hand, raked together the last of the old year's haystack and pitched small forkfuls over the wire fence to a few mildly interested cattle. High in the air small clouds like puffs of cannon smoke were driven eastward by the March wind. The wind could be heard whishing in the brush on the ridge crests, but no breath of it penetrated down into the ranch-cup.

The little boy, Jody, emerged from the house eating a thick piece of buttered bread. He saw Billy working on the last of the haystack. Jody tramped down scuffing his shoes in a way he had been told was destructive to good shoe-leather. A flock of white pigeons flew out of the black cypress tree as Jody passed, and circled the tree and landed again. A half-grown tortoise-shell cat leaped from the bunkhouse porch, galloped on stiff legs across the road, whirled and galloped back again. Jody picked up a stone to help the game along, but he was too late, for the cat was under the porch before the stone could be discharged. He threw the stone into the cypress tree and started the white pigeons on another whirling flight.

Arriving at the used-up haystack, the boy leaned against the barbed wire fence. "Will that be all of it, do you think?" he asked.

The middle-aged ranch-hand stopped his careful raking and stuck his fork into the ground. He took off his black hat and smoothed down his hair. "Nothing left of it that isn't soggy from ground moisture," he said. He replaced his hat and rubbed his dry leathery hands together.

"Ought to be plenty mice," Jody suggested.

"Lousy with them," said Billy. "Just crawling with mice."

"Well, maybe, when you get all through, I could call the dogs and hunt the mice."

"Sure, I guess you could," said Billy Buck. He lifted a forkful of the damp ground-hay and threw it into the air. Instantly three mice leaped out and burrowed frantically under the hay again.

Jody sighed with satisfaction. Those plump, sleek, arrogant mice were doomed. For eight months they had lived and multiplied in the haystack. They had been immune from cats, from traps, from poison and from Jody. They had grown smug in their security, overbearing and fat. Now the time of disaster had come; they would not survive another day.

Billy looked up at the top of the hills that surrounded the ranch. "Maybe you better ask your father before you do it," he suggested.

"Well, where is he? I'll ask him now."

"He rode up to the ridge ranch after dinner. He'll be back pretty soon."

Jody slumped against the fence post. "I don't think he'd care."

As Billy went back to his work he said ominously, "You'd better ask him anyway. You know how he is."

Jody did know. His father, Carl Tiflin, insisted upon giving permission for anything that was done on the ranch, whether it was important or not. Jody sagged farther against the post until he was sitting on the ground. He looked up at the little puffs of wind-driven cloud. "Is it like to rain, Billy?"

"It might. The wind's good for it, but not strong enough."

"Well, I hope it don't rain until after I kill those damn mice."
He looked over his shoulder to see whether Billy had noticed
the mature profanity. Billy worked on without comment.

Jody turned back and looked at the side-hill where the road
from the outside world came down. The hill was washed with
lean March sunshine. Silver thistles, blue lupins and a few
poppies bloomed among the sage bushes. Halfway up the hill
Jody could see Doubletree Mutt, the black dog, digging in a
squirrel hole. He paddled for a while and then paused to
kick bursts of dirt out between his hind legs, and he dug with
an earnestness which belied the knowledge he must have had
that no dog had ever caught a squirrel by digging in a hole.

Suddenly, while Jody watched, the black dog stiffened, and
backed out of the hole and looked up the hill toward the cleft
in the ridge where the road came through. Jody looked up too.
For a moment Carl Tiflin on horseback stood out against the
pale sky and then he moved down the road toward the house.
He carried something white in his hand.

The boy started to his feet. "He's got a letter," Jody cried.
He trotted away toward the ranch house, for the letter would
probably be read aloud and he wanted to be there. He reached
the house before his father did, and ran in. He heard Carl
dismount from his creaking saddle and slap the horse on the
side to send it to the barn where Billy would unsaddle it and
turn it out.

Jody ran into the kitchen. "We got a letter!" he cried.

His mother looked up from a pan of beans. "Who has?"

"Father has. I saw it in his hand."

Carl strode into the kitchen then, and Jody's mother asked,
"Who's the letter from, Carl?"

He frowned quickly. "How did you know there was a letter?"

She nodded her head in the boy's direction. "Big-Britches Jody told me."

Jody was embarrassed.

His father looked down at him contemptuously. "He *is* getting to be a Big-Britches," Carl said. "He's minding everybody's business but his own. Got his big nose into everything."

Mrs. Tiflin relented a little. "Well, he hasn't enough to keep him busy. Who's the letter from?"

Carl still frowned on Jody. "I'll keep him busy if he isn't careful." He held out a sealed letter. "I guess it's from your father."

Mrs. Tiflin took a hairpin from her head and slit open the flap. Her lips pursed judiciously. Jody saw her eyes snap back and forth over the lines. "He says," she translated, "he says he's going to drive out Saturday to stay for a little while. Why, this is Saturday. The letter must have been delayed." She looked at the postmark. "This was mailed day before yesterday. It should have been here yesterday." She looked up questioningly at her husband, and then her face darkened angrily. "Now what have you got that look on you for? He doesn't come often."

Carl turned his eyes away from her anger. He could be stern with her most of the time, but when occasionally her temper arose, he could not combat it.

"What's the matter with you?" she demanded again.

In his explanation there was a tone of apology Jody himself might have used. "It's just that he talks," Carl said lamely. "Just talks."

"Well, what of it? You talk yourself."

"Sure I do. But your father only talks about one thing."

"Indians!" Jody broke in excitedly. "Indians and crossing the plains!"

Carl turned fiercely on him. "You get out, Mr. Big-Britches! Go on, now! Get out!"

Jody went miserably out the back door and closed the screen with elaborate quietness. Under the kitchen window his shamed, downcast eyes fell upon a curiously shaped stone, a stone of such fascination that he squatted down and picked it up and turned it over in his hands.

The voices came clearly to him through the open kitchen window. "Jody's damn well right," he heard his father say. "Just Indians and crossing the plains. I've heard that story about how the horses got driven off about a thousand times. He just goes on and on, and he never changes a word in the things he tells."

When Mrs. Tiflin answered her tone was so changed that Jody, outside the window, looked up from his study of the stone. Her voice had become soft and explanatory. Jody knew how her face would have changed to match the tone. She said quietly, "Look at it this way, Carl. That was the big thing in my father's life. He led a wagon train clear across the plains to the coast, and when it was finished, his life was done. It was a big thing to do, but it didn't last long enough. Look!" she continued, "it's as though he was born to do that, and after he finished it, there wasn't anything more for him to do but think about it and talk about it. If there'd been any farther west to go, he'd have gone. He's told me so himself. But at last there was the ocean. He lives right by the ocean where he had to stop."

She had caught Carl, caught him and entangled him in her soft tone.

"I've seen him," he agreed quietly. "He goes down and stares off west over the ocean." His voice sharpened a little. "And then he goes up to the Horseshoe Club in Pacific Grove, and he tells people how the Indians drove off the horses."

She tried to catch him again. "Well, it's everything to him. You might be patient with him and pretend to listen."

Carl turned impatiently away. "Well, if it gets too bad, I can always go down to the bunkhouse and sit with Billy," he said irritably. He walked through the house and slammed the front door after him.

Jody ran to his chores. He dumped the grain to the chickens without chasing any of them. He gathered the eggs from the nests. He trotted into the house with the wood and interlaced it so carefully in the wood-box that two armloads seemed to fill it to overflowing.

His mother had finished the beans by now. She stirred up the fire and brushed off the stove-top with a turkey wing. Jody peered cautiously at her to see whether any rancor toward him remained. "Is he coming today?" Jody asked.

"That's what his letter said."

"Maybe I better walk up the road to meet him."

Mrs. Tiflin clanged the stove-lid shut. "That would be nice," she said. "He'd probably like to be met."

"I guess I'll just do it then."

Outside, Jody whistled shrilly to the dogs. "Come on up the hill," he commanded. The two dogs waved their tails and ran ahead. Along the roadside the sage had tender new tips. Jody tore off some pieces and rubbed them on his hands until the air was filled with the sharp wild smell. With a rush the dogs leaped from the road and yapped into the brush after a rabbit. That was the last Jody saw of them, for when they failed to catch the rabbit, they went back home.

Jody plodded on up the hill toward the ridge top. When he reached the little cleft where the road came through, the afternoon wind struck him and blew up his hair and ruffled his shirt. He looked down on the little hills and ridges below and then out at the huge green Salinas Valley. He could see the white town of Salinas far out in the flat and the flash of its windows under the waning sun. Directly below him, in an oak tree, a crow congress had convened. The tree was black with crows all cawing at once.

Then Jody's eyes followed the wagon road down from the ridge where he stood, and lost it behind a hill, and picked it up again on the other side. On that distant stretch he saw a cart slowly pulled by a bay horse. It disappeared behind the hill. Jody sat down on the ground and watched the place where the cart would reappear again. The wind sang on the hilltops and the puff-ball clouds hurried eastward.

Then the cart came into sight and stopped. A man dressed in black dismounted from the seat and walked to the horse's head. Although it was so far away, Jody knew he had unhooked the check-rein, for the horse's head dropped forward. The horse moved on, and the man walked slowly up the hill beside it. Jody gave a glad cry and ran down the road toward them. The squirrels bumped along off the road, and a roadrunner flirted its tail and raced over the edge of the hill and sailed out like a glider.

Jody tried to leap into the middle of his shadow at every step. A stone rolled under his foot and he went down. Around a little bend he raced, and there, a short distance ahead, were his grandfather and the cart. The boy dropped from his unseemly running and approached at a dignified walk.

The horse plodded stumble-footedly up the hill and the old man walked beside it. In the lowering sun their giant shadows flickered darkly behind them. The grandfather was dressed in a black broadcloth suit and he wore kid congress gaiters and a black tie on a short, hard collar. He carried his black slouch hat in his hand. His white beard was cropped close and his white eyebrows overhung his eyes like mustaches. The blue eyes were sternly merry. About the whole face and figure there was a granite dignity, so that every motion seemed an impossible thing. Once at rest, it seemed the old man would be stone, would never move again. His steps were slow and certain. Once made, no step could ever be retraced; once headed in a direction, the path would never bend nor the pace increase nor slow.

When Jody appeared around the bend, Grandfather waved his hat slowly in welcome, and he called, "Why, Jody! Come down to meet me, have you?"

Jody sidled near and turned and matched his step to the old man's step and stiffened his body and dragged his heels a little. "Yes, sir," he said. "We got your letter only today."

"Should have been here yesterday," said Grandfather. "It certainly should. How are all the folks?"

"They're fine, sir." He hesitated and then suggested shyly, "Would you like to come on a mouse hunt tomorrow, sir?"

"Mouse hunt, Jody?" Grandfather chuckled. "Have the people of this generation come down to hunting mice? They aren't very strong, the new people, but I hardly thought mice would be game for them."

"No, sir. It's just play. The haystack's gone. I'm going to drive out the mice to the dogs. And you can watch, or even beat the hay a little."

The stern, merry eyes turned down on him. "I see. You don't eat them, then. You haven't come to that yet."

Jody explained, "The dogs eat them, sir. It wouldn't be much like hunting Indians, I guess."

"No, not much—but then later, when the troops were hunting Indians and shooting children and burning tepees, it wasn't much different from your mouse hunt."

They topped the rise and started down into the ranch cup, and they lost the sun from their shoulders. "You've grown," Grandfather said. "Nearly an inch, I should say."

"More," Jody boasted. "Where they mark me on the door, I'm up more than an inch since Thanksgiving even."

Grandfather's rich throaty voice said, "Maybe you're getting too much water and turning to pith and stalk. Wait until you head out, and then we'll see."

Jody looked quickly into the old man's face to see whether his feelings should be hurt, but there was no will to injure, no punishing nor putting-in-your-place light in the keen blue eyes. "We might kill a pig," Jody suggested.

"Oh, no! I couldn't let you do that. You're just humoring me. It isn't the time and you know it."

"You know Riley, the big boar, sir?"

"Yes. I remember Riley well."

"Well, Riley ate a hole into that same haystack, and it fell down on him and smothered him."

"Pigs do that when they can," said Grandfather.

"Riley was a nice pig, for a boar, sir. I rode him sometimes, and he didn't mind."

A door slammed at the house below them, and they saw Jody's mother standing on the porch waving her apron in welcome. And they saw Carl Tiflin walking up from the barn to be at the house for the arrival.

The sun had disappeared from the hills by now. The blue smoke from the house chimney hung in flat layers in the purpling ranch-cup. The puff-ball clouds, dropped by the falling wind, hung listlessly in the sky.

Billy Buck came out of the bunkhouse and flung a wash basin of soapy water on the ground. He had been shaving in mid-week, for Billy held Grandfather in reverence, and Grandfather said that Billy was one of the few men of the new generation who had not gone soft. Although Billy was in middle age, Grandfather considered him a boy. Now Billy was hurrying toward the house too.

When Jody and Grandfather arrived, the three were waiting for them in front of the yard gate.

Carl said, "Hello, sir. We've been looking for you."

Mrs. Tiflin kissed Grandfather on the side of his beard, and stood still while his big hand patted her shoulder. Billy shook hands solemnly, grinning under his straw mustache. "I'll put up your horse," said Billy, and he led the rig away.

Grandfather watched him go, and then, turning back to the group, he said as he had said a hundred times before, "There's a good boy. I knew his father, old Mule-tail Buck. I never knew why they called him Mule-tail except he packed mules."

Mrs. Tiflin turned and led the way into the house. "How long are you going to stay, Father? Your letter didn't say."

"Well, I don't know. I thought I'd stay about two weeks. But I never stay as long as I think I'm going to."

In a short while they were sitting at the white oilcloth table eating their supper. The lamp with the tin reflector hung over the table. Outside the dining-room windows the big moths battered softly against the glass.

Grandfather cut his steak into tiny pieces and chewed slowly. "I'm hungry," he said. "Driving out here got my appetite up. It's like when we were crossing. We all got so hungry every night we could hardly wait to let the meat get done. I could eat about five pounds of buffalo meat every night."

"It's moving around does it," said Billy. "My father was a government packer. I helped him when I was a kid. Just the two of us could about clean up a deer's ham."

"I knew your father, Billy," said Grandfather. "A fine man he was. They called him Mule-tail Buck. I don't know why except he packed mules."

"That was it," Billy agreed. "He packed mules."

Grandfather put down his knife and fork and looked around the table. "I remember one time we ran out of meat—" His voice dropped to a curious low sing-song, dropped into a tonal groove the story had worn for itself. "There was no buffalo, no antelope, not even rabbits. The hunters couldn't even shoot a coyote. That was the time for the leader to be on the watch. I was the leader, and I kept my eyes open. Know why? Well, just the minute the people began to get hungry they'd start slaughtering the team oxen. Do you believe that? I've heard of parties that just ate up their draft cattle. Started from the middle and worked toward the ends. Finally they'd eat the lead pair, and then the wheelers. The leader of a party had to keep them from doing that."

In some manner a big moth got into the room and circled the hanging kerosene lamp. Billy got up and tried to clap it between his hands. Carl struck with a cupped palm and caught the moth and broke it. He walked to the window and dropped it out.

"As I was saying," Grandfather began again, but Carl interrupted him. "You'd better eat some more meat. All the rest of us are ready for our pudding."

Jody saw a flash of anger in his mother's eyes. Grandfather picked up his knife and fork. "I'm pretty hungry, all right," he said. "I'll tell you about that later."

When supper was over, when the family and Billy Buck sat in front of the fireplace in the other room, Jody anxiously watched Grandfather. He saw the signs he knew. The bearded head leaned forward; the eyes lost their sternness and looked wonderingly into the fire; the big lean fingers laced themselves on the black knees. "I wonder," he began, "I just wonder whether I ever told you how those thieving Piutes drove off thirty-five of our horses."

"I think you did," Carl interrupted. "Wasn't it just before you went up into the Tahoe country?"

Grandfather turned quickly toward his son-in-law. "That's right. I guess I must have told you that story."

"Lots of times," Carl said cruelly, and he avoided his wife's eyes. But he felt the angry eyes on him, and he said, " 'Course I'd like to hear it again."

Grandfather looked back at the fire. His fingers unlaced and laced again. Jody knew how he felt, how his insides were collapsed and empty. Hadn't Jody been called a Big-Britches that very afternoon? He arose to heroism and opened himself to the term Big-Britches again. "Tell about Indians," he said softly.

Grandfather's eyes grew stern again. "Boys always want to hear about Indians. It was a job for men, but boys want to hear about it. Well, let's see. Did I ever tell you how I wanted each wagon to carry a long iron plate?"

Everyone but Jody remained silent. Jody said, "No. You didn't."

"Well, when the Indians attacked, we always put the wagons in a circle and fought from between the wheels. I thought that if every wagon carried a long plate with rifle holes, the men could stand the plates on the outside of the wheels when the wagons were in the circle and they would be protected. It would save lives and that would make up for the extra weight of the iron. But of course the party wouldn't do it. No party had done it before and they couldn't see why they should go to the expense. They lived to regret it, too."

Jody looked at his mother, and knew from her expression that she was not listening at all. Carl picked at a callus on his thumb and Billy Buck watched a spider crawling up the wall.

Grandfather's tone dropped into its narrative groove again. Jody knew in advance exactly what words would fall. The story droned on, speeded up for the attack, grew sad over the wounds, struck a dirge at the burials on the great plains. Jody sat quietly watching Grandfather. The stern blue eyes were detached. He looked as though he were not very interested in the story himself.

When it was finished, when the pause had been politely respected as the frontier of the story, Billy Buck stood up and stretched and hitched his trousers. "I guess I'll turn in," he said. Then he faced Grandfather. "I've got an old powder horn and a cap and ball pistol down to the bunkhouse. Did I ever show them to you?"

Grandfather nodded slowly. "Yes, I think you did, Billy. Reminds me of a pistol I had when I was leading the people across." Billy stood politely until the little story was done, and then he said, "Good night," and went out of the house.

Carl Tiflin tried to turn the conversation then. "How's the country between here and Monterey? I've heard it's pretty dry."

"It is dry," said Grandfather. "There's not a drop of water in the Laguna Seca. But it's a long pull from '87. The whole country was powder then, and in '61 I believe all the coyotes starved to death. We had fifteen inches of rain this year."

"Yes, but it all came too early. We could do with some now." Carl's eye fell on Jody. "Hadn't you better be getting to bed?"

Jody stood up obediently. "Can I kill the mice in the old haystack, sir?"

"Mice? Oh! Sure, kill them all off. Billy said there isn't any good hay left."

Jody exchanged a secret and satisfying look with Grandfather. "I'll kill every one tomorrow," he promised.

Jody lay in his bed and thought of the impossible world of Indians and buffaloes, a world that had ceased to be forever. He wished he could have been living in the heroic time, but he knew he was not of heroic timber. No one living now, save possibly Billy Buck, was worthy to do the things that had been done. A race of giants had lived then, fearless men, men of a staunchness unknown in this day. Jody thought of the wide plains and of the wagons moving across like centipedes. He thought of Grandfather on a huge white horse, marshaling the people. Across his mind marched the great phantoms, and they marched off the earth and they were gone.

He came back to the ranch for a moment, then. He heard the dull rushing sound that space and silence make. He heard one of the dogs, out in the doghouse, scratching a flea and bumping his elbow against the floor with every stroke. Then the wind arose again and the black cypress groaned and Jody went to sleep.

He was up half an hour before the triangle sounded for breakfast. His mother was rattling the stove to make the flames roar when Jody went through the kitchen. "You're up early," she said. "Where are you going?"

"Out to get a good stick. We're going to kill the mice today."

"Who is 'we'?"

"Why, Grandfather and I."

"So you've got him in it. You always like to have someone in with you in case there's blame to share."

"I'll be right back," said Jody. "I just want to have a good stick ready for after breakfast."

He closed the screen door after him and went out into the cool blue morning. The birds were noisy in the dawn and the ranch cats came down from the hill like blunt snakes. They had been hunting gophers in the dark, and although the four cats were full of gopher meat, they sat in a semi-circle at the back door and mewed piteously for milk. Doubletree Mutt and Smasher moved sniffing along the edge of the brush, performing the duty with rigid ceremony, but when Jody whistled, their heads jerked up and their tails waved. They plunged down to him, wriggling their skins and yawning. Jody patted their heads seriously, and moved on to the weathered scrap pile. He selected an old broom handle and a short piece of inch-square scrap wood. From his pocket he took a shoelace and tied the ends of the sticks loosely together to make a flail. He whistled his new weapon through the air and struck the ground experimentally, while the dogs leaped aside and whined with apprehension.

Jody turned and started down past the house toward the old haystack ground to look over the field of slaughter, but Billy Buck, sitting patiently on the back steps, called to him, "You better come back. It's only a couple of minutes till breakfast."

Jody changed his course and moved toward the house. He leaned his flail against the steps. "That's to drive the mice out," he said. "I'll bet they're fat. I'll bet they don't know what's going to happen to them today."

"No, nor you either," Billy remarked philosophically, "nor me, nor anyone."

Jody was staggered by this thought. He knew it was true. His imagination twitched away from the mouse hunt. Then his mother came out on the back porch and struck the triangle, and all thoughts fell in a heap.

Grandfather hadn't appeared at the table when they sat down. Billy nodded at his empty chair. "He's all right? He isn't sick?"

"He takes a long time to dress," said Mrs. Tiflin. "He combs his whiskers and rubs up his shoes and brushes his clothes."

Carl scattered sugar on his mush. "A man that's led a wagon train across the plains has got to be pretty careful how he dresses."

Mrs. Tiflin turned on him. "Don't do that, Carl! Please don't!" There was more of threat than of request in her tone. And the threat irritated Carl.

"Well, how many times do I have to listen to the story of the iron plates, and the thirty-five horses? That time's done. Why can't he forget it, now it's done?" He grew angrier while he talked, and his voice rose. "Why does he have to tell them over and over? He came across the plains. All right! Now it's finished. Nobody wants to hear about it over and over."

The door into the kitchen closed softly. The four at the table sat frozen. Carl laid his mush spoon on the table and touched his chin with his fingers.

Then the kitchen door opened and Grandfather walked in. His mouth smiled tightly and his eyes were squinted. "Good morning," he said, and he sat down and looked at his mush dish.

Carl could not leave it there. "Did—did you hear what I said?"

Grandfather jerked a little nod.

"I don't know what got into me, sir. I didn't mean it. I was just being funny."

Jody glanced in shame at his mother, and he saw that she was looking at Carl, and that she wasn't breathing. It was an awful thing that he was doing. He was tearing himself to pieces to talk like that. It was a terrible thing to him to retract a word, but to retract it in shame was infinitely worse.

Grandfather looked sidewise. "I'm trying to get right side up," he said gently. "I'm not being mad. I don't mind what you said, but it might be true, and I would mind that."

"It isn't true," said Carl. "I'm not feeling well this morning. I'm sorry I said it."

"Don't be sorry, Carl. An old man doesn't see things sometimes. Maybe you're right. The crossing is finished. Maybe it should be forgotten, now it's done."

Carl got up from the table. "I've had enough to eat. I'm

going to work. Take your time, Billy!" He walked quickly out of the dining-room. Billy gulped the rest of his food and followed soon after. But Jody could not leave his chair.

"Won't you tell any more stories?" Jody asked.

"Why, sure I'll tell them, but only when—I'm sure people want to hear them."

"I like to hear them, sir."

"Oh! Of course you do, but you're a little boy. It was a job for men, but only little boys like to hear about it."

Jody got up from his place. "I'll wait outside for you, sir. I've got a good stick for those mice."

He waited by the gate until the old man came out on the porch. "Let's go down and kill the mice now," Jody called.

"I think I'll just sit in the sun, Jody. You go kill the mice."

"You can use my stick if you like."

"No, I'll just sit here a while."

Jody turned disconsolately away, and walked down toward the old haystack. He tried to whip up his enthusiasm with thoughts of the fat juicy mice. He beat the ground with his flail. The dogs coaxed and whined about him, but he could not go. Back at the house he could see Grandfather sitting on the porch, looking small and thin and black.

Jody gave up and went to sit on the steps at the old man's feet.

"Back already? Did you kill the mice?"

"No, sir. I'll kill them some other day."

The morning flies buzzed close to the ground and the ants dashed about in front of the steps. The heavy smell of sage slipped down the hill. The porch boards grew warm in the sunshine.

Jody hardly knew when Grandfather started to talk. "I shouldn't stay here, feeling the way I do." He examined his strong old hands. "I feel as though the crossing wasn't worth doing." His eyes moved up the side-hill and stopped on a motionless hawk perched on a dead limb. "I tell those old stories, but they're not what I want to tell. I only know how I want people to feel when I tell them.

"It wasn't Indians that were important, nor adventures, nor even getting out here. It was a whole bunch of people made into one big crawling beast. And I was the head. It was westering and westering. Every man wanted something for himself, but the big beast that was all of them wanted only westering. I was the leader, but if I hadn't been there, some-one else would have been the head. The thing had to have a head.

"Under the little bushes the shadows were black at white noonday. When we saw the mountains at last, we cried—all of us. But it wasn't getting here that mattered, it was move-ment and westering.

"We carried life out here and set it down the way those ants carry eggs. And I was the leader. The westering was as big as God, and the slow steps that made the movement piled up and piled up until the continent was crossed.

"Then we came down to the sea, and it was done." He stopped and wiped his eyes until the rims were red. "That's what I should be telling instead of stories."

When Jody spoke, Grandfather started and looked down at him. "Maybe I could lead the people some day," Jody said.

The old man smiled. "There's no place to go. There's the ocean to stop you. There's a line of old men along the shore hating the ocean because it stopped them."

"In boats I might, sir."

"No place to go, Jody. Every place is taken. But that's not the worst—no, not the worst. Westering has died out of the people. Westering isn't a hunger any more. It's all done.

Your father is right. It is finished." He laced his fingers on his knee and looked at them.

Jody felt very sad. "If you'd like a glass of lemonade I could make it for you."

Grandfather was about to refuse, and then he saw Jody's face. "That would be nice," he said. "Yes, it would be nice to drink a lemonade."

Jody ran into the kitchen where his mother was wiping the last of the breakfast dishes. "Can I have a lemon to make a lemonade for Grandfather?"

His mother mimicked— "And another lemon to make a lemonade for you."

"No, ma'am. I don't want one."

"Jody! You're sick!" Then she stopped suddenly. "Take a lemon out of the cooler," she said softly. "Here, I'll reach the squeezer down to you."

THE PEASANT MAREY

by FYODOR DOSTOEVSKY

I⟩T was the second day in Easter week. The air was warm, the sky was blue, the sun was high, warm, bright, but my soul was very gloomy. I sauntered behind the prison barracks. I stared at the palings of the stout prison fence, counting them; but I had no inclination to count them, though it was my habit to do so. This was the second day of the "holidays" in the prison; the convicts were not taken out to work, there were numbers of men drunk, loud abuse and quarreling were springing up continually in every corner. There were hideous, disgusting songs, and card-parties installed beside the platform-beds. Several of the convicts who had been sentenced by their comrades, for special violence, to be beaten till they were half dead, were lying on the platform-bed, covered with sheepskins till they should recover and come to themselves again; knives had already been drawn several times. For these two days of holiday all this had been torturing me till it made me ill. And indeed I could never endure without repulsion the noise and disorder of drunken people, and especially in this place. On these days even the prison officials did not look into the prison, made no searches, did not look for vodka, understanding that they must allow even these outcasts to enjoy themselves once a year, and that things would be even worse if they did not. At last a sudden fury flamed up in my heart. A political prisoner called M. met me; he looked at me gloomily, his eyes flashed and his lips

quivered. *"Je hais ces brigands!"* he hissed at me through his
teeth, and walked on. I returned to the prison ward, though
only a quarter of an hour before I had rushed out of it as
though I were crazy, when six stalwart fellows had all together
flung themselves upon the drunken Tatar Gazin to suppress
him and had begun beating him; they beat him stupidly, a camel
might have been killed by such blows, but they knew that this
Hercules was not easy to kill, and so they beat him without
uneasiness. Now on returning I noticed on the bed in the
furthest corner of the room Gazin lying unconscious, almost
without sign of life. He lay covered with a sheepskin, and
everyone walked round him, without speaking; though they
confidently hoped that he would come to himself next morning, yet if luck was against him, maybe from a beating like that,
the man would die. I made my way to my own place opposite
the window with the iron grating, and lay on my back with my
hands behind my head and my eyes shut. I liked to lie like that;
a sleeping man is not molested, and meanwhile one can dream
and think. But I could not dream, my heart was beating un-
easily, and M.'s words, *"Je hais ces brigands!"* were echoing in
my ears. But why describe my impressions? I sometimes dream
even now of those times at night, and I have no dreams more
agonizing. Perhaps it will be noticed that even to this day I
have scarcely once spoken in print of my life in prison. *The
House of the Dead* I wrote fifteen years ago in the character of
an imaginary person, a criminal who had killed his wife. I may
add by the way that since then, very many persons have supposed, and even now maintain, that I was sent to penal servitude
for the murder of my wife.

Gradually I sank into forgetfulness and by degrees was lost
in memories. During the whole course of my four years in
prison I was continually recalling all my past, and seemed
to live over again the whole of my life in recollection. These

memories rose up of themselves, it was not often that I summoned them of my own will. Each would begin from some
point, some little thing, at times unnoticed, and then by degrees there would rise up a complete picture, some vivid and
complete impression. I used to analyze these impressions, give
new features to what had happened long ago, and best of all, I
used to correct it, correct it continually, that was my great
amusement. On this occasion, I suddenly for some reason remembered an unnoticed moment in my early childhood when
I was only nine years old—a moment which I should have
thought I had utterly forgotten; but at that time I was particularly fond of memories of my early childhood. I remembered
the month of August in our country house: a dry bright day but
rather cold and windy; summer was waning and soon we should
have to go to Moscow to be bored all winter with French lessons, and I was so sorry to leave the country. I walked past the
threshing-floor and, going down the ravine, I went up to the
dense thicket of bushes that covered the further side of the ravine
as far as the copse. And I plunged right into the midst of the
bushes, and heard a peasant plowing alone on the clearing about
thirty paces away. I knew that he was plowing up the steep
hill and the horse was moving with effort, and from time to time
the peasant's call "Come up!" floated upwards to me. I knew
almost all our peasants, but I did not know who it was plowing
now, and, indeed, I did not care, I was absorbed in my own
affairs. I was busy, too; I was breaking off switches from the
nut trees to whip the frogs with. Nut sticks made such fine
whips, but they do not last; while birch twigs are just the opposite. I was interested, too, in beetles and other insects; I used
to collect them, some were very ornamental. I was very fond,
too, of the nimble red and yellow lizards with black spots on
them, but I was afraid of snakes. Snakes, however, were much
more rare than lizards. There were not many mushrooms there.

To get mushrooms one had to go to the birch wood, and I was about to set off there. And there was nothing in the world that I loved so much as the wood with its mushrooms and wild berries, with its beetles and its birds, its hedgehogs and squirrels, with its damp smell of dead leaves which I loved so much, and even as I write I smell the fragrance of our birch wood: these impressions will remain for my whole life. Suddenly in the midst of the profound stillness I heard a clear and distinct shout, "Wolf!" I shrieked and, beside myself with terror, calling out at the top of my voice, ran out into the clearing and straight to the peasant who was plowing.

It was our peasant Marey. I don't know if there is such a name, but everyone called him Marey—a thick set, rather well-grown peasant of fifty, with a good many gray hairs in his dark brown, spreading beard. I knew him, but had scarcely ever happened to speak to him till then. He stopped his horse on hearing my cry, and when, breathless, I caught with one hand at his plow and with the other at his sleeve, he saw how frightened I was.

"There is a wolf!" I cried, panting.

He flung up his head, and could not help looking round for an instant, almost believing me.

"Where is the wolf?"

"A shout . . . someone shouted: 'wolf' . . ." I faltered out.

"Nonsense, nonsense! A wolf? Why, it was your fancy! How could there be a wolf?" he muttered, reassuring me. But I was trembling all over, and still kept tight hold of his smock frock, and I must have been quite pale. He looked at me with an uneasy smile, evidently anxious and troubled over me.

"Why, you have had a fright, *aïe, aïe!*" He shook his head. "There, dear. . . . Come little one, *aïe!*"

He stretched out his hand, and all at once stroked my cheek.

"Come, come, there; Christ be with you! Cross yourself!"

But I did not cross myself. The corners of my mouth were twitching, and I think that struck him particularly. He put out his thick, black-nailed, earth-stained finger and softly touched my twitching lips.

"*Aïe,* there, there," he said to me with a slow, almost motherly smile. "Dear, dear, what is the matter? There; come, come!"

I grasped at last that there was no wolf, and that the shout that I had heard was my fancy. Yet that shout had been so clear and distinct, but such shouts (not only about wolves) I had imagined once or twice before, and I was aware of that. (These hallucinations passed away later as I grew older.)

"Well, I will go then," I said, looking at him timidly and inquiringly.

"Well, do, and I'll keep watch on you as you go. I won't let the wolf get you," he added, still smiling at me with the same motherly expression. "Well, Christ be with you! Come, run along then." And he made the sign of the cross over me and then over himself. I walked away, looking back almost at every tenth step. Marey stood still with his mare as I walked away, and looked after me and nodded to me every time I looked round. I must own I felt a little ashamed at having let him see me so frightened, but I was still very much afraid of the wolf as I walked away, until I reached the first barn half-way up the slope of the ravine; there my fright vanished completely, and all at once our yard-dog Volchok flew to meet me. With Volchok I felt quite safe, and I turned round to Marey for the last time; I could not see his face distinctly, but I felt that he was still nodding and smiling affectionately at me. I waved to him; he waved back at me and started his little mare. "Come up!" I heard his call in the distance again, and the little mare pulled at the plow again.

All this I recalled all at once, I don't know why, but with extraordinary minuteness of detail. I suddenly roused myself and sat up on the sleeping-platform, and, I remember, found myself still smiling quietly at my memories. I brooded over them for another minute.

When I got home that day I told no one of my "adventure" with Marey. And indeed it was hardly an adventure. And in fact I soon forgot Marey. When I met him now and then afterwards, I never even spoke to him about the wolf or anything else; and all at once now, twenty years afterwards in Siberia, I remembered this meeting with such distinctness to the smallest detail. So it must have lain hidden in my soul, though I knew nothing of it, and rose suddenly to my memory when it was wanted; I remembered the soft motherly smile of the poor serf, the way he signed me with the cross and shook his head. "There, there, you have had a fright, little one!" And I remembered particularly the thick earth-stained finger with which he softly and with timid tenderness touched my quivering lips. Of course anyone would have reassured a child, but something quite different seemed to have happened in that solitary meeting; and if I had been his own son, he could not have looked at me with eyes shining with greater love. And what made him like that? He was our serf and I was his little master, after all. No one would know that he had been kind to me and reward him for it. Was he, perhaps, very fond of little children? Some people are. It was a solitary meeting in the deserted fields, and only God, perhaps, may have seen from above with what deep and humane civilized feeling, and with what a delicate, almost feminine tenderness, the heart of a coarse, brutally ignorant Russian serf, who had as yet no expectation, no idea even of his freedom, may be filled. Was not this, perhaps, what Konstantin Aksakov meant when he spoke of the high degree of culture of our peasantry?

And when I got down off the bed and looked around me, I remember I suddenly felt that I could look at these unhappy creatures with quite different eyes, and that suddenly by some miracle all hatred and anger had vanished utterly from my heart. I walked about, looking into the faces that I met. That shaven peasant, branded on his face as a criminal, bawling his hoarse, drunken song, may be that very Marey; I cannot look into his heart.

I met M. again that evening. Poor fellow! he could have no memories of Russian peasants, and no other view of these people but: *"Je hais ces brigands!"* Yes, the Polish prisoners had more to bear than I.

CLAY

by JAMES JOYCE

THE MATRON had given her leave to go out as soon as the women's tea was over and Maria looked forward to her evening out. The kitchen was spick and span: the cook said you could see yourself in the big copper boilers. The fire was nice and bright and on one of the side-tables were four very big barmbracks. These barmbracks seemed uncut; but if you went closer you would see that they had been cut into long thick even slices and were ready to be handed round at tea. Maria had cut them herself.

Maria was a very, very small person indeed but she had a very long nose and a very long chin. She talked a little through her nose, always soothingly: *"Yes, my dear,"* and *"No, my dear."* She was always sent for when the women quarreled over their tubs and always succeeded in making peace. One day the matron had said to her:

"Maria, you are a veritable peace-maker!"

And the sub-matron and two of the Board ladies had heard the compliment. And Ginger Mooney was always saying what she wouldn't do to the dummy who had charge of the irons if it wasn't for Maria. Everyone was so fond of Maria.

The women would have their tea at six o'clock and she would be able to get away before seven. From Ballsbridge to the Pillar, twenty minutes; from the Pillar to Drumcondra, twenty minutes; and twenty minutes to buy the things. She would be there before eight. She took out her purse with the silver clasps and read again the words *A Present from Belfast*. She was very fond of that purse because Joe had brought it to her five years before when he and Alphy had gone to Belfast on a Whit-Monday trip. In the purse were two half-crowns and some coppers. She would have five shillings clear after paying tram fare. What a nice evening they would have, all the children singing! Only she hoped that Joe wouldn't come in drunk. He was so different when he took any drink.

Often he had wanted her to go and live with them; but she would have felt herself in the way (though Joe's wife was ever so nice with her) and she had become accustomed to the life of the laundry. Joe was a good fellow. She had nursed him and Alphy too; and Joe used often say:

"Mamma is mamma but Maria is my proper mother."

After the break-up at home the boys had got her that position in the *Dublin by Lamplight* laundry, and she liked it. She used to have such a bad opinion of Protestants but now she thought they were very nice people, a little quiet and serious, but still very nice people to live with. Then she had her plants in the conservatory and she liked looking after them. She had lovely ferns and wax-plants and, whenever anyone came to visit her, she always gave the visitor one or two slips from her conservatory. There was one thing she didn't like and that was the tracts on the walls; but the matron was such a nice person to deal with, so genteel.

When the cook told her everything was ready she went into the women's room and began to pull the big bell. In a few minutes the women began to come in by twos and threes, wiping their steaming hands in their petticoats and pulling down the sleeves of their blouses over their red steaming arms. They settled down before their huge mugs which the cook and the dummy filled up with hot tea, already mixed with milk and

sugar in huge tin cans. Maria superintended the distribution
of the barmbrack and saw that every woman got her four slices.
There was a great deal of laughing and joking during the meal.
Lizzie Fleming said Maria was sure to get the ring and, though
Fleming had said that for so many Hallow Eves, Maria had
to laugh and say she didn't want any ring or man either; and
when she laughed her gray-green eyes sparkled with disappointed shyness and the tip of her nose nearly met the tip of
her chin. Then Ginger Mooney lifted up her mug of tea and
proposed Maria's health while all the other women clattered
with their mugs on the table, and said she was sorry she hadn't
a sup of porter to drink it in. And Maria laughed again till
the tip of her nose nearly met the tip of her chin and till her
minute body nearly shook itself asunder because she knew that
Mooney meant well though, of course, she had the notions of a
common woman.

But wasn't Maria glad when the women had finished their
tea and the cook and the dummy had begun to clear away the
tea-things! She went into her little bedroom and, remembering that the next morning was a mass morning, changed the
hand of the alarm from seven to six. Then she took off her
working skirt and her house-boots and laid her best skirt out
on the bed and her tiny dress-boots beside the foot of the bed.
She changed her blouse too and, as she stood before the mirror,
she thought of how she used to dress for mass on Sunday morning when she was a young girl; and she looked with quaint
affection at the diminutive body which she had so often adorned.
In spite of its years she found it a nice tidy little body.

When she got outside the streets were shining with rain and
she was glad of her old brown waterproof. The tram was full
and she had to sit on the little stool at the end of the car, facing
all the people, with her toes barely touching the floor. She
arranged in her mind all she was going to do and thought how

much better it was to be independent and to have your own
money in your pocket. She hoped they would have a nice
evening. She was sure they would but she could not help
thinking what a pity it was Alphy and Joe were not speaking.
They were always falling out now but when they were boys
together they used to be the best of friends: but such was life.

She got out of her tram at the Pillar and ferreted her way
quickly among the crowds. She went into Downes's cake-shop
but the shop was so full of people that it was a long time before
she could get herself attended to. She bought a dozen of mixed
penny cakes, and at last came out of the shop laden with a big
bag. Then she thought what else would she buy: she wanted
to buy something really nice. They would be sure to have
plenty of apples and nuts. It was hard to know what to buy
and all she could think of was cake. She decided to buy
some plumcake but Downes's plumcake had not enough almond
icing on top of it so she went over to a shop in Henry Street.
Here she was a long time in suiting herself and the stylish
young lady behind the counter, who was evidently a little annoyed by her, asked her was it wedding-cake she wanted to
buy. That made Maria blush and smile at the young lady; but
the young lady took it all very seriously and finally cut a thick
slice of plumcake, parceled it up and said:

"Two-and-four, please."

She thought she would have to stand in the Drumcondra tram
because none of the young men seemed to notice her but an
elderly gentleman made room for her. He was a stout gentleman and he wore a brown hard hat; he had a square red face
and a grayish mustache. Maria thought he was a colonel-
looking gentleman and she reflected how much more polite he
was than the young men who simply stared straight before
them. The gentleman began to chat with her about Hallow
Eve and the rainy weather. He supposed the bag was full of

good things for the little ones and said it was only right that the youngsters should enjoy themselves while they were young. Maria agreed with him and favored him with demure nods and hems. He was very nice with her, and when she was getting out at the Canal Bridge she thanked him and bowed, and he bowed to her and raised his hat and smiled agreeably; and while she was going up along the terrace, bending her tiny head under the rain, she thought how easy it was to know a gentleman even when he has a drop taken.

Everybody said: *"O, here's Maria!"* when she came to Joe's house. Joe was there, having come home from business, and all the children had their Sunday dresses on. There were two big girls in from next door and games were going on. Maria gave the bag of cakes to the eldest boy, Alphy, to divide and Mrs. Donnelly said it was too good of her to bring such a big bag of cakes and made all the children say:

"Thanks, Maria."

But Maria said she had brought something special for papa and mamma, something they would be sure to like, and she began to look for her plumcake. She tried in Downes's bag and then in the pockets of her waterproof and then on the hall-stand but nowhere could she find it. Then she asked all the children had any of them eaten it—by mistake, of course—but the children all said no and looked as if they did not like to eat cakes if they were to be accused of stealing. Everybody had a solution for the mystery and Mrs. Donnelly said it was plain that Maria had left it behind her in the tram. Maria, remembering how confused the gentleman with the grayish mustache had made her, colored with shame and vexation and disappointment. At the thought of the failure of her little surprise and of the two and four-pence she had thrown away for nothing she nearly cried outright.

But Joe said it didn't matter and made her sit down by the

fire. He was very nice with her. He told her all that went
on in his office, repeating for her a smart answer which he had
made to the manager. Maria did not understand why Joe
laughed so much over the answer he had made but she said that
the manager must have been a very overbearing person to deal
with. Joe said he wasn't so bad when you knew how to take
him, that he was a decent sort so long as you didn't rub him
the wrong way. Mrs. Donnelly played the piano for the children and they danced and sang. Then the two next-door girls
handed round the nuts. Nobody could find the nutcrackers
and Joe was nearly getting cross over it and asked how did they
expect Maria to crack nuts without a nutcracker. But Maria
said she didn't like nuts and that they weren't to bother about
her. Then Joe asked would she take a bottle of stout and Mrs.
Donnelly said there was port wine too in the house if she would
prefer that. Maria said she would rather they didn't ask her
to take anything: but Joe insisted.

So Maria let him have his way and they sat by the fire talking
over old times and Maria thought she would put in a good
word for Alphy. But Joe cried that God might strike him stone
dead if ever he spoke a word to his brother again and Maria
said she was sorry she had mentioned the matter. Mrs. Donnelly told her husband it was a great shame for him to speak
that way of his own flesh and blood but Joe said that Alphy
was no brother of his and there was nearly being a row on the
head of it. But Joe said he would not lose his temper on account
of the night it was and asked his wife to open some more
stout. The two next-door girls had arranged some Hallow
Eve games and soon everything was merry again. Maria was
delighted to see the children so merry and Joe and his wife in
such good spirits. The next-door girls put some saucers on the
table and then led the children up to the table, blindfold. One
got the prayer-book and the other three got the water; and when

one of the next-door girls got the ring Mrs. Donnelly shook her finger at the blushing girl as much as to say: *O, I know all about it!* They insisted then on blindfolding Maria and leading her up to the table to see what she would get; and, while they were putting on the bandage, Maria laughed and laughed again till the tip of her nose nearly met the tip of her chin.

They led her up to the table amid laughing and joking and she put her hand out in the air as she was told to do. She moved her hand about here and there in the air and descended on one of the saucers. She felt a soft wet substance with her fingers and was surprised that nobody spoke or took off her bandage. There was a pause for a few seconds; and then a great deal of scuffling and whispering. Somebody said something about the garden, and at last Mrs. Donnelly said something very cross to one of the next-door girls and told her to throw it out at once: that was no play. Maria understood that it was wrong that time and so she had to do it over again: and this time she got the prayer-book.

After that Mrs. Donnelly played Miss McCloud's Reel for the children and Joe made Maria take a glass of wine. Soon they were all quite merry again and Mrs. Donnelly said Maria would enter a convent before the year was out because she had got the prayer-book. Maria had never seen Joe so nice to her as he was that night, so full of pleasant talk and reminiscences. She said they were all very good to her.

At last the children grew tired and sleepy and Joe asked Maria would she not sing some little song before she went, one of the old songs. Mrs. Donnelly said: *"Do, please, Maria!"* and so Maria had to get up and stand beside the piano. Mrs. Donnelly bade the children be quiet and listen to Maria's song. Then she played the prelude and said *"Now, Maria!"* and Maria, blushing very much, began to sing in a tiny quavering voice. She sang *I Dreamt that I Dwelt*, and when she came to the second verse she sang again:

> *I dreamt that I dwelt in marble halls*
> *With vassals and serfs at my side*
> *And of all who assembled within those walls*
> *That I was the hope and the pride.*
>
> *I had riches too great to count, could boast*
> *Of a high ancestral name,*
> *But I also dreamt, which pleased me most,*
> *That you loved me still the same.*

But no one tried to show her her mistake; and when she had ended her song Joe was very much moved. He said that there was no time like the long ago and no music for him like poor old Balfe, whatever other people might say; and his eyes filled up so much with tears that he could not find what he was looking for and in the end he had to ask his wife to tell him where the corkscrew was.

DAUGHTER

by ERSKINE CALDWELL

At sunrise a Negro on his way to the big house to feed the mules had taken the word to Colonel Henry Maxwell, and Colonel Henry phoned the sheriff. The sheriff had hustled Jim into town and locked him up in the jail, and then he went home and ate breakfast.

Jim walked around the empty cellroom while he was buttoning his shirt, and after that he sat down on the bunk and tied his shoelaces. Everything that morning had taken place so quickly that he had not even had time to get a drink of water. He got up and went to the water bucket near the door, but the sheriff had forgotten to put water in it.

By that time there were several men standing in the jailyard. Jim went to the window and looked out when he heard them talking. Just then another automobile drove up, and six or seven men got out. Other men were coming towards the jail from both directions of the street.

"What was the trouble out at your place this morning, Jim?" somebody said.

Jim stuck his chin between the bars and looked at the faces in the crowd. He knew everyone there.

While he was trying to figure out how everybody in town had heard about his being there, somebody else spoke to him.

"It must have been an accident, wasn't it, Jim?"

A colored boy hauling a load of cotton to the gin drove up

the street. When the wagon got in front of the jail, the boy whipped up the mules with the ends of the reins and made them trot.

"I hate to see the State have a grudge against you, Jim," somebody said.

The sheriff came down the street swinging a tin dinner-pail in his hand. He pushed through the crowd, unlocked the door, and set the pail inside.

Several men came up behind the sheriff and looked over his shoulder into the jail.

"Here's your breakfast my wife fixed up for you, Jim. You'd better eat a little, Jim boy."

Jim looked at the pail, at the sheriff, at the open jail door, and he shook his head.

"I don't feel hungry," he said. "Daughter's been hungry, though—awful hungry."

The sheriff backed out the door, his hand going to the handle of his pistol. He backed out so quickly that he stepped on the toes of the men behind him.

"Now, don't you get careless, Jim boy," he said. "Just sit and calm yourself."

He shut the door and locked it. After he had gone a few steps towards the street, he stopped and looked into the chamber of his pistol to make sure it had been loaded.

The crowd outside the window pressed in closer. Some of the men rapped on the bars until Jim came and looked out. When he saw them, he stuck his chin between the iron and gripped his hands around it.

"How come it to happen, Jim?" somebody asked. "It must have been an accident, wasn't it?"

Jim's long thin face looked as if it would come through the bars. The sheriff came up to the window to see if everything was all right.

"Now, just take it easy, Jim boy," he said.

The man who had asked Jim to tell what had happened, elbowed the sheriff out of the way. The other men crowded closer.

"How come, Jim?" the man said. "Was it an accident?"

"No," Jim said, his fingers twisting about the bars. "I picked up my shotgun and done it."

The sheriff pushed towards the window again.

"Go on, Jim, and tell us what it's all about."

Jim's face squeezed between the bars until it looked as though only his ears kept his head from coming through.

"Daughter said she was hungry, and I just couldn't stand it no longer. I just couldn't stand to hear her say it."

"Don't get all excited now, Jim boy," the sheriff said, pushing forward one moment and being elbowed away the next.

"She waked up in the middle of the night again and said she was hungry. I just couldn't stand to hear her say it."

Somebody pushed all the way through the crowd until he got to the window.

"Why, Jim, you could have come and asked me for something for her to eat, and you know I'd have given you all I got in the world."

The sheriff pushed forward once more.

"That wasn't the right thing to do," Jim said. "I've been working all year and I made enough for all of us to eat."

He stopped and looked down into the faces on the other side of the bars.

"I made enough working on shares, but they came and took it all away from me. I couldn't go around begging after I'd made enough to keep us. They just came and took it all off. Then Daughter woke up again this morning saying she was hungry, and I just couldn't stand it no longer."

"You'd better go and get on the bunk now, Jim boy," the sheriff said.

"It don't seem right that the little girl ought to be shot like that," somebody said.

"Daughter said she was hungry," Jim said. "She'd been saying that for all of the past month. Daughter'd wake up in the middle of the night and say it. I just couldn't stand it no longer."

"You ought to have sent her over to my house, Jim. Me and my wife could have fed her something, somehow. It don't look right to kill a little girl like her."

"I'd made enough for all of us," Jim said. "I just couldn't stand it no longer. Daughter'd been hungry all the past month."

"Take it easy, Jim boy," the sheriff said, trying to push forward.

The crowd swayed from side to side.

"And so you just picked up the gun this morning and shot her?" somebody asked.

"When she woke up this morning saying she was hungry, I just couldn't stand it."

The crowd pushed closer. Men were coming towards the jail from all directions, and those who were then arriving pushed forward to hear what Jim had to say.

"The State has got a grudge against you now, Jim," somebody said, "but somehow it don't seem right."

"I can't help it," Jim said. "Daughter woke up again this morning that way."

The jailyard, the street, and the vacant lot on the other side were filled with men and boys. All of them were pushing forward to hear Jim. Word had spread all over town by that time that Jim Carlisle had shot and killed his eight-year-old daughter, Clara.

"Who does Jim share-crop for?" somebody asked.

"Colonel Henry Maxwell," a man in the crowd said. "Colonel Henry has had Jim out there about nine or ten years."

"Henry Maxwell didn't have no business coming and taking all the shares. He's got plenty of his own. It ain't right for Henry Maxwell to come and take Jim's, too."

The sheriff was pushing forward once more.

"The State's got a grudge against Jim now," somebody said. "Somehow it don't seem right, though."

The sheriff pushed his shoulder into the crowd of men and worked his way in closer.

A man shoved the sheriff away.

"Why did Henry Maxwell come and take your share of the crop, Jim?"

"He said I owed it to him because one of his mules died about a month ago."

The sheriff got in front of the barred window.

"You ought to go to the bunk now and rest some, Jim boy," he said. "Take off your shoes and stretch out, Jim boy."

He was elbowed out of the way.

"You didn't kill the mule, did you, Jim?"

"The mule dropped dead in the barn," Jim said. "I wasn't nowhere around. It just dropped dead."

The crowd was pushing harder. The men in front were jammed against the jail, and the men behind were trying to get within earshot. Those in the middle were squeezed against each other so tightly they could not move in any direction. Everyone was talking louder.

Jim's face pressed between the bars and his fingers gripped the iron until the knuckles were white.

The milling crowd was moving across the street to the vacant lot. Somebody was shouting. He climbed up on an automobile and began swearing at the top of his lungs.

A man in the middle of the crowd pushed his way out and went to his automobile. He got in and drove off alone.

Jim stood holding to the bars and looking through the window. The sheriff had his back to the crowd, and he was saying something to Jim. Jim did not hear what he said.

A man on his way to the gin with a load of cotton stopped to find out what the trouble was. He looked at the crowd in the vacant lot for a moment, and then he turned around and looked at Jim behind the bars. The shouting across the street was growing louder.

"What's the trouble, Jim?"

Somebody on the other side of the street came to the wagon. He put his foot on a spoke in the wagon wheel and looked up at the man on the cotton while he talked.

"Daughter woke up this morning again saying she was hungry," Jim said.

The sheriff was the only person who heard him.

The man on the load of cotton jumped to the ground, tied the reins to the wagon wheel, and pushed through the crowd to the car where all the shouting and swearing was being done. After listening for a while, he came back to the street, called a Negro who was standing with several other Negroes on the corner, and handed him the reins. The Negro drove off with the cotton towards the gin, and the man went back into the crowd.

Just then the man who had driven off alone in his car came back. He sat for a moment behind the steering wheel, and then he jumped to the ground. He opened the rear door and took out a crowbar that was as long as he was tall.

"Pry that jail door open and let Jim out," somebody said. "It ain't right for him to be in there."

The crowd in the vacant lot was moving again. The man who had been standing on top of the automobile jumped to the ground, and the men moved towards the street in the direction of the jail.

The first man to reach it jerked the six-foot crowbar out of the soft earth where it had been jabbed.

The sheriff backed off.

"Now, take it easy, Jim boy," he said.

He turned and started walking rapidly up the street towards his house.

IN ANOTHER COUNTRY

by ERNEST HEMINGWAY

I<small>N THE</small> fall the war was always there, but we did not go to it any more. It was cold in the fall in Milan and the dark came very early. Then the electric lights came on, and it was pleasant along the streets looking in the windows. There was much game hanging outside the shops, and the snow powdered in the fur of the foxes and the wind blew their tails. The deer hung stiff and heavy and empty, and small birds blew in the wind and the wind turned their feathers. It was a cold fall and the wind came down from the mountains.

We were all at the hospital every afternoon, and there were different ways of walking across the town through the dusk to the hospital. Two of the ways were alongside canals, but they were long. Always, though, you crossed a bridge across a canal to enter the hospital. There was a choice of three bridges. On one of them a woman sold roasted chestnuts. It was warm, standing in front of her charcoal fire, and the chestnuts were warm afterward in your pocket. The hospital was very old and very beautiful, and you entered through a gate and walked across a courtyard and out a gate on the other side. There were usually funerals starting from the courtyard. Beyond the old hospital were the new brick pavilions, and there we met every afternoon and were all very polite and interested in what was the matter, and sat in the machines that were to make so much difference.

The doctor came up to the machine where I was sitting and

said: "What did you like best to do before the war? Did you practice a sport?"

I said: "Yes, football."

"Good," he said. "You will be able to play football again better than ever."

My knee did not bend and the leg dropped straight from the knee to the ankle without a calf, and the machine was to bend the knee and make it move as in riding a tricycle. But it did not bend yet, and instead the machine lurched when it came to the bending part. The doctor said: "That will all pass. You are a fortunate young man. You will play football again like a champion."

In the next machine was a major who had a little hand like a baby's. He winked at me when the doctor examined his hand, which was between two leather straps that bounced up and down and flapped the stiff fingers, and said: "And will I too play football, captain-doctor?" He had been a very great fencer, and before the war the greatest fencer in Italy.

The doctor went to his office in a back room and brought a photograph which showed a hand that had been withered almost as small as the major's, before it had taken a machine course, and after was a little larger. The major held the photograph with his good hand and looked at it very carefully. "A wound?" he asked.

"An industrial accident," the doctor said.

"Very interesting, very interesting," the major said, and handed it back to the doctor.

"You have confidence?"

"No," said the major.

There were three boys who came each day who were about the same age I was. They were all three from Milan, and one of them was to be a lawyer, and one was to be a painter, and one had intended to be a soldier, and after we were finished with the machines, sometimes we walked back together to the Café Cova, which was next door to the Scala. We walked the short way through the communist quarter because we were four together. The people hated us because we were officers, and from a wine-shop someone called out, "A basso gli ufficiali!' as we passed. Another boy who walked with us sometimes and made us five wore a black silk handkerchief across his face because he had no nose then and his face was to be rebuilt. He had gone out to the front from the military academy and been wounded within an hour after he had gone into the front line for the first time. They rebuilt his face, but he came from a very old family and they could never get the nose exactly right. He went to South America and worked in a bank. But this was a long time ago, and then we did not any of us know how it was going to be afterward. We only knew then that there was always the war, but that we were not going to it any more.

We all had the same medals, except the boy with the black silk bandage across his face, and he had not been at the front long enough to get any medals. The tall boy with a very pale face who was to be a lawyer had been a lieutenant of Arditi and had three medals of the sort we each had only one of. He had lived a very long time with death and was a little detached. We were all a little detached, and there was nothing that held us together except that we met every afternoon at the hospital. Although, as we walked to the Cova through the tough part of town, walking in the dark, with light and singing coming out of the wine-shops, and sometimes having to walk into the street when the men and women would crowd together on the sidewalk so that we would have had to jostle them to get by, we felt held together by there being something that had happened that they, the people who disliked us, did not understand.

We ourselves all understood the Cova, where it was rich and warm and not too brightly lighted, and noisy and smoky at certain hours, and there were always girls at the tables and the illustrated papers on a rack on the wall. The girls at the Cova were very patriotic, and I found that the most patriotic people in Italy were the café girls—and I believe they are still patriotic.

The boys at first were very polite about my medals and asked me what I had done to get them. I showed them the papers, which were written in very beautiful language and full of *fratellanza* and *abnegazione,* but which really said, with the adjectives removed, that I had been given the medals because I was an American. After that their manner changed a little toward me, although I was their friend against outsiders. I was a friend, but I was never really one of them after they had read the citations, because it had been different with them and they had done very different things to get their medals. I had been wounded, it was true; but we all knew that being wounded, after all, was really an accident. I was never ashamed of the ribbons, though, and sometimes, after the cocktail hour, I would imagine myself having done all the things they had done to get their medals; but walking home at night through the empty streets with the cold wind and all the shops closed, trying to keep near the street lights, I knew that I would never have done such things, and I was very much afraid to die, and often lay in bed at night by myself, afraid to die and wondering how I would be when I went back to the front again.

The three with the medals were like hunting-hawks; and I was not a hawk, although I might seem a hawk to those who had never hunted; they, the three, knew better and so we drifted apart. But I stayed good friends with the boy who had been wounded his first day at the front, because he would never know now how he would have turned out; so he could never be accepted either, and I liked him because I thought perhaps he would not have turned out to be a hawk either.

The major, who had been the great fencer, did not believe in bravery, and spent much time while we sat in the machines correcting my grammar. He had complimented me on how I spoke Italian, and we talked together very easily. One day I had said that Italian seemed such an easy language to me that I could not take a great interest in it; everything was so easy to say. "Ah, yes," the major said. "Why, then, do you not take up the use of grammar?" So we took up the use of grammar, and soon Italian was such a difficult language that I was afraid to talk to him until I had the grammar straight in my mind.

The major came very regularly to the hospital. I do not think he ever missed a day, although I am sure he did not believe in the machines. There was a time when none of us believed in the machines, and one day the major said it was all nonsense. The machines were new then and it was we who were to prove them. It was an idiotic idea, he said, "a theory, like another." I had not learned my grammar, and he said I was a stupid impossible disgrace, and he was a fool to have bothered with me. He was a small man and he sat straight up in his chair with his right hand thrust into the machine and looked straight ahead at the wall while the straps thumped up and down with his fingers in them.

"What will you do when the war is over if it is over?" he asked me. "Speak grammatically!"

"I will go to the States."

"Are you married?"

"No, but I hope to be."

"The more of a fool you are," he said. He seemed very angry. "A man must not marry."

"Why, Signor Maggiore?"

"Don't call me 'Signor Maggiore.'"

"Why must not a man marry?"

"He cannot marry. He cannot marry," he said angrily. "If he is to lose everything, he should not place himself in a position to lose that. He should not place himself in a position to lose. He should find things he cannot lose."

He spoke very angrily and bitterly, and looked straight ahead while he talked.

"But why should he necessarily lose it?"

"He'll lose it," the major said. He was looking at the wall. Then he looked down at the machine and jerked his little hand out from between the straps and slapped it hard against his thigh. "He'll lose it," he almost shouted. "Don't argue with me!" Then he called to the attendant who ran the machines. "Come and turn this damned thing off."

He went back into the other room for the light treatment and the massage. Then I heard him ask the doctor if he might use his telephone and he shut the door. When he came back into the room, I was sitting in another machine. He was wearing his cape and had his cap on, and he came directly toward my machine and put his arm on my shoulder.

"I am so sorry," he said, and patted me on the shoulder with his good hand. "I would not be rude. My wife has just died. You must forgive me."

"Oh—" I said, feeling sick for him. "I am *so* sorry."

He stood there biting his lower lip. "It is very difficult," he said. "I cannot resign myself."

He looked straight past me and out through the window. Then he began to cry. "I am utterly unable to resign myself," he said and choked. And then crying, his head up looking at nothing, carrying himself straight and soldierly, with tears on both his cheeks and biting his lips, he walked past the machines and out the door.

The doctor told me that the major's wife, who was very young and whom he had not married until he was definitely invalided out of the war, had died of pneumonia. She had been sick only a few days. No one expected her to die. The major did not

come to the hospital for three days. Then he came at the usual
hour, wearing a black band on the sleeve of his uniform. When
he came back, there were large framed photographs around the
wall, of all sorts of wounds before and after they had been cured
by the machines. In front of the machine the major used were
three photographs of hands like his that were completely restored. I do not know where the doctor got them. I always
understood we were the first to use the machines. The photographs did not make much difference to the major because he
only looked out of the window.

A STORY

by DYLAN THOMAS

I F YOU can call it a story. There's no
real beginning or end and there's very
little in the middle. It is all about a
day's outing, by charabanc, to Porthcawl, which, of course, the
charabanc never reached, and it happened when I was so high
and much nicer.

I was staying at the time with my uncle and his wife. Although she was my aunt, I never thought of her as anything
but the wife of my uncle, partly because he was so big and
trumpeting and red-hairy and used to fill every inch of the hot
little house like an old buffalo squeezed into an airing cupboard,
and partly because she was so small and silk and quick and
made no noise at all as she whisked about on padded paws,
dusting the china dogs, feeding the buffalo, setting the mouse-
traps that never caught her; and once she sleaked out of the
room, to squeak in a nook or nibble in the hayloft, you forgot
she had ever been there.

But there he was, always, a steaming hulk of an uncle, his
braces straining like hawsers, crammed behind the counter of
the tiny shop at the front of the house, and breathing like a
brass band; or guzzling and blustery in the kitchen over his
gutsy supper, too big for everything except the great black boats
of his boots. As he ate, the house grew smaller; he billowed
out over the furniture, the loud check meadow of his waistcoat
littered, as though after a picnic, with cigarette ends, peelings,

cabbage stalks, birds' bones, gravy; and the forest fire of his hair crackled among the hooked hams from the ceiling. She was so small she could hit him only if she stood on a chair; and every Saturday night at half-past ten he would lift her up, under his arm, onto a chair, in the kitchen so that she could hit him on the head with whatever was handy, which was always a china dog. On Sundays, and when pickled, he sang high tenor, and had won many cups.

The first I heard of the annual outing was when I was sitting one evening on a bag of rice behind the counter, under one of my uncle's stomachs, reading an advertisement for sheep-dip, which was all there was to read. The shop was full of my uncle, and when Mr. Benjamin Franklyn, Mr. Weazley, Noah Bowen, and Will Sentry came in, I thought it would burst. It was like all being together in a drawer that smelled of cheese and turps, and twist tobacco and sweet biscuits and snuff and waistcoat. Mr. Benjamin Franklyn said that he had collected enough money for the charabanc and twenty cases of pale ale and a pound apiece over that he would distribute among the members of the outing when they first stopped for refreshment, and he was about sick and tired, he said, of being followed by Will Sentry.

"All day long, wherever I go," he said, "he's after me like a collie with one eye. I got a shadow of my own *and* a dog. I don't need no Tom, Dick or Harry pursuing me with his dirty muffler on."

Will Sentry blushed, and said, "It's only oily. I got a bicycle."

"A man has no privacy at all," Mr. Franklyn went on. "I tell you he sticks so close I'm afraid to go out the back in case I sit in his lap. It's a wonder to me," he said, "he don't follow me into bed at night."

"Wife won't let," Will Sentry said.

And that started Mr. Franklyn off again, and they tried to soothe him down by saying, "Don't you mind Will Sentry." "No harm in old Will." "He's only keeping an eye on the money, Benjie."

"Aren't I honest?" asked Mr. Franklyn in surprise. There was no answer for some time; then Noah Bowen said, "You know what the committee is. Ever since Bob the Fiddle they don't feel safe with a new treasurer."

"Do you think *I'm* going to drink the outing funds, like Bob the Fiddle did?" said Mr. Franklyn.

"You *might*," said my uncle, slowly.

"I resign," said Mr. Franklyn.

"Not with our money you won't," Will Sentry said.

"Who put the dynamite in the salmon pool?" said Mr. Weazley, but nobody took any notice of him. And, after a time, they all began to play cards in the thickening dusk of the hot, cheesy shop, and my uncle blew and bugled whenever he won, and Mr. Weazley grumbled like a dredger, and I fell to sleep on the gravy-scented mountain meadow of uncle's waistcoat.

On Sunday evening, after Bethesda, Mr. Franklyn walked into the kitchen where my uncle and I were eating sardines from the tin with spoons because it was Sunday and his wife would not let us play draughts. She was somewhere in the kitchen, too. Perhaps she was inside the grandmother clock, hanging from the weights and breathing. Then, a second later, the door opened again and Will Sentry edged into the room, twiddling his hard, round hat. He and Mr. Franklyn sat down on the settee, stiff and mothballed and black in their chapel and funeral suits.

"I brought the list," said Mr. Franklyn. "Every member fully paid. You ask Will Sentry."

My uncle put on his spectacles, wiped his whiskery mouth with a handkerchief big as a Union Jack, laid down his spoon of sardines, took Mr. Franklyn's list of names, removed the spectacles so that he could read, and then ticked the names off one by one.

"Enoch Davies. Aye. He's good with his fists. You never know. Little Gerwain. Very melodious bass. Mr. Cadwalladwr. That's right. He can tell opening time better than my watch. Mr. Weazley. Of course. He's been to Paris. Pity he suffers so much in the charabanc. Stopped us nine times last year between the Beehive and the Red Dragon. Noah Bowen. Ah, very peaceable. He's got a tongue like a turtledove. Never a argument with Noah Bowen. Jenkins Loughor. Keep him off economics. It cost us a plateglass window. And ten pints for the Sergeant. Mr. Jervis. Very tidy."

"He tried to put a pig in the charra," Will Sentry said.

"Live and let live," said my uncle.

Will Sentry blushed.

"Sinbad the Sailor's Arms. Got to keep in with him. Old O. Jones."

"Why old O. Jones?" said Will Sentry.

"Old O. Jones always goes," said my uncle.

I looked down at the kitchen table. The tin of sardines was gone. By Gee, I said to myself, Uncle's wife is quick as a flash.

"Cuthbert Johnny Fortnight. Now there's a card," said my uncle.

"He whistles after women," Will Sentry said.

"So do you," said Mr. Benjamin Franklyn, "in your mind."

My uncle at last approved the whole list, pausing only to say, when he came across one name, "If we weren't a Christian community, we'd chuck that Bob the Fiddle in the sea."

"We can do that in Porthcawl," said Mr. Franklyn, and soon after that he went, Will Sentry no more than an inch behind him, their Sunday-bright boots squeaking on the kitchen cobbles.

And then, suddenly, there was my uncle's wife standing in front of the dresser, with a china dog in one hand. By Gee, I said to myself again, did you ever see such a woman, if that's what she is. The lamps were not lit yet in the kitchen and she stood in a wood of shadows, with the plates on the dresser behind her shining—like pink and white eyes.

"If you go on that outing on Saturday, Mr. Thomas," she said to my uncle in her small, silk voice, "I'm going home to my mother's."

Holy Mo, I thought, she's got a mother. Now that's one old bald mouse of a hundred and five I won't be wanting to meet in a dark lane.

"It's me or the outing, Mr. Thomas."

I would have made my choice at once, but it was almost half a minute before my uncle said, "Well, then, Sarah, it's the outing, my love." He lifted her up, under his arm, onto a chair in the kitchen, and she hit him on the head with the china dog. Then he lifted her down again, and then I said good night.

For the rest of the week my uncle's wife whisked quiet and quick round the house with her darting duster, my uncle blew and bugled and swole, and I kept myself busy all the time being up to no good. And then at breakfast time on Saturday morning, the morning of the outing, I found a note on the kitchen table. It said, "There's some eggs in the pantry. Take your boots off before you go to bed." My uncle's wife had gone, as quick as a flash.

When my uncle saw the note, he tugged out the flag of his handkerchief and blew such a hubbub of trumpets that the plates on the dresser shook. "It's the same every year," he said. And then he looked at me. "But this year it's different. *You'll* have to come on the outing, too, and what the members will say I dare not think."

The charabanc drew up outside, and when the members of the outing saw my uncle and me squeeze out of the shop together, both of us cat-licked and brushed in our Sunday best, they snarled like a zoo.

"Are you bringing a *boy?*" asked Mr. Benjamin Franklyn as we climbed into the charabanc. He looked at me with horror.

"Boys is nasty," said Mr. Weazley.

"He hasn't paid his contributions," Will Sentry said.

"No room for boys. Boys get sick in charabancs."

"So do you, Enoch Davies," said my uncle.

"Might as well bring *women.*"

The way they said it, women were worse than boys.

"Better than bringing grandfathers."

"Grandfathers is nasty, too," said Mr. Weazley.

"What can we do with him when we stop for refreshments?"

"I'm a grandfather," said Mr. Weazley.

"Twenty-six minutes to opening time," shouted an old man in a panama hat, not looking at a watch. They forgot me at once.

"Good old Mr. Cadwalladwr," they cried, and the charabanc started off down the village street.

A few cold women stood at their doorways, grimly watching us go. A very small boy waved goodbye, and his mother boxed his ears. It was a beautiful August morning.

We were out of the village, and over the bridge, and up the hill toward Steeplehat Wood when Mr. Franklyn, with his list of names in his hand, called out loud, "Where's old O. Jones?"

"Where's old O.?"

"We've left old O. behind."

"Can't go without old O."

And though Mr. Weazley hissed all the way, we turned and drove back to the village, where, outside the Prince of Wales,

old O. Jones was waiting patiently and alone with a canvas
bag.

"I didn't want to come at all," old O. Jones said as they
hoisted him into the charabanc and clapped him on the back
and pushed him on a seat and stuck a bottle in his hand, "but
I always go." And over the bridge and up the hill and under
the deep green wood and along the dusty road we wove, slow
cows and ducks flying by, until "Stop the bus!" Mr. Weazley
cried, "I left my teeth on the mantelpiece."

"Never you mind," they said, "you're not going to bite nobody," and they gave him a bottle with a straw.

"I might want to smile," he said.

"Not you," they said.

"What's the time, Mr. Cadwalladwr?"

"Twelve minutes to go," shouted back the old man in the
panama, and they all began to curse him.

The charabanc pulled up outside the Mountain Sheep, a small,
unhappy public house with a thatched roof like a wig with ring-
worm. From a flagpole by the Gents fluttered the flag of Siam.
I knew it was the flag of Siam because of cigarette cards. The
landlord stood at the door to welcome us, simpering like a wolf.
He was a long, lean, black-fanged man with a greased love-
curl and pouncing eyes. "What a beautiful August day!" he
said, and touched his love-curl with a claw. That was the way
he must have welcomed the Mountain Sheep before he ate it,
I said to myself. The members rushed out, bleating, and into
the bar.

"You keep an eye on the charra," my uncle said, "see nobody
steals it now."

"There's nobody to steal it," I said, "except some cows," but
my uncle was gustily blowing his bugle in the bar. I looked
at the cows opposite, and they looked at me. There was nothing else for us to do. Forty-five minutes passed, like a very

slow cloud. The sun shone down on the lonely road, the lost, unwanted boy, and the lake-eyed cows. In the dark bar they were so happy they were breaking glasses. A Shoni-Onion Breton man, with a beret and a necklace of onions, bicycled down the road and stopped at the door.

"*Quelle un grand matin, monsieur,*" I said.

"There's French, boy bach!" he said.

I followed him down the passage, and peered into the bar. I could hardly recognize the members of the outing. They had all changed color. Beetroot, rhubarb and puce, they hollered and rollicked in that dark, damp hole like enormous ancient bad boys, and my uncle surged in the middle, all red whiskers and bellies. On the floor was broken glass and Mr. Weazley.

"Drinks all round," cried Bob the Fiddle, a small, absconding man with bright blue eyes and a plump smile.

"Who's been robbing the orphans?"

"Who sold his little babby to the gyppoes?"

"Trust old Bob, he'll let you down."

"You will have your little joke," said Bob the Fiddle, smiling like a razor, "but I forgive you, boys."

Out of the fug and babel I heard: "Where's old O. Jones?" "Where are you, old O.?" "He's in the kitchen cooking his dinner." "He never forgets his dinner time." "Good old O. Jones." "Come out and fight." "No, not now, later." "No, now when I'm in a temper." "Look at Will Sentry, he's proper snobbled." "Look at his willful feet." "Look at Mr. Weazley lording it on the floor."

Mr. Weazley got up, hissing like a gander. "That boy pushed me down deliberate," he said, pointing to me at the door, and I slunk away down the passage and out to the mild, good cows.

Time clouded over, the cows wondered, I threw a stone at them and they wandered, wondering, away. Then out blew my Uncle, ballooning, and one by one the members lumbered after him in a grizzle. They had drunk the Mountain Sheep dry. Mr. Weazley had won a string of onions that the Shoni-Onion man had raffled in the bar.

"What's the good of onions if you left your teeth on the mantelpiece?" he said. And when I looked through the back window of the thundering charabanc, I saw the pub grow smaller in the distance. And the flag of Siam, from the flag-pole by the Gents, fluttered now at half mast.

The Blue Bull, the Dragon, the Star of Wales, the Twll in the Wall, the Sour Grapes, the Shepherd's Arms, the Bells of Aberdovey: I had nothing to do in the whole wild August world but remember the names where the outing stopped and keep an eye on the charabanc. And whenever it passed a public house, Mr. Weazley would cough like a billy goat and cry, "Stop the bus, I'm dying of breath." And back we would all have to go.

Closing time meant nothing to the members of that outing. Behind locked doors, they hymned and rumpused all the beautiful afternoon. And, when a policeman entered the Druid's Tap by the back door, and found them all choral with beer, "Sssh!" said Noah Bowen, "the pub is shut."

"Where do you come from?" he said in his buttoned, blue voice.

They told him.

"I got a auntie there," the policeman said. And very soon he was singing "Asleep in the Deep."

Off we drove again at last, the charabanc bouncing with tenors and flagons, and came to a river that rushed along among willows.

"Water!" they shouted.

"Porthcawl!" sang my uncle.

"Where's the donkeys?" said Mr. Weazley.

And out they lurched, to paddle and whoop in the cool, white, winding water. Mr. Franklyn, trying to polka on the slippery stones, fell in twice. "Nothing is simple," he said with dignity as he oozed up the bank.

"It's cold!" they cried.

"It's lovely!"

"It's smooth as a moth's nose!"

"It's *better* than Porthcawl!"

And dusk came down warm and gentle on thirty wild, wet, pickled, splashing men without a care in the world at the end of the world in the west of Wales. And, "Who goes there?" called Will Sentry to a wild duck flying.

They stopped at the Hermit's Nest for a rum to keep out the cold. "I played for Aberavon in 1898," said a stranger to Enoch Davies.

"Liar," said Enoch Davies.

"I can show the photos," said the stranger.

"Forged," said Enoch Davies.

"And I'll show you my cap at home."

"Stolen."

"I got friends to prove it," the stranger said in a fury.

"Bribed," said Enoch Davies.

On the way home, through the simmering moonsplashed dark, old O. Jones began to cook his supper on a primus stove in the middle of the charabanc. Mr. Weazley coughed himself blue in the smoke. "Stop the bus!" he cried, "I'm dying of breath." We all climbed down into the moonlight. There was not a public house in sight. So they carried out the remaining cases, and the primus stove, and old O. Jones himself, and took them into a field, and sat down in a circle in the field and drank and sang while old O. Jones cooked sausage and mash and the moon flew above us. And there I drifted to sleep against my uncle's mountainous waistcoat, and, as I slept, "Who goes there?" called out Will Sentry to the flying moon.

MR. HIGGINBOTHAM'S CATASTROPHE

by NATHANIEL HAWTHORNE

A YOUNG fellow, a tobacco pedlar by trade, was on his way from Morristown, where he had dealt largely with the Deacon of the Shaker settlement, to the village of Parker's Falls, on Salmon River. He had a neat little cart, painted green, with a box of cigars depicted on each side panel, and an Indian chief, holding a pipe and a golden tobacco stalk, on the rear. The pedlar drove a smart little mare, and was a young man of excellent character, keen at a bargain, but none the worse liked by the Yankees, who, as I have heard them say, would rather be shaved with a sharp razor than a dull one. Especially was he beloved by the pretty girls along the Connecticut, whose favor he used to court by presents of the best smoking tobacco in his stock, knowing well that the country lasses of New England are generally great performers on pipes. Moreover, as will be seen in the course of my story, the pedlar was inquisitive, and something of a tattler, always itching to hear the news and anxious to tell it again.

After an early breakfast at Morristown, the tobacco pedlar, whose name was Dominicus Pike, had travelled seven miles through a solitary piece of woods, without speaking a word to anybody but himself and his little gray mare. It being nearly seven o'clock, he was as eager to hold a morning gossip as a city shopkeeper to read the morning paper. An opportunity seemed at hand when, after lighting a cigar with a sunglass, he looked up, and perceived a man coming over the brow of the hill at the foot of which the pedlar had stopped his green cart. Dominicus watched him as he descended, and noticed that he carried a bundle over his shoulder on the end of a stick, and travelled with a weary, yet determined pace. He did not look as if he had started in the freshness of the morning, but had footed it all night, and meant to do the same all day.

"Good morning, mister," said Dominicus, when within speaking distance. "You go a pretty good jog. What's the latest news at Parker's Falls?"

The man pulled the broad brim of a gray hat over his eyes, and answered, rather sullenly, that he did not come from Parker's Falls, which, as being the limit of his own day's journey, the pedlar had naturally mentioned in his inquiry.

"Well, then," rejoined Dominicus Pike, "let's have the latest news where you did come from. I'm not particular about Parker's Falls. Any place will answer."

Being thus importuned, the traveller—who was as ill-looking a fellow as one would desire to meet in a solitary piece of woods —appeared to hesitate a little, as if he was either searching his memory for news, or weighing the expediency of telling it. At last, mounting on the step of the cart, he whispered in the ear of Dominicus, though he might have shouted aloud and no other mortal would have heard him.

"I do remember one little trifle of news," said he. "Old Mr. Higginbotham, of Kimballton, was murdered in his orchard, at eight o'clock last night, by an Irishman and a nigger. They strung him up to the branch of a Saint Michael's pear-tree, where nobody would find him till the morning."

As soon as this horrible intelligence was communicated, the stranger betook himself to his journey again, with more speed than ever, not even turning his head when Dominicus invited him to smoke a Spanish cigar and relate all the particulars. The pedlar whistled to his mare and went up the hill, pondering on the doleful fate of Mr. Higginbotham, whom he had known in the way of trade, having sold him many a bunch of long nines, and a great deal of pigtail, lady's twist, and fig tobacco. He was rather astonished at the rapidity with which the news had spread. Kimballton was nearly sixty miles distant in a straight line; the murder had been perpetrated only at eight o'clock the preceding night; yet Dominicus had heard of it at seven in the morning, when, in all probability, poor Mr. Higginbotham's own family had but just discovered his corpse, hanging on the Saint Michael's pear-tree. The stranger on foot must have worn seven-league boots to travel at such a rate.

"Ill news flies fast, they say," thought Dominicus Pike; "but this beats railroads. The fellow ought to be hired to go express with the President's Message."

The difficulty was solved by supposing that the narrator had made a mistake of one day in the date of the occurrence, so that our friend did not hesitate to introduce the story at every tavern and country store along the road, expending a whole bunch of Spanish wrappers among at least twenty horrified audiences. He found himself invariably the first bearer of the intelligence, and was so pestered with questions that he could not avoid filling up the outline, till it became quite a respectable narrative. He met with one piece of corroborative evidence. Mr. Higginbotham was a trader; and a former clerk of his, to whom Dominicus related the facts, testified that the old gentleman was accustomed to return home through the orchard about nightfall, with the money and valuable papers of the store in his pocket. The clerk manifested but little grief at Mr. Higginbotham's catastrophe, hinting, what the pedlar had discovered in his own dealings with him, that he was a crusty old fellow, as close as a vice. His property would descend to a pretty niece who was now keeping school in Kimballton.

What with telling the news for the public good, and driving bargains for his own, Dominicus was so much delayed on the road that he chose to put up at a tavern, about five miles short of Parker's Falls. After supper, lighting one of his prime cigars, he seated himself in the bar-room, and went through the story of the murder, which had grown so fast that it took him half an hour to tell. There were as many as twenty people in the room, nineteen of whom received it all for gospel. But the twentieth was an elderly farmer, who had arrived on horseback a short time before, and was now seated in a corner smoking his pipe. When the story was concluded, he rose up very deliberately, brought his chair right in front of Dominicus, and stared him full in the face, puffing out the vilest tobacco smoke the pedlar had ever smelt.

"Will you make affidavit," demanded he, in the tone of a country justice taking an examination, "that old Squire Higginbotham of Kimballton was murdered in his orchard the night before last, and found hanging on his great pear-tree yesterday morning?"

"I tell the story as I heard it, mister," answered Dominicus, dropping his half-burnt cigar; "I don't say that I saw the thing done. So I can't take my oath that he was murdered exactly in that way."

"But I can take mine," said the farmer, "that if Squire Higginbotham was murdered night before last, I drank a glass of bitters with his ghost this morning. Being a neighbor of mine, he called me into his store, as I was riding by, and treated me, and then asked me to do a little business for him on the road. He didn't seem to know any more about his own murder than I did."

"Why, then, it can't be a fact!" exclaimed Dominicus Pike.

"I guess he'd have mentioned, if it was," said the old farmer; and he removed his chair back to the corner, leaving Dominicus quite down in the mouth.

Here was a sad resurrection of old Mr. Higginbotham! The pedlar had no heart to mingle in the conversation any more, but comforted himself with a glass of gin and water, and went to bed, where, all night long, he dreamed of hanging on the Saint Michael's pear-tree. To avoid the old farmer (whom he so detested that his suspension would have pleased him better than Mr. Higginbotham's), Dominicus rose in the gray of the morning, put the little mare into the green cart, and trotted swiftly away towards Parker's Falls. The fresh breeze, the dewy road, and the pleasant summer dawn revived his spirits and might have encouraged him to repeat the old story had there been anybody awake to hear it. But he met neither ox team, light wagon, chaise, horseman, nor foot traveler, till, just as he crossed Salmon River, a man came trudging down to the bridge with a bundle over his shoulder, on the end of a stick.

"Good morning, mister," said the pedlar, reining in his mare. "If you come from Kimballton or that neighborhood, maybe you can tell me the real fact about this affair of old Mr. Higginbotham. Was the old fellow actually murdered two or three nights ago, by an Irishman and a nigger?"

Dominicus had spoken in too great a hurry to observe, at first, that the stranger himself had a deep tinge of Negro blood. On hearing this sudden question, the Ethiopian appeared to change his skin, its yellow hue becoming a ghastly white, while, shaking and stammering, he thus replied:

"No! no! There was no colored man! It was an Irishman that hanged him last night, at eight o'clock. I came away at seven! His folks can't have looked for him in the orchard yet."

Scarcely had the yellow man spoken, when he interrupted himself, and though he seemed weary enough before, continued his journey at a pace which would have kept the pedlar's mare on a smart trot. Dominicus stared after him in great perplexity. If the murder had not been committed till Tuesday night, who was the prophet that had foretold it, in all its circumstances, on Tuesday morning? If Mr. Higginbotham's corpse were not yet discovered by his own family, how came the mulatto, at above thirty miles' distance, to know that he was hanging in the orchard, especially as he had left Kimballton before the unfortunate man was hanged at all? These ambiguous circumstances, with the stranger's surprise and terror, made Dominicus think of raising a hue and cry after him, as an accomplice in the murder, since a murder, it seemed, had really been perpetrated.

"But let the poor devil go," thought the pedlar. "I don't want his black blood on my head; and hanging the nigger wouldn't unhang Mr. Higginbotham. Unhang the old gentleman! It's a sin, I know; but I should hate to have him come to life a second time, and give me the lie!"

With these meditations, Dominicus Pike drove into the street of Parker's Falls, which, as everybody knows, is as thriving a village as three cotton factories and a slitting mill can make it. The machinery was not in motion, and but a few of the shop doors unbarred, when he alighted in the stableyard of the tavern, and made it his first business to order the mare four quarts of oats. His second duty, of course, was to impart Mr. Higginbotham's catastrophe to the hostler. He deemed it advisable, however, not to be too positive as to the date of the direful fact, and also to be uncertain whether it were perpetrated by an Irishman and a mulatto, or by the son of Erin alone. Neither did he profess to relate it on his own authority, or that of any one person, but mentioned it as a report generally diffused.

The story ran through the town like fire among girdled

trees, and became so much the universal talk that nobody could tell whence it had originated. Mr. Higginbotham was as well known at Parker's Falls as any citizen of the place, being part owner of the slitting mill, and a considerable stockholder in the cotton factories. The inhabitants felt their own prosperity interested in his fate. Such was the excitement, that the Parker's Falls *Gazette* anticipated its regular day of publication, and came out with half a form of blank paper and a column of double pica emphasized with capitals, and headed HORRID MURDER OF MR. HIGGINBOTHAM! Among other dreadful details, the printed account described the mark of the cord round the dead man's neck, and stated the number of thousand dollars of which he had been robbed; there was much pathos also about the affliction of his niece, who had gone from one fainting fit to another, ever since her uncle was found hanging on the Saint Michael's pear-tree with his pockets inside out. The village poet likewise commemorated the young lady's grief in seventeen stanzas of a ballad. The selectmen held a meeting, and, in consideration of Mr. Higginbotham's claims on the town, determined to issue handbills, offering a reward of five hundred dollars for the apprehension of his murderers and the recovery of the stolen property.

Meanwhile, the whole population of Parker's Falls, consisting of shopkeepers, mistresses of boarding-houses, factory girls, millmen, and school-boys, rushed into the street and kept up such a terrible loquacity as more than compensated for the silence of the cotton machines, which refrained from their usual din out of respect to the deceased. Had Mr. Higginbotham cared about posthumous renown, his untimely ghost would have exulted in this tumult. Our friend Dominicus, in his vanity of heart, forgot his intended precautions, and mounting on the town pump, announced himself as the bearer of the authentic intelligence which had caused so wonderful a sensation. He immediately became the great man of the moment, and had just begun a new edition of the narrative, with a voice like a field preacher, when the mail stage drove into the village street. It had travelled all night, and must have shifted horses at Kimballton, at three in the morning.

"Now we shall hear all the particulars," shouted the crowd.

The coach rumbled up to the piazza of the tavern, followed by a thousand people; for if any man had been minding his own business till then, he now left it at sixes and sevens, to hear the news. The pedlar, foremost in the race, discovered two passengers, both of whom had been startled from a comfortable nap to find themselves in the centre of a mob. Every man assailing them with separate questions, all propounded at once, the couple were struck speechless, though one was a lawyer and the other a young lady.

"Mr. Higginbotham! Mr. Higginbotham! Tell us the particulars about old Mr. Higginbotham!" bawled the mob. "What is the coroner's verdict? Are the murderers apprehended? Is Mr. Higginbotham's niece come out of her fainting fits? Mr. Higginbotham! Mr. Higginbotham!"

The coachman said not a word, except to swear awfully at the hostler for not bringing him a fresh team of horses. The lawyer inside had generally his wits about him even when asleep; the first thing he did, after learning the cause of the excitement, was to produce a large, red pocket-book. Meantime Dominicus Pike, being an extremely polite young man, and also suspecting that a female tongue would tell the story as glibly as a lawyer's, had handed the lady out of the coach. She was a fine, smart girl, now wide awake and bright as a button, and had such a sweet pretty mouth, that Dominicus would almost as lief have heard a love tale from it as a tale of murder.

"Gentlemen and ladies," said the lawyer to the shop-keepers, the millmen, and the factory girls, "I can assure you that some unaccountable mistake, or, more probably, a willful falsehood, maliciously contrived to injure Mr. Higginbotham's credit, has excited this singular uproar. We passed through Kimballton at three o'clock this morning, and most certainly should have been informed of the murder, had any been perpetrated. But I have proof nearly as strong as Mr. Higginbotham's own oral testimony, in the negative. Here is a note relating to a suit of his in the Connecticut courts, which was delivered me from that gentleman himself. I find it dated at ten o'clock last evening."

So saying, the lawyer exhibited the date and signature of the note, which irrefragably proved either that this perverse Mr. Higginbotham was alive when he wrote it, or—as some deemed the more probable case, of two doubtful ones—that he was so absorbed in worldly business as to continue to transact it even after his death. But unexpected evidence was forthcoming. The young lady, after listening to the pedlar's explanation, merely seized a moment to smooth her gown and put her curls in order, and then appeared at the tavern door, making a modest signal to be heard.

"Good people," said she, "I am Mr. Higginbotham's niece."

A wondering murmur passed through the crowd on beholding her so rosy and bright; that same unhappy niece, whom they had supposed, on the authority of the Parker's Falls *Gazette*, to be lying at death's door in a fainting fit. But some shrewd fellows had doubted, all along, whether a young lady would be quite so desperate at the hanging of a rich old uncle.

"You see," continued Miss Higginbotham, with a smile, "that this strange story is quite unfounded as to myself; and I believe I may affirm it to be equally so in regard to my dear uncle Higginbotham. He has the kindness to give me a home in his house, though I contribute to my own support by teaching a school. I left Kimballton this morning to spend the vacation of commencement week with a friend, about five miles from Parker's Falls. My generous uncle, when he heard me on the stairs, called me to his bedside, and gave me two dollars and fifty cents to pay my stage fare, and another dollar for my extra expenses. He then laid his pocketbook under his pillow, shook hands with me, and advised me to take some biscuit in my bag, instead of breakfasting on the road. I feel confident, therefore, that I left my beloved relative alive, and trust that I shall find him so on my return."

The young lady courtesied at the close of her speech, which was so sensible and well worded, and delivered with such grace and propriety, that everybody thought her fit to be preceptress of the best academy in the State. But a stranger would have supposed that Mr. Higginbotham was an object of abhorrence at Parker's Falls, and that a thanksgiving had been proclaimed for his murder, so excessive was the wrath of the inhabitants on learning their mistake. The millmen resolved to bestow public honors on Dominicus Pike, only hesitating whether to tar and feather him, ride him on a rail, or refresh him with an ablution at the town pump, on the top of which he had declared himself the bearer of the news. The selectmen, by advice of the lawyer, spoke of prosecuting him for a misdemeanor, in circulating unfounded reports, to the great disturbance of the peace of the Commonwealth. Nothing saved Dominicus, either from mob law or a court of justice, but an eloquent appeal made by the young lady in his behalf. Addressing a few words of heartfelt gratitude to his benefactress, he mounted the green cart and rode out of town, under a discharge of artillery from the school-boys, who found plenty of ammunition in the neighboring claypits and mud holes. As he turned his head to exchange a farewell glance with Mr. Higginbotham's niece, a ball, of the consistence of hasty pudding, hit him slap in the mouth, giving him a most grim aspect. His whole person was so bespattered with the like filthy missiles, that he had almost a mind to ride back and supplicate for the threatened ablution at the town pump; for, though not meant in kindness, it would now have been a deed of charity.

However, the sun shone bright on poor Dominicus, and the mud, an emblem of all stains of undeserved opprobrium, was easily brushed off when dry. Being a funny rogue, his heart soon cheered up; nor could he refrain from a hearty laugh at the uproar which his story had excited. The handbills of the selectment would cause the commitment of all the vagabonds in the State; the paragraph in the Parker's Falls *Gazette* would be reprinted from Maine to Florida, and perhaps form an item in the London newspapers; and many a miser would tremble for his money bags and life, on learning that catastrophe of Mr. Higginbotham. The pedlar meditated with much fervor on the charms of the young schoolmistress, and swore that Daniel Webster never spoke nor looked so like an angel as Miss Higginbotham, while defending him from the wrathful populace at Parker's Falls.

Dominicus was now on the Kimballton turnpike, having all along determined to visit that place, though business had drawn him out of the most direct road from Morristown. As he approached the scene of the supposed murder, he continued to revolve the circumstances in his mind, and was astonished at the aspect which the whole case assumed. Had nothing occurred to corroborate the story of the first traveller, it might now have been considered as a hoax; but the yellow man was evidently acquainted either with the report or the fact; and there was a mystery in his dismayed and guilty look on being abruptly questioned. When, to this singular combination of incidents, it was added that the rumor tallied exactly with Mr. Higginbotham's character and habits of life, and that he had an orchard, and a Saint Michael's pear-tree near which he always passed at night-

fall: the circumstantial evidence appeared so strong that Dominicus doubted whether the autograph produced by the lawyer,
or even the niece's direct testimony, ought to be equivalent.
Making cautious inquiries along the road, the pedlar further
learned that Mr. Higginbotham had in his service an Irishman
of doubtful character, whom he had hired without a recommendation, on the score of economy.

"May I be hanged myself," exclaimed Dominicus Pike aloud,
on reaching the top of a lonely hill, "if I'll believe old Higginbotham is unhanged, till I see him with my own eyes, and hear
it from his own mouth! And as he's a real shaver, I'll have
the minister or some other responsible man for an indorser."

It was growing dusk when he reached the toll-house on Kimballton turnpike, about a quarter of a mile from the village of
this name. His little mare was fast bringing him up with a
man on horseback, who trotted through the gate a few rods in
advance of him, nodded to the toll-gatherer, and kept on towards the village. Dominicus was acquainted with the tollman,
and, while making change, the usual remarks on the weather
passed between them.

"I suppose," said the pedlar, throwing back his whiplash, to
bring it down like a feather on the mare's flank, "you have not
seen anything of old Mr. Higginbotham within a day or two?"

"Yes," answered the toll-gatherer. "He passed the gate just
before you drove up, and yonder he rides now, if you can see
him through the dusk. He's been to Woodfield this afternoon,
attending a sheriff's sale there. The old man generally shakes
hands and has a little chat with me; but tonight, he nodded—
as if to say, 'Charge my toll'—and jogged on; for wherever he
goes, he must always be at home by eight o'clock."

"So they tell me," said Dominicus.

"I never saw a man look so yellow and thin as the squire
does," continued the toll-gatherer. "Says I to myself, tonight,

he's more like a ghost or an old mummy than good flesh and blood."

The pedlar strained his eyes through the twilight, and could just discern the horseman now far ahead on the village road. He seemed to recognize the rear of Mr. Higginbotham; but through the evening shadows, and amid the dust from the horse's feet, the figure appeared dim and unsubstantial; as if the shape of the mysterious old man were faintly moulded of darkness and gray light. Dominicus shivered.

"Mr. Higginbotham has come back from the other world, by way of the Kimballton turnpike," thought he.

He shook the reins and rode forward, keeping about the same distance in the rear of the gray old shadow, till the latter was concealed by a bend of the road. On reaching this point, the pedlar no longer saw the man on horseback, but found himself at the head of the village street, not far from a number of stores and two taverns, clustered round the meeting-house steeple. On his left were a stone wall and a gate, the boundary of a wood-lot, beyond which lay an orchard, farther still, a mowing field, and last of all, a house. These were the premises of Mr. Higginbotham, whose dwelling stood beside the old highway, but had been left in the background by the Kimballton turnpike. Dominicus knew the place; and the little mare stopped short by instinct, for he was not conscious of tightening the reins.

"For the soul of me, I cannot get by this gate!" said he, trembling. "I never shall be my own man again, till I see whether Mr. Higginbotham is hanging on the Saint Michael's pear-tree!"

He leaped from the cart, gave the rein a turn round the gate post, and ran along the green path of the wood-lot as if Old Nick were chasing behind. Just then the village clock tolled eight, and as each deep stroke fell, Dominicus gave a fresh bound and flew faster than before, till, dim in the solitary centre of the orchard, he saw the fated pear-tree. One great branch stretched from the old contorted trunk across the path, and threw the darkest shadow on that one spot. But something seemed to struggle beneath the branch!

The pedlar had never pretended to more courage than befits a man of peaceable occupation, nor could he account for his valor on this awful emergency. Certain it is, however, that he rushed forward, prostrated a sturdy Irishman with the butt end of his whip, and found—not indeed hanging on the Saint Michael's pear-tree, but trembling beneath it, with a halter round his neck—the old, identical Mr. Higginbotham!

"Mr. Higginbotham," said Dominicus tremulously, "you're an honest man, and I'll take your word for it. Have you been hanged or not?"

If the riddle be not already guessed, a few words will explain the simple machinery by which this "coming event" was made to "cast its shadow before." Three men had plotted the robbery and murder of Mr. Higginbotham; two of them, successively, lost courage and fled, each delaying the crime one night by their disappearance; the third was in the act of perpetration, when a champion, blindly obeying the call of fate, like the heroes of old romance, appeared in the person of Dominicus Pike.

It only remains to say that Mr. Higginbotham took the pedlar into high favor, sanctioned his addresses to the pretty schoolmistress, and settled his whole property on their children, allowing themselves the interest. In due time, the old gentleman capped the climax of his favors by dying a Christian death, in bed, since which melancholy event Dominicus Pike has removed from Kimballton and established a large tobacco manufactory in my native village.

THE CORN DIES

by JEAN GIONO

(TRANSLATED BY JOHN RODKER)

A SPLENDID harvest. Tight in the ear, short-strawed, pale-bearded, yet sparse enough to show the stony soil beneath. And still the mass seemed solid, and swung its thick pile from side to side in the breeze, like a huge brass platter. There it stretched, grave and serious bordered by pale oats beginning to ripen too. At moments some wild impulse, some girlish restlessness, would take them. Then they raced to the skyline with ragged streaming locks. From that vantage point they gazed down on the opposite slope, its Val Noir, its Vaudrey Valley, its Val d'Enchat or its Combe de Pierre Mousse. There was never anything else. They would always have to stay where they were, with only the fir plantations, the sombre trees and the dense foliage to look at, as though every black ram in the world had been flayed, and the pelts spread out to dry over every inch of ground, and cover every tree. And then the little oats would seem to shudder and begin to rush downhill again, passing like a pale wind over the lovely cornflowers that lit up bright as stars.

The fields of corn were dancing. Weighed down and solemn. Beating with huge freckled hands on a limp drumskin. It thudded as the heart thuds, the very earth seemed reverberating with its muffled kroom-kroom. The fields of corn were dancing,

73

shooting a frantic lark into the air from time to time, which trilled over and over:

"Brrrning, Brrrning . . ."

till the sky's blue waves swept it under.

The Hebron no longer existed. Now all its vast body swarmed with wild mint, goats and grass snakes. The huge rocks, like caps to its watery knees, stood out grimly in the litter of bleached bones and pebbles: the lovely watery leg no longer curved closely about the rock. It was all dead and motionless. The great arms of the mountain stream that, all withered, still stretched as occasional sumps among the alders, were covered with swarms of flies sucking the putrid water. In the forest vale nothing stirred. The woodcutters had departed for the remote high glades. From time to time a woodman or so would come out of the trees. There they stood a moment in the clearing, blinking at the hot sun, before beginning to cross the dry river. The stout boots echoed among the stones. Climbing they would reach La Columette's, and there get their wine-gourds filled. Pale as turnips they were, smelling of fungi and the dark. Yet half an hour at the iron tables of the cafe, and all the coolness had been drained out of them. They would begin to sweat, and scratch themselves, and smell like ancient leather. Then they would cross over the Hebron again, making for the remote depths of the forest.

It was no good gazing at the poplars. Frail as smoke though they were, they stood as motionless as cast iron.

The village wash-house. Now and then the pipe would purl a drop, and the pool would tremble slightly. But the second after it was flat and dead as ice, revealing through the depths the accumulated soap and dirt of innumerable washing days. So densely did it cling together, there in the depths, it seemed a forest under water.

Only the wheat went on dancing, kroom, kroom, kroom, thudding always deeper and more strongly as the heat increased, while everything in which the life was frail slowly perished, and everything in which the life was firmly, cautiously, rooted, the dense woods, the watery grottoes, and the mountain tarns, huddled closer in upon themselves, striving to retain their moisture. Meanwhile the corn danced, rubbing its freckled hands over the limp drumskin, kroom, kroom, kroom, endlessly, uninterruptedly, both day and night, dancing thuddingly like a heart.

Samsombre met Simon in the village square.

It was full noon, and the air was oppressive: oppressive and glittering like a marble haystack.

"Well?" said Simon.

"To-morrow!" said Samsombre.

The coolness had all gone from the shadows under the elm, and the sick fountain moaned and hiccoughed and gave forth a mossy smell.

For a moment they stayed there, hardly daring to venture into the sun again.

Boromé came round the corner. He saw them and stopped.

"To-morrow!" shouted Samsombre.

"Your place?" asked Boromé.

"Yes."

Sailor came out of Columette's.

"To-morrow!" shouted Samsombre.

"Good," said Sailor.

"I'll tell Clodomir," said Simon, "and Jofroi. Barbe-Baille and Doron. You see Martin, Picollet, Pélissier, Belfruit and Cateland."

"We'll begin with the big field," said Samsombre, "the one near Durban's land. How will he manage this time, I wonder. His corn should be ready for cutting too."

"That's true," said Simon. "But he's generally back round this time."

After a moment Samsombre said:

"My word, it's hot. Well, so long."

"So long," said Simon, ". . . till to-morrow."

The vast silence of high summer encompassed them.

That evening Samsombre called on the priest.

"Well, will you be coming to-morrow?" he said to him.

"Of course," M. Lignières made answer. "What makes you ask?"

"Oh, nothing . . ." said Samsombre, ". . . but the years pass—you never know . . . one goes on getting older."

M. Lignières rested a bony hand on Samsombre's arm, and first he said:

"You're sweating."

"It's hot," said Samsombre.

"For that sort of thing," said M. Lignières, "one's never too old. Of course I'll go. At least I can be of some help. Which are we doing first?"

"The big field."

"You've seen the others?"

"Yes."

"When do we start?"

"At three."

"Would you like me to ring the church bell?"

"Ah! that's an idea," said Samsombre.

"Good. What could have made you think," said M. Lignières, "that I shouldn't go harvesting with you this year. We haven't stopped needing each other's help, have we? Well, till to-morrow, then."

"Good-bye, Lignières," said Samsombre.

"Funny," he thought, "why, I left the 'Sir' out."

At three in the morning the church bell rang. People were already afoot. But first to leave was Samsombre, with the mare carrying the sack of bread, the two hams and the wine-barrel.

Simon carefully picked out a scythe and then a stone. There were three of them. He weighed them one against the other.

"I'm going," said Marie.

"It's a long way."

"I should be afraid alone here," said Marie. "There won't be a soul left in the village."

"Is it heavy?" asked father.

"No," said little Jean.

He was carrying the billhook and the water-bottle. As they passed by Boromé's house, he threw a glance into the stable. It was empty, except for a big half-finished basket standing there. As they came to the threshing-floor by the cross-roads, he gazed down on the meadows. The willows were scarcely distinguishable. It was light enough, but a heavy mist obscured everything. Overhead there was the sound of Samsombre's mare picking its way over the stones. Barbe-Baille blew the lamp out, opened the door, peered at the dawn and put down his scythe: then shut the door, picked up the scythe and started.

The women, Adeline, Mélanie, Héloise, Maxima, Zélie and Mariette, came down the street. They had their heavy boots on. Colombe Boromé was taking the short cut.

"Oh! Colombe!"

M. Lignières came out of the church, locked the door, raised an arm and slid the key under one of the beams of the porch. He was wearing his corduroy trousers, and a gleaming white, newly washed shirt. His face was shaved and shining, and his hair was newly cut. A happy smile played over his lips.

In front of Picollet's house he shouted.

"Irma."

"What," she said from the window, buttoning her cotton blouse.

"Is my scythe ready?"

"It's just inside, M. le curé. Behind the door. I won't come down, I'm still dressing. Picollet's gone off already. Oh, that man. Behind the door . . . have you got it?"

"Don't bother. I've got it. Hurry," said M. Lignières, "or you'll be last."

Bearing the scythe on his shoulder, he set off.

Adeline and Mélanie seemed to have muscles of iron. Already they were up by the maples. Little Jean walked behind father. The billhook now rested on his shoulder. Father takes a step, I take a step. What big steps I'm taking. . . . He was wearing lovely corduroy trousers, whose rustling made sweet music in his ears, and boots as hard as horn. Héloise, Zélie, and Mariette were taking the short cut. Maxima had stopped where the roads branched, and was wondering:

"Which road shall I take?"

Barbe-Baille was coming up the hill behind her with his long legs. Then Sailor, Boromé and Philomène Samsombre, leading her two children by the hand, while a little behind came Simon, bringing up the rear.

They took the road, and Maxima fell in with them. The three others went up by the fields.

On the bluff high over them, Samsombre's field came in sight, one mass of corn.

As they went pebbles were constantly rattling downwards beneath their feet. Heads began to appear higher than the box-trees.

Slowly the light grew stronger, but the heat was still bearable. Yet so still and heavy was the air that only by taking great gulps was it possible to breathe.

Marie shut her door and began to climb the road. Her crutch

made progress difficult. The village was as silent as a stone. It took her a long time to pass the first slopes. At last she was on the other side.

"How shall we begin?"

"Following the rise," says Samsombre.

The cornfield is as steep as a wall.

Simon puts an edge on his scythe. Lignières puts an edge on his scythe. Barbe-Baille shoots out his arm in a great sweep. Boromé keeps step with him. Samsombre attacks the corner. Sailor takes off his shirt. Three are already deep in the corn. Four are in line, six over by the alders, four over by the oaks. The women are waiting for the first swathes. Adeline is already gathering them up. Zélie leans forward. Mariette advances. Héloise moves her arms in readiness. Maxima tucks up her sleeves.

The ten by the alders mow upright. The four by the oaks move obliquely: the fifteen in front sway together. Simon is next to Lignières, Lignières is short in the arm. He does his best, but leaves a wisp standing after every fourth sweep of the scythe. Simon makes a fifth sweep to the right and mows the wisp through. Lignières takes a short step to the left after each cut. There are no wisps now. Simon straightens up. At intervals his scythe sweeps inquisitively out towards Lignières. Boromé makes his sweep, then raises the left foot.

Mariette catches the sheaves up. She twists a string of straw, she ties the sheaf, she casts it back. Héloise goes so fast, she is almost under the reapers' feet.

"Mind your head."

Mélanie, Maxima, Zélie pile it into shocks.

Little Jean cuts binders with his hook. Leonard twists them. Mille carries them to the women. Little Jean stops. Now Leon-

ard takes the hook. Mille twists binders. Little Jean takes them
off.

Mariette sends out a hand behind, takes hold of the twist, embraces a sheaf, ties it up and throws it behind. Mélanie takes it
and Zélie places it. Héloise throws down her sheaf, Maxima
takes it, Zélie places it.

"Oh! my back."

Simon raises his scythe. Lignières advances. Boromé finishes
the cut and raises a foot. The corn topples over between all
three, like water flowing.

The centre of the field still sings its "kroom, kroom, kroom."
Not a breath of wind. It is hot. They are thirsty. Little Jean
carries the water-bottle to his father. Old Jofroi never touches
wine at work. Mariette sends out a hand behind. There is no
binder waiting. Her head turns: ". . . Well, children!"

"Here," says Leonard.

She clasps the sheaf, ties it, flings it away. Zélie places it.
Simon sweeps his scythe into a dense mass of corn with a mighty
swing of the shoulders. Lignières raises his scythe. Boromé
slips on a rock. The corn goes on flowing. Simon takes a
stone and puts an edge on his blade. He goes back to his mowing. Lignières sharpens his blade. Samsombre does likewise. Boromé wipes the sweat off his brow, and hitches his
belt up. Old Jofroi is over by the alders. He raises the pitcher,
and spurts the water into his mouth. His face is scarlet. He
draws in his loins. The pains in his back were bad before setting
out. He makes a grimace, straightens himself up and begins to
mow again, limping as he starts. Those over by the alders go
on relentlessly devouring the corn. The women can no longer
keep pace tying up the sheaves. Those over by the oaks have
broken their line: the prim straight line now looks crooked as a
goat's leg. Sailor lags behind. He had stopped to fasten his

woollen body-belt. It came undone, and now has to be wound round himself again.

The sun can be felt rising on the other side of Ferrand, about to burst forth. The mountain-side facing the sun is intensely blue, darting with rays, a floating powdery blue.

Simon reaps with a slow wide sweep that mows beautifully. He is tall. As he cuts he throws his body forward. His reach is long; he leaves a wide clear space all round him. Lignières can still do pretty well for his age. But he stands too stiff. His loins don't do their part, it's suppleness he lacks. He thinks he can do it all with his shoulders, and his scythe turns up as he cuts. His mowing is not even. Boromé is best of all. He is far in front. He eats up the corn like a rat. There is always a pocket round him.

Mariette counts as she follows in Simon's wake.

"One, two, three."

Behind Lignières, three: behind Samsombre, four: behind Boromé, five. Five sheaves and they must step three paces forward to catch up, he is so far in front.

Suddenly the sun bounds over Ferrand peak, beginning to bear down on everything with its vast trenchant might. The air is full of the sound of corn, the stertorous breathing of the men, the singing flight of scythes, and the women's sighs. Lignières stops. He rests his scythe against his body, takes off his shirt. Immediately a horn of wheat appears in front of him. A salient of standing wheat advancing on him. Simon is pressing forward on his left. Samsombre on his right. Lignières, his torso bare, sets to again. Mariette picks up his shirt and puts it near the shock. Simon stops, leans the scythe against his hips, takes off his shirt. Lignières catches up to Simon. Mariette picks up the shirt and puts it near the shock. Samsombre takes off his shirt, Mariette gathers the sheaf, ties it up, gives it to Zélie and gives her Samsombre's shirt. Boromé takes off his shirt and tightens his belt. The four backs are scarlet. Lignières's shoulders are hairy. Old Jofroi cries:

"Jeannot."

Little Jean runs through the stubble.

Father takes off his shirt. He has huge tufts of grey hair on his chest like a ram, and bundles of knotted muscles in his shoulders. They quiver on both sides of his head like the beam of a balance, when he picks up his scythe again, and hurls himself on the corn.

Sailor seems to be dancing with his arms high over his head. He is kicking an ant heap to pieces. Zélie unbuttons her blouse, tucking the collar in. She opens the neck as much as she can. It shows the skin all scarlet, and she rubs her buttocks with the flat of her hand.

Simon raises his scythe; so do Lignières, Boromé, Samsombre. Working in unison they sweep through the corn in a wide arc, and it sinks down suddenly in front of them. For a moment, all are working to the same rhythm, left-right in cadence, in step, with the same thrust of the foot. That helps. They speed forward. Lignières bites his lips. It is hard to keep up. Simon is thirty-five. Boromé's muscles are hard as iron, and Samsombre is cutting his own corn. Zélie has taken off her bodice, now she wears only her chemise, open at the neck, and a petticoat. Mariette does the same. Leonard takes his shirt off. Little Jean cuts more binders. Leonard twists them, Mille takes them to the women. A score of swathes are waiting to be gathered. Mariette sends out a hand, takes hold of a twist, gathers the sheaf together, ties it, stands erect again, draws in her loins and throws the sheaf back. Mélanie takes it, stands erect and carries it to the shock. Simon raises his scythe. Lignières sweeps outwards. Boromé swings back. Samsombre is in his element. The corn falls in front of them like the waters of the Hebron when it leaps over the rocks, and full of mud, cascades through the valley, with great webbed feet, and spumy flying manes like a troop of horses.

The sun spins in the sky like a chalk crusher. All the dust of the earth seems to be filling the sky. There it remains, dense, unyielding, motionless. The trees, the very grass are white with it. The toppling wheat smokes as if on fire, and sends up clouds of dust that quiver and gleam in the drab air. Not a vestige of colour remains on the mountain-side. The earth is grey, the corn is grey, the sky is grey. The heat sinks down on the world like a mountain of cinders.

Simon, Lignières, Boromé, Samsombre, naked to the waist, go on battling with the grain. When they straighten up, all that is visible is the colour of the eye, shadowed by a hat. The rest is a compost of dust and sweat and blood. The blood held off only by the frail skin.

Over everything the same greyness. Everything burns and the wheat smokes. Those over by the alders are naked. Those over by the oaks are naked. Sailor has taken off his belt: he ties his trousers with a wisp of straw. The fourteen scythes pierce into the corn, the legs move forward, the feet trample the stubble, hands twist binders, hands stretch out for twists, tie sheaves, add sheaves to shocks. Fists clench handles of scythes, press down on scythes, draw back, clutch tighter, balance and swing out again. Feet move forward, backs bend, loins ache, heads buzz, eyes throb. Teeth bite, and noses pump up air. Mouths gasp, throats are afire. Pangs of anguish shoot long flames through spines. The earth is grey, the sky is grey. The sun crushes all things under it. Fists clench. Feet move forward. Hands gather up corn. Arms shuffle sheaves. Hands take twists. Fingers tie knots, shoulders cast sheaves, hands catch sheaves by ties, arms pull, shoulders lift, hands set them to the shock. The earth is grey, the corn is grey. The sun crushes its chalk faster than ever. Breasts ache, loins ache, thighs ache, heads weigh tons, and the hair is an intolerable weight. Eyeballs quiver, teeth bite, petticoats burn the thighs like fire.

Little Jean, flat on his stomach in the grey shadow, lies still and motionless. His face is turned to the earth. Leonard no longer moves. Mille no longer moves. Over by the alders, over by the oaks, over by the straight cut there are no more men now, no more women. Nothing but hands, arms, fists, legs, feet, calves, shoulders, fingers, teeth, mouths, loins, buttocks, breasts, thighs still pulsating with the struggle against the heat, against the corn, against the sun. The vast solitary sun crushes its chalk of summer down on the whole universe.

Lignières puts down his scythe.

"Oh," he says, drawing in his loins and straightening his back.

Simon stops, Samsombre stops, Boromé and Sailor, in the distance, Héloise, Zélie, Mélanie, Maxima, Adeline, those by the alders, those over by the oaks, each and all come to a stop. It is too hot. The four in the distance away there, by the alders, can be seen stopping, looking at each other. They raise their hands in the air, towards those taking the straight cut, for Samsombre is among them, the master for the day. Samsombre puts his fingers to his mouth and whistles. Those by the alders put their scythes on their shoulders and move towards the alder thicket. Those by the oaks wait. When Samsombre has whistled, they too put their scythes on their shoulders and move towards the shadow of the oaks. The others have put their scythes on their shoulders and are walking towards the maples.

"A good morning's work," says Lignières.

"A long morning," says Simon.

Samsombre goes off to the mare where the bread, the ham and the wine are. He drags his leg as he walks.

Marie is waiting under the maples. She has got ready beds of dried leaves for all of them, but Simon's heap is thickest. Not that it is noticeable though, she has only bedded them more tightly down. He will notice the difference when he throws himself upon it.

Lignières lies down. So does Boromé. Simon too. And he pulls his hat down over his eyes.

Samsombre returns carrying a bag of bread and a ham.

"I'm going for the wine."

He goes off dragging his leg, and returns with a small barrel.

"Oh! Lignières!"

"Oh!"

Lignières pushes his hat up off his face.

"Here!"

Samsombre holds out the bread and ham.

"Cut it," says Lignières.

"This much?"

"Yes, thanks."

"Oh, Simon!"

"Cut it."

"Is this all right?"

"Yes, that's right."

"Oh! Boromé!"

Boromé sits up on the leaves and gets out his knife.

"Marie, help yourself."

"Lie down, Samsombre," she says, "I'll take the food over to those by the alders, and then over to those by the oaks. Let me be of some use!"

"Good," says Samsombre.

He takes some ham and lies down. Simon eats lying down. He bends his right arm, and bites the bread. He bends his left arm, and bites the ham. Then both arms fall at his side and he goes on chewing for a long time.

Lignières is lying on his side. Boromé is sitting up.

Marie takes the bag, she tucks the crutch under her arm, and goes off towards the alders.

The cornfield no longer sings. Softly, with what is left of the standing wheat, it sighs a little iron sigh. The sun beats down so heavily, you can hear the trees crack.

Marie, the only moving figure, crosses the empty field.

Samsombre sits up. Boromé, his face buried in the leaves, snores. Lignières sleeps. He clenches his lips, but he does not move. Simon sleeps. Marie, sitting, gazes beyond the leaves at the vast face of the sun. Not a movement. The earth is glittering and dead like marble. Samsombre whistles.

Lignières is first to rise. The first two, three, steps, he seems to be walking on knife blades.

Away off, they come out of the shade of the alders. They tramp towards the wheat like huge staggering beetles with the scythe blades trembling over their heads.

Little Jean wakes in bewilderment, hardly able to breathe, his nose and his mouth blocked. A violent fit of sneezing buffets him like a diver who has hit his head on the bottom.

"Forward march!"

At five, Samsombre's field is finished. A hundred shocks, each a score of sheaves. At the top of the field, the ears were small, the straw short and the sheaves like children born before their time. Then they all ate, standing, silent in the midst of the flat field.

The first arrivals were waiting in front of the church. They sat down on the steps.

"Well, what about to-morrow?" said Samsombre.

They looked at each other.

"To-morrow, we could go over to my place," said Boromé, "if you'd care."

"Yes," said Sailor, "only next, we ought to be thinking of mine, it mustn't be left too long in the valley. It's out of the sun too much."

"Mine, that can wait," said Boromé.

"Mine too," said Sailor.

"Best begin with Sailor's field."

"Well, then we'll meet at the same time."

"The only thing is," said Lignières, "you'd better not put too much reliance on the church bell. To-morrow's Sunday: I'll be saying Mass before we leave."

He took the key from under the beam in the porch, and opened the church door.

The bell rang towards three the next morning. Four or five soft strokes rose like bubbles into the green of the dawn, and burst softly, high in the air on Ferrand brow.

Simon rose.

There were lights in the church.

Adeline and Mélanie were walking down the street.

Barbe-Baille opened his door, put down his scythe, shut the door, took up the scythe and departed.

"Babeau, my back aches," said Jofroi. "I'm getting old."

He got up . . . his knees creaking.

"Devil take it," he swore, his hands on his buttocks.

Little Jean was still asleep.

"Oh!" said Jofroi touching his chin.

Little Jean awoke. The first thing he saw was his father standing by his bed. He was so full of the grey wheat he could almost vomit. The dawn was ripening gradually.

"Not tired?" asked Boromé, that evening, when they stood in front of the church.

"Forty-three shocks," thought Sailor, "if the yield's all right, I shan't do badly."

"Well, same time to-morrow."

Lignières took the key from under the beam in the porch and opened the church.

The bell rang at three again.

Simon got up.

Adeline went down into the street. She knocked at Mélanie's door.

"Mélanie!"

After a moment the window opened.

"I'm dressing."

Barbe-Baille shut his door, took his scythe and departed.

"Let the child stay at home to-day," said Babeau.

Jofroi had gone closer to the window. His naked foot was resting on a chair. He was cutting his corns with a knife.

Sailor passed by his barn. He gazed at the bare earth. He counted his steps. "One, two, three, four."

He was picturing his corn.

"I'll borrow a plank from Taillas," he said.

Footsteps sounded upon the road.

Mélanie went by, loins limp and with trailing feet. Boromé's horse followed slowly after, bearing the three bags of bread and ham. Barbe-Baille walked with his scythe on his shoulder, bending beneath it as though it were socketed into a pine. . . .

"You're resting to-morrow?" asked Babeau.

"No, to-morrow's our turn."

"You might have said so sooner."

"If that's all you think one has to think about?"

"But all the things I've got to get ready. The ham, the bread, everything. Heavens! And how do you feel in yourself . . . your back?"

"It'll do," said Jofroi.

He sat down in his wooden armchair, put his hands on his knees and slowly let the small of his back sink against the back.

"There," he said sighing.

With all his weight he leant against it.

Marie was melting some salt in a basin of water. Simon was lying face down on his bed. Marie soaked a towel in the water. Then she went to him.

"Where is it?" she said.

Simon sighed.

"There," he said.

He pointed to the crease in his loins, just over the buttocks.

"Take your hand away."

She laid the cold biting towel on the skin that the heat and sweat had split open.

"God damn it for a life," moaned Simon.

Lignières was stretched out on his bed. Without moving his body, he put out an arm and picked his stick from the floor. Then holding it carefully, he knocked a piece of bread off the table onto the floor. With his stick he went on drawing it closer, till he could take it with his hand. Then he began to eat, the crumbs crunching in his mouth like maize.

"What time are they starting?" said Babeau.

Jofroi opened an eye.

"At three."

"That bitch of a bell," said Simon: then awoke.

The bell was ringing. There was the dawn all clad in green. Nothing moved in the whole universe. The earth was more motionless than ever, now that so much corn was cut.

Marie slept.

Simon rose. He bent down for his boots . . . stumbled. . . .
"God damn it for a life!" he muttered in his teeth.

There were balls of fire under his knees. They burst between his thighs and legs whenever he bent his knees, and sparks of fire shot into the flesh like red-hot iron. A belt of thorns tore at his thighs. The collar of his shirt weighed heavier than a horse-collar.

"Marie!"

He touched her cheek.

"I'm off."

She tried to rise. But only her scrawny chicken's neck lifted itself up.

"I'm done," she said.

"Stay here then."

She watched him go. His feet dragged. He was as full of mutterings as water about to boil.

"Jofroi, Jofroi," called Babeau.

He lay there like a stone, then buried deep in sleep, asked:
"What?"

"Three o'clock."

"Good," he said.

She shook him.

"It's our turn to-day."

He woke.

"What?"

"They're coming to us. It's our corn to-day."

He looked at the green dawn.

"It's a dog's life," he groaned.

Barbe-Baille opened his door, put down his scythe, shut the door, put out his hand to the scythe, and moved his loins forward and back two or three times to prove the extremity of their pain. He took his scythe and departed.

That night, Boromé went through the motions of sitting down a few times, to test how far those legs of his would still serve him.

"Aie!" he said at last.

Colombe sighed.

"Oh, that corn, that corn! And they won't be finished till Sunday."

She could hear her man yawning in the room above: it sounded like the bellowing of a bull.

A hundred shocks at Samsombre's, forty-three at Sailor's, fifty-eight at Boromé's, sixty-four at Jofroi's, forty at Simon's, twenty, sixteen, thirty-four, Saturday, Sunday, Monday, Tuesday. The earth is dead, the sun beats more and more fiercely down, bearing down so heavily on the earth that nothing moves now, nothing at all: it crushes so much powdered chalk and stifling air that the whole universe is white, at the last gasp. And yet the corn of Mariette, Adeline, Héloise, Durban, Taillas, Zélie, and Barbe-Baille is still standing.

Three o'clock.

The bell rings.

"Oh, curse and blast it," groans Simon from his bed.

"Jofroi!"

Not a movement.

"Jofroi," Babeau says to him, "don't go, you'll kill yourself at your age."

"They've done for me," says Jofroi.

And gets up.

"God in heaven!" he cries.

"Damn it for a life!" mutters Boromé between his teeth.

Barbe-Baille throws open his door, puts down his scythe.

"The bitch's bastard!"

Lignières comes out of church. He leaves the door open. He

has grown as thin as a whistle. He stretches himself, and as
he does so groans.

"Oh! Suffering Christ, our Saviour!"

Towards five in the morning, the bell began to ring softly.
Simon heard it.

"Curse!" he thought. "The corn!"

Heavy waves of grey corn swirled through the still air on the
vibrations of the bell. A ball of dust exploded inside his head.
His ears were full of the sound of corn; the spatter of raining
chalk dust and the throbbing of the sun. He turned over to
shut its rays out of his eyes.

"Curse!"

Huge nails of pain pierced him through and through.

"But we finished, we finished yesterday! Why are they ringing?"

The ringing came to an end.

"Ah!" he sighed.

A frightful weariness seemed to crush all his muscles.

When M. Lignières had finished ringing, he came down. He
was still in his corduroy trousers and heavy boots, just as he had
thrown himself down to sleep. He ran his hand over his week-
old beard. It pricked like stubble where it covered the jaw,
stretched up to his eyes, and along his nose, and filled the hollows in his cheeks.

The church door opened, screeched and fell shut again.

He looked. Héloise Catelan had just entered.

"It's time to begin," M. Lignières told himself.

He had to sit down on his bed to pull off the corduroy trousers,
and get into his light buckled shoes. . . . His nose was full of
earthy dust. . . . The air he breathed still tasted of flaming summer. . . . He licked the corner of his lips. . . . It was salty with
all his dried-up sweat, and rough as a hog's back.

Then stretching out his two tired arms.

"It's only because I can't. . . ." he told himself.

He slipped his surplice over the dirty shirt. There was blood on both his hands.

He looked into the church. Four were waiting. Then he called.

"Clarisse!"

"Monsieur l'abbé?"

She came up to him.

"You serve me at Mass," he said.

"An old woman like me?"

"Yes, take the sacring bell, go before."

"You will tell me what to do, monsieur l'abbé?"

"Yes, I'll tell you!"

They went into the church together. It was broad daylight.

"Will you get me a chair?" said M. Lignières. "I know it isn't seemly, but I'm tired."

He watched her as she fetched the chair.

Héloise, Lydia, Augusta gazed at M. Lignières and his week-old growth.

"I'm tired," he said aloud. "There's been ten days of it."

"At your age," they replied, "you shouldn't be."

A pigeon flew in through the open window, and Augusta, fluttering her apron, tried to frighten it away.

"Let it be," said M. Lignières, "it's not doing any harm."

He moved his chair closer to his book.

"I'll read to you sitting, if you don't mind?"

"Oh, please! monsieur l'abbé," they said, all together.

"In a moment I'll stand up," he said, with a soft apologetic laugh. The pigeon pecked at the stoup. Then it began to spill the water over itself, and beat its wings. It was all white, all clean, all steaming in the scattering water.

"Pigeon," said M. Lignières, "if you want to stay, stay, but keep quiet and listen."

THIS TOWN AND SALAMANCA

by ALLAN SEAGER

So WHEN he returned, we asked him why had he gone to live there and he said he'd just heard of it and thought it might be a nice place to live in for a while. He had lived in an old house built around a court. The walls were four feet thick and the windows were larger on the inside than they were on the outside; the sills slanted. They kept goats' milk there on the window-sills because the stone made the air cool. You could see the sticks of a hawk's nest hanging over one corner of the roof, and Jesus the landlady's son—he looked up here to see if we thought it was funny that a man should be named Jesus, but none of us said anything. We read a great deal—he often whistled to it evenings. Yes, the food was good. They had a sausage with tomatoes in it that was very good and the wine was not like French wine, it was heavier and sweeter. And there were no fireplaces for heating but things they called braseros. They were big pans like that with his arms stretched and on cold mornings they set it alight and covered the flame with ashes. They would put the brasero under a big table. The table had a sort of plush cover to it that hung down to the floor with slits in it. You put your feet through the slits and wrapped the cover around your waist. Then although your feet roasted, you could still see your breath and you couldn't stay in the room long because of the fumes, and sitting by the brasero gave you chilblains but they were a

94

common thing and no one minded. Klug asked him about the women. Were they—you know? The women were all right he said. The peasant girls were very pretty but they faded early and got fat. Yes, but, Klug said impatiently, but he was talking then about the riots, how they used beer bottles full of black powder for bombs and when they bombed the convent, the nuns all ran out crying and waving their arms after the explosion and some fell on their knees and prayed in the midst of the rioters but the bomb had not even chipped the wall, it was four feet thick. All the houses were like that with big thick walls and the streets were narrow and the town was quiet. They could not hang the washing in the courtyards because it was too cool for it to dry, so they spread it on rocks beside the river when they finished. It was a very old town and they lived in the same way year after year. Gordon asked him about the spiritual remnants of medievalism. He answered that the people were very pious and went to the cathedral to pray for everything, even lost articles. The cathedral had small windows and the light was yellow inside not like the gray light inside the cathedrals in Ile de France.

Well, I thought, as they talked on into the evening, it is not anything like that here. You see I remember this particular evening very clearly and all that we said, because it was the last time John had anything new to tell us, and from that time on, he has lived here with us in this town. We never thought he would settle here. It is a good enough town but nothing to the places he has seen, not even the kind of place you would close your book to watch if you went through on the train. First there are the ball-bearing factory and the electric bell factory, with the other factories hidden behind them; then there are trees hiding the houses with their backs turned toward you and vegetable gardens beside the tracks; and then you would see the spire, not of a cathedral, but of the Methodist church, and the town would soon dwindle away into the cornfields and just after that you could look at your watch to see how long before Chicago. It is not like Salamanca, but the four of us were born and grew up here and only John had gone away. And when he came home to see his mother, he would tell us these things that made us seem fools to ourselves for having stayed but we were busy with our work and could not follow him. There are maple trees on both sides of the streets and in summer it is like driving through a tunnel of green leaves.

You see he never answered Gordon's intelligent questions and he always disappointed Klug who thinks that all the women in foreign countries wait on street corners after dark winking and motioning yonder with their heads. John seldom was an actor in his own play—he merely looked, it seemed, and told us what he saw. It was the best way, keeping himself out, but they would not admit it, so they kept on with the questions. They admitted it to themselves though. Klug said he thought of the peasant girls with their ankles shining under their tucked-up skirts doing the washing by the river bank when he was scrubbing his hands after taking the cancer out of Mrs. Gira, the Polish washwoman, and the nurse was counting the used wet sponges and the hospital smell made his stomach turn. And when the aldermen brought the plans of the new railroad station to Gordon and sat down to talk and object for hours, he saw the smoke drifting from where the bomb exploded and the nuns praying in the confusion and one of the aldermen had spots on his waistcoat that he kept picking at. Though we had nothing but questions when he came, we all knew that the questions were merely little signs to show that we too might very well have been there and seen these things, and that it was nothing more important than chance that we

had stayed here. He talked late and I remember there was a
bat lurching to and fro under a light down the street.

Mrs. Gira got well though and it is a fine new railroad station.

II

He was in an old boat-house whistling. We heard him when
we came down the path. The boat-house was so old the
shingles curled and weeds grew on the roof, and we used to
tell him that some day the whole thing would give way with
him in it and he would have to swim out with the rafters round
his neck. He had borrowed the use of it from Old Man Suggs
who hadn't kept a boat in years. When we were kids I remember seeing it when we went to the river-flats to look for dog-
tooth violets. It was a motor launch and he sold it when the
tomato cannery started up. Every summer the river is full of
blobs of red tomato pulp and no one wants to go out in a boat
then. But John was building a sail boat. It was May then and
he had worked all his spare time on it since the August before;
every Saturday afternoon, and nights after supper he would go
down and work by the light of three oil lamps he got from his
mother. That was the winter we played so much poker and
sometimes we would go to the boat-house at midnight and ask
John to take a hand. He was always pleasant about it, without
any scruples against gambling, but he never stopped working
and we would shout above the hammer blows, "Where do you
think you're going in this boat when it's finished? Going to
haul tomatoes for the cannery?" He would laugh and say that
a good many waters would wet this hull before she was much
older. We would laugh because we knew he had got the phrase
out of some book, and we would start up the path. The ripples
on the water always shone in the lamplight and we could
hear his hammer as far as the dirt road where we turned to

Klug's house. Often we played till midnight. I won a lot of money that winter.

When we entered the boat-house we could see it was nearly finished. It looked very big and white and seemed not too much to have put a winter's work into. He was planing some teak for the deck, and when we came near there was the acrid leathery odor of the fresh shavings. We had seen pictures of yachts, and once or twice the ore boats on the big lakes, but the things we saw every day, the houses, trees and grain elevators, went straight up from the ground. They had roots. If they had not, as they seemed, been always in one place, they always would be. John's boat was a strange shape, curved for the water. Even in the dim boat-house, propped up with blocks, she seemed ready for movement. I looked at John with the handle of the plane easy in his hand, a carpenter's tool, and we were going to be "professional" men, and I knew he would go away. The boat had sprung from some matrix within him that we would never understand, just as he was puzzled when Gordon asked him how long she was and how many tons weight as if she were a heifer fattened for market. When we went out of the boat-house, Klug said, "So long, skipper."

He went away in the boat as I had thought he would and after this he never came back for long at a time. God knows how he got the blocks from under her without any help, but one afternoon he launched her all by himself, and in ten days he had her rigged and the galley full of stores. He sailed away without saying anything to anyone, down our little river into the Ohio and then into the Mississippi and out into the Gulf below New Orleans. He was gone all summer into October. I saw him on the street when he returned. He was tanned almost black. We shook hands and I said:

"Where did you go? Did you have a good trip?"

He looked at me a moment before answering. "Trip" means

a journey you take in a car during your two-weeks' vacation in the summer, maybe to Yellowstone or the Grand Canyon or Niagara. It is a relaxation from your work. I could see as I said it that "trip" was the wrong word, but just how far wrong, it took me years to find out and then I never was certain. I thought of his boat, a strange and unfamiliar shape, and how he, whom we had seen unsuspectingly every day through his boyhood, had made it.

"Yes, I had a good time."

"Where did you go?"

"Well, down into the Gulf and around."

"Cuba?"

"Yes, I put in at Havana," and then as if he had at last found something he could tell me, "you know, Klug would like that place—they've got a park there where you can get free beer. It's owned by a brewing company and you can go there and drink all you want, free."

"Where else did you go?"

"Oh, the Tortugas, Hayti, Vera Cruz."

He showed me a gold piece he had got off a pawnbroker in Port-au-Prince. He said it was a moidore. He was nineteen then.

III

When he returned next time, he was less reticent. It was not because he was proud of being a traveler but more, I think, that he saw we really wanted to hear about the distant places he had been. When his boat was coming into the harbor of Singapore, he said you could see the junks waiting with their crinkled sails. And when the ship came near, they sailed right in front of the bow as close as they could. Sometimes they didn't make it and they all smashed up and drowned. He said they did it to cut off the devils following behind. The day after he told us that

Gordon asked Tom Sing, who runs the chop suey joint, if he believed in devils but Tom only grinned. Gordon said it was the oriental inscrutability. Gordon is quite serious.

During the next ten years John did all the things we said we'd do that time in the apple orchard. He joined the army to fly and left the army after a time and went to Italy. I went to his house from the office the day he got home. He was dressed in white, lunging at himself in a long mirror with a foil in his hand. The French held their foils this way with the thumb so, but the Italians that way. After that he was a sailor on one of the crack clippers that still bring the wheat up from Australia, and from Liverpool I had a postcard with a picture of Aintree racecourse on the back. It said, "Give Gordon my congratulations." Gordon had been elected mayor and we were very proud of him. How John heard of it we couldn't figure out.

One time there was a card from Aden and another from Helsingfors. You can see he traveled. No one in the town had ever gone so far and people used to stop his mother on the street to ask where he was then, not that they really cared but because the thread that tied them to him as a local boy tied them also to the strange name his mother answered when they asked.

When he was a sailor in the Pacific, spinal meningitis broke out on board. Eighteen people died and they put the bodies down in the hold. The ship's doctor examined all the crew and said John was the healthiest and the captain ordered him to go below and sew up the bodies in shrouds and heave them overboard.

John got a roll of canvas, a reel of pack-thread, a leather palm-guard and a needle and went down into the hold. He rigged up an electric light in a wire cage and swung it from a hook over his head. The eighteen lay there in a row. They were quite stiff, and when the ship rolled, sometimes an arm would come up and pause until the ship rolled back. But they were in the shadow and he did not watch them much because the sewing was hard work about an hour to each one. He jabbed his finger with the needle three or four times and that made it harder. When he got one ready, he would put it over his shoulder and stagger up the companionway to the deck.

High up above him beside the funnel, to escape the risk of infection, stood an Anglican parson, one of the passengers. He had an open prayer book and said the service very quickly, the leaves fluttering in the wind. Then John would pick up the corpse again and heave it over the side. Sometimes a shark ripped the shroud almost as it hit the water; others he could see jerked from the ring of foam of their impact and carried quickly below. There were at least a dozen sharks and John said he knew his work was useless and he took bigger and bigger stitches in the canvas. There was quite a wind and John could never hear the whole service because the wind blew the words away but a few snatches would come down to him. He and the parson were all alone, the other people having hidden from fear; and they did not speak to each other. When John brought up the last corpse, it had been a Portuguese merchant from Manila on his way to Goa to see his daughter, the wind stopped suddenly and there was a moment of calm. ". . . to the deep to be turned into corruption," the parson said. John picked up the merchant, balanced him on the rail and shoved him over and the sharks came.

IV

"And Eloise said it was when she was getting the coffee after dinner. Mr. and Mrs. Booth were setting in the parlor and Mr. Booth was drinking brandy like he always does and both of them quiet as mutes at a funeral when all at once the door bell rang and Eloise answered it and there stood John Baldwin.

My, I think he's handsome. Oh, he's much better looking than him. And he asked could he see Mr. Booth and Eloise said he could; he was right in the parlor. So Mr. Baldwin come in but he wouldn't give Eloise his hat. He kept it and said he was only staying a minute. Well Eloise said she went to the kitchen to get another cup naturally expecting Mr. Baldwin would have some coffee and when she come back through the dining-room she was so surprised she nearly dropped it.

"She said Mr. Baldwin was standing right in front of Mr. Booth and he says, 'Dennis, I've come for your wife.' Just like that. And Mr. Booth says, 'What do you mean—you've come for my wife?' Eloise said she got behind the window drapes so they wouldn't see her and Mr. Baldwin says, 'Frances loves me. I want you to divorce her.' Mr. Booth was drunk on all that brandy and he jumped up and began to shout that it was damned cool and a lot of things about throwing Mr. Baldwin out of the house only Eloise don't think for a minute he could have even if he was sober. Why, John Baldwin's way over six feet and a sailor and always fighting with them little swords and all, but Mr. Booth got white, he was so mad, and Mrs. Booth she didn't say anything. She just sat there and looked at them and Eloise said it was like Mr. Baldwin didn't hear a word Mr. Booth said because he was looking at Mrs. Booth all the time and when Mr. Booth stopped talking Mr. Baldwin looked up at him quick like you do when a clock stops. Then he just says, 'Well, Dennis,' and Mr. Booth began to swear something terrible but he didn't try to throw him out, he didn't even come close to him. Then Mr. Baldwin looked at Mrs. Booth and smiled and says, 'Come along, Frances,' and Mrs. Booth smiled back and they walked right out of the house without her even packing any clothes. And that's all there was to it. Eloise says Mrs. Booth walked right out of her house into a new life, never to return. And Mrs. Booth they say has gone to Paris to get a divorce from Mr. Booth. Well, all I got to say is, it serves him right—he was always running around after them dirty little factory girls. Certainly he was. Everybody knows it. Why you know that little Muller girl, the one with the fox fur. Why Eloise says that. . . ."

I stopped listening then. I always liked to look even at the Italian flags on bottles of olive oil when I was a kid. I had the same feeling then: no one does things like that here, walking into a man's house and taking his wife. If you want a man's wife, you meet her by chance in Chicago and she goes on being his wife afterwards. Or maybe it was like the boat. We hadn't lived with him. He was only the things he had done and those at a distance. Now that he had begun his marriage this way I did not think he would change the pattern, but that was before I knew he intended to settle here.

He was, I thought then, rootless and invincible. He didn't seem to want what we had, what we had remained here and worked for. Which comes down to this, I suppose, and little more: the same trees every day when you go to work, in summer hanging over the lawns beside the walks, and bare with snow at the forks of the limbs and the sound of snow shovels scraping the walks; and when you look up, the line of the roof of the house next door against the sky. You could call it peace. It is just peace with no brilliance. I remembered how bright the gold piece was in his hand.

But he didn't go away again. He settled here very quietly and took a nice little house. He and Frances were very happy, and we all used to say how glad we were that they were so happy. We used to say it very loudly to ourselves and sometimes to him, and we put ourselves out to help him meet people. He had been away so long that he had forgot or never had known them. We got him into the golf club the first week he was in the bank. Everything we could show him about the town we did gladly.

After he had been married a year, we all came to Gordon's one night to drink beer. Most of the evening we taught John poker, and after that we just sat around and talked. John said:

"You know Roy Curtis from out Fruit Ridge way? Well, he came in today and wanted to borrow ten thousand dollars to buy another hundred acres. That piece there by the bridge. Belongs to Dick Sheppard."

"He'll raise wheat. There's no money in wheat now," we said.

"That's what I told him, but he wants to have a shot at it just the same. He offered a second mortgage. I don't know though. What do you think?"

We told him that Roy Curtis was a fool if he thought he could make money in wheat at fifty-six cents a bushel.

"He's got a combine you know. He says he'll have five hundred acres in wheat, and he and his boy can work it all by themselves."

We remembered when he'd bought the combine. Five hundred acres is too small for a combine. This isn't Dakota.

"You wouldn't lend him the money, then? He's coming in Thursday. It's good security, a second mortgage on his place."

We told him that we wouldn't lend the money, but John had drunk a lot of beer. He kept on talking about it.

"He's a smart farmer, Roy. Look at that house he's got there. It's a fine place, as good as any of these here in town. Got a Packard and a big radio. Why, he said he got Rome on that radio the other night. He didn't make his money doing foolish things. I don't know about the loan."

Roy's aunt had left him money, but that was while John was away. We didn't tell him. I said:

"Do you fence any now, John?"

He got up laughing and went out into the hall and got a mashie out of Gordon's golf bag and came in with it. He began standing with a bent leg and one hand flung up behind him. He went through the lunges and parries laughing.

"Getting fat," he said, "I can't do 'em any more."

I had to leave then because I had to be at the office early next day. John was still talking about the loan when I left. It had been raining and the wind had blown down leaves from the maples. The evening had been unsatisfactory and I thought about it as I walked along. I was in sight of my house before I thought why, and I stopped to pick off the red leaves stuck to my shoes.

I remembered him in white with his face grave. "You see, the French hold a foil this way. It's not like the Italians. I learned in Marseilles." That was the way he used to talk. We knew all about loans; we knew all about him now. Of course I could never do more than just remind him of these things because he was so happy. But I did not think he would ever go away again to return and tell us these things, because of his happiness. Suddenly I felt old. It was as if we had trusted him to keep our youth for us and he had let it go. But our youth only.

THE THREE STRANGERS

by THOMAS HARDY

AMONG the few features of agricultural England which retain an appearance but little modified by the lapse of centuries may be reckoned the high, grassy and furzy downs, coombs, or ewe-leases, as they are indifferently called, that fill a large area of certain counties in the south and southwest. If any mark of human occupation is met with hereon, it usually takes the form of the solitary cottage of some shepherd.

Fifty years ago such a lonely cottage stood on such a down, and may possibly be standing there now. In spite of its loneliness, however, the spot, by actual measurement, was not more than five miles from a county-town. Yet that affected it little. Five miles of irregular upland, during the long inimical seasons, with their sleets, snows, rains, and mists, afford withdrawing space enough to isolate a Timon or a Nebuchadnezzar; much less, in fair weather, to please that less repellent tribe, the poets, philosophers, artists, and others who "conceive and meditate of pleasant things."

Some old earthen camp or barrow, some clump of trees, at least some starved fragment of ancient hedge is usually taken advantage of in the erection of these forlorn dwellings. But, in the present case, such a kind of shelter had been disregarded. Higher Crowstairs, as the house was called, stood quite detached and undefended. The only reason for its precise situation seemed to be the crossing of two footpaths at right angles hard by, which may have crossed there and thus for a good five hundred years. Hence the house was exposed to the elements on all sides. But, though the wind up here blew unmistakably when it did blow, and the rain hit hard whenever it fell, the various weathers of the winter season were not quite so formidable on the coomb as they were imagined to be by dwellers on low ground. The raw rimes were not so pernicious as in the hollows, and the frosts were scarcely so severe. When the shepherd and his family who tenanted the house were pitied for their sufferings from the exposure, they said that upon the whole they were less inconvenienced by "wuzzes and flames" (hoarses and phlegms) than when they had lived by the stream of a snug neighboring valley.

The night of March 28, 182–, was precisely one of the nights that were wont to call forth these expressions of commiseration. The level rainstorm smote walls, slopes, and hedges like the clothyard shafts of Senlac and Crecy. Such sheep and outdoor animals as had no shelter stood with their buttocks to the winds; while the tails of little birds trying to roost on some scraggy thorn were blown inside-out like umbrellas. The gable-end of the cottage was stained with wet, and the eavesdroppings flapped against the wall. Yet never was commiseration for the shepherd more misplaced. For that cheerful rustic was entertaining a large party in glorification of the christening of his second girl.

The guests had arrived before the rain began to fall, and they were all now assembled in the chief or living room of the dwelling. A glance into the apartment at eight o'clock on this eventful evening would have resulted in the opinion that it was as cozy and comfortable a nook as could be wished for in boisterous weather. The calling of its inhabitant was proclaimed by a number of highly polished sheep crooks without stems that were hung ornamentally over the fireplace, the curl of

each shining crook varying from the antiquated type engraved
in the patriarchal pictures of old family Bibles to the most
approved fashion of the last local sheep-fair. The room was
lighted by half a dozen candles having wicks only a trifle smaller
than the grease which enveloped them, in candlesticks that were
never used but at high-days, holy-days, and family feasts. The
lights were scattered about the room, two of them standing on
the chimney piece. This position of candles was in itself significant. Candles on the chimney piece always meant a party.

On the hearth, in front of a back-brand to give substance,
blazed a fire of thorns, that crackled "like the laughter of the
fool."

Nineteen persons were gathered here. Of these, five women,
wearing gowns of various bright hues, sat in chairs along the
wall; girls shy and not shy filled the window-bench; four men,
including Charley Jake the hedge-carpenter, Elijah New the
parish-clerk, and John Pitcher, a neighboring dairyman, the
shepherd's father-in-law, lolled in the settle; a young man and
maid, who were blushing over tentative *pourparlers* on a life-
companionship, sat beneath the corner-cupboard; and an elderly
engaged man of fifty or upward moved restlessly about from
spots where his betrothed was not to the spot where she was.
Enjoyment was pretty general, and so much the more prevailed
in being unhampered by conventional restrictions. Absolute confidence in each other's good opinion begat perfect ease, while
the finishing stroke of manner, amounting to a truly princely
serenity, was lent to the majority by the absence of any expression or trait denoting that they wished to get on in the world,
enlarge their minds, or do any eclipsing thing whatever—which
nowadays so generally nips the bloom and *bonhomie* of all except the two extremes of the social scale.

Shepherd Fennel had married well, his wife being a dairyman's daughter from a vale at a distance, who brought fifty

guineas in her pocket—and kept them there, till they should be required for ministering to the needs of a coming family. This frugal woman had been somewhat exercised as to the character that should be given to the gathering. A sit-still party had its advantages; but an undisturbed position of ease in chairs and settles was apt to lead on the men to such an unconscionable deal of toping that they would sometimes fairly drink the house dry. A dancing-party was the alternative; but this, while avoiding the foregoing objection on the score of good drink, had a counterbalancing disadvantage in the matter of good victuals, the ravenous appetites engendered by the exercise causing immense havoc in the buttery. Shepherdess Fennel fell back upon the intermediate plan of mingling short dances with short periods of talk and singing, so as to hinder any ungovernable rage in either. But this scheme was entirely confined to her own gentle mind: the shepherd himself was in the mood to exhibit the most reckless phases of hospitality.

The fiddler was a boy of those parts, about twelve years of age, who had a wonderful dexterity in jigs and reels, though his fingers were so small and short as to necessitate a constant shifting for the high notes, from which he scrambled back to the first position with sounds not of unmixed purity of tone. At seven the shrill tweedle-dee of this youngster had begun, accompanied by a booming ground-bass from Elijah New, the parish-clerk, who had thoughtfully brought with him his favorite musical instrument, the serpent. Dancing was instantaneous, Mrs. Fennel privately enjoining the players on no account to let the dance exceed the length of a quarter of an hour.

But Elijah and the boy, in the excitement of their position, quite forgot the injunction. Moreover, Oliver Giles, a man of seventeen, one of the dancers, who was enamored of his partner, a fair girl of thirty-three rolling years, had recklessly handed a new crown-piece to the musicians, as a bribe to keep going as

long as they had muscle and wind. Mrs. Fennel, seeing the
steam begin to generate on the countenances of her guests,
crossed over and touched the fiddler's elbow and put her hand
on the serpent's mouth. But they took no notice, and fearing
she might lose her character of genial hostess if she were to
interfere too markedly, she retired and sat down helpless. And
so the dance whizzed on with cumulative fury, the performers
moving in their planet-like courses, direct and retrograde, from
apogee to perigee, till the hand of the well-kicked clock at the
bottom of the room had traveled over the circumference of an
hour.

While these cheerful events were in course of enactment
within Fennel's pastoral dwelling, an incident having considerable bearing on the party had occurred in the gloomy night
without. Mrs. Fennel's concern about the growing fierceness
of the dance corresponded in point of time with the ascent of
a human figure to the solitary hill of Higher Crowstairs from
the direction of the distant town. This personage strode on
through the rain without a pause, following the little-worn
path which, further on in its course, skirted the shepherd's cottage.

It was nearly the time of full moon, and on this account,
though the sky was lined with a uniform sheet of dripping
cloud, ordinary objects out of doors were readily visible. The
sad, wan light revealed the lonely pedestrian to be a man of
supple frame; his gait suggested that he had somewhat passed
the period of perfect and instinctive agility, though not so far
as to be otherwise than rapid of motion when occasion required.
At a rough guess, he might have been about forty years of age.
He appeared tall, but a recruiting sergeant, or other person accustomed to the judging of men's heights by the eye, would
have discerned that this was chiefly owing to his gauntness, and
that he was not more than five-feet-eight or nine.

Notwithstanding the regularity of his tread, there was caution in it, as in that of one who mentally feels his way; and
despite the fact that it was not a black coat nor a dark garment
of any sort that he wore, there was something about him which
suggested that he naturally belonged to the black-coated tribes
of men. His clothes were of fustian, and his boots hobnailed,
yet in his progress he showed not the mud-accustomed bearing
of hobnailed and fustianed peasantry.

By the time that he had arrived abreast of the shepherd's
premises the rain came down, or rather came along, with yet
more determined violence. The outskirts of the little settlement partially broke the force of wind and rain, and this induced him to stand still. The most salient of the shepherd's
domestic erections was an empty sty at the forward corner of
his hedgeless garden, for in these latitudes the principle of
masking the homelier features of your establishment by a conventional frontage was unknown. The traveler's eye was attracted to this small building by the pallid shine of the wet
slates that covered it. He turned aside, and, finding it empty,
stood under the pent-roof for shelter.

While he stood, the boom of the serpent within the adjacent
house, and the lesser strains of the fiddler, reached the spot as
an accompaniment to the surging hiss of the flying rain on the
sod, its louder beating on the cabbage-leaves of the garden, on
the eight or ten beehives just discernible by the path, and its
dripping from the eaves into a row of buckets and pans that
had been placed under the walls of the cottage. For at Higher
Crowstairs, as at all such elevated domiciles, the grand difficulty
of housekeeping was an insufficiency of water; and a casual rain-
fall was utilized by turning out, as catchers, every utensil that
the house contained. Some queer stories might be told of the
contrivances for economy in suds and dishwaters that are absolutely necessitated in upland habitations during the droughts of

summer. But at this season there were no such exigencies; a mere acceptance of what the skies bestowed was sufficient for an abundant store.

At last the notes of the serpent ceased and the house was silent. This cessation of activity aroused the solitary pedestrian from the reverie into which he had elapsed, and, emerging from the shed, with an apparently new intention, he walked up the path to the house-door. Arrived here, his first act was to kneel down on a large stone beside the row of vessels, and to drink a copious draught from one of them. Having quenched his thirst, he rose and lifted his hand to knock, but paused with his eye upon the panel. Since the dark surface of the wood revealed absolutely nothing, it was evident that he must be mentally looking through the door, as if he wished to measure thereby all the possibilities that a house of this sort might include, and how they might bear upon the question of his entry.

In his indecision he turned and surveyed the scene around. Not a soul was anywhere visible. The garden path stretched downward from his feet, gleaming like the track of a snail; the roof of the little well (mostly dry), the well-cover, the top rail of the garden-gate, were varnished with the same dull liquid glaze; while, far away in the vale, a faint whiteness of more than usual extent showed that the rivers were high in the meads. Beyond all this winked a few bleared lamplights through the beating drops—lights that denoted the situation of the county-town from which he had appeared to come. The absence of all notes of life in that direction seemed to clinch his intentions, and he knocked at the door.

Within, a desultory chat had taken the place of movement and musical sound. The hedge-carpenter was suggesting a song to the company, which nobody just then was inclined to under-take, so that the knock afforded a not unwelcome diversion.

"Walk in!" said the shepherd, promptly.

The latch clicked upward, and out of the night our pedestrian appeared upon the door-mat. The shepherd arose, snuffed two of the nearest candles, and turned to look at him.

Their light disclosed that the stranger was dark in complexion and not unprepossessing as to feature. His hat, which for a moment he did not remove, hung low over his eyes, without concealing that they were large, open, and determined, moving with a flash rather than a glance round the room. He seemed pleased with his survey, and, baring his shaggy head, said, in a rich, deep voice: "The rain is so heavy, friends, that I ask leave to come in and rest awhile."

"To be sure, Stranger," said the shepherd. "And faith, you've been lucky in choosing your time, for we are having a bit of a fling for a glad cause—though, to be sure, a man could hardly wish that glad cause to happen more than once a year."

"Nor less," spoke up a woman. "For 'tis best to get your family over and done with, as soon as you can, so as to be all the earlier out of the fag o't."

"And what may be this glad cause?" asked the stranger.

"A birth and christening," said the shepherd.

The stranger hoped his host might not be made unhappy either by too many or too few of such episodes and, being invited by a gesture to a pull at the mug, he readily acquiesced. His manner, which, before entering, had been so dubious, was now altogether that of a careless and candid man.

"Late to be traipsing athwart this coomb—hey?" said the engaged man of fifty.

"Late it is, Master, as you say.—I'll take a seat in the chimney corner, if you have nothing to urge against it, Ma'am; for I am a little moist on the side that was next the rain."

Mrs. Shepherd Fennel assented, and made room for the self-invited comer, who, having got completely inside the chimney corner, stretched out his legs and arms with the expansiveness of a person quite at home.

"Yes, I am rather cracked in the vamp," he said freely, seeing that the eyes of the shepherd's wife fell upon his boots, "and I am not well fitted either. I have had some rough times lately, and have been forced to pick up what I can get in the way of wearing, but I must find a suit better fit for working-days when I reach home."

"One of hereabouts?" she inquired.

"Not quite that—further up the country."

"I thought so. And so be I; and by your tongue you come from my neighborhood."

"But you would hardly have heard of me," he said quickly. "My time would be long before yours, Ma'am, you see."

This testimony to the youthfulness of his hostess had the effect of stopping her cross-examination.

"There is only one thing more wanted to make me happy," continued the newcomer, "and that is a little baccy, which I am sorry to say I am out of."

"I'll fill your pipe," said the shepherd.

"I must ask you to lend me a pipe likewise."

"A smoker, and no pipe about 'ee?"

"I have dropped it somewhere on the road."

The shepherd filled and handed him a new clay pipe, saying, as he did so, "Hand me your baccy-box—I'll fill that too, now I am about it."

The man went through the movement of searching his pockets.

"Lost that too?" said his entertainer, with some surprise.

"I am afraid so," said the man with some confusion. "Give it to me in a screw of paper." Lighting his pipe at the candle with a suction that drew the whole flame into the bowl, he resettled

himself in the corner and bent his looks upon the faint steam
from his damp legs, as if he wished to say no more.

Meanwhile the general body of guests had been taking little
notice of this visitor by reason of an absorbing discussion in
which they were engaged with the band about a tune for the
next dance. The matter being settled, they were about to stand
up when an interruption came in the shape of another knock
at the door.

At sound of the same the man in the chimney corner took up
the poker and began stirring the brands as if doing it thoroughly
were the one aim of his existence; and a second time the shepherd said, "Walk in!" In a moment another man stood upon
the straw-woven door-mat. He too was a stranger.

This individual was one of a type radically different from the
first. There was more of the commonplace in his manner, and
a certain jovial cosmopolitanism sat upon his features. He was
several years older than the first arrival, his hair being slightly
frosted, his eyebrows bristly, and his whiskers cut back from
his cheeks. His face was rather full and flabby, and yet it was
not altogether a face without power. A few grog-blossoms
marked the neighborhood of his nose. He flung back his long
drab greatcoat, revealing that beneath it he wore a suit of cinder-
gray shade throughout, large heavy seals, of some metal or other
that would take a polish, dangling from his fob as his only
personal ornament. Shaking the water drops from his low-
crowned glazed hat, he said, "I must ask for a few minutes'
shelter, comrades, or I shall be wetted to my skin before I get
to Casterbridge."

"Make yourself at home, Master," said the shepherd, perhaps a
trifle less heartily than on the first occasion. Not that Fennel
had the least tinge of niggardliness in his composition; but the
room was far from large, spare chairs were not numerous, and

damp companions were not altogether desirable at close quarters for the women and girls in their bright-colored gowns.

However, the second comer, after taking off his greatcoat, and hanging his hat on a nail in one of the ceiling-beams as if he had been specially invited to put it there, advanced and sat down at the table. This had been pushed so closely into the chimney corner, to give all available room to the dancers, that its inner edge grazed the elbow of the man who had ensconced himself by the fire; and thus the two strangers were brought into close companionship. They nodded to each other by way of breaking the ice of unacquaintance, and the first stranger handed his neighbor the family mug—a huge vessel of brown ware, having its upper edge worn away like a threshold by the rub of whole generations of thirsty lips that had gone the way of all flesh, and bearing the following inscription burnt upon its rotund side in yellow letters:

THERE IS NO FUN
UNTiL i CUM.

The other man, nothing loth, raised the mug to his lips, and drank on, and on, and on—till a curious blueness overspread the countenance of the shepherd's wife, who had regarded with no little surprise the first stranger's free offer to the second of what did not belong to him to dispense.

"I knew it!" said the toper to the shepherd with much satisfaction. "When I walked up your garden before coming in, and saw the hives all of a row, I said to myself, 'Where there's bees there's honey, and where there's honey there's mead.' But mead of such a truly comfortable sort as this I really didn't expect to meet in my older days." He took yet another pull at the mug, till it assumed an ominous elevation.

"Glad you enjoy it!" said the shepherd warmly.

"It is goodish mead," assented Mrs. Fennel, with an absence

of enthusiasm which seemed to say that it was possible to buy praise for one's cellar at too heavy a price. "It is trouble enough to make—and really I hardly think we shall make any more. For honey sells well, and we ourselves can make shift with a drop o' small mead and metheglin for common use from the comb-washings."

"Oh, but you'll never have the heart!" reproachfully cried the stranger in cinder-gray, after taking up the mug a third time and setting it down empty. "I love mead, when 'tis old like this, as I love to go to church o' Sundays, or to relieve the needy any day of the week."

"Ha, ha, ha!" said the man in the chimney corner, who, in spite of the taciturnity induced by the pipe of tobacco, could not or would not refrain from this slight testimony to his comrade's humor.

Now the old mead of those days, brewed of the purest first-year or maiden honey, four pounds to the gallon—with its due complement of white of eggs, cinnamon, ginger, cloves, mace, rosemary, yeast, and processes of working, bottling, and cellaring —tasted remarkably strong; but it did not taste so strong as it actually was. Hence, presently, the stranger in cinder-gray at the table, moved by its creeping influence, unbuttoned his waistcoat, threw himself back in his chair, spread his legs, and made his presence felt in various ways.

"Well, well, as I say," he resumed, "I am going to Caster-bridge, and to Casterbridge I must go. I should have been almost there by this time; but the rain drove me into your dwelling, and I'm not sorry for it."

"You don't live in Casterbridge?" said the shepherd.

"Not as yet; though I shortly mean to move there."

"Going to set up in trade, perhaps?"

"No, no," said the shepherd's wife. "It is easy to see that the gentleman is rich, and don't want to work at anything."

The cinder-gray stranger paused, as if to consider whether he would accept that definition of himself. He presently rejected it by answering, "Rich is not quite the word for me, Dame. I do work, and I must work. And even if I only get to Casterbridge by midnight I must begin work there at eight tomorrow morning. Yes, het or wet, blow or snow, famine or sword, my day's work tomorrow must be done."

"Poor man! Then, in spite o' seeming, you be worse off than we," replied the shepherd's wife.

"'Tis the nature of my trade, men and maidens. 'Tis the nature of my trade more than my poverty. . . . But really and truly I must up and off, or I shan't get a lodging in the town." However, the speaker did not move, and directly added, "There's time for one more draught of friendship before I go; and I'd perform it at once if the mug were not dry."

"Here's a mug o' small," said Mrs. Fennel. "Small, we call it, though to be sure 'tis only the first wash o' the combs."

"No," said the stranger, disdainfully. "I won't spoil your first kindness by partaking o' your second."

"Certainly not," broke in Fennel. "We don't increase and multiply every day, and I'll fill the mug again." He went away to the dark place under the stairs where the barrel stood. The shepherdess followed him.

"Why should you do this?" she said, reproachfully, as soon as they were alone. "He's emptied it once, though it held enough for ten people; and now he's not contented wi' the small, but must needs call for more o' the strong! And a stranger unbeknown to any of us. For my part, I don't like the look o' the man at all."

"But he's in the house, my honey; and 'tis a wet night, and a christening. Daze it, what's a cup of mead more or less? There'll be plenty more next bee-burning."

"Very well—this time, then," she answered, looking wistfully at the barrel. "But what is the man's calling, and where is he one of, that he should come in and join us like this?"

"I don't know. I'll ask him again."

The catastrophe of having the mug drained dry at one pull by the stranger in cinder-gray was effectually guarded against this time by Mrs. Fennel. She poured out his allowance in a small cup, keeping the large one at a discreet distance from him. When he had tossed off his portion the shepherd renewed his inquiry about the stranger's occupation.

The latter did not immediately reply, and the man in the chimney corner, with sudden demonstrativeness, said, "Anybody may know my trade—I'm a wheelwright."

"A very good trade for these parts," said the shepherd.

"And anybody may know mine—if they've the sense to find it out," said the stranger in cinder-gray.

"You may generally tell what a man is by his claws," observed the hedge-carpenter, looking at his own hands. "My fingers be as full of thorns as an old pincushion is of pins."

The hands of the man in the chimney corner instinctively sought the shade, and he gazed into the fire as he resumed his pipe. The man at the table took up the hedge-carpenter's remark, and added smartly, "True; but the oddity of my trade is that, instead of setting a mark upon me, it sets a mark upon my customers."

No observation being offered by anybody in elucidation of this enigma, the shepherd's wife once more called for a song. The same obstacles presented themselves as at the former time—one had no voice, another had forgotten the first verse. The stranger at the table, whose soul had now risen to a good working temperature, relieved the difficulty by exclaiming that, to start the company, he would sing himself. Thrusting one thumb into the armhole of his waistcoat, he waved the other hand in the air, and, with an extemporizing gaze at the shining sheep-crooks above the mantelpiece, began:

> *O my trade it is the rarest one,*
> > *Simple shepherds all—*
> *My trade is a sight to see;*
> *For my customers I tie, and take them up on high,*
> *And waft 'em to a far countree!*

The room was silent when he had finished the verse—with one exception, that of the man in the chimney corner, who at the singer's word, "Chorus!" joined him in a deep bass voice of musical relish:

> *And waft 'em to a far countree!*

Oliver Giles, John Pitcher the dairyman, the parish-clerk, the engaged man of fifty, the row of young women against the wall, seemed lost in thought not of the gayest kind. The shepherd looked meditatively on the ground, the shepherdess gazed keenly at the singer, and with some suspicion; she was doubting whether this stranger were merely singing an old song from recollection, or was composing one there and then for the occasion. All were as perplexed at the obscure revelation as the guests at Belshazzar's Feast, except the man in the chimney corner, who quietly said, "Second verse, stranger," and smoked on.

The singer thoroughly moistened himself from his lips inward, and went on with the next stanza as requested:

> *My tools are but common ones,*
> > *Simple shepherds all—*
> *My tools are no sight to see:*
> *A little hempen string, and a post whereon to swing,*
> *Are implements enough for me!*

Shepherd Fennel glanced round. There was no longer any doubt that the stranger was answering his question rhythmically. The guests one and all started back with suppressed exclamations. The young woman engaged to the man of fifty fainted halfway, and would have proceeded, but finding him wanting in alacrity for catching her she sat down trembling.

"Oh, he's the ——!" whispered the people in the background, mentioning the name of an ominous public officer. "He's come to do it! 'Tis to be at Casterbridge jail tomorrow—the man for sheep-stealing—the poor clockmaker we heard of, who used to live away at Shottsford and had no work to do—Timothy Summers, whose family were astarving, and so he went out of Shottsford by the highroad, and took a sheep in open daylight, defying the farmer and the farmer's wife and the farmer's lad, and every man jack among 'em. He" (and they nodded toward the stranger of the deadly trade) "is come from up the country to do it because there's not enough to do in his own county-town, and he's got the place here now our own county-man's dead; he's going to live in the same cottage under the prison wall."

The stranger in cinder-gray took no notice of this whispered string of observations, but again wetted his lips. Seeing that his friend in the chimney corner was the only one who reciprocated his joviality in any way, he held out his cup toward that appreciative comrade, who also held out his own. They clinked together, the eyes of the rest of the room hanging upon the singer's actions. He parted his lips for the third verse; but at that moment another knock was audible upon the door. This time the knock was faint and hesitating.

The company seemed scared; the shepherd looked with consternation toward the entrance, and it was with some effort that he resisted his alarmed wife's deprecatory glance, and uttered for the third time the welcoming words, "Walk in!"

The door was gently opened, and another man stood upon the

mat. He, like those who had preceded him, was a stranger. This time it was a short, small personage, of fair complexion, and dressed in a decent suit of dark clothes.

"Can you tell me the way to ——?" he began: when, gazing round the room to observe the nature of the company among whom he had fallen, his eyes lighted on the stranger in cinder-gray. It was just at the instant when the latter, who had thrown his mind into his song with such a will that he scarcely heeded the interruption, silenced all whispers and inquiries by bursting into his third verse:

> *Tomorrow is my working day,*
> > *Simple shepherds all—*
> *Tomorrow is a working day for me:*
> *For the farmer's sheep is slain, and the lad who did it ta'en,*
> *And on his soul may God ha' merc-y!*

The stranger in the chimney corner, waving cups with the singer so heartily that his mead splashed over on the hearth, repeated in his bass voice as before:

> *And on his soul may God ha' merc-y!*

All this time the third stranger had been standing in the doorway. Finding now that he did not come forward or go on speaking, the guests particularly regarded him. They noticed to their surprise that he stood before them the picture of abject terror—his knees trembling, his hand shaking so violently that the door-latch by which he supported himself rattled audibly: his white lips were parted, and his eyes fixed on the merry officer of justice in the middle of the room. A moment more and he had turned, closed the door, and fled.

"What a man can it be?" said the shepherd.

The rest, between the awfulness of their late discovery and the odd conduct of this third visitor, looked as if they knew not what to think, and said nothing. Instinctively they withdrew further and further from the grim gentleman in their midst, whom some of them seemed to take for the Prince of Darkness himself, till they formed a remote circle, an empty space of floor being left between them and him—

> . . . *circulas, cujus centrum diabolus.*

The room was so silent—though there were more than twenty people in it—that nothing could be heard but the patter of the rain against the window-shutters, accompanied by the occasional hiss of a stray drop that fell down the chimney into the fire, and the steady puffing of the man in the corner, who had now resumed his pipe of long clay.

The stillness was unexpectedly broken. The distant sound of a gun reverberated through the air—apparently from the direction of the county-town.

"Be jiggered!" cried the stranger who had sung the song, jumping up.

"What does that mean?" asked several.

"A prisoner escaped from the jail—that's what it means."

All listened. The sound was repeated, and none of them spoke but the man in the chimney corner, who said quietly, "I've often been told that in this county they fire a gun at such times; but I never heard it till now."

"I wonder if it is *my* man?" murmured the personage in cinder-gray.

"Surely it is!" said the shepherd involuntarily. "And surely we've zeed him! That little man who looked in at the door by now, and quivered like a leaf when he zeed ye and heard your song!"

"His teeth chattered, and the breath went out of his body," said the dairyman.

"And his heart seemed to sink within him like a stone," said Oliver Giles.

"And he bolted as if he'd been shot at," said the hedge-carpenter.

"True—his teeth chattered, and his heart seemed to sink; and he bolted as if he'd been shot at," slowly summed up the man in the chimney corner.

"I didn't notice it," remarked the hangman.

"We were all awondering what made him run off in such a fright," faltered one of the women against the wall, "and now 'tis explained!"

The firing of the alarm-gun went on at intervals, low and sullenly, and their suspicions became a certainty. The sinister gentleman in cinder-gray roused himself. "Is there a constable here?" he asked, in thick tones. "If so, let him step forward."

The engaged man of fifty stepped quavering out from the wall, his betrothed beginning to sob on the back of the chair.

"You are a sworn constable?"

"I be, Sir."

"Then pursue the criminal at once, with assistance, and bring him back here. He can't have gone far."

"I will, Sir, I will—when I've got my staff. I'll go home and get it, and come sharp here, and start in a body."

"Staff!—never mind your staff; the man'll be gone!"

"But I can't do nothing without my staff—can I, William, and John, and Charles Jake? No; for there's the king's royal crown apainted on en in yaller and gold, and the lion and the unicorn, so as when I raise en up and hit my prisoner, 'tis made a lawful blow thereby. I wouldn't 'tempt to take up a man without my staff—no, not I. If I hadn't the law to gie me courage, why, instead o' my taking up him he might take up me!"

"Now, I'm a king's man myself, and can give you authority

enough for this," said the formidable officer in gray. "Now then, all of ye, be ready. Have ye any lanterns?"

"Yes—have ye any lanterns?—I demand it!" said the constable.

"And the rest of you able-bodied—"

"Able-bodied men—yes—the rest of ye!" said the constable.

"Have you some good stout staves and pitchforks—"

"Staves and pitchforks—in the name o' the law! And take 'em in yer hands and go in quest, and do as we in authority tell ye!"

Thus aroused, the men prepared to give chase. The evidence was, indeed, though circumstantial, so convincing, that but little argument was needed to show the shepherd's guests that after what they had seen it would look very much like connivance if they did not instantly pursue the unhappy third stranger, who could not as yet have gone more than a few hundred yards over such uneven country.

A shepherd is always well provided with lanterns; and, lighting these hastily, and with hurdle-staves in their hands, they poured out of the door, taking a direction along the crest of the hill, away from the town, the rain having fortunately a little abated.

Disturbed by the noise, or possibly by unpleasant dreams of her baptism, the child who had been christened began to cry heart-brokenly in the room overhead. These notes of grief came down through the chinks of the floor to the ears of the women below, who jumped up one by one, and seemed glad of the excuse to ascend and comfort the baby, for the incidents of the last half-hour greatly oppressed them. Thus in the space of two or three minutes the room on the ground-floor was deserted quite.

But it was not for long. Hardly had the sound of footsteps died away when a man returned round the corner of the house from the direction the pursuers had taken. Peeping in at the

door, and seeing nobody there, he entered leisurely. It was the
stranger of the chimney corner, who had gone out with the rest.
The motive of his return was shown by his helping himself to a
cut piece of skimmer-cake that lay on a ledge beside where he
had sat, and which he had apparently forgotten to take with
him. He also poured out half a cup more mead from the
quantity that remained, ravenously eating and drinking these as
he stood. He had not finished when another figure came in
just as quietly—his friend in cinder-gray.

"Oh—you here?" said the latter, smiling. "I thought you had
gone to help in the capture." And this speaker also revealed the
object of his return by looking solicitously round for the fascinating mug of old mead.

"And I thought you had gone," said the other, continuing his
skimmer-cake with some effort.

"Well, on second thoughts, I felt there were enough without
me," said the first confidentially, "and such a night as it is, too.
Besides, 'tis the business o' the Government to take care of its
criminals—not mine."

"True; so it is. And I felt as you did, that there were enough
without me."

"I don't want to break my limbs running over the humps and
hollows of this wild country."

"Nor I neither, between you and me."

"These shepherd-people are used to it—simple-minded souls,
you know, stirred up to anything in a moment. They'll have
him ready for me before the morning, and no trouble to me at
all."

"They'll have him, and we shall have saved ourselves all labor
in the matter."

"True, true. Well, my way is to Casterbridge; and 'tis as
much as my legs will do to take me that far. Going the same
way?"

"No, I am sorry to say! I have to get home over there" (he nodded indefinitely to the right), "and I feel as you do, that it is quite enough for my legs to do before bedtime."

The other had by this time finished the mead in the mug, after which, shaking hands heartily at the door, and wishing each other well, they went their several ways.

In the meantime the company of pursuers had reached the end of the hog's-back elevation which dominated this part of the down. They had decided on no particular plan of action; and, finding that the man of the baleful trade was no longer in their company, they seemed quite unable to form any such plan now. They descended in all directions down the hill, and straightway several of the party fell into the snare set by Nature for all misguided midnight ramblers over this part of the cretaceous formation. The "lanchets," or flint slopes, which belted the escarpment at intervals of a dozen yards, took the less cautious ones unawares, and losing their footing on the rubbly steep they slid sharply downward, the lanterns rolling from their hands to the bottom, and there lying on their sides till the horn was scorched through.

When they had again gathered themselves together, the shepherd, as the man who knew the country best, took the lead, and guided them round these treacherous inclines. The lanterns, which seemed rather to dazzle their eyes and warn the fugitive than to assist them in the exploration, were extinguished, due silence was observed; and in this more rational order they plunged into the vale. It was a grassy, briery, moist defile, affording some shelter to any person who had sought it; but the party perambulated it in vain, and ascended on the other side. Here they wandered apart, and after an interval closed together again to report progress. At the second time of closing in they found themselves near a lonely ash, the single tree on this part of the coomb, probably sown there by a passing bird

some fifty years before. And here, standing a little to one side
of the trunk, as motionless as the trunk itself appeared the man
they were in quest of, his outline being well defined against the
sky beyond. The band noiselessly drew up and faced him.

"Your money or your life!" said the constable sternly to the
still figure.

"No, no," whispered John Pitcher. " 'Tisn't our side ought to
say that. That's the doctrine of vagabonds like him, and we be
on the side of the law."

"Well, well," replied the constable, impatiently; "I must say
something, mustn't I? and if you had all the weight o' this
undertaking upon your mind, perhaps you'd say the wrong
thing, too!—Prisoner at the bar, surrender in the name of the
Father—the Crown, I mane!"

The man under the tree seemed now to notice them for the
first time, and, giving them no opportunity whatever for ex-
hibiting their courage, he strolled slowly toward them. He was,
indeed, the little man, the third stranger; but his trepidation
had in a great measure gone.

"Well, travelers," he said, "did I hear you speak to me?"

"You did; you've got to come and be our prisoner at once!"
said the constable. "We arrest 'ee on the charge of not biding
in Casterbridge jail in a decent proper manner to be hung to-
morrow morning. Neighbors, do your duty, and seize the
culpet!"

On hearing the charge, the man seemed enlightened, and,
saying not another word, resigned himself with preternatural
civility to the search-party, who, with their staves in their hands,
surrounded him on all sides, and marched him back toward the
shepherd's cottage.

It was eleven o'clock by the time they arrived. The light
shining from the open door, a sound of men's voices within,
proclaimed to them as they approached the house that some new

events had arisen in their absence. On entering they discovered the shepherd's living-room to be invaded by two officers
from Casterbridge jail, and a well-known magistrate who lived
at the nearest county-seat, intelligence of the escape having become generally circulated.

"Gentlemen," said the constable, "I have brought back your
man—not without risk and danger; but everyone must do his
duty! He is inside this circle of able-bodied persons, who have
lent me useful aid, considering their ignorance of Crown work.
—Men, bring forward your prisoner!" And the third stranger
was led to the light.

"Who is this?" said one of the officials.

"The man," said the constable.

"Certainly not," said the turnkey; and the first corroborated
his statement.

"But how can it be otherwise?" asked the constable. "Or why
was he so terrified at sight o' the singing instrument of the law
who sat there?" Here he related the strange behavior of the third
stranger on entering the house during the hangman's song.

"Can't understand it," said the officer coolly. "All I know is
that it is not the condemned man. He's quite a different character from this one; a gauntish fellow, with dark hair and eyes,
rather good-looking, and with a musical bass voice that if you
heard it once you'd never mistake as long as you lived."

"Why, souls—'twas the man in the chimney corner!"

"Hey—what?" said the magistrate, coming forward after inquiring particulars from the shepherd in the background.
"Haven't you got the man after all?"

"Well, Sir," said the constable, "he's the man we were in search
of, that's true; and yet he's not the man we were in search of.
For the man we were in search of was not the man we wanted,
Sir, if you understand my everyday way; for 'twas the man in
the chimney corner!"

"A pretty kettle of fish altogether!" said the magistrate. "You had better start for the other man at once."

The prisoner now spoke for the first time. The mention of the man in the chimney corner seemed to have moved him as nothing else could do. "Sir," he said, stepping forward to the magistrate, "take no more trouble about me. The time is come when I may as well speak. I have done nothing; my crime is that the condemned man is my brother. Early this afternoon I left home at Shottsford to tramp it all the way to Casterbridge jail to bid him farewell. I was benighted, and called here to rest and ask the way. When I opened the door I saw before me the very man, my brother, that I thought to see in the condemned cell at Casterbridge. He was in this chimney corner; and jammed close to him, so that he could not have got out if he had tried, was the executioner who'd come to take his life, singing a song about it and not knowing that it was his victim who was close by, joining in to save appearances. My brother looked a glance of agony at me, and I know he meant, 'Don't reveal what you see; my life depends on it.' I was so terrorstruck that I could hardly stand, and, not knowing what I did, I turned and hurried away."

The narrator's manner and tone had the stamp of truth, and his story made a great impression on all around. "And do you know where your brother is at the present time?" asked the magistrate.

"I do not. I have never seen him since I closed this door."

"I can testify to that, for we've been between ye ever since," said the constable.

"Where does he think to fly to?—what is his occupation?"

"He's a watch-and-clock-maker, Sir."

"'A said 'a was a wheelwright—a wicked rogue," said the constable.

"The wheels of clocks and watches he meant, no doubt," said

Shepherd Fennel. "I thought his hands were palish for's trade."

"Well, it appears to me that nothing can be gained by retaining this poor man in custody," said the magistrate; "your business lies with the other, unquestionably."

And so the little man was released off-hand; but he looked nothing the less sad on that account, it being beyond the power of magistrate or constable to raze out the written troubles in his brain, for they concerned another whom he regarded with more solicitude than himself. When this was done, and the man had gone his way, the night was found to be so far advanced that it was deemed useless to renew the search before the next morning.

Next day, accordingly, the quest for the clever sheep-stealer became general and keen, to all appearance at least. But the intended punishment was cruelly disproportioned to the transgression, and the sympathy of a great many country-folk in that district was strongly on the side of the fugitive. Moreover, his marvelous coolness and daring in hob-and-nobbing with the hangman, under the unprecedented circumstances of the shepherd's party, won their admiration. So that it may be questioned if all those who ostensibly made themselves so busy in exploring woods and fields and lanes were quite so thorough when it came to the private examination of their own lofts and outhouses. Stories were afloat of a mysterious figure being occasionally seen in some old overgrown trackway or other, remote from turnpike roads, but when a search was instituted in any of these suspected quarters nobody was found. Thus the days and weeks passed without tidings.

In brief, the bass-voiced man of the chimney corner was never recaptured. Some said that he went across the sea, others that he did not, but buried himself in the depths of a populous city. At any rate, the gentleman in cinder-gray never did his morning's work at Casterbridge, nor met anywhere at all, for business purposes, the genial comrade with whom he had passed an hour of relaxation in the lonely house on the coomb.

The grass has long been green on the graves of Shepherd Fennel and his frugal wife; the guests who made up the christening party have mainly followed their entertainers to the tomb; the baby in whose honor they all had met is a matron in the sere and yellow leaf. But the arrival of the three strangers at the shepherd's that night, and the details connected therewith, is a story as well-known as ever in the country about Higher Crowstairs.

THE LEGEND OF
SLEEPY HOLLOW

by WASHINGTON IRVING

A pleasing land of drowsy head it was,
Of dreams that wave before the half-shut eye;
And of gay castles in the clouds that pass,
For ever flushing round a summer sky.

CASTLE OF INDOLENCE

IN THE bosom of one of the spacious coves which indent the eastern shore of the Hudson, at that broad expansion of the river denominated by the ancient Dutch navigators the Tappan Zee, and where they always prudently shortened sail, and implored the protection of St. Nicholas when they crossed, there lies a small market-town or rural port, which by some is called Greensburgh, but which is more generally and properly known by the name of Tarry Town. This name was given, we are told, in former days, by the good housewives of the adjacent country, from the inveterate propensity of their husbands to linger about the village tavern on market days. Be that as it may, I do not vouch for the fact, but merely advert to it, for the sake of being precise and authentic. Not far from this village, perhaps about two miles, there is a little valley, or rather lap of land, among high hills, which is one of the quietest places in the whole world. A small brook glides through it, with just murmur enough to lull one to repose; and the occasional

133

whistle of a quail or tapping of a woodpecker is almost the only sound that ever breaks in upon the uniform tranquillity.

I recollect that, when a stripling, my first exploit in squirrel-shooting was in a grove of tall walnut-trees that shades one side of the valley. I had wandered into it at noon time, when all nature is peculiarly quiet, and was startled by the roar of my own gun, as it broke the Sabbath stillness around, and was prolonged and reverberated by the angry echoes. If ever I should wish for a retreat, whither I might steal from the world and its distractions, and dream quietly away the remnant of a troubled life, I know of none more promising than this little valley.

From the listless repose of the place, and the peculiar character of its inhabitants, who are descendants from the original Dutch settlers, this sequestered glen has long been known by the name of SLEEPY HOLLOW, and its rustic lads are called the Sleepy Hollow Boys throughout all the neighboring country. A drowsy dreamy influence seems to hang over the land, and to pervade the very atmosphere. Some say that the place was bewitched by a high German doctor, during the early days of the settlement; others, that an old Indian chief, the prophet or wizard of his tribe, held his powwows there before the country was discovered by Master Hendrick Hudson. Certain it is, the place still continues under the sway of some witching power, that holds a spell over the minds of the good people, causing them to walk in a continual reverie. They are given to all kinds of marvelous beliefs; are subject to trances and visions; and frequently see strange sights, and hear music and voices in the air. The whole neighborhood abounds with local tales, haunted spots, and twilight superstitions; stars shoot and meteors glare oftener across the valley than in any other part of the country, and the nightmare, with her whole nine fold, seems to make it the favorite scene of her gambols.

The dominant spirit, however, that haunts this enchanted region, and seems to be commander-in-chief of all the powers of the air, is the apparition of a figure on horseback without a head. It is said by some to be the ghost of a Hessian trooper, whose head had been carried away by a cannon-ball, in some nameless battle during the Revolutionary War; and who is ever and anon seen by the country folk, hurrying along in the gloom of night, as if on the wings of the wind. His haunts are not confined to the valley, but extend at times to the adjacent roads, and especially to the vicinity of a church at no great distance. Indeed, certain of the most authentic historians of those parts, who have been careful in collecting and collating the floating facts concerning this specter, allege that the body of the trooper having been buried in the churchyard, the ghost rides forth to the scene of battle in nightly quest of his head; and that the rushing speed with which he sometimes passes along the Hollow, like a midnight blast, is owing to his being belated, and in a hurry to get back to the churchyard before daybreak.

Such is the general purport of this legendary superstition, which has furnished materials for many a wild story in that region of shadows; and the specter is known at all the country firesides by the name of the Headless Horseman of Sleepy Hollow.

It is remarkable that the visionary propensity I have mentioned is not confined to the native inhabitants of the valley, but is unconsciously imbibed by everyone who resides there for a time. However wide awake they may have been before they entered that sleepy region, they are sure, in a little time, to inhale the witching influence of the air, and begin to grow imaginative— to dream dreams, and see apparitions.

I mention this peaceful spot with all possible laud; for it is in such little retired Dutch valleys, found here and there embosomed in the great state of New York, that population, manners, and customs remain fixed; while the great torrent of migration and improvement, which is making such incessant changes in other parts of this restless country, sweeps by them unobserved. They are like those little nooks of still water which border a rapid stream; where we may see the straw and bubble riding quietly at anchor, or slowly revolving in their mimic harbor, undisturbed by the rush of the passing current. Though many years have elapsed since I trod the drowsy shades of Sleepy Hollow, yet I question whether I should not still find the same trees and the same families vegetating in its sheltered bosom.

In this by-place of nature there abode, in a remote period of American history, that is to say, some thirty years since, a worthy wight of the name of Ichabod Crane; who sojourned, or, as he expressed it, "tarried," in Sleepy Hollow, for the purpose of instructing the children of the vicinity. He was a native of Connecticut; a state which supplies the Union with pioneers for the mind as well as for the forest, and sends forth yearly its legions of frontier woodmen and country schoolmasters. The cognomen of Crane was not inapplicable to his person. He was tall, but exceedingly lank, with narrow shoulders, long arms and legs, hands that dangled a mile out of his sleeves, feet that might have served for shovels, and his whole frame most loosely hung together. His head was small, and flat at top, with huge ears, large green glassy eyes, and a long snipe nose, so that it looked like a weather-cock, perched upon his spindle neck, to tell which way the wind blew. To see him striding along the profile of a hill on a windy day, with his clothes bagging and fluttering about him, one might have mistaken him for the genius of famine descending upon the earth, or some scarecrow eloped from a cornfield.

His school-house was a low building of one large room, rudely constructed of logs; the windows partly glazed, and partly patched with leaves of old copy-books. It was most ingeniously

secured at vacant hours, by a withe twisted in the handle of the
door, and stakes set against the window-shutters; so that, though
a thief might get in with perfect ease, he would find some embarrassment in getting out; an idea most probably borrowed by
the architect, Yost Van Houten, from the mystery of an eel-pot.
The school-house stood in a rather lonely but pleasant situation,
just at the foot of a woody hill, with a brook running close by,
and a formidable birch-tree growing at one end of it. From
hence the low murmur of his pupils' voices, conning over their
lessons, might be heard in a drowsy summer's day, like the hum
of a bee-hive; interrupted now and then by the authoritative voice
of the master, in the tone of menace or command; or, peradventure, by the appalling sound of the birch, as he urged some tardy
loiterer along the flowery path of knowledge. Truth to say, he
was a conscientious man, and ever bore in mind the golden
maxim, "Spare the rod and spoil the child." Ichabod Crane's
scholars certainly were not spoiled.

I would not have it imagined, however, that he was one of
those cruel potentates of the school, who joy in the smart of their
subjects; on the contrary, he administered justice with discrimination rather than severity; taking the burthen off the backs of the
weak, and laying it on those of the strong. Your mere puny
stripling, that winced at the least flourish of the rod, was passed
by with indulgence; but the claims of justice were satisfied by
inflicting a double portion on some little tough, wrong-headed,
broad-skirted Dutch urchin, who sulked and swelled and grew
dogged and sullen beneath the birch. All this he called "doing
his duty by their parents"; and he never inflicted a chastisement
without following it by the assurance, so consolatory to the smart-
ing urchin, that "he would remember it and thank him for it
the longest day he had to live."

When school-hours were over, he was even the companion and
playmate of the larger boys; and on holiday afternoons would

convoy some of the smaller ones home, who happened to have pretty sisters, or good housewives for mothers, noted for the comforts of the cupboard. Indeed, it behoved him to keep on good terms with his pupils. The revenue arising from his school was small, and would have been scarcely sufficient to furnish him with daily bread, for he was a huge feeder, and though lank, had the dilating powers of an anaconda; but to help out his maintenance, he was, according to country custom in those parts, boarded and lodged at the houses of the farmers, whose children he instructed. With these he lived successively a week at a time; thus going the rounds of the neighborhood, with all his worldly effects tied up in a cotton handkerchief.

That all this might not be too onerous on the purses of his rustic patrons, who are apt to consider the costs of schooling a grievous burden, and schoolmasters as mere drones, he had various ways of rendering himself both useful and agreeable. He assisted the farmers occasionally in the lighter labors of their farms; helped to make hay; mended the fences; took the horses to water; drove the cows from pasture; and cut wood for the winter fire. He laid aside, too, all the dominant dignity and absolute sway with which he lorded it in his little empire, the school, and became wonderfully gentle and ingratiating. He found favor in the eyes of the mothers by petting the children, particularly the youngest; and like the lion bold, which whilom so magnanimously the lamb did hold, he would sit with a child on one knee, and rock a cradle with his foot for whole hours together.

In addition to his other vocations, he was the singing-master of the neighborhood, and picked up many bright shillings by instructing the young folks in psalmody. It was a matter of no little vanity to him, on Sundays, to take his station in front of the church gallery, with a band of chosen singers; where, in his own mind, he completely carried away the palm from the parson. Certain it is, his voice resounded far above all the rest of the con-

gregation; and there are peculiar quavers still to be heard in
that church, and which may even be heard half a mile off, quite
to the opposite side of the mill-pond, on a still Sunday morning,
which are said to be legitimately descended from the nose of
Ichabod Crane. Thus, by divers little make-shifts, in that ingenious way which is commonly denominated "by hook and
by crook," the worthy pedagogue got on tolerably enough, and
was thought, by all who understand nothing of the labor of
head-work, to have a wonderfully easy life of it.

The schoolmaster is generally a man of some importance in the
female circle of a rural neighborhood; being considered a kind
of idle gentleman-like personage, of vastly superior taste and ac-
complishments to the rough country swains, and, indeed, inferior
in learning only to the parson. His appearance, therefore, is apt
to occasion some little stir at the tea-table of a farm-house and the
addition of a supernumerary dish of cakes or sweetmeats, or peradventure the parade of a silver teapot. Our man of letters,
therefore, was peculiarly happy in the smiles of all the country
damsels. How he would figure among them in the churchyard
between services on Sundays! gathering grapes for them from
the wild vines that overran the surrounding trees; reciting for
their amusement all the epitaphs on the tombstones; or sauntering with a whole bevy of them along the banks of the adjacent
mill-pond; while the more bashful country bumpkins hung
sheepishly back, envying his superior elegance and address.

From his half-itinerant life, also, he was a kind of traveling
gazette, carrying the whole budget of local gossip from house
to house; so that his appearance was always greeted with satisfaction. He was, moreover, esteemed by the women as a man
of great erudition, for he had read several books quite through,
and was a perfect master of Cotton Mather's *History of New
England Witchcraft,* in which, by the way, he most firmly and
potently believed.

He was, in fact, an odd mixture of small shrewdness and simple credulity. His appetite for the marvelous, and his powers of digesting it, were equally extraordinary; and both had been increased by his residence in this spell-bound region. No tale was too gross or monstrous for his capacious swallow. It was often his delight, after his school was dismissed in the afternoon, to stretch himself on the rich bed of clover, bordering the little brook that whimpered by his school-house, and there con over old Mather's direful tales, until the gathering dusk of the evening made the printed page a mere mist before his eyes. Then, as he wended his way by swamp and stream and awful woodland, to the farm-house where he happened to be quartered, every sound of nature, at that witching hour, fluttered his excited imagination: the moan of the whip-poor-will * from the hill-side; the boding cry of the tree-toad, that harbinger of storm; the dreary hooting of the screech-owl, or the sudden rustling in the thicket of birds frightened from their roost. The fire-flies, too, which sparkled most vividly in the darkest places, now and then startled him, as one of uncommon brightness would stream across his path; and if by chance a huge blackhead of a beetle came winging his blundering flight against him, the poor varlet was ready to give up the ghost, with the idea that he was struck with a witch's token. His only resource on such occasions, either to drown thought or drive away evil spirits, was to sing psalm tunes;—and the good people of Sleepy Hollow, as they sat by their doors of an evening, were often filled with awe at hearing his nasal melody, "in linked sweetness long drawn out," floating from the distant hill, or along the dusky road.

Another of his sources of fearful pleasure was to pass long winter evenings with the old Dutch wives, as they sat spinning by the fire, with a row of apples roasting and spluttering along

---

* The whip-poor-will is a bird which is only heard at night. It receives its name from its note, which is thought to resemble those words.

the hearth, and listen to their marvelous tales of ghosts and goblins, and haunted fields, and haunted brooks, and haunted bridges, and haunted houses, and particularly of the headless horseman, or Galloping Hessian of the Hollow, as they sometimes called him. He would delight them equally by his anecdotes of witchcraft, and of the direful omens and portentous sights and sounds in the air, which prevailed in the earlier times of Connecticut; and would frighten them woefully with speculations upon comets and shooting stars; and with the alarming fact that the world did absolutely turn round, and that they were half the time topsy-turvy!

But if there was a pleasure in all this, while snugly cuddling in the chimney-corner of a chamber that was all of a ruddy glow from the crackling wood fire, and where, of course, no specter dared to show its face, it was dearly purchased by the terrors of his subsequent walk homewards. What fearful shapes and shadows beset his path amidst the dim and ghastly glare of a snowy night!—With what wistful look did he eye every trembling ray of light streaming across the waste fields from some distant window!—How often was he appalled by some shrub covered with snow, which, like a sheeted specter, beset his very path!—How often did he shrink with curdling awe at the sound of his own steps on the frosty crust beneath his feet! and dread to look over his shoulder, lest he should behold some uncouth being tramping close behind him!—and how often was he thrown into complete dismay by some rushing blast, howling among the trees, in the idea that it was the Galloping Hessian on one of his nightly scourings!

All these, however, were mere terrors of the night, phantoms of the mind that walk in darkness; and though he had seen many specters in his time, and been more than once beset by Satan in divers shapes, in his lonely perambulations, yet daylight put an end to all these evils; and he would have passed a pleasant life of it, in despite of the devil and all his works, if his path had not been crossed by a being that causes more perplexity to mortal man than ghosts, goblins, and the whole race of witches put together, and that was—a woman.

Among the musical disciples who assembled one evening in each week to receive his instructions in psalmody, was Katrina Van Tassel, the daughter and only child of a substantial Dutch farmer. She was a blooming lass of fresh eighteen; plump as a partridge; ripe and melting and rosy-cheeked as one of her father's peaches, and universally famed, not merely for her beauty, but her vast expectations. She was, withal, a little of a coquette, as might be perceived even in her dress, which was a mixture of ancient and modern fashions, as most suited to set off her charms. She wore ornaments of pure yellow gold, which her great-great-grandmother had brought over from Saardam; the tempting stomacher of the olden time; and withal a provokingly short petticoat, to display the prettiest foot and ankle in the country round.

Ichabod Crane had a soft and foolish heart towards the sex, and it is not to be wondered at that so tempting a morsel soon found favor in his eyes, more especially after he had visited her in her paternal mansion. Old Baltus Van Tassel was a perfect picture of a thriving, contented, liberal-hearted farmer. He seldom, it is true, sent either his eyes or his thoughts beyond the boundaries of his own farm; but within those, everything was snug, happy, and well-conditioned. He was satisfied with his wealth, but not proud of it; and piqued himself upon the hearty abundance, rather than the style in which he lived. His stronghold was situated on the banks of the Hudson, in one of those green, sheltered, fertile nooks in which the Dutch farmers are so fond of nestling. A great elm-tree spread its broad branches over it, at the foot of which bubbled up a spring of the softest and sweetest water, in a little well formed of a barrel, and then

stole sparkling away through the grass to a neighboring brook
that bubbled along among alders and dwarf willows. Hard by
the farm-house was a vast barn that might have served for a
church, every window and crevice of which seemed bursting
forth with the treasures of the farm; the flail was busily resounding within it from morning to night; swallows and martins
skimmed twittering about the eaves; and rows of pigeons, some
with one eye turned up, as if watching the weather, some with
their heads under their wings, or buried in their bosoms, and
others swelling, and cooing, and bowing about their dames, were
enjoying the sunshine on the roof. Sleek unwieldy porkers were
grunting in the repose and abundance of their pens, whence sallied forth now and then troops of sucking pigs, as if to snuff the
air. A stately squadron of snowy geese were riding in an ad-
joining pond, convoying whole fleets of ducks; regiments of
turkeys were gobbling through the farm-yard, and guinea-fowls
fretting about it, like ill-tempered house-wives, with their peevish,
discontented cry. Before the barn door strutted the gallant cock,
that pattern of a husband, a warrior, and a fine gentleman, clapping his burnished wings, and crowing in the pride and gladness
of his heart—sometimes tearing up the earth with his feet, and
then generously calling his ever-hungry family of wives and children to enjoy the rich morsel which he had discovered.

The pedagogue's mouth watered as he looked upon his sumptuous promise of luxurious winter fare. In his devouring mind's
eye he pictured to himself every roasting-pig running about with
a pudding in his belly, and an apple in his mouth; the pigeons
were snugly put to bed in a comfortable pie, and tucked in with
a coverlet of crust; the geese were swimming in their own
gravy; and the ducks pairing cozily in dishes, like snug married
couples, with a decent competency of onion sauce. In the porkers he saw carved out the future sleek side of bacon and juicy
relishing ham; not a turkey but he beheld daintily trussed up,

with its gizzard under its wing, and, peradventure, a necklace of savory sausages; and even bright chanticleer himself lay sprawling on his back in a side dish, with uplifted claws, as if craving that quarter which his chivalrous spirit disdained to ask while living.

As the enraptured Ichabod fancied all this, and as he rolled his great green eyes over the fat meadow-lands, the rich fields of wheat, of rye, of buckwheat, and Indian corn, and the orchards burthened with ruddy fruit, which surrounded the warm tenement of Van Tassel, his heart yearned after the damsel who was to inherit these domains, and his imagination expanded with the idea, how they might be readily turned into cash, and the money invested in immense tracts of wild land, and shingle palaces in the wilderness. Nay, his busy fancy already realized his hopes, and presented to him the blooming Katrina, with a whole family of children, mounted on the top of a wagon loaded with household trumpery, with pots and kettles dangling beneath; and he beheld himself bestriding a pacing mare, with a colt at her heels, setting out for Kentucky, Tennessee, or the Lord knows where.

When he entered the house, the conquest of his heart was complete. It was one of those spacious farm-houses, with high-ridged, but lowly-sloping roofs, built in the style handed down from the first Dutch settlers; the low projecting eaves forming a piazza along the front, capable of being closed up in bad weather. Under this were hung flails, harness, various utensils of husbandry, and nets for fishing in the neighboring river. Benches were built along the sides for summer use; and a great spinning-wheel at one end, and a churn at the other, showed the various uses to which this important porch might be devoted. From this piazza the wondering Ichabod entered the hall, which formed the center of the mansion and the place of usual residence. Here rows of resplendent pewter, ranged on a long dresser, dazzled his eyes. In one corner stood a huge bag of wool ready to be spun;

in another, a quantity of linsey-woolsey just from the loom; ears of Indian corn, and strings of dried apples and peaches, hung in gay festoons along the wall, mingled with the gaud of red peppers; and a door left ajar gave him a peep into the best parlor, where the claw-footed chairs and dark mahogany tables shone like mirrors; andirons, with their accompanying shovel and tongs, glistened from their covert of asparagus tops; mock oranges and conch-shells decorated the mantel-piece; strings of various colored birds' eggs were suspended above it; a great ostrich egg was hung from the center of the room, and a corner-cupboard, knowingly left open, displayed immense treasures of old silver and well-mended china.

From the moment Ichabod laid his eyes upon these regions of delight, the peace of his mind was at an end, and his only study was how to gain the affections of the peerless daughter of Van Tassel. In this enterprise, however, he had more real difficulties than generally fell to the lot of a knight-errant of yore, who seldom had anything but giants, enchanters, fiery dragons, and such like easily conquered adversaries, to contend with; and had to make his way merely through gates of iron and brass, and walls of adamant, to the castle keep, where the lady of his heart was confined; all which he achieved as easily as a man would carve his way to the center of a Christmas pie, and then the lady gave him her hand as a matter of course. Ichabod, on the contrary, had to win his way to the heart of a country coquette, beset with a labyrinth of whims and caprices, which were forever presenting new difficulties and impediments; and he had to encounter a host of fearful adversaries of real flesh and blood, the numerous rustic admirers who beset every portal to her heart, keeping a watchful and angry eye upon each other, but ready to fly out in the common cause against any new competitor.

Among these the most formidable was a burly, roaring, roistering blade, of the name of Abraham, or, according to the Dutch abbreviation, Brom Van Brunt, the hero of the country round, which rang with his feats of strength and hardihood. He was broad-shouldered and double-jointed, with short curly black hair, and a bluff but not unpleasant countenance, having a mingled air of fun and arrogance. From his Herculean frame and great powers of limb, he had received the nickname of BROM BONES, by which he was universally known. He was famed for great knowledge and skill in horsemanship, being as dexterous on horseback as a Tartar. He was foremost at all races and cock-fights, and, with the ascendency which bodily strength acquires in rustic life, was the umpire in all disputes, setting his hat on one side, and giving his decisions with an air and tone admit-ting of no gainsay or appeal. He was always ready for either a fight or frolic, but had more mischief than ill-will in his com-position; and, with all his overbearing roughness, there was a strong dash of waggish good humor at bottom. He had three or four boon companions, who regarded him as their model, and at the head of whom he scoured the country, attending every scene of feud or merriment for miles round. In cold weather he was distinguished by a fur cap, surmounted with a flaunting fox's tail; and when the folks at a country gathering descried this well-known crest at a distance, whisking about among a squad of hard riders, they always stood by for a squall. Sometimes his crew would be heard dashing along past the farm-houses at midnight, with hoop and halloo, like a troop of Don Cossacks, and the old dames, startled out of their sleep, would listen for a moment, till the hurry-scurry had clattered by, and then ex-claim, "Ay, there goes BROM BONES and his gang!" The neigh-bors looked upon him with a mixture of awe, admiration, and good-will; and when any madcap prank or rustic brawl occurred in the vicinity, always shook their heads and warranted Brom Bones was at the bottom of it.

This rantipole hero had for some time singled out the blooming Katrina for the object of his uncouth gallantries, and though his amorous toyings were something like the gentle caresses and endearments of a bear, yet it was whispered that she did not altogether discourage his hopes. Certain it is, his advances were signals for rival candidates to retire, who felt no inclination to cross a lion in his amours; insomuch that when his horse was seen tied to Van Tassel's paling on a Sunday night, a sure sign that his master was courting, or, as it is termed, "sparking," within, all other suitors passed by in despair, and carried the war into other quarters.

Such was the formidable rival with whom Ichabod Crane had to contend, and, considering all things, a stouter man than he would have shrunk from the competition, and a wiser man would have despaired. He had, however, a happy mixture of pliability and perseverance in his nature; he was in form and spirit like a supple-jack—yielding, but tough; though he bent, he never broke; and though he bowed beneath the slightest pressure, yet, the moment it was away—jerk! he was as erect, and carried his head as high as ever.

To have taken the field openly against his rival would have been madness; for he was not a man to be thwarted in his amours, any more than that stormy lover, Achilles. Ichabod, therefore, made his advances in a quiet and gently insinuating manner. Under cover of his character of singing-master, he made frequent visits at the farm-house; not that he had anything to apprehend from the meddlesome interference of parents, which is so often a stumbling-block in the path of lovers. Balt Van Tassel was an easy, indulgent soul; he loved his daughter better even than his pipe, and, like a reasonable man and an excellent father, let her have her way in everything. His notable little wife, too, had enough to do to attend to her housekeeping, and manage her poultry; for, as she sagely observed, ducks and geese are foolish things, and must be looked after, but girls can take care of themselves. Thus, while the busy dame bustled about the house, or plied her spinning-wheel at one end of the piazza, honest Balt would sit smoking his evening pipe at the other, watching the achievements of a little wooden warrior, who, armed with a sword in each hand, was most valiantly fighting the wind on the pinnacle of the barn. In the meantime, Ichabod would carry on his suit with the daughter by the side of the spring under the great elm, or sauntering along in the twilight, that hour so favorable to the lover's eloquence.

I profess not to know how women's hearts are wooed and won. To me they have always been matters of riddle and admiration. Some seem to have but one vulnerable point, or door of access; while others have a thousand avenues, and may be captured in a thousand different ways. It is a great triumph of skill to gain the former, but a still greater proof of generalship to maintain possession of the latter, for a man must battle for his fortress at every door and window. He who wins a thousand common hearts is therefore entitled to some renown; but he who keeps undisputed sway over the heart of a coquette is indeed a hero. Certain it is, this was not the case with the redoubtable Brom Bones; and from the moment Ichabod Crane made his advances, the interests of the former evidently declined; his horse was no longer seen tied at the palings on Sunday nights, and a deadly feud gradually arose between him and the preceptor of Sleepy Hollow.

Brom, who had a degree of rough chivalry in his nature, would fain have carried matters to open warfare, and have settled their pretensions to the lady, according to the mode of those most concise and simple reasoners, the knights-errant of yore— by single combat; but Ichabod was too conscious of the superior might of his adversary to enter the lists against him; he had overheard a boast of Bones, that he "would double the schoolmaster up, and lay him on a shelf of his own school-house"; and he was too wary to give him an opportunity. There was something extremely provoking in this obstinately pacific system; it left Brom no alternative but to draw upon the funds of rustic waggery in his disposition, and to play off boorish practical jokes upon his rival. Ichabod became the object of whimsical persecution to Bones and his gang of rough riders. They harried his hitherto peaceful domains; smoked out his singing-school, by stopping up the chimney; broke into the school-house at night, in spite of his formidable fastenings of withe and window stakes, and turned everything topsy-turvy; so that the poor schoolmaster began to think all the witches in the country held their meetings there. But what was still more annoying, Brom took all opportunities of turning him into ridicule in the presence of his mistress, and had a scoundrel dog whom he taught to whine in the most ludicrous manner, and introduced as a rival of Ichabod's to instruct her in psalmody.

In this way matters went on for some time, without producing any material effect on the relative situation of the contending powers. On a fine autumnal afternoon, Ichabod, in pensive mood, sat enthroned on the lofty stool whence he usually watched all the concerns of his little literary realm. In his hand he swayed a ferule, that scepter of despotic power; the birch of justice reposed on three nails behind the throne, a constant terror to evil-doers; while on the desk before him might be seen sundry contraband articles and prohibited weapons, detected upon the persons of idle urchins; such as half-munched apples, pop-guns, whirligigs, fly-cages, and whole legions of rampant little paper game-cocks. Apparently there had been some appalling act of justice recently inflicted, for his scholars were all busily intent upon their books, or slyly whispering behind them with one eye kept upon the master; and a kind of buzzing stillness reigned throughout the school-room. It was suddenly interrupted by the appearance of a Negro, in tow-cloth jacket and trousers, a round-crowned fragment of a hat, like the cap of Mercury, and mounted on the back of a ragged, wild, half-broken colt, which he managed with a rope by way of halter. He came clattering up to the school door with an invitation to Ichabod to attend a merry-making, or "quilting frolic," to be held that evening at Mynheer Van Tassel's; and having delivered his message with that air of importance and effort at fine language which a Negro is apt to display on petty embassies of the kind, he dashed over the brook, and was seen scampering away up the hollow, full of the importance and hurry of his mission.

All was now bustle and hubbub in the late quiet school-room. The scholars were hurried through their lessons without stopping at trifles; those who were nimble skipped over half with impunity, and those who were tardy had a smart application now and then in the rear, to quicken their speed, or help them over a tall word. Books were flung aside without being put away on the shelves; inkstands were overturned, benches thrown down, and the whole school was turned loose an hour before the usual time, bursting forth like a legion of young imps, yelping and racketing about the green in joy at their early emancipation.

The gallant Ichabod now spent at least an extra half-hour at his toilet, brushing and furbishing up his best, and indeed only suit of rusty black, and arranging his locks by a bit of broken looking-glass that hung up in the school-house. That he might make his appearance before his mistress in the true style of a cavalier, he borrowed a horse from the farmer with whom he was domiciliated, a choleric old Dutchman, of the name of Hans Van Ripper, and, thus gallantly mounted, issued forth like a knight-errant in quest of adventures. But it is meet I should, in the true spirit of romantic story, give some account of the looks and equipments of my hero and his steed. The animal he bestrode was a broken-down plough-horse that had outlived almost everything but his viciousness. He was gaunt and shagged, with a ewe neck and a head like a hammer; his rusty mane and tail were tangled and knotted with burrs; one eye had lost its pupil, and was glaring and spectral; but the other had the gleam of a genuine devil in it. Still he must have had fire and mettle in his day, if we may judge from the name he bore of Gunpowder. He had, in fact, been a favorite steed of his master's, the choleric Van Ripper, who was a furious rider, and had infused, very probably, some of his own spirit into the animal; for, old and broken-down as he looked, there was more of the lurking devil in him than in any young filly in the country.

Ichabod was a suitable figure for such a steed. He rode with short stirrups, which brought his knees nearly up to the pommel of the saddle; his sharp elbows stuck out like grasshoppers; he carried his whip perpendicularly in his hand, like a scepter, and, as his horse jogged on, the motion of his arms was not unlike the flapping of a pair of wings. A small wool hat rested on the top of his nose, for so his scanty strip of forehead might be called; and the skirts of his black coat fluttered out almost to the horse's tail. Such was the appearance of Ichabod and his steed, as they shambled out of the gate of Hans Van Ripper, and it was altogether such an apparition as is seldom to be met with in broad daylight.

It was, as I have said, a fine autumnal day, the sky was clear and serene, and nature wore that rich and golden livery which we always associate with the idea of abundance. The forests had put on their sober brown and yellow, while some trees of the tenderer kind had been nipped by the frosts into brilliant dyes of orange, purple, and scarlet. Streaming files of wild ducks began to make their appearance high in the air; the bark of the squirrel might be heard from the groves of beech and hickory nuts, and the pensive whistle of the quail at intervals from the neighboring stubble field.

The small birds were taking their farewell banquets. In the fulness of their revelry, they fluttered, chirping and frolicking, from bush to bush and tree to tree, capricious from the very profusion and variety around them. There was the honest cock-robin, the favorite game of stripling sportsmen, with its loud, querulous note; and the twittering blackbirds flying in sable clouds; and the golden-winged woodpecker, with his crimson crest, his broad black gorget, and splendid plumage; and the cedar-bird, with its red-tipt wings and yellow-tipt tail, and its little montero cap of feathers; and the blue jay, that noisy coxcomb, in his gay light-blue coat and white underclothes, screaming and chattering, nodding and bobbing and bowing, and pretending to be on good terms with every songster of the grove.

As Ichabod jogged slowly on his way, his eye, ever open to every symptom of culinary abundance, ranged with delight over the treasures of jolly autumn. On all sides he beheld vast stores of apples; some hanging in oppressive opulence on the trees; some gathered into baskets and barrels for the market; others heaped up in rich piles for the cider-press. Further on he beheld great fields of Indian corn, with its golden ears peeping from their leafy coverts, and holding out the promise of cakes and hasty-pudding; and the yellow pumpkins lying beneath them, turning up their fair round bellies to the sun, and giving ample prospects of the most luxurious of pies; and anon he passed the fragrant buckwheat fields breathing the odor of the bee-hive, and as he beheld them, soft anticipations stole over his mind of dainty slapjacks, well buttered, and garnished with honey or treacle, by the delicate little dimpled hand of Katrina Van Tassel.

Thus feeding his mind with many sweet thoughts and "sugared suppositions," he journeyed along the sides of a range of hills which look out upon some of the goodliest scenes of the mighty Hudson. The sun gradually wheeled his broad disc down into the west. The wide bosom of the Tappan Zee lay motionless and glassy, except that here and there a gentle undulation waved and prolonged the blue shadow of the distant mountain. A few amber clouds floated in the sky, without a breath of air to move them. The horizon was of a fine golden tint, changing gradually into a pure apple-green, and from that into the deep blue of the mid-heaven. A slanting ray lingered on the woody crests of the precipices that overhung some parts of the river, giving greater depth to the dark-gray and purple of their rocky sides. A sloop was loitering in the distance, dropping slowly down with the tide, her sail hanging uselessly against the mast; and as the reflection of the sky gleamed along the still water, it seemed as if the vessel was suspended in the air.

It was towards evening that Ichabod arrived at the castle of the Heer Van Tassel, which he found thronged with the pride and flower of the adjacent country. Old farmers, a spare leathern-faced race, in homespun coats and breeches, blue stockings, huge shoes, and magnificent pewter buckles. Their brisk withered little dames, in close crimped caps, long-waisted short gowns, homespun petticoats, with scissors and pincushions, and gay calico pockets hanging on the outside. Buxom lasses, almost as antiquated as their mothers, excepting where a straw hat, a fine riband, or perhaps a white frock, gave symptoms of city innovation. The sons, in short square-skirted coats with rows of stupendous brass buttons, and their hair generally queued in the fashion of the times, especially if they could procure an eel-skin for the purpose, it being esteemed throughout the country as a potent nourisher and strengthener of the hair.

Brom Bones, however, was the hero of the scene, having come to the gathering on his favorite steed Daredevil, a creature like himself, full of mettle and mischief, and which no one but himself could manage. He was, in fact, noted for preferring vicious animals, given to all kinds of tricks, which kept the rider in constant risk of his neck, for he held a tractable, well-broken horse as unworthy of a lad of spirit.

Fain would I pause to dwell upon the world of charms that burst upon the enraptured gaze of my hero, as he entered the state parlor of Van Tassel's mansion. Not those of the bevy of buxom lasses, with their luxurious display of red and white; but the ample charms of a genuine Dutch country tea-table in the sumptuous time of autumn. Such heaped-up platters of cakes of various and almost indescribable kinds, known only to experienced Dutch housewives! There was the doughty dough-nut, the tenderer oly koek, and the crisp and crumbling cruller; sweet-cakes and short-cakes, ginger-cakes and honey-cakes, and the whole family of cakes. And then there were apple-pies and peach-pies and pumpkin-pies; besides slices of ham and smoked beef; and, moreover, delectable dishes of preserved plums, and peaches, and pears, and quinces; not to mention broiled shad and roasted chickens; together with bowls of milk and cream, all mingled higgledy-piggledy, pretty much as I have enumerated them, with the motherly tea-pot sending up its clouds of vapor from the midst—Heaven bless the mark! I want breath and time to discuss this banquet as it deserves, and am too eager to get on with my story. Happily, Ichabod Crane was not in so great a hurry as his historian, but did ample justice to every dainty.

He was a kind and thankful creature, whose heart dilated in proportion as his skin was filled with good cheer, and whose spirits rose with eating as some men's do with drink. He could not help, too, rolling his large eyes round him as he ate, and chuckling with the possibility that he might one day be lord of all this scene of almost unimaginable luxury and splendor. Then he thought, how soon he'd turn his back upon the old school-house, snap his fingers in the face of Hans Van Ripper and every other niggardly patron, and kick any itinerant pedagogue out of doors that should dare to call him comrade!

Old Baltus Van Tassel moved about among his guests with a face dilated with content and good humor, round and jolly as the harvest moon. His hospitable attentions were brief, but expressive, being confined to a shake of the hand, a slap on the shoulder, a loud laugh, and a pressing invitation to "fall to, and help themselves."

And now the sound of the music from the common room or hall summoned to the dance. The musician was an old gray-headed Negro, who had been the itinerant orchestra of the neighborhood for more than half a century. His instrument was as old and battered as himself. The greater part of the time he scraped on two or three strings, accompanying every movement of the bow with a motion of the head; bowing almost to the ground, and stamping with his foot whenever a fresh couple were to start.

Ichabod prided himself upon his dancing as much as upon his vocal powers. Not a limb, not a fiber about him was idle; and to have seen his loosely hung frame in full motion, and clattering about the room, you would have thought Saint Vitus himself, that blessed patron of the dance, was figuring before you in person. He was the admiration of all the Negroes; who, having gathered, of all ages and sizes, from the farm and the neighborhood, stood forming a pyramid of shining black faces, at every door and window, gazing with delight at the scene, rolling their white eye-balls, and showing grinning rows of ivory from ear to ear. How could the flogger of urchins be otherwise than animated and joyous? the lady of his heart was his partner in the dance, and smiling graciously in reply to all his amorous oglings; while Brom Bones, sorely smitten with love and jealousy, sat brooding by himself in one corner.

When the dance was at an end, Ichabod was attracted to a knot of the sager folks, who, with old Van Tassel, sat smoking at one end of the piazza, gossiping over former times, and drawing out long stories about the war.

This neighborhood, at the time of which I am speaking, was one of those highly favored places which abound with chronicle and great men. The British and American line had run near it during the war; it had, therefore, been the scene of marauding, and infested with refugees, cow-boys, and all kinds of border chivalry. Just sufficient time had elapsed to enable each story-teller to dress up his tale with a little becoming fiction, and, in the indistinctness of his recollection, to make himself the hero of every exploit.

There was the story of Doffue Martling, a large bluebearded Dutchman, who had nearly taken a British frigate with an old iron nine-pounder from a mud breastwork, only that his gun burst at the sixth discharge. And there was an old gentleman who shall be nameless, being too rich a mynheer to be lightly mentioned, who, in the battle of White Plains, being an excellent master of defense, parried a musket-ball with a small sword, insomuch that he absolutely felt it whiz round the blade, and glance off at the hilt; in proof of which he was ready at any time to show the sword, with the hilt a little bent. There were several more that had been equally great in the field, not one of whom but was persuaded that he had a considerable hand in bringing the war to a happy termination.

But all these were nothing to the tales of ghosts and apparitions that succeeded. The neighborhood is rich in legendary treasures of the kind. Local tales and superstitions thrive best in these sheltered long-settled retreats; but are trampled under-foot by the shifting throng that forms the population of most of our country places. Besides, there is no encouragement for ghosts in most of our villages, for they have scarcely had time to finish their first nap, and turn themselves in their graves, before their surviving friends have traveled away from the neighborhood; so that when they turn out at night to walk their rounds, they have no acquaintance left to call upon. This is perhaps the reason why we so seldom hear of ghosts except in our long-established Dutch communities.

The immediate cause, however, of the prevalence of supernatural stories in these parts, was doubtless owing to the vicinity of Sleepy Hollow. There was a contagion in the very air that blew from that haunted region; it breathed forth an atmosphere of dreams and fancies infecting all the land. Several of the Sleepy Hollow people were present at Van Tassel's, and, as usual, were doling out their wild and wonderful legends. Many dismal tales were told about funeral trains, and mourning cries and wailings heard and seen about the great tree where the unfortunate Major André was taken, and which stood in the neighborhood. Some mention was made also of the woman in white, that haunted the dark glen at Raven Rock, and was often heard to shriek on winter nights before a storm, having perished there in the snow. The chief part of the stories, however, turned upon the favorite specter of Sleepy Hollow, the headless horseman, who had been heard several times of late, patrolling the country; and, it was said, tethered his horse nightly among the graves in the churchyard.

The sequestered situation of this church seems always to have made it a favorite haunt of troubled spirits. It stands on a knoll surrounded by locust-trees and lofty elms, from among which its decent white-washed walls shine modestly forth, like Christian purity, beaming through the shades of retirement. A gentle slope descends from it to a silver sheet of water, bordered by high trees, between which peeps may be caught at the blue hills of the Hudson. To look upon its grass-grown yard, where the sunbeams seem to sleep so quietly, one would think that there at least the dead might rest in peace. On one side of the church extends a wide woody dell, along which raves a large brook among broken rocks and trunks of fallen trees. Over a deep black part of the stream, not far from the church, was formerly thrown a wooden bridge; the road that led to it, and the bridge itself, were thickly shaded by overhanging trees, which cast a gloom about it, even in the daytime; but occasioned a fearful darkness at night. Such was one of the favorite haunts of the headless horseman, and the place where he was most frequently encountered. The tale was told of old Brouwer, a most heretical disbeliever in ghosts, how he met the horseman returning from his foray into Sleepy Hollow, and was obliged to get up behind him; how they galloped over bush and brake, over hill and swamp, until they reached the bridge; when the horseman suddenly turned into a skeleton, threw old Brouwer into the brook, and sprang away over the tree-tops with a clap of thunder.

This story was immediately matched by a thrice marvelous adventure of Brom Bones, who made light of the Galloping Hessian as an arrant jockey. He affirmed that, on returning one night from the neighboring village of Sing-Sing, he had been overtaken by this midnight trooper; that he had offered to race with him for a bowl of punch, and should have won it too, for Daredevil beat the goblin horse all hollow, but, just as they came to the church bridge, the Hessian bolted, and vanished in a flash of fire.

All these tales, told in that drowsy undertone with which men talk in the dark, the countenances of the listeners only now and then receiving a casual gleam from the glare of a pipe, sank deep in the mind of Ichabod. He repaid them in kind, with large extracts from his invaluable author, Cotton Mather, and added many marvelous events that had taken place in his native state of Connecticut, and fearful sights which he had seen in his nightly walks about Sleepy Hollow.

The revel now gradually broke up. The old farmers gathered together their families in their wagons, and were heard for some time rattling along the hollow roads, and over the distant hills. Some of the damsels mounted on pillions behind their favorite swains, and their light-hearted laughter, mingling with the clatter of hoofs, echoed along the silent woodlands, sounding fainter and fainter until they gradually died away—and the late scene of noise and frolic was all silent and deserted. Ichabod only lingered behind, according to the custom of country lovers, to have a *tête-à-tête* with the heiress, fully convinced that he was now on the high road to success. What passed at this interview I will not pretend to say, for in fact I do not know. Something, I fear me, must have gone wrong, for he certainly sallied forth, after no very great interval, with an air quite desolate and chop-fallen. Oh, these women! these women! Could that girl have been playing off any of her coquettish tricks?—Was her encouragement of the poor pedagogue all a mere sham to secure her conquest of his rival?—Heaven only knows, not I!—Let it suffice to say, Ichabod stole forth with the air of one who had been sacking a hen-roost, rather than a fair lady's heart. Without looking to the right or left to notice the scene of rural wealth on which he had so often gloated, he went straight to the stable, and with several hearty cuffs and kicks, roused his steed most uncourteously from the comfortable quarters in which he was soundly sleeping, dreaming of mountains of corn and oats, and whole valleys of timothy and clover.

It was the very witching time of night that Ichabod, heavy-hearted and crest-fallen, pursued his travels homewards, along the sides of the lofty hills which rise above Tarry Town, and which he had traversed so cheerily in the afternoon. The hour was as dismal as himself. Far below him the Tappan Zee spread its dusky and indistinct waste of waters, with here and there the tall mast of a sloop riding quietly at anchor under the land. In the dead hush of midnight he could even hear the barking of the watch-dog from the opposite shore of the Hudson; but it was so vague and faint as only to give an idea of his distance from this faithful companion of man. Now and then, too, the long-drawn crowing of a cock, accidentally awakened, would sound far, far off, from some farm-house away among the hills—but it was like a dreaming sound in his ear. No signs of life occurred near him, but occasionally the melancholy chirp of a cricket, or perhaps the guttural twang of a bull-frog, from a neighboring marsh, as if sleeping uncomfortably, and turning suddenly in his bed.

All the stories of ghosts and goblins that he had heard in the afternoon now came crowding upon his recollection. The night grew darker and darker; the stars seemed to sink deeper in the sky, and driving clouds occasionally hid them from his sight. He had never felt so lonely and dismal. He was, moreover, approaching the very place where many of the scenes of the ghost-stories had been laid. In the center of the road stood an enormous tulip-tree, which towered like a giant above all the other trees of the neighborhood, and formed a kind of landmark. Its limbs were gnarled and fantastic, large enough to form trunks for ordinary trees, twisting down almost to the earth, and rising again into the air. It was connected with the tragical story of the unfortunate André, who had been taken prisoner hard by; and was universally known by the name of Major André's tree. The common people regarded it with a mixture of respect and superstition, partly out of sympathy for the fate of its ill-starred namesake and partly from the tales of strange sights and doleful lamentations told concerning it.

As Ichabod approached this fearful tree, he began to whistle; he thought his whistle was answered; it was but a blast sweeping sharply through the dry branches. As he approached a little nearer, he thought he saw something white hanging in the midst of the tree—he paused and ceased whistling; but on looking more narrowly, perceived that it was a place where the tree had been scathed by lightning, and the white wood laid bare. Suddenly he heard a groan—his teeth chattered, and his knees smote against the saddle; it was but the rubbing of one huge bough upon another, as they were swayed about by the breeze. He passed the tree in safety, but new perils lay before him.

About two hundred yards from the tree a small brook crossed the road, and ran into a marshy and thickly wooded glen, known by the name of Wiley's Swamp. A few rough logs, laid side by side, served for a bridge over this stream. On that side of the road where the brook entered the wood, a group of oaks and chestnuts, matted thick with wild grapevines, threw a cavernous gloom over it. To pass this bridge was the severest trial. It was at this identical spot that the unfortunate André was captured, and under the covert of those chestnuts and vines were the sturdy yeomen concealed who surprised him. This has ever since been considered a haunted stream, and fearful are the feelings of the schoolboy who has to pass it alone after dark.

As he approached the stream, his heart began to thump; he summoned up, however, all his resolution, gave his horse half a score of kicks in the ribs, and attempted to dash briskly across the bridge; but instead of starting forward, the perverse old animal made a lateral movement, and ran broadside against the fence. Ichabod, whose fears increased with the delay, jerked the reins on the other side, and kicked lustily with the contrary foot: it was all in vain; his steed started, it is true, but it was only to plunge to the opposite side of the road into a thicket of brambles and alder-bushes. The schoolmaster now bestowed both whip and heel upon the starveling ribs of old Gunpowder, who dashed forward, snuffling and snorting, but came to a stand just by the bridge, with a suddenness that had nearly sent his rider sprawling over his head. Just at this moment a plashy tramp by the side of the bridge caught the sensitive ear of Ichabod. In the dark shadow of the grove, on the margin of the brook, he beheld something huge, mis-shapen, black and towering. It stirred not, but seemed gathered up in the gloom, like some gigantic monster ready to spring upon the traveler.

The hair of the affrighted pedagogue rose upon his head with terror. What was to be done? To turn and fly was now too late; and besides, what chance was there of escaping ghost or goblin, if such it was, which could ride upon the wings of the wind? Summoning up, therefore, a show of courage, he demanded in stammering accents—"Who are you?" He received no reply. He repeated his demand in a still more agitated voice. Still there was no answer. Once more he cudgelled the sides of the inflexible Gunpowder, and, shutting his eyes, broke forth with involuntary fervor into a psalm tune. Just then the shadowy object of alarm put itself in motion, and with a scramble and a bound, stood at once in the middle of the road. Though the night was dark and dismal, yet the form of the unknown might now in some degree be ascertained. He appeared to be a horseman of large dimensions, and mounted on a black horse of powerful frame. He made no offer of molestation or sociability, but kept aloof on one side of the road, jogging along on the blind side of old Gunpowder, who had now got over his fright and waywardness.

Ichabod, who had no relish for this strange midnight companion, and bethought himself of the adventure of Brom Bones with the Galloping Hessian, now quickened his steed, in hopes of leaving him behind. The stranger, however, quickened his horse to an equal pace. Ichabod pulled up, and fell into a walk, thinking to lag behind—the other did the same. His heart began to sink within him; he endeavored to resume his psalm tune, but his parched tongue clove to the roof of his mouth, and he could not utter a stave. There was something in the moody and dogged silence of this pertinacious companion that was mysterious and appalling. It was soon fearfully accounted for. On mounting a rising ground, which brought the figure of his fellow-traveler in relief against the sky, gigantic in height, and muffled in a cloak, Ichabod was horror-struck on perceiving that he was headless!—but his horror was still more increased on observing that the head, which should have rested on his shoulders, was carried before him on the pommel of the saddle: his terror rose to desperation; he rained a shower of kicks and blows upon Gunpowder, hoping, by a sudden movement, to give his companion the slip—but the specter started full jump with him. Away then they dashed, through thick and thin; stones flying and sparks flashing at every bound. Ichabod's flimsy garments fluttered in the air, as he stretched his long lank body away over his horse's head, in the eagerness of his flight.

They had now reached the road which turns off to Sleepy Hollow; but Gunpowder, who seemed possessed with a demon, instead of keeping up it, made an opposite turn, and plunged headlong down the hill to the left. This road leads through a sandy hollow, shaded by trees for about a quarter of a mile, where it crosses the bridge famous in goblin story, and just beyond swells the green knoll on which stands the white-washed church.

As yet the panic of the steed had given his unskilful rider an apparent advantage in the chase; but just as he had got half way through the hollow, the girths of the saddle gave way, and he felt it slipping from under him. He seized it by the pommel, and endeavored to hold it firm, but in vain; and had just time to save himself by clasping old Gunpowder round the neck, when the saddle fell to the earth, and he heard it trampled under-foot by his pursuer. For a moment the terror of Hans Van Ripper's wrath passed across his mind—for it was his Sunday saddle; but this was no time for petty fears; the goblin was hard on his haunches; and (unskilful rider that he was!) he had much ado to maintain his seat; sometimes slipping on one side, sometime on the other, and sometimes jolted on the high ridge of his horse's back-bone, with a violence that he verily feared would cleave him asunder.

An opening in the trees now cheered him with the hopes that the church bridge was at hand. The wavering reflection of a silver star in the bosom of the brook told him that he was not mistaken. He saw the walls of the church dimly glaring under the trees beyond. He recollected the place where Brom Bones' ghostly competitor had disappeared. "If I can but reach that bridge," thought Ichabod, "I am safe." Just then he heard the black steed panting and blowing close behind him; he even fancied that he felt his hot breath. Another convulsive kick in the ribs, and old Gunpowder sprang upon the bridge; he thundered over the resounding planks; he gained the opposite side; and now Ichabod cast a look behind to see if his pursuer should vanish, according to rule, in a flash of fire and brimstone. Just then he saw the goblin rising in his stirrups, and in the very act of hurling his head at him. Ichabod endeavored to dodge the horrible missile, but too late. It encountered his cranium with a tremendous crash—he was tumbled headlong into the dust, and Gunpowder, the black steed, and the goblin rider passed by like a whirlwind.

The next morning the old horse was found without his saddle, and with the bridle under his feet, soberly cropping the grass at his master's gate. Ichabod did not make his appearance at breakfast—dinner-hour came, but no Ichabod. The boys assembled at the school-house, and strolled idly about the banks of the brook; but no schoolmaster. Hans Van Ripper now began to feel some uneasiness about the fate of poor Ichabod and his saddle. An inquiry was set on foot, and after diligent investigation they came upon his traces. In one part of the road leading to the church was found the saddle trampled in the dirt; the tracks of horses' hoofs deeply dented in the road, and evidently at furious speed, were traced to the bridge, beyond which, on the bank of a broad part of the brook, where the water ran deep and black, was found the hat of the unfortunate Ichabod, and close beside it a shattered pumpkin.

The brook was searched, but the body of the schoolmaster was not to be discovered. Hans Van Ripper, as executor of his estate, examined the bundle, which contained all his worldly effects. They consisted of two shirts and a half; two stocks for the neck; a pair or two of worsted stockings; an old pair of corduroy small clothes; a rusty razor; a book of psalm tunes, full of dog's ears; and a broken pitch-pipe. As to the books and furniture of the school-house, they belonged to the community, excepting Cotton Mather's *History of Witchcraft,* a New England Almanac, and a book of dreams and fortune-telling; in which last was a sheet of foolscap much scribbled and blotted in several fruitless attempts to make a copy of verses in honor of the heiress of Van Tassel. These magic books and the poetic scrawl were forthwith consigned to the flames by Hans Van Ripper; who from that time forward determined to send his children no more to school, observing that he never knew any good come of this same reading and writing. Whatever money the schoolmaster possessed, and he had received his quarter's pay but a day or two before, he must have had about his person at the time of his disappearance.

The mysterious event caused much speculation at the church on the following Sunday. Knots of gazers and gossips were collected in the churchyard, at the bridge, and at the spot where the hat and pumpkin had been found. The stories of Brouwer, of Bones, and a whole budget of others, were called to mind; and when they had diligently considered them all, and compared them with the symptoms of the present case, they shook their heads, and came to the conclusion that Ichabod had been carried off by the Galloping Hessian. As he was a bachelor, and in nobody's debt, nobody troubled his head any more about him: the school was removed to a different quarter of the Hollow, and another pedagogue reigned in his stead.

It is true, an old farmer, who had been down to New York on a visit several years after, and from whom this account of the ghostly adventure was received, brought home the intelligence that Ichabod Crane was still alive; that he had left the neighborhood, partly through fear of the goblin and Hans Van Ripper, and partly in mortification at having been suddenly dismissed by the heiress; that he had changed his quarters to a distant part of the country; had kept school and studied law at the same time; he had been admitted to the bar, turned politician, electioneered, written for the newspapers, and finally had been made a justice of the Ten-pound Court. Brom Bones, too, who shortly after his rival's disappearance conducted the blooming Katrina in triumph to the altar, was observed to look exceedingly knowing whenever the story of Ichabod was related, and always burst into a hearty laugh at the mention of the pumpkin; which led some to suspect that he knew more about the matter than he chose to tell.

The old country wives, however, who are the best judges of these matters, maintain to this day that Ichabod was spirited away by supernatural means; and it is a favorite story often told about the neighborhood round the winter evening fire. The bridge became more than ever an object of superstitious awe, and that may be the reason why the road has been altered of late years, so as to approach the church by the border of the millpond. The school-house, being deserted, soon fell to decay, and was reported to be haunted by the ghost of the unfortunate pedagogue; and the plough-boy, loitering homeward of a still summer evening, has often fancied his voice at a distance, chanting a melancholy psalm tune among the tranquil solitudes of Sleepy Hollow.

Postscript

FOUND IN THE HANDWRITING OF MR. KNICKERBOCKER

The preceding tale is given almost in the precise words in which I heard it related at a Corporation meeting of the ancient city of Manhattoes, at which were present many of its sagest and most illustrious burghers. The narrator was a pleasant, shabby, gentlemanly old fellow, in pepper-and-salt clothes, with a sadly humorous face; and one whom I strongly suspected of being poor—he made such efforts to be entertaining. When his story was concluded, there was much laughter and approbation, particularly from two or three deputy aldermen, who had been asleep the greater part of the time. There was, however, one tall, dry-looking old gentleman, with beetling eyebrows, who maintained a grave and rather a severe face throughout: now and then folding his arms, inclining his head, and looking down upon the floor, as if turning a doubt over in his mind. He was one of your wary men, who never laugh, but upon good grounds —when they have reason and the law on their side. When the mirth of the rest of the company had subsided, and silence was restored, he leaned one arm on the elbow of his chair, and sticking the other akimbo, demanded, with a slight but exceedingly sage motion of the head, and contraction of the brow, what was the moral of the story, and what it went to prove?

The story-teller, who was just putting a glass of wine to his lips, as a refreshment after his toils, paused for a moment, looked at his inquirer with an air of infinite deference, and, lowering the glass slowly to the table, observed that the story was intended most logically to prove:—

"That there is no situation in life but has its advantages and pleasures—provided we will but take a joke as we find it:

"That, therefore, he that runs races with goblin troopers is likely to have rough riding of it.

"Ergo, for a country schoolmaster to be refused the hand of a Dutch heiress is a certain step to high preferment in the state."

The cautious old gentleman knit his brows tenfold closer after this explanation, being sorely puzzled by the ratiocination of the syllogism: while, methought, the one in pepper-and-salt eyed him with something of a triumphant leer. At length he observed that all this was very well; but still he thought the story a little on the extravagant—there were one or two points on which he had his doubts.

"Faith, sir," replied the story-teller, "as to that matter, I don't believe one half of it myself."

D. K.

THE MAN THAT CORRUPTED HADLEYBURG

by MARK TWAIN

IT WAS many years ago. Hadleyburg was the most honest and upright town in all the region round about. It had kept that reputation unsmirched during three generations, and was prouder of it than of any other of its possessions. It was so proud of it, and so anxious to insure its perpetuation, that it began to teach the principles of honest dealing to its babies in the cradle, and made the like teachings the staple of their culture thenceforward through all the years devoted to their education. Also, throughout the formative years, temptations were kept out of the way of the young people, so that their honesty could have every chance to harden and solidify, and become a part of their very bone. The neighboring towns were jealous of this honorable supremacy, and affected to sneer at Hadleyburg's pride in it and call it vanity; but all the same they were obliged to acknowledge that Hadleyburg was in reality an incorruptible town; and if pressed they would also acknowledge that the mere fact that a young man hailed from Hadleyburg was all the recommendation he needed when he went forth from his natal town to seek for responsible employment.

But at last, in the drift of time, Hadleyburg had the ill luck to offend a passing stranger—possibly without knowing it, certainly without caring, for Hadleyburg was sufficient unto itself, and cared not a rap for strangers or their opinions. Still, it would have been well to make an exception in this one's case, for he was a bitter man and revengeful. All through his wanderings during a whole year he kept his injury in mind, and gave all his leisure moments to trying to invent a compensating satisfaction for it. He contrived many plans, and all of them were good, but none of them was quite sweeping enough; the poorest of them would hurt a great many individuals, but what he wanted was a plan which would comprehend the entire town, and not let so much as one person escape unhurt. At last he had a fortunate idea, and when it fell into his brain it lit up his whole head with an evil joy. He began to form a plan at once, saying to himself, "That is the thing to do—I will corrupt the town."

Six months later he went to Hadleyburg, and arrived in a buggy at the house of the old cashier of the bank about ten at night. He got a sack out of the buggy, shouldered it, staggered with it through the cottage yard, and knocked at the door. A woman's voice said "Come in," and he entered and set his sack behind the stove in the parlor, saying politely to the old lady who sat reading the *Missionary Herald* by the lamp:

"Pray keep your seat, madam, I will not disturb you. There —now it is pretty well concealed; one would hardly know it was there. Can I see your husband a moment, madam?"

No, he was gone to Brixton, and might not return before morning.

"Very well, madam, it is no matter. I merely wanted to leave that sack in his care, to be delivered to the rightful owner when he shall be found. I am a stranger; he does not know me; I am merely passing through the town tonight to discharge a matter which has been long in my mind. My errand is now completed, and I go pleased and a little proud, and you will never see me again. There is a paper attached to the sack which will explain everything. Good night, madam."

The old lady was afraid of the mysterious big stranger, and was glad to see him go. But her curiosity was roused, and she went straight to the sack and brought away the paper. It began as follows:

TO BE PUBLISHED; or, the right man sought out by private inquiry—either will answer. This sack contains gold coin weighing a hundred and sixty pounds four ounces—

"Mercy on us, and the door not locked!"

Mrs. Richards flew to it all in a tremble and locked it, then pulled down the window-shades and stood frightened, worried, and wondering if there was anything else she could do toward making herself and the money more safe. She listened awhile for burglars, then surrendered to curiosity and went back to the lamp and finished reading the paper:

I am a foreigner, and am presently going back to my own country, to remain there permanently. I am grateful to America for what I have received at her hands during my long stay under her flag; and to one of her citizens—a citizen of Hadleyburg—I am especially grateful for a great kindness done me a year or two ago. Two great kindnesses, in fact. I will explain. I was a gambler. I say I was. I was a ruined gambler. I arrived in this village at night, hungry and without a penny. I asked for help—in the dark; I was ashamed to beg in the light. I begged of the right man. He gave me twenty dollars—that is to say, he gave me life, as I considered it. He also gave me fortune; for out of that money I have made myself rich at the gaming-table. And finally, a remark which he made to me has remained with me to this day, and has at last conquered me; and in conquering has saved the remnant of my morals: I shall gamble no more. Now I have no idea who that man was, but I want him found, and I want him to have this money, to give away, throw away, or keep, as he pleases. It is merely my way of testifying my gratitude to him. If I could stay, I would find him myself; but no matter, he will be found. This is an honest town, an incorruptible town, and I know I can trust it without fear. This man can be identified by the remark which he made to me; I feel persuaded that he will remember it.

And now my plan is this: If you prefer to conduct the inquiry privately, do so. Tell the contents of this present writing to any one who is likely to be the right man. If he shall answer, "I am the man; the remark I made was so-and-so," apply the test—to wit: open the sack, and in it you will find a sealed envelope containing that remark. If the remark mentioned by the candidate tallies with it, give him the money, and ask no further questions, for he is certainly the right man.

But if you shall prefer a public inquiry, then publish this present writing in the local paper—with these instructions added, to wit: Thirty days from now, let the candidate appear at the town-hall at eight in the evening (Friday), and hand his remark, in a sealed envelope, to the Rev. Mr. Burgess (if he will be kind enough to act); and let Mr. Burgess there and then destroy the seals of the sack, open it, and see if the remark is correct; if correct, let the money be delivered, with my sincere gratitude, to my benefactor thus identified.

Mrs. Richards sat down, gently quivering with excitement, and was soon lost in thinkings—after this pattern: "What a strange thing it is! . . . And what a fortune for that kind man who set his bread afloat upon the waters! . . . If it had only been my husband that did it!—for we are so poor, so old and poor! . . ." Then, with a sigh—"But it was not my Edward; no, it was not he that gave a stranger twenty dollars. It is a pity, too; I see

it now. . . ." Then, with a shudder—"But it is *gambler's* money!
the wages of sin: we couldn't take it; we couldn't touch it. I
don't like to be near it; it seems a defilement." She moved to
a farther chair. . . . "I wish Edward would come and take it
to the bank; a burglar might come at any moment; it is dreadful to be here all alone with it."

At eleven Mr. Richards arrived, and while his wife was saying, "I am *so* glad you've come!" he was saying, "I'm so tired
—tired clear out; it is dreadful to be poor, and have to make
these dismal journeys at my time of life. Always at the grind,
grind, grind, on a salary—another man's slave, and he sitting at
home in his slippers, rich and comfortable."

"I am so sorry for you, Edward, you know that; but be comforted: we have our livelihood; we have our good name—"

"Yes, Mary, and that is everything. Don't mind my talk—
it's just a moment's irritation and doesn't mean anything. Kiss
me—there, it's all gone now, and I am not complaining any
more. What have you been getting? What's in the sack?"

Then his wife told him the great secret. It dazed him for a
moment; then he said:

"It weighs a hundred and sixty pounds? Why, Mary, it's
forty thousand dollars—think of it—a whole fortune! Not ten
men in this village are worth that much. Give me the paper."

He skimmed through it and said:

"Isn't it an adventure! Why, it's a romance; it's like the impossible things one reads about in books and never sees in life."
He was well stirred up now; cheerful, even gleeful. He tapped
his old wife on the cheek, and said, humorously, "Why, we're
rich, Mary, rich; all we've got to do is to bury the money and
burn the papers. If the gambler ever comes to inquire, we'll
merely look coldly upon him and say: 'What is this nonsense
you are talking? We have never heard of you and your sack
of gold before;' and then he would look foolish, and—"

"And in the meantime, while you are running on with your jokes, the money is still here, and it is fast getting along toward burglar-time."

"True. Very well, what shall we do—make the inquiry private? No, not that: it would spoil the romance. The public method is better. Think what a noise it will make! And it will make all the other towns jealous; for no stranger would trust such a thing to any town but Hadleyburg, and they know it. It's a great card for us. I must get to the printing-office now, or I shall be too late."

"But stop—stop—don't leave me here alone with it, Edward!"

But he was gone. For only a little while, however. Not far from his own house he met the editor-proprietor of the paper, and gave him the document, and said, "Here is a good thing for you, Cox—put it in."

"It may be too late, Mr. Richards, but I'll see."

At home again he and his wife sat down to talk the charming mystery over; they were in no condition for sleep. The first question was, Who could the citizen have been who gave the stranger the twenty dollars? It seemed a simple one; both answered it in the same breath—

"Barclay Goodson."

"Yes," said Richards, "he could have done it, and it would have been like him, but there's not another in the town."

"Everybody will grant that, Edward—grant it privately, anyway. For six months, now, the village has been its own proper self once more—honest, narrow, self-righteous, and stingy."

"It is what he always called it, to the day of his death—said it right out publicly, too."

"Yes, and he was hated for it."

"Oh, of course; but he didn't care. I reckon he was the best-hated man among us, except the Reverend Burgess."

"Well, Burgess deserves it—he will never get another congregation here. Mean as the town is, it knows how to estimate *him*. Edward, doesn't it seem odd that the stranger should appoint Burgess to deliver the money?"

"Well, yes—it does. That is—that is—"

"Why so much that-*is*-ing? Would *you* select him?"

"Mary, maybe the stranger knows him better than this village does."

"Much *that* would help Burgess!"

The husband seemed perplexed for an answer; the wife kept a steady eye upon him, and waited. Finally Richards said, with the hesitancy of one who is making a statement which is likely to encounter doubt.

"Mary, Burgess is not a bad man."

His wife was certainly surprised.

"Nonsense!" she exclaimed.

"He is not a bad man. I know. The whole of his unpopularity had its foundation in that one thing—the thing that made so much noise."

"That 'one thing,' indeed! As if that 'one thing' wasn't enough, all by itself."

"Plenty. Plenty. Only he wasn't guilty of it."

"How you talk! Not guilty of it! Everybody knows he *was* guilty."

"Mary, I give you my word—he was innocent."

"I can't believe it, and I don't. How do you know?"

"It is a confession. I am ashamed, but I will make it. I was the only man who knew he was innocent. I could have saved him, and—and—well, you know how the town was wrought up —I hadn't the pluck to do it. It would have turned everybody against me. I felt mean, ever so mean; but I didn't dare; I hadn't the manliness to face that."

Mary looked troubled, and for a while was silent. Then she said, stammeringly:

"I—I don't think it would have done for you to—to— One mustn't—er—public opinion—one has to be so careful—so—" It was a difficult road, and she got mired; but after a little she got started again. "It was a great pity, but— Why, we couldn't afford it, Edward—we couldn't indeed. Oh, I wouldn't have had you do it for anything!"

"It would have lost us the good will of so many people, Mary; and then—and then—"

"What troubles me now is, what *he* thinks of us, Edward."

"He? *He* doesn't suspect that I could have saved him."

"Oh," exclaimed the wife, in a tone of relief, "I am glad of that. As long as he doesn't know that you could have saved him, he—he—well, that makes it a great deal better. Why, I might have known he didn't know, because he is always trying to be friendly with us, as little encouragement as we give him. More than once people have twitted me with it. There's the Wilsons, and the Wilcoxes, and the Harknesses, they take a mean pleasure in saying, 'Your *friend* Burgess,' because they know it pesters me. I wish he wouldn't persist in liking us so; I can't think why he keeps it up."

"I can explain it. It's another confession. When the thing was new and hot, and the town made a plan to ride him on a rail, my conscience hurt me so that I couldn't stand it, and I went privately and gave him notice, and he got out of the town and stayed out till it was safe to come back."

"Edward! If the town had found it out—"

"*Don't!* It scares me yet, to think of it. I repented of it the minute it was done; and I was even afraid to tell you, lest your face might betray it to somebody. I didn't sleep any that night, for worrying. But after a few days I saw that no one was going to suspect me, and after that I got to feeling glad I did it. And I feel glad yet, Mary—glad through and through."

"So do I, now, for it would have been a dreadful way to treat him. Yes, I'm glad; for really you did owe him that, you know. But, Edward, suppose it should come out yet, some day!"

"It won't."

"Why?"

"Because everybody thinks it was Goodson."

"Of course they would!"

"Certainly. And of course *he* didn't care. They persuaded poor old Sawlsberry to go and charge it on him, and he went blustering over there and did it. Goodson looked him over, like as if he was hunting for a place on him that he could despise the most, then he says, 'So you are the Committee of Inquiry, are you?' Sawlsberry said that was about what he was. 'Hm. Do they require particulars, or do you reckon a kind of a *general* answer will do?' 'If they require particulars, I will come back, Mr. Goodson; I will take the general answer first.' 'Very well, then, tell them to go to hell—I reckon that's general enough. And I'll give you some advice, Sawlsberry; when you come back for the particulars, fetch a basket to carry the relics of yourself home in.'"

"Just like Goodson; it's got all the marks. He had only one vanity: he thought he could give advice better than any other person."

"It settled the business, and saved us, Mary. The subject was dropped."

"Bless you, I'm not doubting *that*."

Then they took up the gold-sack mystery again, with strong interest. Soon the conversation began to suffer breaks—interruptions caused by absorbed thinkings. The breaks grew more and more frequent. At last Richards lost himself wholly in thought. He sat long, gazing vacantly at the floor, and by and by he began to punctuate his thoughts with little nervous movements of his hands that seemed to indicate vexation. Meantime his wife too had relapsed into a thoughtful silence, and her movements were beginning to show a troubled discomfort. Finally Richards got up and strode aimlessly about the room, plowing his hands through his hair, much as a somnambulist might do who was having a bad dream. Then he seemed to arrive at a definite purpose; and without a word he put on his hat and passed quickly out of the house. His wife sat brooding, with a drawn face, and did not seem to be aware that she was alone. Now and then she murmured, "Lead us not into t— . . . but—but— we are so poor, so poor! . . . Lead us not into. . . . Ah, who would be hurt by it?—and no one would ever know. . . . Lead us. . . ." The voice died out in mumblings. After a little she glanced up and muttered in a half-frightened, half-glad way—

"He is gone! But, oh dear, he may be too late—too late. . . . Maybe not—maybe there is still time." She rose and stood thinking, nervously clasping and unclasping her hands. A slight shudder shook her frame, and she said, out of a dry throat, "God forgive me—it's awful to think such things—but . . . Lord, how we are made—how strangely we are made!"

She turned the light low, and slipped stealthily over and kneeled down by the sack and felt of its ridgy sides with her hands, and fondled them lovingly; and there was a gloating light in her poor old eyes. She fell into fits of absence; and came half out of them at times to mutter, "If we had only waited!—oh, if we had only waited a little, and not been in such a hurry!"

Meantime Cox had gone home from his office and told his wife all about the strange thing that had happened, and they had talked it over eagerly, and guessed that the late Goodson was the only man in the town who could have helped a suffering stranger with so noble a sum as twenty dollars. Then there was a pause, and the two became thoughtful and silent. And by and by nervous and fidgety. At last the wife said, as if to herself,

"Nobody knows this secret but the Richardses . . . and us . . . nobody."

The husband came out of his thinkings with a slight start, and gazed wistfully at his wife, whose face was become very pale; then he hesitatingly rose, and glanced furtively at his hat, then at his wife—a sort of mute inquiry. Mrs. Cox swallowed once or twice, with her hand at her throat, then in place of speech she nodded her head. In a moment she was alone, and mumbling to herself.

And now Richards and Cox were hurrying through the deserted streets, from opposite directions. They met, panting, at the foot of the printing-office stairs; by the night-light there they read each other's face. Cox whispered,

"Nobody knows about this but us?"

The whispered answer was,

"Not a soul—on honor, not a soul!"

"If it isn't too late to—"

The men were starting upstairs; at this moment they were overtaken by a boy, and Cox asked,

"Is that you, Johnny?"

"Yes, sir."

"You needn't ship the early mail—nor *any* mail; wait till I tell you."

"It's already gone, sir."

"*Gone?*" It had the sound of an unspeakable disappointment in it.

"Yes, sir. Time-table for Brixton and all the towns beyond changed today, sir—had to get the papers in twenty minutes earlier than common. I had to rush; if I had been two minutes later—"

The men turned and walked slowly away, not waiting to hear the rest. Neither of them spoke during ten minutes; then Cox said, in a vexed tone,

"What possessed you to be in such a hurry, *I* can't make out."
The answer was humble enough:

"I see it now, but somehow I never thought, you know, until it was too late. But the next time—"

"Next time be hanged! It won't come in a thousand years."

Then the friends separated without a good-night, and dragged themselves home with the gait of mortally stricken men. At their homes their wives sprang up with an eager "Well?"— then saw the answer with their eyes and sank down sorrowing, without waiting for it to come in words. In both houses a discussion followed of a heated sort—a new thing; there had been discussions before, but not heated ones, not ungentle ones. The discussions tonight were a sort of seeming plagiarisms of each other. Mrs. Richards said,

"If you had only waited, Edward—if you had only stopped to think; but no, you must run straight to the printing-office and spread it all over the world."

"It *said* publish it."

"That is nothing; it also said do it privately, if you liked. There, now—is that true, or not?"

"Why, yes—yes, it is true; but when I thought what a stir it would make, and what a compliment it was to Hadleyburg that a stranger should trust it so—"

"Oh, certainly, I know all that; but if you had only stopped to think, you would have seen that you *couldn't* find the right man, because he is in his grave, and hasn't left chick nor child nor relation behind him; and as long as the money went to somebody that awfully needed it, and nobody would be hurt by it, and—and—"

She broke down, crying. Her husband tried to think of some comforting thing to say, and presently came out with this:

"But after all, Mary, it must be for the best—it *must* be; we know that. And we must remember that it was so ordered—"

"Ordered! Oh, everything's *ordered*, when a person has to find some way out when he has been stupid. Just the same, it was *ordered* that the money should come to us in this special way, and it was you that must take it on yourself to go meddling with the designs of Providence—and who gave you the right? It was wicked, that is what it was—just blasphemous presumption, and no more becoming to a meek and humble professor of—"

"But, Mary, you know how we have been trained all our lives long, like the whole village, till it is absolutely second nature to us to stop not a single moment to think when there's an honest thing to be done—"

"Oh, I know it, I know it—it's been one everlasting training and training and training in honesty—honesty shielded, from the very cradle, against every possible temptation, and so it's *artificial* honesty, and weak as water when temptation comes, as we have seen this night. God knows I never had shade nor shadow of a doubt of my petrified and indestructible honesty until now —and now, under the very first big and real temptation, I— Edward, it is my belief that this town's honesty is as rotten as mine is; as rotten as yours is. It is a mean town, a hard, stingy town, and hasn't a virtue in the world but this honesty it is so celebrated for and so conceited about; and so help me, I do believe that if ever the day comes that its honesty falls under great temptation, its grand reputation will go to ruin like a house of cards. There, now, I've made confession, and I feel better; I am a humbug, and I've been one all my life, without knowing it. Let no man call me honest again—I will not have it."

"I—well, Mary, I feel a good deal as you do; I certainly do. It seems strange, too, so strange. I never could have believed it—never."

A long silence followed; both were sunk in thought. At last the wife looked up and said,

"I know what you are thinking, Edward."

Richards had the embarrassed look of a person who is caught.

"I am ashamed to confess it, Mary, but—"

"It's no matter, Edward, I was thinking the same question myself."

"I hope so. State it."

"You were thinking, if a body could only guess out *what the remark was* that Goodson made to the stranger."

"It's perfectly true. I feel guilty and ashamed. And you?"

"I'm past it. Let us make a pallet here; we've got to stand watch till the bank vault opens in the morning and admits the sack. . . . Oh dear, oh dear—if we hadn't made the mistake!"

The pallet was made, and Mary said:

"The open sesame—what could it have been? I do wonder what that remark could have been? But come; we will go to bed now."

"And sleep?"

"No, think."

"Yes, think."

By this time the Coxes too had completed their spat and their reconciliation, and were turning in—to think, to think, and toss, and fret, and worry over what the remark could possibly have been which Goodson made to the stranded derelict; that golden remark; that remark worth forty thousand dollars, cash.

The reason that the village telegraph office was open later than usual that night was this: The foreman of Cox's paper was the local representative of the Associated Press. One might say its honorary representative, for it wasn't four times a year that he could furnish thirty words that would be accepted. But this time it was different. His dispatch stating what he had caught got an instant answer:

Send the whole thing—all the details—twelve hundred words.

A colossal order! The foreman filled the bill; and he was the proudest man in the State. By breakfast-time the next morning the name of Hadleyburg the Incorruptible was on every lip in America, from Montreal to the Gulf, from the glaciers of Alaska to the orange-groves of Florida; and millions and millions of people were discussing the stranger and his money-sack, and wondering if the right man would be found, and hoping some more news about the matter would come soon—right away.

II

Hadleyburg village woke up world-celebrated—astonished—happy—vain. Vain beyond imagination. Its nineteen principal citizens and their wives went about shaking hands with each other, and beaming, and smiling, and congratulating, and saying *this* thing adds a new word to the dictionary—*Hadleyburg,* synonym for *incorruptible*—destined to live in dictionaries forever! And the minor and unimportant citizens and their wives went around acting in much the same way. Everybody ran to the bank to see the gold-sack; and before noon grieved and envious crowds began to flock in from Brixton and all neighboring towns; and that afternoon and next day reporters began to arrive from everywhere to verify the sack and its history and write the whole thing up anew, and make dashing free-hand pictures of the sack, and of Richards's house, and the bank, and the Presbyterian church, and the Baptist church, and the public square, and the town hall where the test would be applied and the money delivered; and damnable portraits of the Richardses, and Pinkerton the banker, and Cox, and the foreman, and Reverend Burgess, and the postmaster—and even of Jack Halliday, who was the loafing, good-natured, no-account, irreverent fisherman, hunter, boys' friend, stray-dogs' friend, typical "Sam Lawson" of the town. The little mean, smirking, oily Pinkerton showed the sack to all comers, and rubbed his sleek palms together pleasantly, and enlarged upon the town's fine old reputation for honesty and upon this wonderful endorsement of it, and hoped and believed that the example would now spread far and wide over the American world, and be epoch-making in the matter of moral regeneration. And so on, and so on.

By the end of a week things had quieted down again; the wild intoxication of pride and joy had sobered to a soft, sweet, silent delight—a sort of deep, nameless, unutterable content. All faces bore a look of peaceful, holy happiness.

Then a change came. It was a gradual change: so gradual that its beginnings were hardly noticed; maybe were not noticed at all, except by Jack Halliday, who always noticed everything; and always made fun of it, too, no matter what it was. He began to throw out chaffing remarks about people not looking quite so happy as they did a day or two ago; and next he claimed that the new aspect was deepening to positive sadness; next, that it was taking on a sick look; and finally he said that everybody was become so moody, thoughtful, and absent-minded that he could rob the meanest man in town of a cent out of the bottom of his breeches pocket and not disturb his reverie.

At this stage—or at about this stage—a saying like this was dropped at bedtime—with a sigh, usually—by the head of each of the nineteen principal households: "Ah, what *could* have been the remark that Goodson made?"

And straightway—with a shudder—came this, from the man's wife:

"Oh, *don't!* What horrible thing are you mulling in your mind? Put it away from you, for God's sake!"

But that question was wrung from those men again the next night—and got the same retort. But weaker.

And the third night the men uttered the question yet again

—with anguish, and absently. This time—and the following night—the wives fidgeted feebly, and tried to say something. But didn't.

And the night after that they found their tongues and responded—longingly,

"Oh, if we *could* only guess!"

Halliday's comments grew daily more and more sparklingly disagreeable and disparaging. He went diligently about, laughing at the town, individually and in mass. But his laugh was the only one left in the village: it fell upon a hollow and mournful vacancy and emptiness. Not even a smile was findable anywhere. Halliday carried a cigar-box around on a tripod, playing that it was a camera, and halted all passers and aimed the thing and said, "Ready!—now look pleasant, please," but not even this capital joke could surprise the dreary faces into any softening.

So three weeks passed—one week was left. It was Saturday evening—after supper. Instead of the aforetime Saturday-evening flutter and bustle and shopping and larking, the streets were empty and desolate. Richards and his old wife sat apart in their little parlor—miserable and thinking. This was become their evening habit now: the lifelong habit which had preceded it, of reading, knitting, and contented chat, or receiving or paying neighborly calls, was dead and gone and forgotten, ages ago —two or three weeks ago; nobody talked now, nobody read, nobody visited—the whole village sat at home, sighing, worrying, silent. Trying to guess out that remark.

The postman left a letter. Richards glanced listlessly at the superscription and the postmark—unfamiliar, both—and tossed the letter on the table and resumed his might-have-beens and his hopeless dull miseries where he had left them off. Two or three hours later his wife got wearily up and was going away to bed without a good-night—custom now—but she stopped near the letter and eyed it awhile with a dead interest, then broke it open, and began to skim it over. Richards, sitting there with his chair tilted back against the wall and his chin between his knees, heard something fall. It was his wife. He sprang to her side, but she cried out:

"Leave me alone, I am too happy. Read the letter—read it!"

He did. He devoured it, his brain reeling. The letter was from a distant State, and it said:

I am a stranger to you, but no matter: I have something to tell. I have just arrived home from Mexico, and learned about that episode. Of course you do not know who made that remark, but I know, and I am the only person living who does know. It was GOODSON. *I knew him well, many years ago. I passed through your village that very night, and was his guest till the midnight train came along. I overheard him make that remark to the stranger in the dark—it was in Hale Alley. He and I talked of it the rest of the way home, and while smoking in his house. He mentioned many of your villagers in the course of his talk—most of them in a very uncomplimentary way, but two or three favorably; among these latter yourself. I say "favorably"—nothing stronger. I remember his saying he did not actually* LIKE *any person in the town—not one; but that you—I* THINK *he said you—am almost sure—had done him a very great service once, possibly without knowing the full value of it, and he wished he had a fortune, he would leave it to you when he died, and a curse apiece for the rest of the citizens. Now, then, if it was you that did him that service, you are his legitimate heir, and entitled to the sack of gold. I know that I can trust to your honor and honesty, for in a citizen of Hadleyburg these virtues are an unfailing inheritance, and so I am going to reveal to you the remark, well satisfied that if you are not the right man you will seek and find the right one and see that poor Goodson's debt of gratitude for the service referred to is paid. This is the remark:* "YOU ARE FAR FROM BEING A BAD MAN: GO, AND REFORM."

HOWARD L. STEPHENSON.

"Oh, Edward, the money is ours, and I am so grateful, *oh,* so grateful—kiss me, dear, it's forever since we kissed—and we needed it so—the money—and now you are free of Pinkerton and his bank, and nobody's slave any more; it seems to me I could fly for joy."

It was a happy half-hour that the couple spent there on the settee caressing each other; it was the old days come again—days that had begun with their courtship and lasted without a break till the stranger brought the deadly money. By and by the wife said:

"Oh, Edward, how lucky it was you did him that grand service, poor Goodson! I never liked him, but I love him now. And it was fine and beautiful of you never to mention it or brag about it." Then, with a touch of reproach, "But you ought to have told *me,* Edward, you ought to have told your wife, you know."

"Well, I—er—well, Mary, you see—"

"Now stop hemming and hawing, and tell me about it, Edward. I always loved you, and now I'm proud of you. Everybody believes there was only one good generous soul in this village, and now it turns out that you—Edward, why don't you tell me?"

"Well—er—er— Why, Mary, I can't!"

"You *can't? Why* can't you?"

"You see, he—well, he—he made me promise I wouldn't."

The wife looked him over, and said, very slowly,

"Made—you—promise? Edward, what do you tell me that for?"

"Mary, do you think I would lie?"

She was troubled and silent for a moment, then she laid her hand within his and said:

"No . . . no. We have wandered far enough from our bearings—God spare us that! In all your life you have never uttered a lie. But now—now that the foundations of things seem to be crumbling from under us, we—we—" She lost her voice for a moment, then said, brokenly, "Lead us not into temptation. . . . I think you made the promise, Edward. Let it rest so. Let us keep away from that ground. Now—that is all gone by; let us be happy again; it is no time for clouds."

Edward found it something of an effort to comply, for his mind kept wandering—trying to remember what the service was that he had done Goodson.

The couple lay awake the most of the night, Mary happy and busy, Edward busy but not so happy. Mary was planning what she would do with the money. Edward was trying to recall that service. At first his conscience was sore on account of the lie he had told Mary—if it was a lie. After much reflection—suppose it *was* a lie? What then? Was it such a great matter? Aren't we always *acting* lies? Then why not *tell* them? Look at Mary—look what she had done. While he was hurrying off on his honest errand, what was she doing? Lamenting because the papers hadn't been destroyed and the money kept! Is theft better than lying?

That point lost its sting—the lie dropped into the background and left comfort behind it. The next point came to the front: *Had* he rendered that service? Well, here was Goodson's own evidence as reported in Stephenson's letter; there could be no better evidence than that—it was even *proof* that he had rendered it. Of course. So that point was settled. . . . No, not quite. He recalled with a wince that this unknown Mr. Stephenson was just a trifle unsure as to whether the performer of it was Richards or some other—and, oh dear, he had put Richards on his honor! He must himself decide whither that money must go—and Mr. Stephenson was not doubting that if he was the wrong man he would go honorably and find the right one. Oh, it was odious to put a man in such a situation—ah, why couldn't Stephenson have left out that doubt! What did he want to intrude that for?

Further reflection. How did it happen that *Richards's* name remained in Stephenson's mind as indicating the right man, and not some other man's name? That looked good. Yes, that looked very good. In fact, it went on looking better and better, straight along—until by and by it grew into positive *proof*. And then Richards put the matter at once out of his mind, for he had a private instinct that a proof once established is better left so.

He was feeling reasonably comfortable now, but there was still one other detail that kept pushing itself on his notice: of course he had done that service—that was settled; but what *was* that service? He must recall it—he would not go to sleep till he had recalled it; it would make his peace of mind perfect. And so he thought and thought. He thought of a dozen things—possible services, even probable services—but none of them seemed adequate, none of them seemed large enough, none of them seemed worth the money—worth the fortune Goodson had wished he could leave in his will. And besides, he couldn't remember having done them, anyway. Now, then—now, then—what *kind* of a service would it be that would make a man so inordinately grateful? Ah—the saving of his soul! That must be it. Yes, he could remember, now, how he once set himself the task of converting Goodson, and labored at it as much as—he was going to say three months; but upon closer examination it shrunk to a month, then to a week, then to a day, then to nothing. Yes, he remembered now, and with un-

welcome vividness, that Goodson had told him to go to thunder and mind his own business—*he* wasn't hankering to follow
Hadleyburg to heaven!

So that solution was a failure—he hadn't saved Goodson's soul.
Richards was discouraged. Then after a little came another idea:
had he saved Goodson's property? No, that wouldn't do—he
hadn't any. His life? That is it! Of course. Why, he might
have thought of it before. This time he was on the right track,
sure. His imagination-mill was hard at work in a minute, now.

Thereafter during a stretch of two exhausting hours he was
busy saving Goodson's life. He saved it in all kinds of difficult and perilous ways. In every case he got it saved satisfac-
torily up to a certain point; then, just as he was beginning to
get well persuaded that it had really happened, a troublesome
detail would turn up which made the whole thing impossible.
As in the matter of drowning, for instance. In that case he
had swum out and tugged Goodson ashore in an unconscious
state with a great crowd looking on and applauding, but when
he had got it all thought out and was just beginning to remember all about it, a whole swarm of disqualifying details arrived on the ground: the town would have known of the circumstance, Mary would have known of it, it would glare like
a limelight in his own memory instead of being an inconspic-
uous service which he had possibly rendered "without knowing its full value." And at this point he remembered that he
couldn't swim, anyway.

Ah—*there* was a point which he had been overlooking from
the start: it had to be a service which he had rendered "possibly
without knowing the full value of it." Why, really, that ought
to be an easy hunt—much easier than those others. And sure
enough, by and by he found it. Goodson, years and years ago,
came near marrying a very sweet and pretty girl, named Nancy
Hewitt, but in some way or other the match had been broken

off; the girl died, Goodson remained a bachelor, and by and by became a soured one and a frank despiser of the human species. Soon after the girl's death the village found out, or thought it had found out, that she carried a spoonful of Negro blood in her veins. Richards worked at these details a good while, and in the end he thought he remembered things concerning them which must have gotten mislaid in his memory through long neglect. He seemed dimly to remember that it was *he* that found out about the Negro blood; that it was he that told the village; that the village told Goodson where they got it; that he thus saved Goodson from marrying the tainted girl; that he had done him this great service "without knowing the full value of it," in fact without knowing that he *was* doing it; but that Goodson knew the value of it, and what a narrow escape he had had, and so went to his grave grateful to his benefactor and wishing he had a fortune to leave him. It was all clear and simple now, and the more he went over it the more luminous and certain it grew; and at last, when he nestled to sleep satisfied and happy, he remembered the whole thing just as if it had been yesterday. In fact, he dimly remembered Goodson's *telling* him his gratitude once. Meantime Mary had spent six thousand dollars on a new house for herself and a pair of slippers for her pastor, and then had fallen peacefully to rest.

That same Saturday evening the postman had delivered a letter to each of the other principal citizens—nineteen letters in all. No two of the envelopes were alike, and no two of the superscriptions were in the same hand, but the letters inside were just like each other in every detail but one. They were exact copies of the letter received by Richards—handwriting and all—and were all signed by Stephenson, but in place of Richards's name each receiver's own name appeared.

All night long eighteen principal citizens did what their caste-brother Richards was doing at the same time—they put in their energies trying to remember what notable service it was that they had unconsciously done Barclay Goodson. In no case was it a holiday job; still they succeeded.

And while they were at this work, which was difficult, their wives put in the night spending the money, which was easy. During that one night the nineteen wives spent an average of seven thousand dollars each out of the forty thousand in the sack—a hundred and thirty-three thousand altogether.

Next day there was a surprise for Jack Halliday. He noticed that the faces of the nineteen chief citizens and their wives bore that expression of peaceful and holy happiness again. He could not understand it, neither was he able to invent any remarks about it that could damage it or disturb it. And so it was his turn to be dissatisfied with life. His private guesses at the reasons for the happiness failed in all instances, upon examination. When he met Mrs. Wilcox and noticed the placid ecstasy in her face, he said to himself, "Her cat has had kittens"—and went and asked the cook: it was not so; the cook had detected the happiness, but did not know the cause. When Halliday found the duplicate ecstasy in the face of "Shadbelly" Billson (village nickname), he was sure some neighbor of Billson's had broken his leg, but inquiry showed that this had not happened. The subdued ecstasy in Gregory Yates's face could mean but one thing—he was a mother-in-law short: it was another mistake. "And Pinkerton—Pinkerton—he has collected ten cents that he thought he was going to lose." And so on, and so on. In some cases the guesses had to remain in doubt, in the others they proved distinct errors. In the end Halliday said to himself, "Anyway it foots up that there's nineteen Hadleyburg families temporarily in heaven: I don't know how it happened; I only know Providence is off duty today."

An architect and builder from the next State had lately ventured to set up a small business in this unpromising village, and his sign had now been hanging out a week. Not a customer yet; he was a discouraged man, and sorry he had come. But his weather changed suddenly now. First one and then another chief citizen's wife said to him privately:

"Come to my house Monday week—but say nothing about it for the present. We think of building."

He got eleven invitations that day. That night he wrote his daughter and broke off her match with her student. He said she could marry a mile higher than that.

Pinkerton the banker and two or three other well-to-do men planned country-seats—but waited. That kind don't count their chickens until they are hatched.

The Wilsons devised a grand new thing—a fancy-dress ball. They made no actual promises, but told all their acquaintanceship in confidence that they were thinking the matter over and thought they should give it—"and if we do, you will be invited, of course." People were surprised, and said, one to another, "Why, they are crazy, those poor Wilsons, they can't afford it." Several among the nineteen said privately to their husbands, "It is a good idea: we will keep still till their cheap thing is over, then *we* will give one that will make it sick."

The days drifted along, and the bill of future squanderings rose higher and higher, wilder and wilder, more and more foolish and reckless. It began to look as if every member of the nineteen would not only spend his whole forty thousand dollars before receiving-day, but be actually in debt by the time he got the money. In some cases light-headed people did not stop with planning to spend, they really spent—on credit. They bought land, mortgages, farms, speculative stock, fine clothes, horses, and various other things, paid down the bonus, and made themselves liable for the rest—at ten days. Presently the sober second thought came, and Halliday noticed that a ghastly anxiety was beginning to show up in a good many faces. Again he was puzzled, and didn't know what to make of it. "The Wilcox kittens aren't dead, for they weren't born; nobody's broken a leg; there's no shrinkage in mother-in-laws; *nothing* has happened—it is an unsolvable mystery."

There was another puzzled man, too—the Rev. Mr. Burgess. For days, wherever he went, people seemed to follow him or to be watching out for him; and if he ever found himself in a retired spot, a member of the nineteen would be sure to appear, thrust an envelope privately into his hand, whisper "To be opened at the town hall Friday evening," then vanish away like a guilty thing. He was expecting that there might be one claimant for the sack—doubtful, however, Goodson being dead —but it never occurred to him that all this crowd might be claimants. When the great Friday came at last, he found that he had nineteen envelopes.

III

The town hall had never looked finer. The platform at the end of it was backed by a showy draping of flags; at intervals along the walls were festoons of flags; the gallery fronts were clothed in flags; the supporting columns were swathed in flags; all this was to impress the stranger, for he would be there in considerable force, and in a large degree he would be connected with the press. The house was full. The 412 fixed seats were occupied; also the 68 extra chairs which had been packed into the aisles; the steps of the platform were occupied; some distinguished strangers were given seats on the platform; at the horseshoe of tables which fenced the front and sides of the platform sat a strong force of special correspondents who had come from everywhere. It was the best-dressed house the town had ever produced. There were some tolerably expensive toilets there, and in several cases the ladies who wore them had the look of being unfamiliar with that kind of clothes. At least the town thought they had that look, but the notion could have arisen from the town's knowledge of the fact that these ladies had never inhabited such clothes before.

The gold-sack stood on a little table at the front of the platform where all the house could see it. The bulk of the house gazed at it with a burning interest, a mouth-watering interest, a wistful and pathetic interest; a minority of nineteen couples gazed at it tenderly, lovingly, proprietarily, and the male half of this minority kept saying over to themselves the moving little impromptu speeches of thankfulness for the audience's applause and congratulations which they were presently going to get up and deliver. Every now and then one of these got a piece of paper out of his vest pocket and privately glanced at it to refresh his memory.

Of course there was a buzz of conversation going on—there always is; but at last when the Rev. Mr. Burgess rose and laid his hand on the sack he could hear his microbes gnaw, the place was so still. He related the curious history of the sack, then went on to speak in warm terms of Hadleyburg's old and well-earned reputation for spotless honesty, and of the town's just pride in this reputation. He said that this reputation was a treasure of priceless value; that under Providence its value had now become inestimably enhanced, for the recent episode had spread this fame far and wide, and thus had focused the eyes of the American world upon this village, and made its name for all time, as he hoped and believed, a synonym for commercial incorruptibility. [*Applause.*] "And who is to be the guardian of this noble treasure—the community as a whole? No! The responsibility is individual, not communal. From this day forth each and every one of you is in his own person its special guardian, and individually responsible that no harm shall come to it. Do you—does each of you—accept this great

trust? [*Tumultuous assent.*] Then all is well. Transmit it
to your children and to your children's children. Today your
purity is beyond reproach—see to it that it shall remain so.
Today there is not a person in your community who could be
beguiled to touch a penny not his own—see to it that you abide
in this grace. [*"We will! we will!"*] This is not the place to
make comparisons between ourselves and other communities—
some of them ungracious toward us; they have their ways, we
have ours; let us be content. [*Applause.*] I am done. Under
my hand, my friends, rests a stranger's eloquent recognition of
what we are; through him the world will always henceforth
know what we are. We do not know who he is, but in your
name I utter your gratitude, and ask you to raise your voices
in endorsement."

The house rose in a body and made the walls quake with
the thunders of its thankfulness for the space of a long minute.
Then it sat down, and Mr. Burgess took an envelope out of his
pocket. The house held its breath while he slit the envelope
open and took from it a slip of paper. He read its contents
—slowly and impressively—the audience listening with tranced
attention to this magic document, each of whose words stood
for an ingot of gold:

"*'The remark which I made to the distressed stranger was
this: "You are very far from being a bad man: go, and reform."'*" Then he continued:

"We shall know in a moment now whether the remark here
quoted corresponds with the one concealed in the sack; and if
that shall prove to be so—and it undoubtedly will—this sack of
gold belongs to a fellow-citizen who will henceforth stand before the nation as the symbol of the special virtue which has
made our town famous throughout the land—Mr. Billson!"

The house had gotten itself all ready to burst into the proper
tornado of applause; but instead of doing it, it seemed stricken

with a paralysis; there was a deep hush for a moment or two, then a wave of whispered murmurs swept the place—of about this tenor: *"Billson!* oh, come, this is *too* thin! Twenty dollars to a stranger—or *anybody—Billson!* tell it to the marines!" And now at this point the house caught its breath all of a sudden in a new access of astonishment, for it discovered that whereas in one part of the hall Deacon Billson was standing up with his head meekly bowed, in another part of it Lawyer Wilson was doing the same. There was a wondering silence now for a while.

Everybody was puzzled, and nineteen couples were surprised and indignant.

Billson and Wilson turned and stared at each other. Billson asked, bitingly,

"Why do *you* rise, Mr. Wilson?"

"Because I have a right to. Perhaps you will be good enough to explain to the house why *you* rise?"

"With great pleasure. Because I wrote that paper."

"It is an impudent falsity! I wrote it myself."

It was Burgess's turn to be paralyzed. He stood looking vacantly at first one of the men and then the other, and did not seem to know what to do. The house was stupefied. Lawyer Wilson spoke up, now, and said,

"I ask the Chair to read the name signed to that paper."

That brought the Chair to itself, and it read out the name,

" 'John Wharton *Billson.'* "

"There!" shouted Billson, "what have you got to say for yourself, now? And what kind of apology are you going to make to me and to this insulted house for the imposture which you have attempted to play here?"

"No apologies are due, sir; and as for the rest of it, I publicly charge you with pilfering my note from Mr. Burgess and substituting a copy of it signed with your own name. There is no other way by which you could have gotten hold of the test-remark; I alone, of living men, possessed the secret of its wording."

There was likely to be a scandalous state of things if this went on; everybody noticed with distress that the short-hand scribes were scribbling like mad; many people were crying "Chair, Chair! Order! Order!" Burgess rapped with his gavel, and said:

"Let us not forget the proprieties due. There has evidently been a mistake somewhere, but surely that is all. If Mr. Wilson gave me an envelope—and I remember now that he did —I still have it."

He took one out of his pocket, opened it, glanced at it, looked surprised and worried, and stood silent a few moments. Then he waved his hand in a wandering and mechanical way, and made an effort or two to say something, then gave it up, despondently. Several voices cried out:

"Read it! read it! What is it?"

So he began in a dazed and sleep-walker fashion:

"*'The remark which I made to the unhappy stranger was this: "You are far from being a bad man.* [*The house gazed at him, marveling.*] *Go, and reform."'* [*Murmurs:* "Amazing! What can this mean?"] This one," said the Chair, "is signed Thurlow G. Wilson."

"There!" cried Wilson, "I reckon that settles it! I knew perfectly well my note was purloined."

"Purloined!" retorted Billson. "I'll let you know that neither you nor any man of your kidney must venture to—"

The Chair. "Order, gentlemen, order! Take your seats, both of you, please."

They obeyed, shaking their heads and grumbling angrily. The house was profoundly puzzled; it did not know what to do with this curious emergency. Presently Thompson got up.

Thompson was the hatter. He would have liked to be a Nine-teener; but such was not for him: his stock of hats was not considerable enough for the position. He said:

"Mr. Chairman, if I may be permitted to make a suggestion, can both of these gentlemen be right? I put it to you, sir, can both have happened to say the very same words to the stranger? It seems to me—"

The tanner got up and interrupted him. The tanner was a disgruntled man; he believed himself entitled to be a Nineteener, but he couldn't get recognition. It made him a little unpleasant in his ways and speech. Said he:

"Sho, *that's* not the point! *That* could happen—twice in a hundred years—but not the other thing. *Neither* of them gave the twenty dollars!"

[*A ripple of applause.*]

Billson. "I did!"

Wilson. "I did!"

Then each accused the other of pilfering.

The Chair. "Order! Sit down, if you please—both of you. Neither of the notes has been out of my possession at any moment."

A Voice. "Good—that settles *that!*"

The Tanner. "Mr. Chairman, one thing is now plain: one of these men has been eavesdropping under the other one's bed, and filching family secrets. If it is not unparliamentary to suggest it, I will remark that both are equal to it. [*The Chair.* "Order! Order!"] I withdraw the remark, sir, and will confine myself to suggesting that *if* one of them has overheard the other reveal the test-remark to his wife, we shall catch him now."

A Voice. "How?"

The Tanner. "Easily. The two have not quoted the remark in exactly the same words. You would have noticed that, if there hadn't been a considerable stretch of time and an exciting quarrel inserted between the two readings."

A Voice. "Name the difference."

The Tanner. "The word *very* is in Billson's note, and not in the other.

Many Voices. "That's so—he's right!"

The Tanner. "And so, if the Chair will examine the test-remark in the sack, we shall know which of these two frauds —[*The Chair.* "Order!"]—which of these two adventurers—[*The Chair.* "Order! Order!"]—which of these two gentlemen —[*laughter and applause*]—is entitled to wear the belt as being the first dishonest blatherskite ever bred in this town—which he has dishonored, and which will be a sultry place for him from now out!" [*Vigorous applause.*]

Many Voices. "Open it!—open the sack!"

Mr. Burgess made a slit in the sack, slid his hand in and brought out an envelope. In it were a couple of folded notes. He said:

"One of these is marked, 'Not to be examined until all written communications which have been addressed to the Chair—if any—shall have been read.' The other is marked '*The Test.*' Allow me. It is worded—to wit:

"'I do not require that the first half of the remark which was made to me by my benefactor shall be quoted with exactness, for it was not striking, and could be forgotten; but its closing fifteen words are quite striking, and I think easily rememberable; unless *these* shall be accurately reproduced, let the applicant be regarded as an impostor. My benefactor began by saying he seldom gave advice to anyone, but that it always bore the hall-mark of high value when he did give it. Then he said this—and it has never faded from my memory: *"You are far from being a bad man—"'"*

Fifty Voices. "That settles it—the money's Wilson's! Wilson! Wilson! Speech! Speech!"

People jumped up and crowded around Wilson, wringing his hand and congratulating fervently—meantime the Chair was hammering with the gavel and shouting:

"Order, gentlemen! Order! Order! Let me finish reading, please." When quiet was restored, the reading was resumed— as follows:

" ' "*Go, and reform—or, mark my words—some day, for your sins, you will die and go to hell or Hadleyburg*—TRY AND MAKE IT THE FORMER." ' "

A ghastly silence followed. First an angry cloud began to settle darkly upon the faces of the citizenship; after a pause the cloud began to rise, and a tickled expression tried to take its place; tried so hard that it was only kept under with great and painful difficulty; the reporters, the Brixtonites, and other strangers bent their heads down and shielded their faces with their hands, and managed to hold in by main strength and heroic courtesy. At this most inopportune time burst upon the stillness the roar of a solitary voice—Jack Halliday's:

"*That's* got the hall-mark on it!"

Then the house let go, strangers and all. Even Mr. Burgess's gravity broke down presently, then the audience considered itself officially absolved from all restraint, and it made the most of its privilege. It was a good long laugh, and a tempestuously wholehearted one, but it ceased at last—long enough for Mr. Burgess to try to resume, and for the people to get their eyes partially wiped; then it broke out again; and afterward yet again; then at last Burgess was able to get out these serious words:

"It is useless to try to disguise the fact—we find ourselves in the presence of a matter of grave import. It involves the honor of your town, it strikes at the town's good name. The difference of a single word between the test-remarks offered by Mr. Wilson and Mr. Billson was itself a serious thing, since it indicated that one or the other of these gentlemen had committed a theft—"

The two men were sitting limp, nerveless, crushed; but at these words both were electrified into movement, and started to get up—

"Sit down!" said the Chair, sharply, and they obeyed. "That, as I have said, was a serious thing. And it was—but for only one of them. But the matter has become graver; for the honor of *both* is now in formidable peril. Shall I go even further, and say in inextricable peril? *Both* left out the crucial fifteen words." He paused. During several moments he allowed the pervading stillness to gather and deepen its impressive effects, then added: "There would seem to be but one way whereby this could happen. I ask these gentlemen—Was there *collusion? —agreement?*"

A low murmur sifted through the house; its import was, "He's got them both."

Billson was not used to emergencies; he sat in a helpless collapse. But Wilson was a lawyer. He struggled to his feet, pale and worried, and said:

"I ask the indulgence of the house while I explain this most painful matter. I am sorry to say what I am about to say, since it must inflict irreparable injury upon Mr. Billson, whom I have always esteemed and respected until now, and in whose invulnerability to temptation I entirely believed—as did you all. But for the preservation of my own honor I must speak—and with frankness. I confess with shame—and I now beseech your pardon for it—that I said to the ruined stranger all of the words contained in the test-remark, including the disparaging fifteen. [*Sensation.*] When the late publication was made I recalled them, and I resolved to claim the sack of coin, for by every right I was entitled to it. Now I will ask you to consider this point, and weigh it well: that stranger's gratitude to me that night knew no bounds; he said himself that he could find no words for it that were adequate, and that if he should ever be able he would repay me a thousand fold. Now, then, I ask you this: Could I expect—could I believe—could I even remotely imagine—that, feeling as he did, he would do so ungrateful a thing as to add those quite unnecessary fifteen words to his test?—set a trap for me?—expose me as a slanderer of my own town before my own people assembled in a public hall? It was preposterous; it was impossible. His test would contain only the kindly opening clause of my remark. Of that I had no shadow of doubt. You would have thought as I did. You would not have expected a base betrayal from one whom you had befriended and against whom you had committed no offense. And so, with perfect confidence, perfect trust, I wrote on a piece of paper the opening words—ending with 'Go, and reform,'—and signed it. When I was about to put it in an envelope I was called into my back office, and without thinking I left the paper lying open on my desk." He stopped, turned his head slowly toward Billson, waited a moment, then added: "I ask you to note this: when I returned, a little later, Mr. Billson was retiring by my street door." [*Sensation.*]

In a moment Billson was on his feet and shouting:

"It's a lie! It's an infamous lie!"

The Chair. "Be seated, sir! Mr. Wilson has the floor."

Billson's friends pulled him into his seat and quieted him, and Wilson went on:

"Those are the simple facts. My note was now lying in a different place on the table from where I had left it. I noticed that, but attached no importance to it, thinking a draught had blown it there. That Mr. Billson would read a private paper was a thing which could not occur to me; he was an honorable man, and he would be above that. If you will allow me to say it, I think his extra word *'very'* stands explained; it is attributable to a defect of memory. I was the only man in the world who could furnish here any detail of the test-remark—by *honorable* means. I have finished."

There is nothing in the world like a persuasive speech to fuddle the mental apparatus and upset the convictions and debauch the emotions of an audience not practiced in the tricks and delusions of oratory. Wilson sat down victorious. The house submerged him in tides of approving applause; friends swarmed to him and shook him by the hand and congratulated him, and Billson was shouted down and not allowed to say a word. The Chair hammered and hammered with its gavel, and kept shouting,

"But let us proceed, gentlemen, let us proceed!"

At last there was a measurable degree of quiet, and the hatter said:

"But what is there to proceed with, sir, but to deliver the money?"

Voices. "That's it! That's it! Come forward, Wilson!"

The Hatter. "I move three cheers for Mr. Wilson, Symbol of the special virtue which—"

The cheers burst forth before he could finish; and in the midst of them—and in the midst of the clamor of the gavel also—some enthusiasts mounted Wilson on a big friend's shoulder and were going to fetch him in triumph to the platform. The Chair's voice now rose above the noise—

"Order! To your places! You forget that there is still a document to be read." When quiet had been restored he took up the document, and was going to read it, but laid it down again, saying, "I forgot; this is not to be read until all written communications received by me have first been read." He took an envelope out of his pocket, removed its enclosure, glanced at it—seemed astonished—held it out and gazed at it—stared at it.

Twenty or thirty voices cried out:

"What is it? Read it! read it!"

And he did—slowly, and wondering:

" 'The remark which I made to the stranger—[*Voices.* "Hello! how's this?"]—was this: "You are far from being a bad man. [*Voices.* "Great Scott!"] Go, and reform." ' [*Voice.* "Oh, saw my leg off!"] Signed by Mr. Pinkerton the banker."

The pandemonium of delight which turned itself loose now was of a sort to make the judicious weep. Those whose withers were unwrung laughed till the tears ran down; the reporters, in throes of laughter, set down disordered pot-hooks which would never in the world be decipherable; and a sleeping dog jumped up, scared out of its wits, and barked itself crazy at the turmoil. All manner of cries were scattered through the din: "We're getting rich—*two* Symbols of Incorruptibility!— without counting Billson!" "*Three!*—count Shadbelly in—we can't have too many!" "All right—Billson's elected!" "Alas, poor Wilson—victim of *two* thieves!"

A Powerful Voice. "Silence! The Chair's fished up something more out of its pocket."

Voices. "Hurrah! Is it something fresh? Read it! read! read!"

The Chair [*reading*]. " 'The remark which I made,' etc.: 'You are far from being a bad man. Go,' etc. Signed, 'Gregory Yates.' "

Tornado of Voices. "Four Symbols!" " 'Rah for Yates!" "Fish again!"

The house was in a roaring humor now, and ready to get all the fun out of the occasion that might be in it. Several Nineteeners, looking pale and distressed, got up and began to work their way toward the aisles, but a score of shouts went up:

"The doors, the doors—close the doors; no Incorruptible shall leave this place! Sit down, everybody!"

The mandate was obeyed.

"Fish again! Read! read!"

The Chair fished again, and once more the familiar words began to fall from its lips—" 'You are far from being a bad man—' "

"Name! name! What's his name?"

" 'L. Ingoldsby Sargent.' "

"Five elected! Pile up the Symbols! Go on, go on!"

" 'You are far from being a bad—' "

"Name! name!"

" 'Nicholas Whitworth.' "

"Hooray! hooray! it's a symbolical day!"

Somebody wailed in, and began to sing this rhyme (leaving out "it's") to the lovely *Mikado* tune of "When a man's afraid, a beautiful maid—"; the audience joined in, with joy; then, just in time, somebody contributed another line—

"And don't you this forget—"

The house roared it out. A third line was at once furnished—

"Corruptibles far from Hadleyburg are—"

The house roared that one too. As the last note died, Jack Halliday's voice rose high and clear, freighted with a final line—

"But the Symbols are here, you bet!"

That was sung, with booming enthusiasm. Then the happy house started in at the beginning and sang the four lines through twice, with immense swing and dash, and finished up with a crashing three-times-three and a tiger for "Hadleyburg the Incorruptible and all Symbols of it which we shall find worthy to receive the hall-mark tonight."

Then the shoutings at the Chair began again, all over the place:

"Go on! go on! Read! read some more! Read all you've got!"

"That's it—go on! We are winning eternal celebrity!"

A dozen men got up now and began to protest. They said that this farce was the work of some abandoned joker, and was an insult to the whole community. Without a doubt these signatures were all forgeries—

"Sit down! sit down! Shut up! You are confessing. We'll find *your* names in the lot."

"Mr. Chairman, how many of those envelopes have you got?"

The Chair counted.

"Together with those that have been already examined, there are nineteen."

A storm of derisive applause broke out.

"Perhaps they all contain the secret. I move that you open them all and read every signature that is attached to a note of that sort—and read also the first eight words of the note."

"Second the motion!"

It was put and carried—uproariously. Then poor old Richards got up, and his wife rose and stood at his side. Her head was bent down, so that none might see that she was crying. Her husband gave her his arm, and so supporting her, he began to speak in a quavering voice:

"My friends, you have known us two—Mary and me—all our lives, and I think you have liked us and respected us—"

The Chair interrupted him:

"Allow me. It is quite true—that which you are saying, Mr. Richards: this town *does* know you two; it *does* like you; it *does* respect you; more—it honors you and *loves* you—"

Halliday's voice rang out:

"That's the hall-marked truth, too! If the Chair is right, let the house speak up and say it. Rise! Now, then—hip! hip! hip!—all together!"

The house rose in mass, faced toward the old couple eagerly, filled the air with a snowstorm of waving handkerchiefs, and delivered the cheers with all its affectionate heart.

The Chair then continued:

"What I was going to say is this: We know your good heart, Mr. Richards, but this is not a time for the exercise of charity toward offenders. [*Shouts of "Right! right!"*] I see your generous purpose in your face, but I cannot allow you to plead for these men—"

"But I was going to—"

"Please take your seat, Mr. Richards. We must examine the rest of these notes—simple fairness to the men who have already been exposed requires this. As soon as that has been done— I give you my word for this—you shall be heard."

Many Voices. "Right!—the Chair is right—no interruption can be permitted at this stage! Go on!—the names! the names! —according to the terms of the motion!"

The old couple sat reluctantly down, and the husband whispered to the wife, "It is pitifully hard to have to wait; the shame will be greater than ever when they find we were only going to plead for *ourselves.*"

Straightway the jollity broke loose again with the reading of the names.

" 'You are far from being a bad man—' Signature, 'Robert J. Titmarsh.'

" 'You are far from being a bad man—' Signature, 'Eliphalet Weeks.'

" 'You are far from being a bad man—' Signature, 'Oscar B. Wilder.' "

At this point the house lit upon the idea of taking the eight words out of the Chairman's hands. He was not unthankful for that. Thenceforward he held up each note in its turn, and waited. The house droned out the eight words in a massed and measured and musical deep volume of sound (with a daringly close resemblance to a well-known church chant)—"'You are f-a-r from being a b-a-a-a-d man.'" Then the Chair said, "Signature, 'Archibald Wilcox.'" And so on, and so on, name after name, and everybody had an increasingly and gloriously good time except the wretched Nineteen. Now and then, when a particularly shining name was called, the house made the Chair wait while it chanted the whole of the test-remark from the beginning to the closing words, "And go to hell or Hadleyburg—try and make it the for-or-m-e-r!" and in these special cases they added a grand and agonized and imposing "A-a-a-a-men!"

The list dwindled, dwindled, dwindled, poor old Richards keeping tally of the count, wincing when a name resembling his own was pronounced, and waiting in miserable suspense for the time to come when it would be his humiliating privilege to rise with Mary and finish his plea, which he was intending to word thus: ". . . for until now we have never done any wrong thing, but have gone our humble way unreproached. We are very poor, we are old, and have no chick nor child to help us; we were sorely tempted, and we fell. It was my purpose when I got up before to make a confession and beg that my name might not be read out in this public place, for it seemed to us that we could not bear it; but I was prevented. It was just; it was our place to suffer with the rest. It has been hard for us. It is the first time we have ever heard our name fall from any one's lips—sullied. Be merciful—for the sake of the better days; make our shame as light to bear as in your charity you can." At this point in his reverie Mary nudged him, perceiving that his mind was absent. The house was chanting, "You are f-a-r," etc.

"Be ready," Mary whispered. "Your name comes now; he has read eighteen."

The chant ended.

"Next! next! next!" came volleying from all over the house. Burgess put his hand into his pocket. The old couple, trembling, began to rise. Burgess fumbled a moment, then said,

"I find I have read them all."

Faint with joy and surprise, the couple sank into their seats, and Mary whispered,

"Oh, bless God, we are saved!—he has lost ours—I wouldn't give this for a hundred of those sacks!"

The house burst out with its *Mikado* travesty, and sang it three times with ever-increasing enthusiasm, rising to its feet when it reached for the third time the closing line—

"But the Symbols are here, you bet!"

and finishing up with cheers and a tiger for "Hadleyburg purity and our eighteen immortal representatives of it."

Then Wingate, the saddler, got up and proposed cheers "for the cleanest man in town, the one solitary important citizen in it who didn't try to steal that money—Edward Richards."

They were given with great and moving heartiness; then somebody proposed that Richards be elected sole guardian and Symbol of the now Sacred Hadleyburg Tradition, with power and right to stand up and look the whole sarcastic world in the face.

Passed, by acclamation; then they sang the *Mikado* again, and ended it with,

"And there's one Symbol left, you bet!"

There was a pause; then—

A Voice. "Now, then, who's to get the sack?"

The Tanner (with bitter sarcasm). "That's easy. The money has to be divided among the eighteen Incorruptibles. They gave the suffering stranger twenty dollars apiece—and that remark— each in his turn—it took twenty-two minutes for the procession to move past. Staked the stranger—total contribution, $360. All they want is just the loan back—and interest—forty thousand dollars altogether."

Many Voices [derisively]. "That's it! Divvy! divvy! Be kind to the poor—don't keep them waiting!"

The Chair. "Order! I now offer the stranger's remaining document. It says: 'If no claimant shall appear [*grand chorus of groans*], I desire that you open the sack and count out the money to the principal citizens of your town, they to take it in trust [*cries of "Oh! Oh! Oh!"*], and use it in such ways as to them shall seem best for the propagation and preservation of your community's noble reputation for incorruptible honesty [*more cries*]—a reputation to which their names and their efforts will add a new and far-reaching luster.' [*Enthusiastic outburst of sarcastic applause.*] That seems to be all. No—here is a postscript:

" 'P. S.—CITIZENS OF HADLEYBURG: There *is* no test-remark— nobody made one. [*Great sensation.*] There wasn't any pauper stranger, nor any twenty-dollar contribution, nor any accompanying benediction and compliment—these are all inventions. [*General buzz and hum of astonishment and delight.*] Allow me to tell my story—it will take but a word or two. I passed through your town at a certain time, and received a deep offense which I had not earned. Any other man would have been content to kill one or two of you and call it square, but to me that would have been a trivial revenge, and inadequate; for the dead do not *suffer.* Besides, I could not kill you all—and, anyway, mad

as I am, even that would not have satisfied me. I wanted to
damage every man in the place, and every woman—and not in
their bodies or in their estate, but in their vanity—the place
where feeble and foolish people are most vulnerable. So I dis-
guised myself and came back and studied you. You were easy
game. You had an old and lofty reputation for honesty, and
naturally you were proud of it—it was your treasure of treasures, the very apple of your eye. As soon as I found out that
you carefully and vigilantly kept yourselves and your children
out of temptation, I knew how to proceed. Why, you simple
creatures, the weakest of all weak things is a virtue which has
not been tested in the fire. I laid a plan, and gathered a list
of names. My project was to corrupt Hadleyburg the Incorruptible. My idea was to make liars and thieves of nearly half
a hundred smirchless men and women who had never in their
lives uttered a lie or stolen a penny. I was afraid of Goodson.
He was neither born nor reared in Hadleyburg. I was afraid
that if I started to operate my scheme by getting my letter laid
before you, you would say to yourselves, "Goodson is the only
man among us who would give away twenty dollars to a poor
devil"—and then you might not bite at my bait. But Heaven
took Goodson; then I knew I was safe, and I set my trap and
baited it. It may be that I shall not catch all the men to whom
I mailed the pretended test secret, but I shall catch the most of
them, if I know Hadleyburg nature. [*Voices.* "Right—he got
every last one of them."] I believe they will even steal ostensible *gamble*-money, rather than miss, poor, tempted, and
mistrained fellows. I am hoping to eternally and everlastingly
squelch your vanity and give Hadleyburg a new renown—one
that will *stick*—and spread far. If I have succeeded, open the
sack and summon the Committee on Propagation and Preservation of the Hadleyburg Reputation.'"

A Cyclone of Voices. "Open it! Open it! The Eighteen to

the front! Committee on Propagation of the Tradition! Forward—the Incorruptibles!"

The Chair ripped the sack wide, and gathered up a handful of bright, broad, yellow coins, shook them together, then examined them—

"Friends, they are only gilded disks of lead!"

There was a crashing outbreak of delight over this news, and when the noise had subsided, the tanner called out:

"By right of apparent seniority in this business, Mr. Wilson is Chairman of the Committee on Propagation of the Tradition. I suggest that he step forward on behalf of his pals, and receive in trust the money."

A Hundred Voices. "Wilson! Wilson! Wilson! Speech! Speech!"

Wilson [*in a voice trembling with anger*]. "You will allow me to say, and without apologies for my language, *damn* the money!"

A Voice. "Oh, and him a Baptist!"

A Voice. "Seventeen Symbols left! Step up, gentlemen, and assume your trust!"

There was a pause—no response.

The Saddler. "Mr. Chairman, we've got *one* clean man left, anyway, out of the late aristocracy; and he needs money, and deserves it. I move that you appoint Jack Halliday to get up there and auction off that sack of gilt twenty-dollar pieces, and give the result to the right man—the man whom Hadleyburg delights to honor—Edward Richards."

This was received with great enthusiasm, the dog taking a hand again; the saddler started the bids at a dollar, the Brixton folk and Barnum's representative fought hard for it, the people cheered every jump that the bids made, the excitement climbed moment by moment higher and higher, the bidders got on their mettle and grew steadily more and more daring, more and more determined, the jumps went from a dollar up to five, then to ten, then to twenty, then fifty, then to a hundred, then—

At the beginning of the auction Richards whispered in distress to his wife: "Oh, Mary, can we allow it? It—it—you see, it is an honor-reward, a testimonial to purity of character, and—and—can we allow it? Hadn't I better get up and—Oh, Mary, what ought we to do?—what do you think we—" [*Halliday's voice. "Fifteen I'm bid!—fifteen for the sack!—twenty! —ah, thanks!—thirty—thanks again! Thirty, thirty, thirty!—do I hear forty?—forty it is! Keep the ball rolling, gentlemen, keep it rolling!—fifty!—thanks, noble Roman! going at fifty, fifty, fifty!—seventy!—ninety!—splendid!—a hundred!—pile it up, pile it up!—hundred and twenty—forty!—just in time!—hundred and fifty!—*TWO *hundred!—superb! Do I hear two h—thanks!—two hundred and fifty!—"*]

"It is another temptation, Edward—I'm all in a tremble—but, oh, we've escaped *one* temptation, and that ought to warn us to— [*"Six did I hear?—thanks!—six fifty, six f—*SEVEN *hundred!"*] And yet Edward, when you think—nobody susp— [*"Eight hundred dollars!—hurrah!—make it nine!—Mr. Parsons, did I hear you say—thanks—nine!—this noble sack of virgin lead going at only nine hundred dollars, gilding and all—come! do I hear—a thousand!—gratefully yours!—did some one say eleven?—a sack which is going to be the most celebrated in the whole Uni—"*] Oh, Edward" (beginning to sob), "we are *so* poor!—but—but—do as you think best—do as you think best."

Edward fell—that is, he sat still; sat with a conscience which was not satisfied, but which was overpowered by circumstances.

Meantime a stranger, who looked like an amateur detective gotten up as an impossible English earl, had been watching the evening's proceedings with manifest interest, and with a contented expression in his face; and he had been privately commenting to himself. He was now soliloquizing somewhat like this: "None of the Eighteen are bidding; that is not satisfactory; I must change that—the dramatic unities require it; they must buy the sack they tried to steal; they must pay a heavy price, too—some of them are rich. And another thing, when I make a mistake in Hadleyburg nature the man that puts that error upon me is entitled to a high honorarium, and some one must pay it. This poor old Richards has brought my judgment to shame; he is an honest man:—I don't understand it, but I acknowledge it. Yes, he saw my deuces *and* with a straight flush, and by rights the pot is his. And it shall be a jack-pot, too, if I can manage it. He disappointed me, but let that pass."

He was watching the bidding. At a thousand, the market broke; the prices tumbled swiftly. He waited—and still watched. One competitor dropped out; then another, and another. He put in a bid or two, now. When the bids had sunk to ten dollars, he added a five; some one raised him a three; he waited a moment, then flung in a fifty-dollar jump, and the sack was his—at $1,282. The house broke out in cheers—then stopped; for he was on his feet, and had lifted his hand. He began to speak.

"I desire to say a word, and ask a favor. I am a speculator in rarities, and I have dealings with persons interested in numismatics all over the world. I can make a profit on this purchase, just as it stands; but there is a way, if I can get your approval, whereby I can make every one of these leaden twenty-dollar pieces worth its face in gold, and perhaps more. Grant me that approval, and I will give part of my gains to your Mr. Richards, whose invulnerable probity you have so justly and cordially recognized tonight; his share shall be ten thousand dollars, and I will hand him the money tomorrow. [*Great applause from the house*. But the "invulnerable probity" made the Richardses blush prettily; however, it went for modesty, and did no harm.] If you will pass my proposition by a good majority—I would like a two-thirds vote—I will regard that as the town's consent, and that is all I ask. Rarities are always helped by any device which will rouse curiosity and compel remark. Now if I may have your permission to stamp upon the faces of each of these ostensible coins the names of the eighteen gentlemen who—"

Nine-tenths of the audience were on their feet in a moment —dog and all—and the proposition was carried with a whirlwind of approving applause and laughter.

They sat down, and all the Symbols except "Dr." Clay Harkness got up, violently protesting against the proposed outrage, and threatening to—

"I beg you not to threaten me," said the stranger, calmly. "I know my legal rights, and am not accustomed to being frightened at bluster." [*Applause.*] He sat down. "Dr." Harkness saw an opportunity here. He was one of the two very rich men of the place, and Pinkerton was the other. Harkness was proprietor of a mint; that is to say, a popular patent medicine. He was running for the Legislature on one ticket, and Pinkerton on the other. It was a close race and a hot one, and getting hotter every day. Both had strong appetites for money; each had bought a great tract of land, with a purpose; there was going to be a new railway, and each wanted to be in the Legislature and help locate the route to his own advantage; a single vote might make the decision, and with it two or three fortunes. The stake was large, and Harkness was a daring speculator. He was sitting close to the stranger. He leaned over while one or another of the other Symbols was entertaining the house with protests and appeals, and asked, in a whisper,

"What is your price for the sack?"

"Forty thousand dollars."

"I'll give you twenty."

"No."

"Twenty-five."

"No."

"Say thirty."

"The price is forty thousand dollars; not a penny less."

"All right, I'll give it. I will come to the hotel at ten in the morning. I don't want it known; will see you privately."

"Very good." Then the stranger got up and said to the house: "I find it late. The speeches of these gentlemen are not without merit, not without interest, not without grace; yet if I may be excused I will take my leave. I thank you for the great favor which you have shown me in granting my petition. I ask the Chair to keep the sack for me until tomorrow, and to hand these three five-hundred-dollar notes to Mr. Richards." They were passed up to the Chair. "At nine I will call for the sack, and at eleven will deliver the rest of the ten thousand to Mr. Richards in person, at his home. Good night."

Then he slipped out, and left the audience making a vast noise, which was composed of a mixture of cheers, the *Mikado* song, dog-disapproval, and the chant, "You are f-a-r from being a b-a-a-d man—a-a-a a-men!"

IV

At home the Richardses had to endure congratulations and compliments until midnight. Then they were left to themselves. They looked a little sad, and they sat silent and thinking. Finally Mary sighed and said,

"Do you think we are to blame, Edward—*much* to blame?" and her eyes wandered to the accusing triplet of big bank notes lying on the table, where the congratulators had been gloating over them and reverently fingering them. Edward did not answer at once; then he brought out a sigh and said, hesitatingly:

"We—we couldn't help it, Mary. It—well, it was ordered. *All* things are."

Mary glanced up and looked at him steadily, but he didn't return the look. Presently she said:

"I thought congratulations and praises always tasted good. But—it seems to me, now—Edward?"

"Well?"

"Are you going to stay in the bank?"

"N-no."

"Resign?"

"In the morning—by note."

"It does seem best."

Richards bowed his head in his hands and muttered:

"Before, I was not afraid to let oceans of people's money pour through my hands, but—Mary, I am so tired, so tired—"

"We will go to bed."

At nine in the morning the stranger called for the sack and took it to the hotel in a cab. At ten Harkness had a talk with him privately. The stranger asked for and got five checks on a metropolitan bank—drawn to "Bearer"—four for $1,500 each, and one for $34,000. He put one of the former in his pocketbook, and the remainder, representing $38,500, he put in an envelope, and with these he added a note, which he wrote after Harkness was gone. At eleven he called at the Richards house and knocked. Mrs. Richards peeped through the shutters, then went and received the envelope, and the stranger disappeared without a word. She came back flushed and a little unsteady on her legs, and gasped out:

"I am sure I recognized him! Last night it seemed to me that maybe I had seen him somewhere before."

"He is the man that brought the sack here?"

"I am almost sure of it."

"Then he is the ostensible Stephenson, too, and sold every important citizen in this town with his bogus secret. Now if he has sent checks instead of money, we are sold, too, after we thought we had escaped. I was beginning to feel fairly comfortable once more, after my night's rest, but the look of that envelope makes me sick. It isn't fat enough; $8,500 in even the largest bank notes makes more bulk than that."

"Edward, why do you object to checks?"

"Checks signed by Stephenson! I am resigned to take the $8,500 if it could come in bank notes—for it does seem that it was so ordered, Mary—but I have never had much courage, and I have not the pluck to try to market a check signed with that disastrous name. It would be a trap. That man tried to catch me; we escaped somehow or other; and now he is trying a new way. If it is checks—"

"Oh, Edward, it is *too* bad!" and she held up the checks and began to cry.

"Put them in the fire! quick! we mustn't be tempted. It is a trick to make the world laugh at *us,* along with the rest, and— Give them to *me,* since you can't do it!" He snatched them and tried to hold his grip till he could get to the stove; but he was human, he was a cashier, and he stopped a moment to make sure of the signature. Then he came near to fainting.

"Fan me, Mary, fan me! They are the same as gold!"

"Oh, how lovely, Edward! Why?"

"Signed by Harkness. What can the mystery of that be, Mary?"

"Edward, do you think—"

"Look here—look at this! Fifteen—fifteen—fifteen—thirty-four. Thirty-eight thousand five hundred! Mary, the sack isn't worth twelve dollars, and Harkness—apparently—has paid about par for it."

"And does it all come to us, do you think—instead of the ten thousand?"

"Why, it looks like it. And the checks are made to 'Bearer,' too."

"Is that good, Edward? What is it for?"

"A hint to collect them at some distant bank, I reckon. Perhaps Harkness doesn't want the matter known. What is that —a note?"

"Yes. It was with the checks."

It was in the "Stephenson" handwriting, but there was no signature. It said:

I am a disappointed man. Your honesty is beyond the reach of temptation. I had a different idea about it, but I wronged you in that, and I beg pardon, and do it sincerely. I honor you—and that is sincere too. This town is not worthy to kiss the hem of your garment. Dear sir, I made a square bet with myself that there were nineteen debauchable men in your self-righteous community. I have lost. Take the whole pot, you are entitled to it.

Richards drew a deep sigh, and said:

"It seems written with fire—it burns so. Mary—I am miserable again."

"I, too. Ah, dear, I wish—"

"To think, Mary—he *believes* in me."

"Oh, don't, Edward—I can't bear it."

"If those beautiful words were deserved, Mary—and God knows I believed I deserved them once—I think I could give the forty thousand dollars for them. And I would put that paper away, as representing more than gold and jewels, and keep it always. But now— We could not live in the shadow of its accusing presence, Mary."

He put it in the fire.

A messenger arrived and delivered an envelope.

Richards took from it a note and read it; it was from Burgess.

You saved me, in a difficult time. I saved you last night. It was at cost of a lie, but I made the sacrifice freely, and out of a grateful heart. None in this village knows so well as I know how brave and good and noble you are. At bottom you cannot respect me, knowing as you do of that matter of which I am accused, and by the general voice condemned; but I beg that you will at least believe that I am a grateful man; it will help me to bear my burden.

[Signed]   BURGESS.

"Saved, once more. And on such terms!" He put the note in the fire. "I—I wish I were dead, Mary, I wish I were out of it all."

"Oh, these are bitter, bitter days, Edward. The stabs, through their very generosity, are so deep—and they come so fast!"

Three days before the election each of two thousand voters suddenly found himself in possession of a prized memento— one of the renowned bogus double-eagles. Around one of its faces was stamped these words: "THE REMARK I MADE TO THE POOR STRANGER WAS—" Around the other face was stamped these: "GO, AND REFORM. [SIGNED] PINKERTON." Thus the entire remaining refuse of the renowned joke was emptied upon a single head, and with calamitous effect. It revived the recent vast laugh and concentrated it upon Pinkerton; and Harkness's election was a walkover.

Within twenty-four hours after the Richardses had received their checks their consciences were quieting down, discouraged; the old couple were learning to reconcile themselves to the sin which they had committed. But they were to learn, now, that a sin takes on new and real terrors when there seems a chance that it is going to be found out. This gives it a fresh and most substantial and important aspect. At church the morning sermon was of the usual pattern; it was the same old things said in the same old way; they had heard them a thousand times and found them innocuous, next to meaningless, and easy to sleep under; but now it was different: the sermon seemed to bristle with accusations; it seemed aimed straight and specially at people who were concealing deadly sins. After church they got away from the mob of congratulators as soon as they could, and hurried homeward, chilled to the bone at they did not know what—vague, shadowy, indefinite fears. And by chance they caught a glimpse of Mr. Burgess as he turned a corner. He paid no attention to their nod of recognition! He hadn't seen it; but they did not know that. What could his conduct mean? It might mean—it might mean—oh, a dozen dreadful things. Was it possible that he knew that Richards could have cleared him of guilt in that bygone time, and had been silently waiting for a chance to even up accounts? At home, in their distress they got to imagining that their servant might have been in the next room listening when Richards revealed the secret to his wife that he knew of Burgess's innocence; next, Richards began to imagine that he had heard the swish of a gown in there at that time; next, he was sure he *had* heard it. They would call Sarah in, on a pretext, and watch her face: if she had been betraying them to Mr. Burgess, it would show in her manner. They asked her some questions—questions which were so random and incoherent and seemingly purposeless that the girl felt sure that the old people's minds had been affected by their sudden good fortune; the sharp and watchful gaze which they bent upon her frightened her, and that completed the business. She blushed, she became nervous and confused, and to the old people these were plain signs of guilt—guilt of some fearful sort or other—without doubt she was a spy and a traitor. When they were alone again they began to piece many unrelated things together and get horrible results out of the combination. When things had got about to the worst, Richards was delivered of a sudden gasp, and his wife asked,

"Oh, what is it?—what is it?"

"The note—Burgess's note! Its language was sarcastic, I see it now." He quoted: " 'At bottom you cannot respect me, *knowing*, as you do, of *that matter* of which I am accused' —oh, it is perfectly plain, now, God help me! He knows that I know! You see the ingenuity of the phrasing. It was a trap —and like a fool, I walked into it. And Mary—?"

"Oh, it is dreadful—I know what you are going to say—he didn't return your transcript of the pretended test-remark."

"No—kept it to destroy us with. Mary, he has exposed us to some already. I know it—I know it well. I saw it in a dozen faces after church. Ah, he wouldn't answer our nod of recognition—*he* knew what he had been doing!"

In the night the doctor was called. The news went around in the morning that the old couple were rather seriously ill— prostrated by the exhausting excitement growing out of their great windfall, the congratulations, and the late hours, the doctor said. The town was sincerely distressed; for these old people were about all it had left to be proud of, now.

Two days later the news was worse. The old couple were delirious, and were doing strange things. By witness of the nurses, Richards had exhibited checks—for $8,500? No—for an amazing sum—$38,500! What could be the explanation of this gigantic piece of luck?

The following day the nurses had more news—and wonderful. They had concluded to hide the checks, lest harm come to them; but when they searched they were gone from under the patient's pillow—vanished away. The patient said:

"Let the pillow alone; what do you want?"

"We thought it best that the checks—"

"You will never see them again—they are destroyed. They came from Satan. I saw the hell-brand on them, and I knew they were sent to betray me to sin." Then he fell to gabbling strange and dreadful things which were not clearly understandable, and which the doctor admonished them to keep to themselves.

Richards was right; the checks were never seen again.

A nurse must have talked in her sleep, for within two days the forbidden gabblings were the property of the town; and they were of a surprising sort. They seemed to indicate that Richards had been a claimant for the sack himself, and that Burgess had concealed that fact and then maliciously betrayed it.

Burgess was taxed with this and stoutly denied it. And he said it was not fair to attach weight to the chatter of a sick old man who was out of his mind. Still, suspicion was in the air, and there was much talk.

After a day or two it was reported that Mrs. Richards's delirious deliveries were getting to be duplicates of her husband's. Suspicion flamed up into conviction, now, and the town's pride in the purity of its one undiscredited important citizen began to dim down and flicker toward extinction.

Six days passed, then came more news. The old couple were dying. Richards's mind cleared in his latest hour, and he sent for Burgess. Burgess said:

"Let the room be cleared. I think he wishes to say something in privacy."

"No!" said Richards: "I want witnesses. I want you all to hear my confession, so that I may die a man, and not a dog. I was clean—artificially—like the rest; and like the rest I fell when temptation came. I signed a lie, and claimed the miserable sack. Mr. Burgess remembered that I had done him a service, and in gratitude (and ignorance) he suppressed my claim and saved me. You know the thing that was charged against Burgess years ago. My testimony, and mine alone, could have cleared him, and I was a coward, and left him to suffer disgrace—"

"No—no—Mr. Richards, you—"

"My servant betrayed my secret to him—"

"No one has betrayed anything to me—"

—"and then he did a natural and justifiable thing, he repented of the saving kindness which he had done me, and he *exposed* me—as I deserved—"

"Never!—I make oath—"

"Out of my heart I forgive him."

Burgess's impassioned protestations fell upon deaf ears; the dying man passed away without knowing that once more he had done poor Burgess a wrong. The old wife died that night.

The last of the sacred Nineteen had fallen a prey to the fiendish sack; the town was stripped of the last rag of its ancient glory. Its mourning was not showy, but it was deep.

By act of the Legislature—upon prayer and petition—Hadleyburg was allowed to change its name to (never mind what—I will not give it away), and leave one word out of the motto that for many generations had graced the town's official seal.

It is an honest town once more, and the man will have to rise early that catches it napping again.

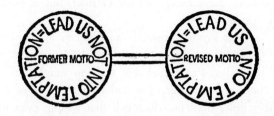

HARMONY

by WILLIAM FAIN

J OHN STEPHENS nodded while Auslander, the American, gave him instructions about how to ride the race. They were at St. Cloud, walking to the paddock. Stephens wished Auslander would not put his arm around his shoulder. Why did people think that because a jockey was a small man it was all right to touch him all the time? He did not much like owners, anyway. It would be a grand sport without them, he thought, and smiled; he had no sense of humor, and for him this was a pretty fair joke. Stephens did not like riding instructions much, either. Did Auslander have any idea of all the things that could happen during a race? Still, he half listened, and nodded.

"I've never run him in the mud, but I don't think he'll mind it," Auslander was saying.

When they got to the paddock, and to the horse Stephens was to ride, Auslander's trainer, Garnier, gave the jockey a leg up. Stephens didn't have much use for Garnier, but at least he offered no instructions.

The race was nothing special—a handicap at a mile and a quarter for four-year-olds and up. Stephens was on a seven-year-old bay called Pantagruel that was top weight although he had no chance of winning. He had won a couple of races the year before but would not do much that spring, even in cheap company; he was nearly burned out and had never had much

heart anyway. Without thinking about it, Stephens knew what
to do.

He got a good hold on Pantagruel as the tapes flew up, and
took him to the rail. At the Fouilleuse, the horse had moved
up on his own initiative to be about ten lengths off the leaders.
Coming into the stretch, Stephens began to ride him. That is,
he started scrubbing, moving with the horse, encouraging him
with hands and heels but not whipping him. The horse responded pretty well; Stephens had been patient, and Pantagruel
had a little run in him. He moved up to third, halfway down
the stretch, and Stephens began to think the old horse might
get there. He was gaining, but not fast; he could make only
a little run. Then, suddenly, the horse running second, an aged
chestnut mare of Archer's, stopped, and Pantagruel passed her.
Stephens saw it was no use whipping; the horse in front, which
Dumesnil was riding, was making it all right and should win
by a good four lengths. Stephens eased Pantagruel and held
on to second by half a length. That was better than he had
expected. Second money was seventy thousand francs; ten per
cent of that was seven thousand.

Riding back to the scales, Stephens picked mud off his face.
He was used to it. The waiting race was his specialty.

A man and a woman watched him ride back and talked about
him; of course he didn't hear them.

"In his old age, Stephens is making combinations," the man
said angrily.

"He looks terrible," the woman said. "His face looks like
death. It's almost black."

"That's only mud, from being behind all the time," the man
said. "The Englishman has just lost an unlosable race."

"No, under the mud he looks awful. His face looks a hundred years old."

"He must be almost fifty," the man said. "Perhaps he is

senile. Really, his way of riding becomes ridiculous. He should retire. He has plenty of money. He never spends any."

Stephens was not very tired. Every race is somewhat tiring, especially at the beginning of the season, but this one had been easy. Pantagruel was a steady old horse—no good, but easy to ride.

Stephens went to the jockeys' room. Pantagruel was his only mount of the day. He was bringing himself along slowly, as he had done every spring in recent years, riding only a horse or two a day and gradually bringing his weight down and getting into form. Besides, at forty-nine, and after being fired (everyone believed) by Perrault the fall before, he was not being offered many mounts.

He didn't speak to anyone in the jockeys' room. He rarely did. He washed and dressed carefully, cleaning the mud out from under his nails and combing his heavy black hair neatly, using plenty of brilliantine. He put on clean white riding breeches, a tweed sports jacket, and well-shined black boots. If the woman who had pitied him as he rode back with mud on his face had seen him walking out of the jockeys' room, she would have been surprised. Cleaned up and dressed in fresh clothes, his binocular case slung over his shoulder, stopping to take a cigarette from his case and light it with his gold lighter, furrowing his brow as he lit it, then drawing in a good lungful of smoke with enjoyment, then letting the smoke out as the wrinkles in his brow smoothed out, he looked only about thirty-five, and quite chipper. Though he had little interest in women, he liked to be neatly dressed. He got a haircut and a manicure once a week. He was careful about money, but he liked good things—well-cut breeches, boots that cost forty thousand francs a pair, a good wristwatch, a good cigarette case, a good lighter, Charvet eau de cologne on his face after a shower.

Having the best of things like that cost very little more in the long run, he reasoned. Cheap boots wore out quickly, for example.

Auslander came up as Stephens was lighting his cigarette. He was a fat man with gray hair. His face was flushed. "Nice, kid, very nice," Auslander said. Stephens figured he had had a place bet. "Next time we'll do better."

"I expect that's the best he'll do," Stephens said.

"He needed a race, that's all. Don't you think?"

"He runs good when he's fresh, Mr. Auslander. That's about the best he'll do. He's getting to be an old horse."

"I liked the way you rode him, Jack," Auslander said. "You didn't take too much out of him. He'll be all the better for it. We'll win a race with him, and I'm going to put you up again, too."

Stephens looked at the tote board. Pantagruel had paid forty-three francs for a ten-franc place bet.

"Did you back him for the place, Mr. Auslander?" he asked.

"Just five hundred each way, to encourage him," Auslander said.

The stingy liar, Stephens thought. "You were lucky," he said.

"Jack, I'm going to give you a good many mounts this spring, and see how we do," Auslander said.

"What do you want with me?" Stephens said. "Garnier's got young Luzzi on contract."

"Oh, there can't be any contract," Auslander said quickly. "I don't care about the Perrault business, but—"

"I don't want a contract just now," Stephens said, just as quickly. "I'm better off on my own."

"Sure," Auslander said. "Well, I expect to use you often."

"Much obliged," Stephens said.

Stephens did not stay for the rest of the races. There was nothing of interest. As he left the racecourse, he stepped on a piece of chewing gum. Scraping the sticky pink stuff from his boot with his little gold penknife, he thought, automatically, Americans.

He went to the parking lot reserved for trainers and jockeys, unlocked his Renault *quatre-chevaux,* and drove home to Paris. He and his wife had an apartment near the Parc Monceau. During his dinner—a steak, salad without dressing, two hard, dry *biscottes*—his wife asked him, "Did it go well today?"

"Not bad," he said. "We were second."

Stephens' wife was a Frenchwoman not much younger than he, whom he had married right after he first came out from England. She took no interest in racing. She did not think much of it as an occupation for a man to be in, and she did not realize that her husband was quite a famous man in France. Although a good deal of money came into the house, she did not believe this would continue; she never had believed so. She saved money, and hoped (without ever saying anything about it) that eventually they would buy a shop—an *epicerie,* a *char-cuterie,* or a bakery. There was nothing like food, she knew; no matter what happened, people ate. Her father had been a baker in Argenteuil. She considered it a little discreditable that her husband was English, and she never brought the matter up, to him or anyone else. They spoke French to each other, though Stephens had never learned the language thoroughly.

A little later, Stephens said, "Auslander, the American, is going to give me some mounts. It was his horse I was second on today. I hear he's got a pretty fair three-year-old."

"There will be a contract?"

"No."

"Ah! Naturally! He is very glad, I'm sure, to make use of you without a contract. You should have insisted. Why do you permit this American to take advantage of you?"

"He already has a contract jockey," Stephens said. "His trainer has this young Italian, this Luzzi."

"That is to say, the American uses you when he wishes, and then puts you to the door," said his wife. "I'm sure it's very interesting for him."

Her voice was high-pitched and irascible, not because of real ill nature but because she had been brought up to believe that life was a struggle in which you must ever be on guard against being tricked. Stephens was used to her piercing voice, laden with suspicion, and it did not bother him. She was his wife, and he assumed that that was the way wives were. He and she got along well; as a matter of fact, he never thought much about whether they got along or not, though sometimes he wished he had someone to talk to about horses.

After dinner, Stephens went out to buy a *Sport Complet*. He sat in a café and read it for half an hour, with a quarter litre of vichy in front of him. The waiter knew him but acted as if he had never seen him before; he considered Stephens a cheapskate. Stephens believed that only fools gave large tips.

When he went home, his wife told him that Garnier had called from Chantilly. She said he wanted Stephens out there at seven the next morning for the workouts. "If I were in your place, I shouldn't go," she said. "You are not under contract. He's taking advantage of you."

Stephens didn't answer.

"Well, will you go?" she asked.

"I'll decide in the morning," Stephens said.

Stephens did not go to Chantilly in the morning. He wanted to; he liked morning workouts almost more than anything else in racing. But a full-fledged jockey does not exercise horses except for the man who holds his contract, or in preparation for a classic race in which he is to ride. He could not go.

He saw Auslander at the races that afternoon, at Le Tremblay. Auslander said he wanted to talk to him, and they walked through the gardens by the paddock, where flowers were planted all along the paths. Le Tremblay was so pretty that Stephens could hardly take it seriously as a racecourse.

"I was hoping you'd be out this morning," Auslander said.

"I'm not available in the mornings, Mr. Auslander," Stephens said.

"We might work out a contract later."

"I don't want a contract," Stephens told him. "How many horses have you? Ten? You don't need me."

Auslander was a man who hated to lose at anything. "I need your help, Jack," he said. "I need your advice. Why don't you come out and take a look tomorrow? I'd like your opinion on what I've got."

"No harm in that, I suppose," Stephens said.

"I've got to be getting along," Auslander said. "My sister-in-law is in the stands. You wouldn't have a winner, would you, Jack? I'd like to give her one. What do you like in the Prix Matchem? Domrémy should be able to take it, don't you think?"

"I've no idea at all, Mr. Auslander," Stephens said.

Auslander went back to the stands and told his sister-in-law Stephens had given him a strong tip on Domrémy. The horse finished third. "Next time," Auslander said.

Stephens rode only once that day, in the last race. It was a cheap handicap at a mile and three-quarters for three-year-olds. In England, they would have thought it a long way to send three-year-olds early in the year. But these were horses of no quality, anyway.

Stephens rode a Norseman colt belonging to Médizélatis, the Greek. As usual, Stephens waited, going along in last place for a mile. Coming into the final turn, he was next to last, and he felt then that the colt was ready to move. He had no class but he could run all day. Stephens took the colt to the far out-side to make his run, but the field of twenty horses swung very wide, and the colt was carried wider still, losing half a dozen lengths.

Seeing that he was beaten, Stephens did not persevere. He galloped past the winning post in seventh or eighth position, beaten a good ten lengths. The Greek's trainer, Barsant, stopped him as he went to dress.

"Why did you go to the outside?" he asked angrily. "There was room for a regiment of cavalry on the rail."

"Where were you watching from?" Stephens asked him.

"From the top of the stands," Barsant said. "There was a veritable *autostrade* on the rail for you. It appears you are too old to take chances now."

"The race is over," Stephens said. He walked away from Barsant and went to the dressing room.

It was a little race of no importance, but it annoyed him that he had made a mistake. Every jockey makes mistakes, and they do not ordinarily upset him, and no one holds them against him as long as he gets his share of winners. An apprentice that everybody's talking about may make three in one day, but if he is getting good mounts and also rides a couple of winners that day, the mistakes are forgotten. When a jockey is going down, people remember his mistakes, and he remembers them; there are not enough good mounts to blot them out. Of course, Stephens didn't think he was going down, but things were not going well at the moment.

The worst of the race just over was that it reminded him of his last ride for Perrault. Octave Perrault, the automobile man, was the biggest owner in Europe. Stephens, his contract rider, had ridden Astolat, the best three-year-old in Europe, in all his races. Astolat was second in the Guineas (the mile was too short for him) and won the Jockey-Club and the Grand Prix de Paris. In the big fall race at a mile and a half, the Prix de l'Arc de Triomphe, Stephens waited and kept Astolat far back under a tight hold as they climbed the long green hill at Longchamp, and then began moving him up as they came down the hill and into the turn. He swung Astolat to the outside on the turn, the field drifted out, and Stephens had to take him wider and wider, losing ground all the time.

Astolat was a good colt, the best in the race, a long-striding colt with stamina, and he lost no momentum in making the turn—no rhythm of his stride—but he was too far back, and as he passed the winning post, he was second, beaten a neck. He passed the winner in the next few strides, and the crowd booed Stephens back to the scales.

Perrault had been in racing a long time, and yet he believed that if you have the best bloodstock, the best trainer, the best jockey, the best lads, the best stud farm with the best grass in Normandy, one of the best biologists in France as an adviser on breeding, and the best equipment, right down to the leather in the saddles, you should never lose a race. Perrault's secretary telephoned Stephens that night and told him to come to the great man's office. Stephens went. Perrault had a whole building in the Faubourg St. Denis—a big modern thing, with lots of glass. The building was dark when Stephens arrived. A silent elevator operator took him up in a silent elevator, and he walked down the bare modern hall to Perrault's office. Perrault, a heavy, frowning man with black-rimmed glasses, sat behind his desk.

"Well, what happened, Stephens?" he asked.

On the way there, Stephens had thought he might tell Perrault that Astolat was a long-striding colt who liked to run by himself, away from other horses, and that he wouldn't have kept his stride if Stephens had squeezed him through on the rail. There was some truth in it; the horse did like to run alone on the outside. Stephens liked riding the Perrault horses. He liked being first jockey for the greatest stable in Europe. Perrault had, over the past twenty years, developed a breed of horses of his own—long-striding horses that never tired, that were always going on at the end. They did not have a great deal of what the French call, in race horses, *brio,* but they had an everlasting sturdiness and gameness. Stephens liked to ride them. He believed no one suited them as he did. He could tell Perrault none of this. "I'm taking myself off all your horses, Mr. Perrault," he said.

Since then, things had gone badly. He had not had many good mounts, and he had lost some races that he might have won. The Auslander connection might help. He had had a little luck with Pantagruel. But Stephens had got the mount on Pantagruel only because Luzzi was riding another horse for Garnier. Stephens had no use for Luzzi, but the kid was riding well just now. He had had a lot of luck the past year.

At dinner, Stephens' wife said, "It went well today?"

"No luck today," Stephens said.

At six the next morning, Stephens got up and drove to Chantilly. There were no cars on the road. It had rained during the night, and everything was fresh and clean. It would be a fine day. The leaves were a little behind the leaves in Paris, but they were all coming out. He drove along slowly.

Garnier had a big place out at Chantilly, opposite the Piste de Lamorlaye, where he had Auslander's horses and those of four or five other owners. The stables were stone, forming a big square with green clipped lawn in the center. Stephens parked his car and walked into the big courtyard. Auslander and Garnier were standing there on the grass with Jim Craye, Garnier's head lad. Stephens walked across the grass and shook hands with them.

"Mr. Auslander wants me to put you on Tekel, the Admiral

Drake colt," Garnier said. "We've got him eligible for everything at Longchamp, but I don't know if he'll do anything."

Garnier spoke in English. Around a French stable, everybody can speak English; even the French grooms usually talk English to the horses. There is a theory that horses find English more soothing.

" 'E's a nice little 'orse," Jim Craye said. He was a little Cockney with bright-blue eyes and a jutting chin and no teeth, who had come from England fifty years before. He was one of the handful of Englishmen left around the stables at Chantilly. Although they were all getting to be old men, they were in great demand. Even French trainers believe that an Englishman is better than anybody else with a horse. Jim had been a good jockey, years ago.

"I could've sold him last week for two million, and bought Dupré's colt," Auslander said. "Maybe I should've done it."

"He didn't do anything last year, did he?" Stephens asked.

"I only ran him twice," Garnier said. "I didn't expect him to do anything. I'm against two-year-olds' racing, on principle."

Garnier was a short, stout, sallow man with a little black mustache. He had become a trainer because his father had been one. He never expected his horses to win; he was always against racing them. And yet, because he was always patient and careful, he won a lot of races for his clients.

"Tekel hasn't grown much during the winter," Auslander said. "I should've sold him and bought something else."

" 'E's a nice little 'orse," Jim Craye said. " 'E'll win 'is ryce."

"Bring him out, Jim," Garnier said. "Let's have a look at him."

Jim Craye went and led Tekel, a rather small, almost black colt, out of his box.

"What do you think, Jack?" Auslander asked anxiously.

"I've no idea at all, Mr. Auslander," Stephens said. "He looks all right. Bit small, but that doesn't matter."

There was the sound of a car stopping quickly, and Luzzi, the Italian jockey, came into the courtyard. He shook hands with everybody, Stephens last.

"So you going to help me, eh, old man?" Luzzi said to Stephens, smiling. Luzzi was a dark-haired kid of nineteen, with sharp dark eyes in a face still soft and without the lines and angles a jockey's face eventually gets. He looked almost girlish.

"That's right," Stephens said.

The first lot of horses was brought out of the stalls, fifteen of them, and jockeys and lads mounted them. Stephens got on Tekel's back. Jim Craye said, "Don't 'urry 'im and don't bother 'im. 'E's not mean, but 'e's got a mind of 'is own, as you might say."

The fifteen of them rode out in a long line, Luzzi first on a chestnut five-year-old, Stephens next on Tekel, and Jim Craye third, on a three-year-old bay colt. They rode to the grassy training course, the Piste de Lamorlaye, across the road. The horses walked slowly, dancing a little and stretching their necks. They were all feeling good. So were the lads. They whistled tunelessly as they rode along in the early-morning light. The sound of many birds was loud on the training course.

Garnier and Auslander walked across, and Garnier asked Stephens to work Tekel a mile. "Start off at the château," Garnier said. "Jim will get away ahead of you. Pass him after half a mile, and finish out a mile here. Let him run the last half mile, understand, but don't *ride* him."

Jim Craye started off, going ahead fifteen lengths. Stephens rode behind, taking his time. They went along that way for a while, Tekel galloping nicely. Stephens watched old Craye, riding far forward in the saddle, light and spry as a boy, coaxing the best out of a horse that would never be worth anything. Jim was closer to seventy than to sixty. It was a pleasure to watch him. After half a mile, Stephens let Tekel run a little and passed the other horse easily. Tekel had a nice run in him, Stephens found, although he had a rather short stride and Stephens could not tell whether the run would last long under pressure. At the end of the mile, he pulled Tekel up by Garnier and Auslander and slid off.

"What do you think?" Auslander asked.

"He's a very nice colt, Mr. Auslander," Stephens said, patting Tekel's muzzle. "I should think he'd do."

"Do you think he's a Poule d'Essai colt?" Auslander asked. The Poule d'Essai des Poulains is the French Two Thousand Guineas, a classic mile for three-year-olds.

"Hard to tell. I shouldn't sell him if I were you, though."

"I've got him in a mile race at Longchamp in a week," Garnier said. "I'm not sure he's ready for it."

"He's ready," Stephens said.

"You think he can win?" Auslander said. "It's the Prix St. James. There's not much in it."

"He's ready to run a good race, that's all I know," Stephens said.

"Well, anyway, one thing sure, I'm not going to sell him," Auslander said happily. Then he added, "Not right away, anyhow."

Stephens went back to the stables. He had hung his sports jacket in the tack room. He got it and put it over the gray turtleneck sweater he was wearing. As he went out again, he passed Tekel's stall. Jim Craye was standing beside it, and the colt was kicking the wooden wall. "Know what 'e wants?" Craye said. " 'E wants 'is breakfast. 'E'll kick down the barn if 'e don't get it."

Stephens had known Jim Craye for thirty-five years, off and on. In the days when Stephens was an apprentice at Newmarket, Craye was a jockey living in France but sometimes riding in England for a French stable.

"You've a nice berth here, Jim," Stephens said.

"Can't complain," Jim said.

"Do you ever go to the races these days?"

"I've not been on a racecourse in ten years," Jim said. "Too busy out 'ere."

Things went along pretty quietly for a while. Stephens rode better as the season wore on, but he did not win often. He won the Prix St. James—a trial for the Poule d'Essai—on Tekel, by a neck. Auslander complained that Stephens had made it too close. Stephens began to find Auslander more and more tiresome; like all owners, he was obsessed with winning.

Every morning now, Stephens went out to Chantilly to work horses for Garnier. He was happy doing this. He began to wonder if he enjoyed only practice races on the training course, where the result was decided in advance. He did not care as much as he had about winning on the racecourse. He lost some races that he could have won. Sometimes he lost because, without thinking it out, he felt that he could not win smoothly and easily, that there would be something forced and strained about winning, which was distasteful to him. He could not explain these feelings to himself, and of course he could not explain them to owners and trainers, so he did not get many good mounts. He did not mind, except for the money, he told himself, and he reminded himself now and then that he had plenty of money.

He had enjoyed being one of the great jockeys of Europe. It did not seriously occur to him now that he was ceasing to be that. His self-esteem was high still. He knew that he was as strong as ever, and that his sense of pace, his knowledge of when to move, and his understanding of a horse were as fine as ever. He told himself that he would like to ride a really great horse, like Astolat, again, one for whom everything was easy and smooth, one of those long-striding, irresistible Perrault horses. If he had a great horse, he would give him a great ride.

Stephens rode Tekel in all his workouts and became fond of the little colt. Tekel had a neat, extremely pure action, although his stride was perhaps too short for him to get a distance in good company. He was courageous; if, in training, Stephens permitted another horse to come up to him at the end of a workout, Tekel would draw away on his own courage, without urging. He had some temperament; in the morning, walking to the training course, he would shy in pretended fright at every shadow. But it was all good-natured and innocent. Stephens found that once he had called on Tekel for an effort, that was enough. The horse did not like to be reminded of what he was supposed to do when he was already doing it. Once he had begun to run, the best thing was to sit absolutely still on him. " 'E knows what 'e was put on earth for," Jim Craye said. Stephens never whipped him and did not intend to. He and Tekel went well together. He thought Tekel was good, and might be very good.

Auslander and Garnier decided to run Tekel in the Poule d'Essai, and Stephens won with him fairly easily, letting him go to the front after half a mile. Tekel was improving all the time. In Chantilly, he began to be mentioned as a horse that might be one of the good ones. Auslander got very enthusiastic and talked of the Jockey Club and the Grand Prix.

Luzzi, Garnier's contract jockey, heard this talk and complained that Garnier should have let him ride Tekel. Garnier told him that Stephens happened to fit the colt, and that besides, it was a whim of Mr. Auslander's to have Stephens ride him. Luzzi couldn't do anything, for though Garnier had first call on Luzzi he was not obliged to use him. Still, Luzzi was resentful and talked against Stephens in the jockeys' rooms at the racecourses and in the bars of Chantilly.

One day, in a little race at St. Cloud, Stephens and Luzzi
were both riding. Stephens brought his horse through on the
rail and won handily, but in slipping through to take the lead
near the last turn, his horse brushed against Luzzi's. After the
race, walking to the jockeys' room, Luzzi said to him, "You
think you're pretty hot, old man, don't you?"

"I didn't bother you," Stephens said. "You weren't going anywhere."

"You think you're hot," Luzzi said. "Sometime someone will
slam you so hard you'll go down and you won't get up."

"Never mind about me," Stephens said, and walked away.

From then on, Luzzi said something unpleasant to Stephens
every time he saw him. The other jockeys encouraged him and
hoped that something would happen between him and Stephens.
There was a feeling that because Stephens did not drink and
talk with the others at the Derby, the Jockey Club, or any of
the other Chantilly bars, he was too pleased with himself. *"M.
Stephens, c'est un* gentleman," they said, using the English word
derisively.

Stephens paid no attention to Luzzi. He had always gone
his own way. He had never been liked.

Luzzi was not popular, either. He was a foreigner. He had
ridden only one other season in France. He was young and
successful. Feeling unpopular and unsure of himself, Luzzi believed he could make himself liked by quarreling with Stephens.
This was only a little successful. Some of the others even resented it, feeling that, after all, they had disliked Stephens first.

Auslander decided to run Tekel in the Prix Lupin, one of
the big spring tests for three-year-olds. The Lupin is at a mile
and five-sixteenths. Stephens and Garnier told him this was too
far.

"You mean he can't win?" Auslander asked.

"Oh, he might win," Stephens said.

"It's not his distance," Garnier said. "A mile is about his

limit. He might go farther in the fall, when he's grown a little."

"God damn it," Auslander said. "I think I've got a classic colt here. I want to run him in the Jockey Club." The Jockey Club, at a mile and a half, is the French Derby.

"I'd much rather wait, Mr. Auslander," Garnier said. "If you give this little horse some time, he'll win plenty of nice races for you. You don't want to run him in the Jockey Club."

"That's just what I do want," Auslander said. So it was decided to try him first in the Lupin.

The race was run on a Sunday, at Longchamp. It rained during the night and morning, but the sun came out before noon. Longchamp is the loveliest racecourse in the world, with the long sweeping green turns of the course, the speckled shade of the walking ring under the chestnut trees, and the calm, cheerful trees themselves. Fresh from the rain, the chestnut trees slick and wet, the sky a fresh light blue, and all the green a richer green, it was more beautiful than usual that day. A racecourse is at its best and happiest, Stephens thought, before the first race on an important day when the weather is fine. Then everything is clean and everything is before you. The lawns have not been littered with torn-up pari-mutuel tickets. No one has been saddened or angered by losing.

Stephens and Garnier went out on the course to see how the going was. It was heavy. Tekel had never run in the mud, and Stephens had a feeling he was too fragile to relish it. The heavy going and the distance would combine to stop him. "It's asking too much of him," Stephens said to Garnier.

"Just see that he does the best he can," Garnier said.

"He'll do that," Stephens said.

"If we can win this, it will do you a lot of good," Garnier said. "You'll be getting mounts from a lot of people."

"I'll win if I can," Stephens said. "I've won the better part of the classics in Europe. What's it matter if I win this or not?"

"They forget those other races," Garnier said.

Stephens rode in one race besides the Prix Lupin that day—a mile for three-year-old maidens that came just before the Lupin. He had taken the mount, on a big, nervous, unmanageable gelding of the Vicomtesse de Rantigny-Luzarches, because he wanted to find out ahead of the main race what the course was like. He had worked the horse once or twice at Chantilly, and did not believe he could do anything.

The field was big—twenty-five runners—and Stephens' number was 23. Luzzi, No. 24, was to start next to him on a colt of the Nawab of Bhopal. As the horses circled around behind the barrier, Stephens knew he would have trouble. His mount was in a lather, trembling and rearing, the way the ones that amount to nothing so often do. At the start, when the tapes flew up, he swerved to the left and slammed into Luzzi's colt, knocking him almost to his knees. After that, there was no chance for either of them. They just galloped along behind the field.

After the race, Luzzi came up to Stephens outside the jockeys' room and said, "I don't let anybody do that to me." His lips were white and compressed, because he had decided he must hit Stephens.

"It was an accident," Stephens said.

"I don't allow that," Luzzi said, uncertain of the right words and trying to work himself into the state of fury he wished to be in.

Luzzi knew a little about boxing. He feinted low with his left hand, and then hit Stephens between the eyes with his right, knocking him down.

Stephens knew nothing of boxing. He had not been in a fight since childhood. But he had imagined being in fights, and it had never occurred to him that he could be beaten in one. He jumped up after a second and awkwardly pushed his right fist at Luzzi. Luzzi stuck his left in Stephens' face before Stephens' fist could land. The punch hit Stephens' nose, and he went down again, caught off balance. He got up quickly, and Luzzi struck him again between the eyes. As he was getting up the third time, some people grabbed Luzzi and pulled him away.

The fight had lasted only a few seconds. Not many of the big crowd had seen it, but gossip travels as quickly as tips around a racecourse, and soon everyone knew that Luzzi had beaten up the Englishman. Many people who really did not care one way or the other, but who had heard that Stephens thought he was better than anyone else, or who had at some time lost a bet on a mount of Stephens', said it was about time.

Stephens walked into the jockeys' room in a fury. He was furious partly because his nose was bleeding and the blood was dripping down over the Vicomtesse de Rantigny-Luzarches's yellow-and-white silks, which seemed to him a dirty, disgusting, and ridiculous thing to have happen. He felt sick at his stomach. He washed and changed into Auslander's silks—gray, with red hoops on the sleeves, and black "A"s on the back and on the black cap—and as he was combing his hair, Garnier came in. The bleeding had stopped, but Stephens still felt sick. His face ached, and he would soon have two black eyes.

Garnier's pudgy, sallow, unhappy face had a look of embarrassment. "This is terrible," he said. "You understand, you don't need to ride."

Stephens, concentrating on combing his thick black hair, didn't look around. "Who will you put up?" he asked. "Luzzi?"

"Of course not," Garnier said. "I can get Kemp."

"Kemp's nearly as old as I am," Stephens said. "Do you think your horse'll do better with him?"

"You're not well," Garnier said.

"Don't be a bloody fool," Stephens said. "I'm riding him unless you order me off."

"I'm not doing that," Garnier said.

"Does Auslander order me off him? Is that it?"

"No, but he's worried. That's natural."

"Tell him to stop worrying," Stephens said. "He can buy
his tickets. I expect to win this race."

Garnier walked out to the paddock with Stephens and gave
him a leg up on Tekel. Everyone there looked at Stephens'
battered face. He had been ready to hear them laugh, but no
one did. His face hurt, though, and he felt old and sick.
Auslander came up beside Garnier, smiling worriedly. He said
nothing.

There was a field of eleven for the Lupin, and Stephens believed only three could trouble him: Mohilal, a good colt of
the Aga Khan's that had finished well in his two races of the
year; Djérama, a Boussac colt that had won his three starts,
and Heronwood, a Rothschild horse that had chased Tekel in
the Prix St. James and the Poule d'Essai. Boussac also had entered another three-year-old, called Phactaris, that would be sacrificed to make the pace.

The race started. The Boussac pacemaker went to the front
at the signal. Stephens took up Tekel and held him in fourth
position. Mohilal was second and Djérama third. They continued that way up the hill. Tekel was full of run in spite of
the heavy going, and Stephens' arms ached from holding him.
As they entered the little wood just below the crest of the hill,
Stephens sensed that Phactaris, the Boussac flier, was having it
too easy. There was not enough pace. He let out a wrap on
Tekel, who bounded forward to draw even with Djérama, and
an instant later the two of them went after Mohilal almost together. Tekel was running willingly, and after he and Djé-

rama had moved past Mohilal, he gradually drew away from Djérama, and Stephens sent him after Phactaris, still four lengths in front and holding on courageously. Coming down the hill, Stephens let Tekel all the way out and clucked to him, and he moved right past Phactaris in a few bounds to take the lead. Phactaris dropped out of the race, Djérama and Mohilal stayed fairly close in second and third, and Heronwood, the Rothschild colt, began to move up.

At the bottom of the hill, Tekel faltered for an instant and seemed to flounder in the sticky mud. Stephens sat absolutely still on him, and Tekel regained his stride. Stephens knew the colt was terribly tired, though he was still going well.

Taking the last turn, Stephens sat like a rock on Tekel, not moving his hands, not looking back for fear the movement might throw Tekel off stride, though he knew the Rothschild colt would be coming at him. There was no change in Tekel's neat, flawless stride. The race was too long for him, it was beyond his powers and he was exhausted, but his heart was fine, so he kept right on, running smoothly and cleanly, with no choppiness, through the holding mud. Stephens continued to sit still. It was not his way of riding—his race was the waiting race and then the drive in the last half mile—but this was the way to ride Tekel. The horse must do it all; Stephens' job was to make it as easy for him as possible.

At the beginning of the stretch, Heronwood came at Tekel, not with a rush but with a steady, plodding attack. Three hundred yards from the end, Heronwood's head was even with Stephens' left boot. When Heronwood was a neck behind Tekel, Tekel felt the challenge and began to fight it off, drawing away a little from the colt. Then he faltered again, and slid a little; his legs would not quite obey his heart. Heronwood gained a head on him.

Stephens had the whip in his left hand. He put it between

his teeth, took the reins in his left hand without easing the
slight pressure he always kept on the bit, took the whip in his
right hand, and started whipping. Heronwood was so close Stephens could not whip lefthanded.

Tekel floundered under the whip as if shocked. Then he
straightened out and moved again. Stephens flogged him as
hard as he could all the way, raising the bat high and bringing it down with a crack on Tekel's crupper again and again,
even after they had passed the finish line a neck in front of
Heronwood.

It was a popular win; the crowd had made Tekel the favorite, and they cheered Stephens back to the scales.

"You see," a man in the crowd said, "he can win when he
wants to."

When Stephens had weighed in, he saw Auslander hurrying
through the enclosure toward him. Stephens avoided him and
went to the jockeys' room. He changed quickly, and got his
car and drove home.

"My God, what has happened to you?" his wife said when
she saw him. "Look at your face!"

Stephens looked at himself in an oak-framed mirror that hung
in the dark hall. Both his eyes were black, and a band of
purple-black spread across the bridge of his nose.

"Not pretty, I admit," he said.

"You've fallen off a horse!" his wife screamed.

"I have not!" Stephens said angrily.

"Ne parle pas comme une idiote." His French tended to be
a literal translation of English.

"You've fallen off a horse," his wife said. "Riding horseback
may be all right for rich men. For a man in your station, it's
ridiculous."

"Perhaps you're right," he said.

"Come into the kitchen and let me take care of your face," she said. "A man who is almost fifty! It's idiotic."

Like an irascible, loving mother, she took care of his face.

For a week, Stephens stayed at home. Garnier telephoned and said he would like to see him. Stephens said he wanted to rest. Garnier told him the commissioners had set down Luzzi for a month. Stephens asked him how Tekel was, and Garnier told him that the horse had limped when he was cooled out after the race, and that he had not been worked since. "His ankles look bad," Garnier said. "There may be a bowed tendon. The vet will tell me in a day or two." Garnier's voice sounded uncomfortable, as though he were trying to keep anger out of it.

"Well, I'm sorry to hear that," Stephens said.

Stephens was sure Tekel would never run with good horses again, and he believed it was his fault. He didn't blame Auslander, who was only the owner.

There is nothing wrong with whipping a horse. It doesn't hurt him much, and many won't run without it. But Stephens knew he had done something ugly when he laid the whip on Tekel. He had asked the colt for more than he could give, and Tekel, with wild generosity, had given it. Tekel had given Stephens everything he might have had in every other race he might run in his life.

Stephens stayed indoors that week, drinking coffee and reading *Sport Complet*—he sent his wife out to get it—and she began saying, "Perfect! You are in retirement, then. Do you wish me to go into service?"

But after a week, when his face looked all right, he said to her, "I'm going out to Chantilly in the morning."

"Why?"

"To ride some of Garnier's horses for him."

"The races!" she said. "I hoped you were finished with that."

"Oh, I'm through with racing," Stephens said. "Sick of it."

"So much the better. What will you do?"

"Exercise horses for Garnier."

"He'll pay you?" she asked.

"Of course."

"How much?"

"About forty thousand a month, I think lads get," Stephens said.

"That's very good. A regular salary, even though it's smaller, is better than depending on the generosity of foreigners." She had always believed that all race-horse owners were foreigners and that jockeys were paid in tips, like waiters.

"We'd better leave Paris," Stephens said. "Too expensive. How would you like to live in Chantilly?"

"We could buy a little store there," she said. "I've always wanted a little business."

"Have you?" Stephens asked, smiling. "Well, I suppose we might. Have to look about a bit first, and go into it carefully."

"Of course," his wife said happily.

In the morning, Stephens drove out to Chantilly. It was green all along the way, now. At the village of Lamorlaye, where he turned off for Garnier's, he passed le Derby. Mme. Bernard, the lean, muscular owner, was flinging water from a bucket out over the stone terrace. He thought that perhaps he'd stop and have a glass of white wine there, after the morning's work. Because he had been so serious about his profession, he had drunk almost nothing for thirty years, but now he thought with pleasure of drinking cold white wine when the workouts were over. He'd drink it out on the terrace there.

In the courtyard at Garnier's, he met Jim Craye. Garnier wasn't up. Jim showed Stephens around, talking about the horses in the slow, steady, gentle way that men have who have worked around horses all their lives. Tekel was not in his stall, and Jim explained that Auslander was selling him. Tekel had not bowed a tendon after all, Jim said, but he was finished just the same.

"You'll be out 'ere regular now?" Jim asked Stephens.

"Yes, I'm going to live out here," Stephens said.

"It's a good place. The boss is all right."

Garnier came down from his house, which was in front of the stables, facing the road. He had not shaved, and was wearing carpet slippers.

"I want you to gallop a little two-year-old for me, Jack," Garnier said. He walked with Stephens to the two-year-old's box. "Take him out," Garnier said.

Stephens led the colt out.

"He's not ready for anything," Garnier said. "Maybe he never will be. Mme. de Rantigny-Luzarches wants to run him at Deauville, but I'm against it. Today we'll just give him a nice gallop."

The other lads were bringing their horses out and mounting. Stephens mounted, and they all rode out across the road to the Piste de Lamorlaye and walked the horses out onto the grass.

The dewy grass, bent from being ridden over, looked blue and purple with the long morning shadows on it. The horses felt fine; they were snorting and shying. The lads felt fine, all whistling their monotonous, tuneless little tunes. Stephens, on a fresh two-year-old that had never been on a racecourse, felt fine, too. In the thickets along the sides of the training course, the birds were just tearing into their songs, as if they knew that the world had been made new that morning—a fresh, new, morning world. Stephens heard them and thought, it's all nonsense about birds singing. They don't really sing songs, they chirp. And yet—although surely no bird listened to the others—it all went fine together when they set to it early in the morning.

MAC'S MASTERPIECE

by FRANK O'CONNOR

TWO OR three times a year Mac, a teacher in the monks' school, took to his bed for four or five days. That was understood. But when he gave up taking food his landlady thought it was getting serious. She told his friends she wanted to have him certified. Not another day would she keep him in the house after the abominable language he had used to her.

His friends, Boyd, Devane and Corbett, came. Mac refused to open the bedroom door. He asked to be allowed to die in peace. It was only when Boyd took a hatchet to the lock that he appeared in his nightshirt, haggard and distraught, a big, melancholy mountain of a man, dribbling, his hair in tumult.

"Almighty God!" he cried. "Won't I even be allowed that one little comfort?"

They wrapped him in blankets and set him by the fire among his discarded toys, his dumb-bells, chest developers, Indian clubs, sabers, shot-gun, camera, cinema, gramophone and piano, while Corbett, the bright young man from the local newspaper, heated the water for the punch. At this Mac came to himself a little and insulted Boyd. Boyd was his foil; a narrow-chested, consumptive-looking chemist with a loud voice and a yapping laugh like a fox's bark. He wore a bowler-hat at various extraordinary angles and was very disputatious.

"Bad luck to you!" growled Boyd. "I don't believe there's anything up with you."

"Nothing up with me!" jeered Mac. "Devane, did you hear that? You know, Devane, that hog, unless you had a broken neck or a broken bottom, he'd say there was nothing up with you. He'd say there was nothing up with Othello or Hamlet. 'Nothing up with you!' Did anybody ever hear such a barbarous locution?"

"Come on away, Corbett," said Boyd angrily. "We might have known the old cod was only play-acting as usual."

"Don't rouse me now," said Mac with quiet scorn.

"Like an old actress when she's going off, pretending her jewelery is stolen."

"I won't be roused," said Mac earnestly. "What's that Lear says—'No, I'll not weep, this heart shall crack. . . .' You Philistine, you Christian Brothers' brat, you low, porter-drinking sot," he snarled with sudden violence, "I have a soul above disputing with you. . . . Devane," he added mournfully, "you understand me. You have a grand Byronian soul."

"I have nervous dyspepsia," groaned Devane, who was organist in the parish church. He felt himself in two or three places. "I get terrible pains here and here."

"I see you now as I saw you twenty years ago with the fire of genius in your eyes," Mac went on. "And now, God help you, you go about the streets as though you were making a living by collecting lost hair-pins."

Devane refused punch. It made his stomach worse, he said.

"You're better off," said Mac, falling serious once more. "I say you're better off. You see your misery plain. You're only a little maggot yourself now, a measly little maggot of a man, hoping the Almighty God won't crush you too soon, but you're a consistent maggot, a maggot by night and by day. But in my dreams I'm still a king, and then comes the awakening, the horror, the gray dawn."

He shuddered, wrapped in his blanket. Corbett rose and began to fiddle with the gramophone.

"Don't break that machine," said Mac irritably. "It cost a lot."

"What you want is a wife," said Corbett. "All those gadgets are only substitute wives. Did you ever get an hour's real pleasure out of any of them? I bet you never play that gramophone."

"You have a low mind, Corbett," snarled Mac. "You impute the basest motives to everyone."

At that very moment Corbett placed the needle on the record. There was a startling series of cracks and then it began to give off *La Donna è Mobile.* Mac jumped up as though he had been shot.

"O God, not that, not that! Turn it off! There, you've done it now."

"What?" asked Corbett innocently.

"Sunlight on the Mediterranean, moonlight on the Swiss lakes, the glow-worms in the grass, young love, hope, passion."

He began to stride up and down the room, swinging his blanket like a toga.

"The last time I heard that"—he stretched out his arm in a wild gesture—" 'twas in Galway on a rainy night. Galway in the rain and the statue of O Conaire in the Park and the long western faces like—like bullocks. There they were over the roulette tables, counting out their coppers; they had big cloth purses. Then suddenly, the what-you-may-call-it organ began. . . . Magic, by God, magic! It mounted and mounted and you knew by the shudder down your spine that 'twas all on fire; a sort of—a sort of pyramid—that's it!—a pyramid of light over your head. Turning and turning, faster and faster, the pyramid,

I mean, and the lights crackling and changing; blue, red, orange. Man, I rushed back to the hotel, fearing something would spoil it on me. The last light was setting over the church tower, woodbine-colored light and a black knot of weeping cloud."

"Bravo, Mac!" said Boyd with his coarse laugh. He stuck his thumbs into the armholes of his waistcoat. "The old warrior is himself again. Haw?"

"Until the next time," said Corbett with a sneer.

"There'll be no next time," said Mac solemnly. "I'm after being down to hell and coming back. I see it all now. The Celtic mist is gone. I see it all clear before me in the Latin light."

And sure enough there was a change in Mac's behavior. He almost gave up drink and began to talk of the necessity for solitude. Solitude, he said, was the mind's true home. Solitude filled the cistern; company emptied it. He would stay at home and read or think. He began to talk of a vast novel on the subject of the clash between idealism and materialism in the Irish soul.

But the discipline was a hard one. Though he told the maid to say he was out, he hated to hear the voices of Boyd or Corbett as they went off together down the quay. One evening as they were moving away he knocked at the window and raised the blind, looking out at them and nodding. He tried to assume a superior, amused air, but there was wistfulness in his eyes. Finally he raised the window.

"Come on out, man!" said Boyd scornfully.

"No, no, I couldn't," replied Mac weakly.

" 'Tis a lovely night."

"What way did ye come?"

"Down High Street. All the shawlies were out singing. Look, 'tis a gorgeous night. Stars! Millions of them!"

Softly in a wheezy tenor Boyd sang *Night of Stars and Night of Love* with declamatory gestures. Mac's resolution wavered.

"Come on in for a minute."

They climbed over the low sill, Boyd still singing and gesturing. As usual, he had an interesting item of news for Mac. The latest scandal; piping hot; another piece of jobbery perpetrated by a religious secret society. Mac groaned.

"My God, 'tis awful," he agreed. " 'Tis, do you know what it is, 'tis scandalous."

"Well, isn't that what we were always looking for?" exclaimed Boyd, shaking his first truculently. "Government by our own? Now we have it. Government by the gunmen and the priests and the secret societies."

" 'Tis our own fault," said Mac gloomily.

"How so-a?"

" 'Tis our own fault. We're the intellect of the country and what good are we? None. Do we ever protest? No. All we do is live in burrows and growl at all the things we find wrong."

"And what else can we do? A handful of us?"

"Thousands of us."

"A handful! How long would I keep me business if I said or did what I thought was right? I make two hundred a year out of parish priests with indigestion. Man, dear, is there one man, one man in this whole town that can call his soul his own?"

"You're all wrong," said Mac crossly, his face going into a thousand wrinkles.

"Is there one man?" shouted Boyd with lifted finger.

"Bogy men!" said Mac, "that's all that frightens ye. Bogy men! If we were in earnest all that tangle of circumstance would melt away."

"Oh, melt away, melt away? Would it, indeed?"

"Of course it would. The human will can achieve anything. The will is the divine faculty in man."

"This is a new sort of theology."

" 'Tisn't theology at all; 'tis common sense. Let me alone now; I thought all this out long ago. The only obstacles we ever see are in ourselves."

"Ah, what nonsense are you talking? How are they in ourselves?"

"When the will is diseased, it creates obstacles where they never existed."

"Answer me," bawled Boyd, spitting into the fire. "Answer my question. Answer it now and let Corbett hear you. How are the obstacles in ourselves? Can a blind man paint a picture, can he? Can a cripple run the thousand yards? Haw?"

"Boyd," said Mac with a fastidious shudder, "you have a very coarse mind."

"I have a very realistic mind."

"You have a very coarse mind; you have the mind of a Christian Brothers' boy. But if you persist in that—that unpleasant strain, I'm more ready to believe that a blind man can paint a picture than that a normal, healthy man can be crippled from birth by a tangle of irrelevant circumstances."

"Circumstances are never irrelevant."

"Between the conception and the achievement all circumstances are irrelevant."

"You don't believe in matther? Isn't that what it all comes to?"

"That has nothing to do with it."

"Do you or do you not believe in matther?" repeated Boyd, throwing his bowler viciously on to the floor.

"I believe in the human will," snapped Mac.

"That means you don't believe in life."

"Not as you see it."

"Because I believe in life," said Boyd, his lantern jaw working sideways. "I believe that in all the life about me a divine purpose is working itself out."

"Oh, God," groaned Mac. "Animal stagnation! Chewing the cud! The City Council! Wolfe Tone Street! Divine purpose, my sweet God! Don't you see, you maggot, you clodhopper, you corner boy, that life can't be directed from outside? If there is a divine purpose—I don't know whether there is or not—it can only express itself through some human agency; and how the devil can you have a human agency if you haven't the individual soul, the man representing humanity? Do you think institutions, poetry, painting, the Roman Empire, were created by maggots and clodhoppers? Do you? Do you? Do you?"

Just then there was a ring at the door and Devane came in, looking more than ever like a collector of lost hair-pins.

"How are you, Devane?" asked Corbett.

"Rotten," said Devane.

"I never saw you any other way," growled Mac.

"I never am any other way," replied Devane.

"You're just in time," said Corbett.

"How so-a?"

"We're getting the will versus determinism; 'tis gorgeous. Go on, Mac. You were talking about the Roman Empire."

Mac suddenly threw himself into a chair, covering his face with his hands.

"My God, my God," he groaned softly between his fingers. "I'm at it again. I'm fifty-four years of age and I'm talking about the human will. A man whose life is over talking about the will. Go away and let me write me novel. For God's sake let me do one little thing before I die."

After that night Mac worked harder than ever. He talked a great deal about his novel. The secret of the Irish soul, he had discovered, was the conflict between the ideal and the reality.

Boyd, with whom he discussed it one night when they met accidentally, disputed this as he disputed everything.

"Idealism my eye!" he said scornfully. "The secret is bloody hypocrisy."

"No, Boyd," protested Mac. "You have a mind utterly without refinement. Hypocrisy is a noble and enlightened vice; 'tis far beyond the capacity of the people of this country. The English have been called hypocritical. Now, nobody could ever talk about the hypocritical Gael. The English had their walled cities, their castles, their artillery, as the price of their hypocrisy; all the unfortunate gulls of Irishmen ever got out of their self-deception was a raggy cloak and a bed in a wood."

"And is that what you're going to say in your novel?"

"I'm going to say lots of things in my novel."

"You'd better mind yourself."

"I'm going to tell the truth at last. I'm going to show that what's wrong with all of you people is your inability to reconcile the debauched sentimentalism of your ideals with the disorderly materialism of your lives."

"What?" Boyd stopped dead, hands in his pockets, head forward. "Are you calling me a sentimentalist?"

"I'm only speaking generally."

"Are you calling me a sentimentalist?"

"I'm not referring to you at all."

"Because I'm no sentimentalist. I'm a realist."

"You're a disappointed idealist like all the rest, that's what you are."

"A disappointed idealist? How do you make that out?"

"Boyd, I see ye all now quite clearly. I see ye as if I was looking at ye from eternity. I see what's wrong with ye. Ye aim too high. Ye hitch yeer wagon to too many bloody stars at the one time. Then comes the first snag and the first compromise. After that ye begin to sink, sink, sink till ye're tied hand and foot, till ye even deny the human soul."

"Are you back to that again? Are you denying the existence of matther again?"

"Materialist! Shabby little materialist, with your sentimental dreams. I see ye all there with yeer heads tied to yeer knees, pretending 'tis circumstance and 'tis nothing only the ropes ye spin out of yeer own guts."

Boyd was furious. It was bad enough to have Mac dodging him, telling the maid to say he was out, forcing him to spend long, lonely evenings; but then to call him a sentimentalist, a materialist, a disappointed idealist! In fact, all Mac's friends resented the new state of things. They jeered at the tidy way he now dressed himself. They jeered at the young woman with whom he was seen taking tea at the Ambassadors'.

Elsie Deignan was a pretty young woman of thirty-two or three. She was a teacher in the nuns' school in the South Parish and had literary leanings. As a result of her experiences with the nuns, she was slightly tinged with anti-clericalism. For the first time in his life Mac felt he had met a woman whose conversation he might conceivably tolerate over an extended period. He fell badly in love.

The resentment of Mac's friends grew when he was seen walking out with her. And there were strange stories in circulation about the things he was saying in his novel. They were all going into it, and in a ridiculous fashion. They were pleased when Corbett told them that Mac's employers, the monks, were getting uneasy, too. Mac knew far too much about the Order. He had often referred scornfully to the disparity between their professions and their practice; was it possible that he was revealing all this? Corbett swore he was; he also said that one chapter described the initiation of a young man into the Knights of Columbanus, skulls, cowls, blindfolding, oaths and all.

"I suppose he thinks he'll be able to retire on the proceeds of it," said Boyd in disgust. "The English will lap that up. I hate a man that fouls his own nest."

"Well, don't we all?" groaned Devane, who alone of the gang was disposed to be merciful.

"That's different," said Boyd. "We can say things like that among ourselves, in the family, so to speak, but we don't want everyone to know about it."

"He showed me a couple of chapters," said Devane mournfully. "I didn't see anything at all in it. Sentimental stuff, that's how it looked to me."

"Ah, but you didn't see the big scenes," said Corbett. "And for a good reason."

"What reason?"

"There are several nasty things about you in it."

"He couldn't say anything about me," said Devane.

"That's all you know."

"By God," said Boyd, "he deserves all he gets. If there's anything worse than a man using his friends for copy, I don't know what it is."

Devane, perturbed, slipped away. After a good deal of thought he went along the quays to Mac's lodgings, his head down, his umbrella hanging over his joined hands, a picture of misery. Mac was busy and cheerful. Sheets of foolscap littered the table. He had been drinking tea.

"So you're still at it," said Devane.

"Still at it."

"You're a brave man."

"How so?"

"All the dove-cots you're after putting a-flutter."

"What the hell are you talking about?"

"I hear the monks are very uneasy."

"About my novel?" asked Mac with a start.

"Yes."

"How did they get to hear of it?"

"How do I know? Corbett says they were talking to the Canon about you."

Mac grew pale.

"Who's spreading stories about me?"

"I don't know, I tell you. What did you say about me?"

"I said nothing about you."

"You'd better not. You'll cause trouble enough."

"Sure, I'm not saying anything about anybody," said Mac, his face beginning to twitch.

"Well, they think you are."

"My God, there's a hole to work in." Mac suddenly sat back, haggard, his hands spread wide before him. "By God, I have a good mind to roast them all. And I didn't get to the serious part at all yet. That's only a description of his childhood."

"I didn't see anything wrong with it—what you showed me," said Devane, rubbing his nose.

"By God, I have," repeated Mac passionately, "a thorough good mind to roast them."

"You're too old," said Devane, and his metallic voice sounded like the spinning of a rattle. "Why don't you have sense? I used to want to be a musician one time. I don't want anything now only to live till I get me pension. You ought to have sense," he went on in a still crankier tone. "Don't you know they'll all round on you, like they did on me the time I got the organ?"

"'Tis the curse of the tribe," declared Mac despairingly. "They hate to see anyone separating himself from the tribe."

"I don't know what it is," said Devane, "and I don't give a damn. I used to be trying to think out explanations, too, one time, but I gave it up. What's the use when you can read Jane Austen? Read Jane Austen, MacCarthy, she's grand and consoling, and there isn't a line in her that would remind you of anything at all. I like Jane Austen and Trollope, and I like Rameau and Lully and Scarlatti, and I'd like Bach too if he was satisfied with writing nice little dance-tunes instead of bloody big elephants of Masses that put you in mind of your last end."

Devane left Mac very depressed. The news about the novel had spread. People discussed it everywhere; his enemies said they had never expected anything else from him; his friends were uneasy and went about asking if they shouldn't, as old friends of Mac's, advise him. They didn't, and as a result the scandal only spread farther.

With Elsie, Mac permitted himself to rage.

"By God, I will roast them now," he said. "I'm going to change the whole center part of the book. I see now where I went wrong. My idea was to show the struggle in a man's soul between idealism and materialism; you know, the Celtic streak, soaring dreams, 'the singing masons building roofs of gold': the quest of the absolute, and then show how 'tis dragged down by the mean little everyday nature of the Celt; the mean, vain, money-grubbing, twisty little nature that kept him from ever doing anything in the world only suffer and twist and whine. But now I see a bigger theme emerging; the struggle with the primitive world—colossal!"

"You're marvelous," said Elsie. "How do you think of it all?"

"Because I'm it," said Mac vehemently. "I am the Celt. I feel it in my blood. The Celts are only emerging into civilization. I and people like me are the forerunners. We feel the whole conflict of the nation in ourselves; the individual soul and at the same time the sense of the tribe; the Latin pride and the primitive desire to merge ourselves in the crowd. I can see how 'twill go. My fellow will have to sink himself time and time again and then at last the trumpet call! His great moment has come. He must say farewell to the old world and stand up, erect and defiant."

Still, Mac found his novel heavy going. It wasn't that ideas didn't come to him; he had too many, but always there was the sense of a hundred malicious faces peering over his shoulder; the Canon and Corbett; Devane, Cronin, Boyd; the headmaster.

Then one evening the maid came to his room.

"Oh, by the way, Mr. MacCarthy, the Canon called looking for you."

"Oh, did he?" said Mac, but his heart missed a beat.

"He said he'd call back another time."

"Did he say what he wanted?"

"No, Mr. MacCarthy, but he seemed a bit worried."

The pages he had written formed a blur before Mac's eyes. He could not write. Instead he put on his hat and went up to Elsie's.

" 'Tis all up," he said.

"What?" she asked.

"Everything. Turned out on the roadside at my age to earn my living what way I can."

"Do you mean you're sacked?"

"No, but I will be. 'Tis only a matter of days. The Canon called to see me. He never called to see me before. But I don't care. Let them throw me out. I'll starve, but I'll show them up."

"You're exaggerating, Dan. Sure, you didn't do anything at all yet."

"No, but they know what I can do. They're afraid of me. They see the end of their world is coming."

"But did anything else happen? Are you guessing all this or did somebody tell you?"

"I only wish to God I did it thirty years ago," said Mac, striding moodily about the room. "That was the time when I was young and strong and passionate. But I'm not afraid of them. I may be a fallen giant, but I'm still a giant. They can destroy me, but I'll pull their damn' temple about their ears, the way Samson did. It's you I'm sorry for, girl. I didn't know I was bringing you into this."

"I'm not afraid," she said.

"Ah, I'm a broken man, a broken man. Ten years ago I could have given you something to be proud of. I had genius then."

After leaving her he called at Dolan's for a drink. Corbett and some of the others were there and Mac felt the necessity for further information. He resolved to get it by bluff. He'd show them just what he thought of all the pother.

"I hear the Church is going to strike," he said with a cynical laugh.

"Did you hear that, too?" exclaimed Corbett.

"So you know?"

"Only that old Brother Reilly was supposed to be up complaining of you to the Canon."

"Aha! So that's it, is it?"

"I hope to goodness it won't be anything serious," said Corbett despondently.

"Oh, I don't care. I won't starve."

"You're a bloody fool," said Cronin, the fat painter who had done the Stations of the Cross for the new parish church. "Don't you know damn' well you won't get another job?"

"I won't. I know quite well I won't."

"And what are you going to do? I declare to God I thought you had more sense. At your age, too! You have a fine cushy job and you won't mind it."

"Not at that price."

"What price? What are you talking about? Haven't we all to stand it and put the best face we can on it?"

"And damn' well you paid for it, Cronin!"

"How so?"

"You're—how long are you painting?—twenty-five years? And worse and worse you're getting till now you're doing Stations of the Cross in the best Bavarian style. Twenty-five years ago you looked as though you might have had the makings of a painter in you, but now what are you? A maggot like the rest of us, a measly little maggot! Oh, you can puff out your chest and eat your mustache as much as you like, but that's what you are. A maggot, a five-bob-an-hour drawing master."

"MacCarthy," said Boyd, "you want your backside kicked, and you're damn' well going to get it kicked."

"And who's going to do it, pray?" asked Mac coolly.

"You wait till you get the Canon down on you; he won't be long about it."

"Aha," said Mac. "So the Canon is our new hero! The Deliverer! This, as I always guessed, is what all the old talk was worth. Ye gas and gas about liberty of conscience, but at the first whiff of powder ye run and hide under the Canon's soutane. Well, here's to the Canon! Anyway, he's a man."

"Are you accusing me of turning me coat?" bawled Boyd.

"Quiet now, Boyd, quiet!"

"Are you?"

"Boyd, I won't even take the trouble to quarrel with you," said Mac gravely. "You've lost even the memory of a man. I suppose when you were twenty-five or so you did hear the clock, but you don't hear it any longer." He sipped his pint and suddenly grew passionate. "Or do you? Do you? Do you hear the inexorable hour when all your wasted years spring out like little toy soldiers from the clock and present arms? And does it never occur to you that one of these days they'll step out and present arms and say: 'Be off now, you bloody old cod! We're going back to barracks!'"

It was late when he left the pub. He was very pleased with himself. He had squelched Cronin, made Boyd ridiculous, reinstated himself with the gang, proved he was still the master of them all. As he came through the side streets he began to feel lonely. When he came to the bridge he leaned over it and watched the river flowing by beneath.

"Christ, what a fool I am! What a fool!" he groaned.

For a long time he stood on the quay outside his own lodgings, afraid to go in. The shapes of human beings began to crowd round him, malevolent and fierce, the Canon, the head, Cronin, Boyd, Devane. They all hated him, all wished him ill, would stop at nothing to destroy him.

In the early morning he went downstairs, made a bonfire of his novel, and sobbed himself to sleep.

STORY COLDLY TOLD

by STELLA BENSON

THE SETTLEMENT of Padda had gone down very much in importance by the time I went to live there. The larger world's distresses had at last affected that remote corner; the big firms were withdrawing their representatives, leaving big houses and compounds to be haunted only by white ants and by the silent echoes of vanished beanos. "They say the lion and the lizard keep the courts where Our Mr. Wilkinson of the Imperial Kerosene Company gloried and drank deep."

The Gildis, a flourishing and rather superior Negro race who inhabit that part of Outer Lesterland, seem to have got tired of foreign influence. Scrobham, the Vice-Consul, always maintained that the Gildis were a decadent race, because, it seems, in the old days they went in for gold-leaf-covered carvings in wood, and in the new days they go in for smuggling arms and kidnaping English and American travelers. But I am not so sure, myself, that this is a sign of decadence. I don't like the Gildis personally, but then I have the belief that the white man and the Negro never can like one another—unless one flatters the other. I don't think liking matters much, anyway, and I get tired of Scrobham's eternal nosing after common denominators and points of contact.

So much had the foreign community at Padda dwindled that, in my time, only the Vice-Consul, Scrobham, a dozen or so of English and American missionaries, a half-caste general-store

manager, a very few tourists and commercial travelers, and myself, represented the white color among the Gildis in Padda city.

The innocent but single-hearted politics of the Gildis had a
good deal to do with this withdrawal of European and American patronage. Anglo-Saxon shoulderers of the White Man's
Burden have a cold dislike of single-hearted politics. They like
double aims; they like native races to be progressive yet docile,
clever yet humble, proud yet servile, practical yet sentimental;
they like colored students to absorb education without applying
it to facts, to read history without drawing a moral from it.
But no imperialist, however confused in his ideals, could possibly approve, consistently, of the goings-on of Orlad, Chief Rak
of the Gildis. He was really all of a twitter about modern political methods, and showed such a restless anxiety to profit by
all the past and current experiments in government—one after
another or all together—that nobody, least of all his subjects,
ever knew from one day to another whether the Gildi nation
lived under a Soviet *régime* or under a dictatorship or owed
allegiance to a divinely appointed monarch or was trying some
other stunt. One could apostrophize Orlad as a second Lenin—
a Gildi Mussolini—a reincarnation of George Washington—a
Karl Marx—a Czar of all the Gildis—a sage and self-effacing
constitutional prince—and please him with each acclamation,
as long as one chose the right title for the right day. I never
met Orlad, the Gildi ruler. I don't think he can be a man of
very much sense, but I am sure he enjoys himself enormously.
Sense in other people is another of the things I don't bother
about much, anyway. When I hear people saying, "Now, that's
sense," it always sounds to me as if they were saying, "*I* might
have said that myself." Whether Orlad's methods were sensible
or not, the result undoubtedly was that he could not keep order
among his subjects or fellow-citizens. The pace was too quick
for them, poor devils. Law succeeded law with such dizzy

rapidity that the only thing a consistent subject could do was to become an outlaw and remain one; in this way, a man could know where he was. The Gildi notables, therefore, took up brigandage in rather the same spirit as the English barons once took up the Magna Carta—as a defense against government instability and as an assertion of their right, as subjects, to know where they stood.

Padda is a small town, three hundred miles from Tra-aan, Orlad's capital—three hundred very rough miles too. The road had been covered, once, by an adventurous Ford car, but in the ordinary way one traveled to Tra-aan, if one had to, by wagon, and put up for six nights at the filthy fortified inns. In the still more ordinary way, one didn't travel to Tra-aan at all, or anywhere else. One reached Padda by river, and lived there for years without finding any reason to go anywhere else. There was very little reason to go to Padda, of course, either. The sisal-export business had once been of great importance there, however, and these great importances die hard. I was the last survival of that particular importance—the last English sisal shipper to be stationed at Padda.

Padda, as I knew it, was just far enough away from the inland center of Gildi activity—Tra-aan—to get the effects of the Chief Rak's political experiments, without any of their advantages. The Communist movement, for instance, which had been initiated in Tra-aan as a neat self-consciously noble plan, organized by "Workers' Soviets"—(in which I believe Comrade Orlad— ex-Chief Rak—was the only worker brave enough to speak)— reached Padda simply in the form of a destructive rabble. Men who left Tra-aan as "Comrades" were simple looters by the time they reached Padda. Communism, in fact, burst upon us like a thunderstorm. Streets in which, for days on end, the dust had only been disturbed by pigs and goats, became quite suddenly hideous with howling "Communists" rounding up recalcitrant converts at the spear's point. I watched the first stages of the business from my roof—as I had watched many invasions before, since my arrival in this disturbed land. The new arrivals, who cannot have been more than five or six hundred strong, were breaking into all houses that were not flying the orthodox red flag. Any red shred flapping from the middle bar of a window would save a house—as long as it was seen in time. All Gildi windows are barred, and a shred of rag is always tied to the middle bar—to frighten devils away, they say—so now it was only a matter of suiting the color of the protecting rag to a new brand of devil.

A crowd of Gildi peasants always seems to me—even after all these years—a queer sight. All peasants in this country dress in black; black is the cheapest dye—made from the bark of the bula shrub that grows all along the river. The combination of black faces, black bodies and black clothes, gives a macabre carnival effect, as though the people were masked mock-revelers at some witch's funeral. I have that feeling, although of course I know that a crowd of Gildi peasants is just as prosaic and commonplace as a crowd of Manchester shop-assistants. I have no use for that Elemental Pagan stuff.

We have had so many disturbances at Padda, and so few that disturbed us, the foreign community, at all, that, for an hour, I watched, with a feeling of god-like detachment, the "Communist" activities in the streets within sight of my roof. A great deal of cackling, fussing and flapping always accompanies all Gildi activities. Today it seemed to me that the "Communist" flappings and cacklings were no more alarming than the flappings and cacklings of a group of Gildi merchants bidding at a market auction. No blood was drawn, as far as I could see. I noticed one old woman collecting donkey-manure all the time, most peacefully, threading her way through the agitation, and once gently tapping on the shoulder a ranting

Communist orator who was standing over a little heap of the treasure she sought. He moved out of her way at once, with great docility. Presently, I thought, that very leader will probably come and pay a formal call on me, and I shall present him—in accordance with Gildi etiquette—with a basket of melons or a dozen bottles of cider, which he will formally accept and (also according to Gildi etiquette) tactfully forget to take away when he leaves my house. Secure in my reliance on precedents, I leaned over my parapet, like the Blessed Damosel. After a while, I heard a kind of croak, and looking round, saw the head of Scrobham, the Vice-Consul, sticking out of the trap-door which was the only egress from the house to the roof. Scrobham's face was stiff with fear, and, for a few seconds, he could scarcely speak. "My God, Palmer, what *shall* we do?" he managed to blurt out. Saying this seemed to ease his utterance a little, and he began stammering out a torrent of really terrifying information. This attack on the city, it seemed, was much more ferocious than anything we had hitherto experienced, and it was particularly directed against us, the foreigners. The invaders had broken into the English mission compound as soon as they arrived, hauled down the Union Jack, locked up all the missionaries, and, after holding some pompous senseless pow-wow they called a Soldiers' Council, condemned them all to death. Whether they would carry out their threat remained to be seen; the whole business was so unlike what we knew of Gildi methods that there seemed nothing to base a surmise on. At any rate, the soldiers were ostentatiously erecting a gallows in the market-place, banners were being paraded with the legend, *Death to the Foreign Traitors,* and an American tourist had been beaten in the street and then hustled away, no one knew where. Scrobham had not been able to get into touch with any other foreigners. He had remained in his office, hoping that some of us would find our way there, until ten minutes ago, when the rabble had broken into his compound and killed his watchman. On which he had escaped over the back wall and come to my house. My house, he said, was entirely deserted; my servants had fled. Up to that point, Scrobham had talked with the fluency and unself-consciousness of fear; never before had I heard him speak without trying to make some personal impression that seemed to me sentimental—trying to wring some implied tribute out of his hearer. But mention of the flight of the servants brought a spark of the old Scrobham back. "Disloyal brutes," he said, and even in my fright I had time to feel irritated. Loyalty in such circumstances is another of the things that don't seem to me real. I am a *job* to my servants, and there is no more reason for my cook-boy to risk his life for me—his job—than there is for me to risk my life in protecting a shipment of sisal.

My first instinct in any emergency is to do nothing—or perhaps it is not my first *instinct* (for almost everyone's first *instinct* is to run away, I suppose)—it is my first mental decision. It seemed to me, as Scrobham spoke, that if the invaders were killing foreigners, we were done for, anyway. True, they were poorly armed—experience of Gildi arms would lead one to suppose that all importation stopped in the 'seventies—and we had up-to-date revolvers at least, but I never can get up any enthusiasm about this business of "selling one's life dearly." If one is obliged to get out, there seems no sense in making it a group exodus; to be accompanied into oblivion by four or five Gildi heroes wouldn't help one at all. So when Scrobham said again, "What is to be done, Palmer?" I said, "Let's go downstairs and get drunk."

"Let's go downstairs and get drunk." Scrobham didn't like that at all. He wanted to do something safe, or, failing that, something noble. Best of all, he would have liked to do something that *looked* noble and *was* safe. However, he followed me downstairs, and all the way down he was murmuring to himself, between chattering teeth, "It's incredible—the whole thing's incredible—incredible." I sympathized with the feeling from which the words sprang; it was a kind of nostalgia, I knew, for the time when all this hadn't happened. "It's incredible" meant "Need I believe it, God—please, please, mayn't it be a dream?" Anybody might feel this, when his world went to pieces, but only a sentimentalist like Scrobham would put a sort of faith in it, would set an illusion to cancel an accomplished fact, would draw a sort of hope from the word *incredible*.

My house, as Scrobham had said, was quite deserted, but as we went through the hall, my clerk, John Monday, came in hurriedly by the side door, making us both jump. I hardly knew him for a moment, as he was dressed in peasant black, instead of his usual Palm Beach style. Monday was of pure Gildi blood, mission-educated; the fact that he had changed the spelling of his name, Mandi, just about explained him, I had always thought. He was a good clerk; occasionally he dined with me, but there was never any ease between us—there never could be; my effort was to disguise patronage, and his, to disguise servility. Only Scrobham could call the point of contact between these two efforts "friendship." However, now I must say, I felt that something important had come on the scene in the mild person of John Monday—something so important that it might be called *hope*—or even *life*. His first words, however, were "Sir, I have brought Miss Sims," and my heart sank. *Sims* was not a word of hope. She was an old woman, an English missionary; I hardly knew her, though, alas, I knew her voice, raised, at street-corners, in thinly melodious affirmation, *"Yes,* Jesus loves me. *Yes,* Jesus loves me . . ."* (translated into Gildi, of course). I expect she was right; she was a selfless old lady, very worthy of His love, no doubt, but to me she seemed to be among the things that didn't matter much. Not that I am against missionaries particularly; it always seems to me that nearly everybody preaches a gospel of some kind—commercial travelers—drunkards—lovely women—golfers—sainted hermits—care-free sinners . . . they all nag at us to listen to their gospels, and the missionaries' nagging is no more tiresome than that of the others.

I find I am telling this story in a very leisurely way, but the curious thing about it is that up to that point it was a very leisurely adventure. I was so profoundly convinced that there was nothing to be done, that time seemed to stand still. John Monday, with a gesture like that of a royal prince unveiling a statue, disclosed Miss Sims sitting peacefully in the cloak-cupboard under the stairs. She smiled at us gallantly, but said nothing—I think because she was in the middle of a prayer. But then John Monday began shyly, "Sir, I think my cousin—" and all the wheels of my mind started going round again. John Monday's cousin, Rak Mandi, after failing in the sisal-growing business owing to the disturbed state of the country, had taken up brigandage and Made Good, as the Americans say. He was one of the most successful brigands in the vicinity of Padda, and owed his success, I think, largely to the fact that he aimed at no sensational *coups*. Small caravans of minor Gildi cotton merchants were his game; he treated his prisoners well and asked—and obtained—moderate ransoms. He never troubled foreigners, and the Chief Rak's government, therefore, had never been forced to take steps to suppress him. "Where is your cousin, John?" I asked.

"Sir, I have reason to believe I could find him," said Monday, bridling. He always bridled when he spoke of his cousin. Evidently he had the whole plan arranged, for he at once led the way through my deserted kitchen and outhouses. Scrobham, Miss Sims and I followed. The servants had evidently downed tools in a hurry; a pot of beans still bubbled on the kitchen fire.

It was really very courageous of John Monday. He was certainly risking his skin for us. "Loyalty," Scrobham would have said; "his Christian training" would have been Miss Sims's guess. I should diagnose his act, myself, as an example of the instinctive Gildi conservatism. Like dogs, Gildis can't bear change, they are faithful to a time-table rather than to a man. John wanted life to get back to normal; in saving us, he instinctively hoped to insure a return to the beloved routine of his life. Still, I can feel grateful, even with a cold heart, and I was certainly very glad of the existence of poor John Monday that day.

At the side-gate we all bumped into one another's backs, for John, our leader, stopped suddenly and looked both ways along the alley before allowing us to cross. Then, at his heels, we all tiptoed across the alley and into the house of a Gildi carpenter, an old acquaintance of mine, who used to do odd jobs for me. The house was full of the carpenter's family and friends, and, one and all, they turned their faces away as we appeared. All naively affected to be busy over some absorbing employment as we walked through their dark home. It was the Gildi way of disclaiming responsibility. There was a red rag ostentatiously tied to the middle bar of the window, I noticed. The carpenter himself was sawing planks, and I wondered whether he had been commissioned to help with the building of the gallows in the market-place. We walked out of the back door of the workshop without uttering a word or meeting a glance. As we crossed the wretched little vegetable garden, Scrobham whispered to me, "Did you notice their expressions?"

"Yes, of course. Why not?"

"Absolutely inscrutable," he murmured. "A marvelous people. An incredible people." Scrobham was himself again.

When we had scrambled over the mud wall of the carpenter's little holding, we found the way open before us to the open country, a flat valley, criss-crossed with beanfields, with an occasional square of gaudy golden buckwheat. John Monday handed us over to a couple of strangers, here, dressed in the usual peasant black, but armed with unusually efficient-looking revolvers.

"Are these your cousin's men, John?" I asked.

"Sir, it is so," said John, bridling.

"I hope we haven't far to go," said Scrobham. "Miss Sims doesn't look in trim for a long trek."

"Oh, I'm up to *anything,*" said the old lady vivaciously.

"The Lair is only about six miles distant," said John pompously.

"Lair!" echoed Scrobham, startled. "Where on earth are we being taken to?"

"We are kidnaped by brigands, Scrobham," I said solemnly. "Resistance is useless."

John Monday took off his hat politely to us as we started, and then he disappeared into the carpenter's house.

I suppose Scrobham thought I was joking, for he walked on without making any comment, chivalrously offering his arm to Miss Sims whenever he came to an irrigation ditch. The old lady tramped on very serenely, tilting her topee over her nose against the sun without the slightest pretense to dignity or grace; she had a silvery mustache and scrawny wisps of gray hair taggling down the back of her tortoise neck, but certainly she had courage. Courage, however, isn't among the social graces, and I thought, as I walked behind Scrobham and Miss Sims, that I could hardly have chosen two less amusing people to be kidnaped with. They might reasonably have been thinking the same thing, but I don't suppose they were, for they were both too noble.

Evidently we were making for the Tuli Len (the Twenty Heads)—a low range of wooded hills that rose, in a series of rather abrupt sandstone shelves, from the checkered valley. I expected that the brigands' "Lair" would be only accessible by means of an arduous climb, and I trembled for the valiant arches of Miss Sims, but it seemed that news of our danger had appealed to all that was Most Chivalrous in Gildi brigand nature, and we found the outlaw, Rak Mandi, and some of his men, awaiting us in a gorge at the very foot of the hills. It was then that we realized for the first time—not only Scrobham, but also I—that we actually were in the hands of brigands— that we could not get away. But even then, Scrobham, with his extraordinary capacity for believing two opposing facts at once, didn't accept the thing prosaically. There was a curious scene during the first hour of our captivity. Rak Mandi ordered Scrobham to sit down at once and write to the Consul-General at Tra-aan, demanding a ransom of a thousand pounds for each of us. Scrobham wrote what he was told, but he wrote it "in quotes," as printers say. He added a whimsical statement of his own view of the situation—that Mandi, "a loyal friend to the British," was putting things in this way to save his own face, but that it need not be taken too seriously. A strong escort should be sent to take us to Tra-aan, and should bring with it a handsome present for the "Loyal" brigand chief—a case of champagne or a good radio set. . . . Rak Mandi asked me to translate this to him (Scrobham was a poor Gildi scholar). I translated Scrobham's vaporings as "The noble Vice-Consul suggests to his noble-noble superior that the Rak Mandi, being evidently generously inclined, might perhaps finally consider a smaller ransom, or even a valuable present of rare English merchandise." The Rak directed me coldly to write an additional letter of my own to the Consul-General saying that he would not bargain at all, and that if the full price were not paid by return—(*return* meant about a fortnight)—a fingertip from each of us would be sent as a reminder.

"He's more serious than you think, Scrobham," I said.

"I should never dream of calling the noble-Rak anything but profoundly serious," said Scrobham, smiling.

We watched the Rak's messenger start. We all felt fairly cheerful, each for a different reason. Scrobham because he believed in the Chivalry of the Gildi Gentleman, Miss Sims because she relied on the protection of her Maker, I because I believed in the British Consul-General. I happened to know that the Consul-General didn't think much of Scrobham and would discount his information to a certain extent. I knew he would act for the best—and act on *my* letter.

In short, the thing was no joke—no fiction—in the eyes of Rak Mandi, and, though quite polite, at any rate at first, he was evidently anxious that we should understand this. He was considerate to us, but only in order to keep us fresh and salable, as it were. He lodged us well. We moved on the second day, and after a fifteen-mile walk, arrived at a herdsman's hut on the lip of a ravine—a breezy place, not half so dirty as you would expect. Indeed, a free man might have chosen it as a week-end camping site; the rising ground behind the hut was carpeted with flowers—yellow lilies—a kind of blood-red balsam—a very delicate wild verbena. Tall pine-woods thirty yards away gave a shade in which our captors allowed us to lie during the worst heat of the day. The food—mostly chicken and eggs, fried in acid batter in the Gildi way—was not bad, though it was monotonous, and one felt the lack of green vegetables. The brigand Rak did us as well as he could, certainly, but only because he was a good husbandman. We were a financial speculation from his point of view—nothing else. At the suggestion of his cousin, John Monday, he had undertaken this speculation; his cousin, he realized, had mysterious missionary motives in recommending the venture, but to him, Rak Mandi, we were just a rather more daring financial flutter than usual. It was impossible for Scrobham to realize this, though, of course, he saw the picturesque value of our seizure and would do full justice to it later, when writing "My Sojourn Among Gildi Brigands" for *Blackwood's Magazine.* Mandi was a "Loyal Gildi" protecting us from "Disloyal Gildis"; the armed men by whom we were always closely surrounded were part of the game, Scrobham thought—part of the "fantastic Gildi instinct for pageantry" that Scrobham so often talked about. Scrobham expected to be treated by Mandi as a gentleman by a gentleman. "These are the descendants, Miss Sims, of the men who wrote *The Gildi To-ali,* a saga of chivalry worthy to be ranked with the epics that have been written round King Arthur or Beowulf. The true Gildi gentleman is a *pukka* gentleman; the word *knightly* best describes him, I think, if he isn't spoilt by corrupting European or American influence. He's a gentleman—with something added—something mystic added. There are stories that have never been explained. . . ."

"Well I never!" said Miss Sims, but still she continued to express a wish that the brigands would soon consent to let her rig herself up a little place to sleep, apart from the rest of us. Their knightliness didn't stretch to that, as yet. I spoke to Rak Mandi about it. Miss Sims had a peculiar longing to be left unwatched while undressing and sleeping, I told him.

"Why? Is It deformed?" asked Rak Mandi.

Privacy became even more difficult to obtain for Miss Sims after I had raised the question. The Rak was not himself impressed by her, but his men were, and wherever she went she was followed by a large, deeply interested band. It was impossible for the simple brigands to believe that Miss Sims was a woman. Her too big topee, her scrawny short hair, her large knobby feet, her goggling spectacles, her harsh brisk voice, the silver bristles on her upper lip, suggested nothing of womanhood to them. The fact that she wore an ankle-length dress of faded flowered cotton only led them to suppose that she was a robed priest of some order new to them. After all, they had no sartorial precedents to rely on, in observing white people. If Scrobham had worn a wreath of jasmine round his bald patch, or if I had worn a morning coat, spats, a brown bowler and no shoes and socks, we should have been no more surprising to the brigands than we were already. It was fixed in their minds that Miss Sims was a venerable eunuch, dedicated to some unknown cult; an abrupt silence fell whenever she spoke, and everything she did was worthy of intense scrutiny.

"These poor creatures seem very interested in me," said Miss Sims on the third difficult day. Unlike Scrobham she was not in the faintest degree interested in them, as people of a foreign race and different civilization—only as *souls*. She had lived thirty-five years among the Gildis without learning the names of one of their gods or devils or hearing a single legend of the country, although, of course, she was aware that they "harbored heathen superstitions." A professional gleam brightened behind her spectacles as she spoke of their interest in her. "I believe they would be a fruitful soil for my message," she added. Scrobham smiled superciliously when she said this, and murmured in a self-conscious aside to me, "The old *vandal!* She hasn't the remotest idea of what she's up against. I suppose it's never occurred to her that she's dealing with a people whose basic knowledge is beyond her conception—whose religion was ancient beyond imagination when Christianity began. Watch the expressions of the men now . . . how incredibly crude her prattle obviously seems to them. . . ."

I watched the brigands' expressions. Miss Sims talked Gildi fluently, but with an atrocious accent. She was saying something like this: "You boys each had a father and mother, didn't you?—a Daddy who was Oh so proud of you and called you little pet names . . . a Mummy who loved you tenderly whatever you did, however naughty you were, who held you up when your little toddling feet strayed into danger, who kissed your little aches and pains to make them well, who forgave all your childish sins. . . ." The brigands lapped it up from the word Go. I saw no trace whatever of Mystic Superiority in their gentle rapt faces. It seemed to me quite obvious that each brigand was obediently sending his dull heart back to the mud hut where he was born—back to the games on the dung-heap—back to the lofty ritual attentions of his father and the other Elders—back to the scrawny pendent breasts of his mother. I felt convinced that Miss Sims's words seemed to each of her brigand listeners fraught with a clairvoyant significance. Only Rak Mandi held himself physically and spiritually apart. It was obvious that Mummies and Daddies held no glamor for him—that in his eyes Miss Sims was a loathsome oddity rather than a shining revelation. Scrobham, who had meanly hoped to see all the brigands turn their backs on Miss Sims and spit, began by muttering, "They have *perfect* manners, these chaps, haven't they?—absolutely perfect natural tact . . ."—then he told me an anecdote about a servant of his—an inscrutable Gildi, of course—who had received some mystic information about the death of an aunt of Scrobham's. . . . "Wise Ingli Lady cross Dark River in far-away High Temple . . ." (Scrobham tried, embarrassingly, to imitate a Gildi looking mystic and inscrutable, and to mimic a dreamy Gildi voice), "and, *at that very hour,* Palmer, my dear aunt had fallen down with heart failure at morning service. . . . You can't *explain* that sort of thing . . . and we have the parvenu impudence to import our silly little messages. . . ." Everybody has heard this kind of story, told by persons of chronically *tourist* intellect—a big web spun from a little cocoon of coincidence.

As the genuine absorption of the brigands in Miss Sims's message became more and more unmistakable, Scrobham gave an ostentatious snort and went out of the hut. I was quite glad to be left to listen sleepily to the talk. With two-thirds of my mind I was trying to calculate how long—at the very quickest—it would take Rak Mandi's messenger to reach Tra-aan. Supposing the Consul-General sent an escort in a caravan of Ford cars. . . . Cars had been used so rarely on that trail that perhaps the possibility had not occurred to the Rak. . . .

I was roused from my calculations by noticing that I had been wrong in supposing all the brigands to be whole-heartedly interested in Miss Sims. One, a big loutish lad near the door, I now saw, had in his hands Scrobham's sweater, which Scrobham had hung on a nail on the wall. It was a gaudy, diamond-criss-crossed thing, and the brigand and his immediate neighbors were handling it with astonishment, turning it this way and that. Almost as soon as I noticed this, Scrobham came into the hut again and saw where his sweater was. For a second he looked annoyed, then he remembered to put on the smile that he always assumed when dealing with Gildis—the smile of a gentleman among gentlemen. He put out his hand genially to take the sweater. The brigand looked at him with an extremely insolent leer in his oily black eyes—and, with slow swaggering movements, put the sweater on. For a moment Scrobham looked nonplussed again, but then his face reverted to its smile—a slightly more urgent smile, suggesting, "A joke's a joke, my dear fellow, and I, for one, am always ready to enjoy a joke against myself, but . . ." In Gildi, he said, "Friend, my garment looks well on you, but you would not wish to leave me with a cold body. . . ." And he actually plucked gently at the shoulder of the sweater. The brigand pushed his hand rudely away and spat on his foot. Scrobham, whose nerves were becoming a little frayed by captivity, suddenly lost his temper and shouted in English: "Give me my sweater, you swine." The brigand snatched up his gun and rattled it under Scrobham's nose. There was something very deadly about the sound. Scrobham sprang back against the wall. Miss Sims's voice ceased. Rak Mandi, at the other end of the hut, said nothing; perhaps he thought it as well that Scrobham should be brought to understand the realities of his position.

The silence lasted only a minute. Then Miss Sims began again. "Up to now, boys, I have been talking of the love of earthly parents, and perhaps some of you may have been thinking there could be no love more unbounded and more beautiful than the love of our dear mothers and fathers. Mothers especially, you will have been thinking; our mothers gave us life out of their own pain, each one of us was sent out into the world by a mother who wept bitter tears when she lost sight of us round the bend of the road, a mother who centered all her hopes on us, and thinks of us night and morning, saying to herself, 'My little boy came to me—a wonderful gift—a holy mystery . . . my little boy . . . now grown a big boy . . . is he all that I hoped and dreamed? Is he keeping himself clean and right and innocent as he was when I first guided his toddling steps upon the earth?' Boys, *at this moment,* perhaps, your mothers are thinking in this way of you—yes, even those mothers who have crossed the dark river of death, away from our earthly sight . . . not even death can quench that wonderful thing called mother-love. . . . Are you *sure,* dear boys, is each one of you *sure,* that none of us here is disappointing those pure hopes? Is there not one of you—I can see him now—whose heart is sore with pride and sin? . . . I ask that boy over there, *could he face his mother at this moment?* No . . . I can see his poor brow, which his mother used to stroke so proudly, all

twisted with the sense of sin. . . ." All the brigands turned to
stare curiously at the forehead of the writhing lout who wore
Scrobham's sweater. He got up irritably from his squatting
attitude and stood with his back to the others, looking ridicu-
lously shy, like a tongue-tied performer at a school speech-day.
In that same vein Miss Sims burbled on, soaring from time to
time to the idea of a heavenly parent, but often returning to
the mother theme, with special reference to the mother of the
wearer of the sweater. After a particularly harrowing description of that mother's tears on receipt of the news that her son
was a thief, a murmur began among the more susceptible brigands, which might be roughly translated as, "Hey, Bill, you
better give that sweater up. It'll bring you bad luck." The
thief shook his shoulders in obstinate refusal, and continued to
stare at the wall, exactly like a stubborn child. Miss Sims
talked on. After a few minutes two fellow-brigands came up
and murmured anxiously to the thief; they pointed first at Miss
Sims, then at the sky, then at the sweater. I could not hear
what they said. I heard the erring brother's reply, though.
He stamped his foot and shouted something like, "I *shan't* give
it back, so *there*. It's *mine*. I took it. It's *mine*, so *there*. . . ."
Then Miss Sims began to pray. She certainly had an extraordi-
narily telling technique. She seemed to be really alone with a
beloved friend, who was, one would almost swear, listening
sympathetically to her from somewhere just above the roof.
Several brigands looked nervously upwards, and even I found
it hard myself to be quite sure that no one was present except
ourselves. Miss Sims's hearer was told all about the brigands—
their essential goodheartedness—their kindness to their captives
—their youth—their mothers' hopes of them—and the sad fact
that one of them had "let the side down," as it were, having
(for the moment only, no doubt) shut his heart against the
light, betrayed the tender love of his mother, denied the un-

speakable gift of an even higher love, and blotted the otherwise
stainless page that the recording angel had allotted to Rak
Mandi's brigand band. I forget the exact point she had reached
when the murmurs directed towards the thief by his fellow-
brigands became so loud that they almost drowned the prayer.
At any rate, at that point the unlucky lout, with a smothered
oath, dragged the sweater violently over his head, threw it furi-
ously on the floor at Scrobham's feet and flounced out of the hut.

Scrobham picked the thing up slowly, looking most deeply
disgusted. I suppose he felt that all his cherished Gildi illusions
were smashed at one blow. While Miss Sims, who—since her
eyes were shut—seemed not to have noticed the return of the
sweater, uttered the rather long peroration of her prayer, Scrobham, in order to dissociate himself from us commoners, went
up to the completely detached Rak Mandi near the further door,
and stood there beside him—two Gentlemen among Plebeians.
And, in the silence that followed Miss Sims's *Amen,* Rak Mandi,
speaking for the first time that afternoon, said to Scrobham,
"Leave me," and after a pause added, "You smell."

That last passage with the Rak seemed to break Scrobham's
heart. He was a man to whom sympathy was the breath of life,
and here there was no sympathy. After that, we three prisoners
kept apart. Miss Sims remained surrounded by her squad of
devoted desperadoes, Scrobham sat in a corner writing in his
pocket-diary notes for the brave, whimsical, reflective account
of his experiences that he afterwards contributed to *Blackwood's.*
I used to sit a good deal at the edge of the pine-wood, watching
ants. It refreshes me to look at insects, though I am not interested in classifying them. I enjoy feeling perfectly free to learn
no lesson—perfectly free from any obligation to pass judgment.
I can say, "This creature does this or that" without being expected to add, "How wrong—how right—how surprising—how

human. . . ." Though a sluggard, I draw no moral at all from Going to the Ant; that's why I go to it.

Two or three days after Miss Sims's first discovery of the brigand susceptibility to her teachings, I was sitting in the shade there, when Rak Mandi came up. I was surprised, for I appreciated the fact that he really had a strong physical distaste for the proximity of white men; he actually did object to our smell, and he would half shut his eyes, sometimes, as if feeling faint with disgust, after studying what must have seemed to him our knobby, uneven, palely blood-tinted faces. Looking at him as he stood over me now, I could see that the Gildi face really is a more perfect face—as a face—than ours, though it is so grossly modeled. It seems to fit more neatly into a more neatly tailored skin; although the skin is blue-black, it is fine, hairless, oiled and exquisite. Certainly Gildi bones are more discreet than ours. I don't like the Gildis, but I rather like their sameness; all this Nordic and Latin physical variety is rather tiresome, since there is so little intellectual variety behind it. Gildis don't seem to bother with individuality much; individuality's one of the things I find it very refreshing to get away from sometimes. "Flesh and blood and bone, that's us," the Gildis seem to say, and God knows that's enough to say—when you come to think of it.

"You must stop that Thing's mouth," said Rak Mandi. (We could hear the drone of Miss Sims's latest message from where we were.) "Otherwise I shall feel obliged . . ."—he gave a little sigh—"to cut Its tongue out."

"Stop Miss Sims preaching!" I echoed. "Why, noble-Rak, surely she is doing no harm. She's happy, the men are happy, you're happy, I'm happy . . . no one's the worse for it. Even if she baptizes them all in due course, I don't see that that need inconvenience you at all. On the contrary, they would probably bring more enthusiasm to their work."

"It is causing my men to be two-hearted," said Rak Mandi,

using a characteristic Gildi expression. "Already two of them have spoken of going away to their own villages—playing traitor to me. My spies have reported to me that It preaches treachery. You must stop Its mouth," he said on a final note—Gildis have no fear of repeating themselves exactly. "Otherwise I shall be obliged—"

"Oh, I'll do my best, noble-Rak," I said hurriedly. "But I'm afraid Miss Sims is very much set on—"

"Stop Its mouth."

I went there and then to the hut, where the indefatigable Miss Sims was conducting her afternoon talk. I stood in the doorway listening for a moment, and was surprised at the progress Miss Sims had made. One or two of her hearers were now quite articulate, asking naive questions and applauding the replies with the sharp "Fla-fla" of Gildi approval; sometimes one brigand would explain away another's expressed problem, like a precocious school-child putting a dullard right, in class. Miss Sims, I was sorry to hear, was actually preaching on the sinfulness of the brigand career. They had been led away by love of gain, she said, comfortingly, it was a mistake fortunately easily put right; they had only to listen to the still small voice—

"Miss Sims," I said. "Sorry to interrupt, but I have an important message for you."

With a loving smile of apology to her audience, she stumped to my side. I gave her Rak Mandi's message pretty baldly.

"My dear Mr. Palmer," she said in a businesslike voice, as she took off her thick glasses and wiped them briskly. (Was there a tear of self-commiseration on them? It was quickly gone.) "You don't suppose that that man's threats will stop me doing my duty?"

I said that the fulfillment of his threat would certainly stop the delivery of her message.

"How can one say that?" she said. "It is for a Higher

Authority to judge of that. It may be that this trial is required of me. . . ."

Miss Sims's motives were as completely hidden from me as those of an ant; I must accept her as I would an ant, saying, "She is this—she is that . . ." and making no comment. She demanded no comment of me; she was self-generating, as an ant is. I found her extremely refreshing at that moment, and as I have often saved a drowning ant, because I so much wanted it to go on, uncoerced, doing its own thing—so I would now have done a good deal to save Miss Sims from interruption in the form of martyrdom. But she would do nothing to save herself. She went back to her place at the end of the room and began talking again about the incompatibility of brigandage with true righteousness.

I heard Rak Mandi shout a word of command outside, and I supposed for a moment that he was trying to withdraw his men from the corrupting influence, but when I turned I saw that he and Scrobham were standing on the edge of the ravine looking down the valley at something exciting. The Rak was holding Scrobham by the arm, and this, for a minute, seemed to me absolutely incredible, until I guessed that some party of rescuers was approaching, and that the prudent Rak was using Scrobham as a protecting shield against rifle-fire. But how could rescuers be in sight? Our letters could scarcely possibly have reached Tra-aan yet—much less have been answered. I ran to the rim of the ravine, and Miss Sims's audience followed me, panting and cackling inquiries.

Up the rough trail that led to our little plateau marched a number of men—quite a hundred or so, I think. Rak Mandi, taken unawares, was obviously at a loss; he was bewildered by the fact that his own sentries were marching quite cheerfully and frankly with the approaching band. And Scrobham—the humiliations of the past forgotten—while trying vainly to wriggle his arm out of the Rak's grasp, further lulled the leader's suspicions by saying, "An escort. . . . I knew they'd send a good escort. You shan't be the loser for our going, noble-Rak—I'll see that your hospitality and loyalty are rewarded. . . ." In any case, the surprise of the sight was too sudden to allow the Rak to organize an effective defense—even had he been sure that he was being attacked.

"But it's much too soon for rescue to be possible, isn't it?" said Miss Sims's precise teacher's croak beside me—and there was an innocently joyful note in it. Martyrdom is no joke, after all. No martyr could help feeling relieved if the Lord should change His plans sometimes.

"We means no harm to nobody," shouted a voice in English from the crowd. I recognized the Chief of Police of Padda—a fat Gildi worthy who had been tactfully out of the way during the "Communist" invasion. I noticed that he, and a good many of the men who accompanied him, were wearing blue sashes diagonally across their black tunics.

I think now that Rak Mandi's men must have been seized by panic. They knew even less than we did what this invasion of strangers meant. But they saw themselves trapped between a life they had recently learned to be ashamed of, and the mysterious forces of the law. They must assert their innocence—their change of heart; they must play their safest card. As the Chief of Police—puffing—reached the plateau, three of the brigands stepped up to their own leader, Rak Mandi, and shot him through the breast.

For a minute it was difficult to see what was happening. I saw the murderers hasten to the policeman and begin an agitated explanation—pointing again and again at Miss Sims. I heard one of them shout, "The noble-Thing's words were like fire in our hearts." I saw Scrobham actually wringing his hands, dancing about, shouting, "You damn swine," again and again. It was the *caddishness* of the thing that seemed so appalling, he afterwards told me. To me, it was simply the death of a living man that seemed appalling, I don't quite know why. I don't think I should have minded at all if it had been Scrobham; that would have been only the death of a skinful of illusions. However, it was Rak Mandi whose clear purposes were thus reduced to nothing.

When we had all calmed down a little, the Chief of Police explained his presence. The kingdom of Gildi, he explained, was now living under a Fascist *régime*—(I happened to notice at that moment that he was standing in the shade of an immense castor-oil plant, and I thought, idiotically, how unnecessarily neatly events sometimes frame themselves). Indeed it seemed that Fascism was quite an old story in Tra-aan by now; the Chief Rak—now Blue-sash Dictator—had had time to establish this new idea with some promise of permanence. His opening activities in suppressing Communism had resulted in the invasion of Padda by the retreating rabble that had driven us out. The Chief Rak's Fascist army had arrived next day— just in time to save the condemned missionaries from the gallows. And John Monday, after prudently waiting a few days to see if any further armies arrived to supplant the Blue-sash *régime,* went to the police with the information that his cousin, "a mountain man," was extending his protection to three more foreign survivors.

"All's well that ends well, I suppose," said Scrobham, looking ambiguously down at the limp body of Rak Mandi. I knew he was thinking of the insults that the proud man had so indifferently thrown at him. "He saved our lives . . . but only from love of gain, of course . . . he wasn't much of a straw to clutch at, poor devil, if the truth were known. . . ."

"Not *really* knightly," I suggested.

"Well—as I say—we owe our lives to him," said Scrobham. "Only a cad would speak critically of the dead."

But as we walked away down the ravine, with a great clatter of clog-shod feet and chatter, I looked up the steep bank to the edge of our plateau, and, just dangling over the broken grassy lip, I saw Rak Mandi's hand—moving. "I'm going back for something," I said to Scrobham. "I'll catch you up."

Rak Mandi, when I reached him, was rolling his head feebly on the grass. His eyes were open; he was bleeding profusely from the mouth and choking a bit. The black skin of his face looked curiously drained. I thought it would ease him if I propped him up against a pine-tree trunk. I managed to do this, but he seemed in danger of toppling over sideways again, so I squatted beside him, propping him up. He said in a strangled voice, "Go further away," and after gasping and choking a moment added, "Go very far away." I left him and stood beneath the next tree. He did not fall over but remained leaning limply against the tree looking at me very coldly. One could see death falling on him, like scarcely visible gossamer veils falling one after another, hiding him very gradually away. I thought how curious it was that we should all have changed our roles—that Scrobham, the gentleman among gentlemen, should have left such a slight epitaph for the man he believed to have saved him—that Miss Sims, the preacher of a gospel of love, should be responsible for this same man's death—that I, who didn't believe in any pretty communications between man and man—least of all between white man and Negro—should be now, so to speak, smoothing the pillow of a Gildi brigand's deathbed. And as I was thinking this, Rak Mandi uttered a low word, his chin dropped—and he, too, changed his role. He changed from a man into a thing. I ran after the others, and sent back two of his own men to bury him.

GOOSEBERRIES

by ANTON CHEKHOV

THE WHOLE sky had been overcast with rain-clouds from early morning; it was a still day, not hot, but heavy, as it is in gray dull weather when the clouds have been hanging over the country for a long while, when one expects rain and it does not come. Ivan Ivanovich, the veterinary surgeon, and Burkin, the high school teacher, were already tired from walking, and the fields seemed to them endless. Far ahead of them they could just see the windmills of the village of Mironositskoe; on the right stretched a row of hillocks which disappeared in the distance behind the village, and they both knew that this was the bank of the river, that there were meadows, green willows, homesteads there, and that if one stood on one of the hillocks one could see from it the same vast plain, telegraph-wires, and a train which in the distance looked like a crawling caterpillar, and that in clear weather one could even see the town. Now, in still weather, when all nature seemed mild and dreamy, Ivan Ivanovich and Burkin were filled with love of the countryside, and both thought how great, how beautiful a land it was.

"Last time we were in Prokofy's barn," said Burkin, "you were about to tell me a story."

"Yes; I meant to tell you about my brother."

Ivan Ivanovich heaved a deep sigh and lighted a pipe to begin to tell his story, but just at that moment the rain began. And

292

five minutes later heavy rain came down, covering the sky, and it was hard to tell when it would be over. Ivan Ivanovich and Burkin stopped in hesitation; the dogs, already drenched, stood with their tails between their legs gazing at them feelingly.

"We must take shelter somewhere," said Burkin. "Let us go to Alehin's; it's close by."

"Come along."

They turned aside and walked through mown fields, sometimes going straight forward, sometimes turning to the right, till they came out on the road. Soon they saw poplars, a garden, then the red roofs of barns; there was a gleam of the river, and the view opened onto a broad expanse of water with a windmill and a white bathhouse: this was Sofino, where Alehin lived.

The watermill was at work, drowning the sound of the rain; the dam was shaking. Here wet horses with drooping heads were standing near their carts, and men were walking about covered with sacks. It was damp, muddy, and desolate; the water looked cold and malignant. Ivan Ivanovich and Burkin were already conscious of a feeling of wetness, messiness, and discomfort all over; their feet were heavy with mud, and when, crossing the dam, they went up to the barns, they were silent, as though they were angry with one another.

In one of the barns there was the sound of a winnowing machine, the door was open, and clouds of dust were coming from it. In the doorway was standing Alehin himself, a man of forty, tall and stout, with long hair, more like a professor or an artist than a landowner. He had on a white shirt that badly needed washing, a rope for a belt, drawers instead of trousers, and his boots, too, were plastered up with mud and straw. His eyes and nose were black with dust. He recognized Ivan Ivanovich and Burkin, and was apparently much delighted to see them.

"Go into the house, gentlemen," he said, smiling; "I'll come directly, this minute."

It was a big two-storied house. Alehin lived in the lower story, with arched ceilings and little windows, where the bailiffs had once lived; here everything was plain, and there was a smell of rye bread, cheap vodka, and harness. He went upstairs into the best rooms only on rare occasions, when visitors came. Ivan Ivanovich and Burkin were met in the house by a maid-servant, a young woman so beautiful that they both stood still and looked at one another.

"You can't imagine how delighted I am to see you, my friends," said Alehin, going into the hall with them. "It is a surprise! Pelageya," he said, addressing the girl, "give our visitors something to change into. And, by the way, I will change too. Only I must first go and wash, for I almost think I have not washed since spring. Wouldn't you like to come into the bathhouse? And meanwhile they will get things ready here."

Beautiful Pelageya, looking so refined and soft, brought them towels and soap, and Alehin went to the bathhouse with his guests.

"It's a long time since I had a wash," he said, undressing. "I have got a nice bathhouse, as you see—my father built it—but I somehow never have time to wash."

He sat down on the steps and soaped his long hair and his neck, and the water round him turned brown.

"Yes, I must say," said Ivan Ivanovich meaningly, looking at his head.

"It's a long time since I washed . . ." said Alehin with embarrassment, giving himself a second soaping, and the water near him turned dark blue, like ink.

Ivan Ivanovich went outside, plunged into the water with a loud splash, and swam in the rain, flinging his arms out wide. He stirred the water into waves which set the white lilies bobbing up and down; he swam to the very middle of the millpond

and dived, and came up a minute later in another place, and
swam on, and kept on diving, trying to touch bottom.

"Oh, my goodness!" he repeated continually, enjoying himself
thoroughly. "Oh, my goodness!" He swam to the mill, talked
to the peasants there, then returned and lay on his back in the
middle of the pond, turning his face to the rain. Burkin and
Alehin were dressed and ready to go, but he still went on swimming and diving. "Oh, my goodness! . . ." he said. "Oh, Lord,
have mercy on me! . . ."

"That's enough!" Burkin shouted to him.

They went back to the house. And only when the lamp was
lighted in the big drawing-room upstairs, and Burkin and Ivan
Ivanovich, attired in silk dressing-gowns and warm slippers,
were sitting in armchairs; and Alehin, washed and combed, in
a new coat, was walking about the drawing-room, evidently
enjoying the feeling of warmth, cleanliness, dry clothes, and
light shoes; and when lovely Pelageya, stepping noiselessly
on the carpet and smiling softly, handed tea and jam on a tray—
only then Ivan Ivanovich began on his story, and it seemed as
though not only Burkin and Alehin were listening, but also the
ladies, young and old, and the officers who looked down upon
them sternly and calmly from their gold frames.

"There are two of us brothers," he began—"I, Ivan Ivanovich,
and my brother, Nikolay Ivanovich, two years younger. I went
in for a learned profession and became a veterinary surgeon,
while Nikolay sat in a government office from the time he was
nineteen. Our father, Chimsha-Himalaisky, was the son of a
private, but he himself rose to be an officer and left us a little
estate and the rank of nobility. After his death the little estate
went in debts and legal expenses; but, anyway, we had spent
our childhood running wild in the country. Like peasant children, we passed our days and nights in the fields and the
woods, looked after horses, stripped the bark off the trees, fished

and so on. . . . And, you know, whoever has once in his life caught perch or has seen the migrating of the thrushes in autumn, watched how they float in flocks over the village on bright, cool days, he will never be a real townsman, and will have a yearning for freedom to the day of his death. My brother was miserable in the government office. Years passed by, and he went on sitting in the same place, went on writing the same papers and thinking of one and the same thing—how to get into the country. And this yearning by degrees passed into a definite desire, into a dream of buying himself a little farm somewhere on the banks of a river or a lake.

"He was a gentle, good-natured fellow, and I was fond of him, but I never sympathized with this desire to shut himself up for the rest of his life in a little farm of his own. It's the correct thing to say that a man needs no more than six feet of earth. But six feet is what a corpse needs, not a man. And they say, too, now, that if our intellectual classes are attracted to the land and yearn for a farm, it's a good thing. But these farms are just the same as six feet of earth. To retreat from town, from the struggle, from the bustle of life, to retreat and bury oneself in one's farm—it's not life, it's egoism, laziness, it's monasticism of a sort, but monasticism without good works. A man does not need six feet of earth or a farm, but the whole globe, all nature, where he can have room to display all the qualities and peculiarities of his free spirit.

"My brother Nikolay, sitting in his government office, dreamed of how he would eat his own cabbages, which would fill the whole yard with such a savory smell, take his meals on the green grass, sleep in the sun, sit for whole hours on the seat by the gate gazing at the fields and the forest. Gardening books and the agricultural hints in calendars were his delight, his favorite spiritual sustenance; he enjoyed reading newspapers, too, but the only things he read in them were the advertisements of so many acres of arable land and a grass meadow with farm-houses and buildings, a river, a garden, a mill and millponds, for sale. And his imagination pictured the garden-paths, flowers and fruit, starling cotes, the carp in the pond, and all that sort of thing, you know. These imaginary pictures were of different kinds according to the advertisements which he came across, but for some reason in every one of them he always had to have gooseberries. He could not imagine a homestead, he could not picture an idyllic nook, without gooseberries.

" 'Country life has its conveniences,' he would sometimes say. 'You sit on the veranda and you drink tea, while your ducks swim on the pond, there is a delicious smell everywhere, and . . . and the gooseberries are growing.'

"He used to draw a map of his property, and in every map there were the same thing—(a) house for the family, (b) servants' quarters, (c) kitchen-garden, (d) gooseberry-bushes. He lived parsimoniously, was frugal in food and drink, his clothes were beyond description; he looked like a beggar, but kept on saving and putting money in the bank. He grew fearfully avaricious. I did not like to look at him, and I used to give him something and send him presents for Christmas and Easter, but he used to save that too. Once a man is absorbed by an idea there is no doing anything with him.

"Years passed: he was transferred to another province. He was over forty, and he was still reading the advertisements in the papers and saving up. Then I heard he was married. Still with the same object of buying a farm and having gooseberries, he married an elderly and ugly widow without a trace of feeling for her, simply because she had filthy lucre. He went on living frugally after marrying her, and kept her short of food, while he put her money in the bank in his name.

"Her first husband had been a postmaster, and with him she was accustomed to pies and homemade wines, while with her second husband she did not get enough black bread; she began to pine away with this sort of life, and three years later she gave up her soul to God. And I need hardly say that my brother never for one moment imagined that he was responsible for her death. Money, like vodka, makes a man queer. In our town there was a merchant who, before he died, ordered a plateful of honey and ate up all his money and lottery tickets with the honey, so that no one might get the benefit of it. While I was inspecting cattle at a railway-station a cattle-dealer fell under an engine and had his leg cut off. We carried him into the waiting-room, the blood was flowing—it was a horrible thing—and he kept asking them to look for his leg and was very much worried about it; there were twenty roubles in the boot on the leg that had been cut off, and he was afraid they would be lost."

"That's a story from a different opera," said Burkin.

"After his wife's death," Ivan Ivanovich went on, after thinking for half a minute, "my brother began looking out for an estate for himself. Of course, you may look about for five years and yet end by making a mistake, and buying something quite different from what you have dreamed of. My brother Nikolay bought through an agent a mortgaged estate of three hundred and thirty acres, with a house for the family, with servants' quarters, with a park, but with no orchard, no gooseberry-bushes, and no duck-pond; there was a river, but the water in it was the color of coffee, because on one side of the estate there was a brickyard and on the other a factory for burning bones. But Nikolay Ivanovich did not grieve much; he ordered twenty gooseberry-bushes, planted them, and began living as a country gentleman.

"Last year I went to pay him a visit. I thought I would go and see what it was like. In his letters my brother called his estate 'Chumbaroklov Waste, alias Himalaiskoe.' I reached 'alias Himalaiskoe' in the afternoon. It was hot. Everywhere there were ditches, fences, hedges, fir-trees planted in rows, and there was no knowing how to get to the yard, where to put one's horse. I went up to the house, and was met by a fat red dog that looked like a pig. It wanted to bark, but was too lazy. The cook, a fat, barefooted woman, came out of the kitchen, and she, too, looked like a pig, and said that her master was resting. I went in to see my brother. He was sitting up in bed with a quilt over his legs; he had grown older, fatter, wrinkled; his cheeks, his nose, and his mouth all stuck out—he looked as though he might begin grunting into the quilt at any moment.

"We embraced each other, and shed tears of joy and of sadness at the thought that we had once been young and now were both gray-headed and near the grave. He dressed, and led me out to show me the estate.

" 'Well, how are you getting on here?' I asked.

" 'Oh, all right, thank God; I am getting on very well.'

"He was no more a poor timid clerk, but a real landowner, a gentleman. He was already accustomed to it, had grown used to it, and liked it. He ate a great deal, went to the bathhouse, was growing stout, was already at law with the village commune and both factories, and was very much offended when the peasants did not call him 'your Honor.' And he concerned himself with the salvation of his soul in a substantial, gentlemanly manner, and performed deeds of charity, not simply, but with an air of consequence. And what deeds of charity! He treated the peasants for every sort of disease with soda and castor oil, and on his name-day had a thanksgiving service in the middle of the village, and then treated the peasants to a gallon of vodka—he thought that was the thing to do. Oh, those horrible gallons of vodka! One day the fat landowner hauls the peasants up before the district captain for trespass, and next day, in honor of a holiday, treats them to a gallon of vodka, and they drink and shout 'Hurrah!' and when they are drunk bow down to his feet. A change of life for the better and being well fed and idle develop in a Russian the most insolent self-conceit. Nikolay Ivanovich, who at one time in the government office was afraid to have any views of his own, now could say nothing that was not gospel truth, and uttered such truths in the tone of a prime minister. 'Education is essential, but for the peasants it is premature.' 'Corporal punishment is harmful as a rule, but in some cases it is necessary and there is nothing to take its place.'

" 'I know the peasants and understand how to treat them,' he would say. 'The peasants like me. I need only to hold up my little finger and the peasants will do anything I like.'

"And all this, observe, was uttered with a wise, benevolent smile. He repeated twenty times over 'We noblemen,' 'I as a noble'; obviously he did not remember that our grandfather was a peasant, and our father a soldier. Even our surname Chimsha-Himalaisky, in reality so incongruous, seemed to him now melodious, distinguished, and very agreeable.

"But the point just now is not he, but myself. I want to tell you about the change that took place in me during the brief hours I spent at his country place. In the evening, when we were drinking tea, the cook put on the table a plateful of gooseberries. They were not bought, but his own gooseberries, gathered for the first time since the bushes were planted. Nikolay Ivanovich laughed and looked for a minute in silence at the gooseberries, with tears in his eyes; he could not speak for excitement. Then he put one gooseberry in his mouth, looked at me with the triumph of a child who has at last received his favorite toy, and said:

" 'How delicious!'

"And he ate them greedily, continually repeating, 'Ah, how delicious! Do taste them!'

"They were sour and unripe, but, as Pushkin says:

*'Dearer to us the falsehood that exalts
Than hosts of baser truths.'*

"I saw a happy man whose cherished dream was so obviously
fulfilled, who had attained his object in life, who had gained
what he wanted, who was satisfied with his fate and himself.
There is always, for some reason, an element of sadness mingled
with my thoughts of human happiness, and, on this occasion, at
the sight of a happy man I was overcome by an oppressive feeling that was close upon despair. It was particularly oppressive
at night. A bed was made up for me in the room next to my
brother's bedroom, and I could hear that he was awake, and
that he kept getting up and going to the plate of gooseberries
and taking one. I reflected how many satisfied, happy people
there really are! What an overwhelming force it is! You look
at life: the insolence and idleness of the strong, the ignorance
and brutishness of the weak, incredible poverty all about us,
overcrowding, degeneration, drunkenness, hypocrisy, lying. . . .
Yet all is calm and stillness in the houses and in the streets; of
the fifty thousand living in a town, there is not one who would
cry out, who would give vent to his indignation aloud. We see
the people going to market for provisions, eating by day, sleeping by night, talking their silly nonsense, getting married, growing old, serenely escorting their dead to the cemetery; but we
do not see and we do not hear those who suffer, and what is terrible in life goes on somewhere behind the scenes. . . . Everything is quiet and peaceful, and nothing protests but mute sta-
tistics: so many people gone out of their minds, so many gallons of vodka drunk, so many children dead from malnutrition.
. . . And this order of things is evidently necessary; evidently
the happy man only feels at ease because the unhappy bear
their burden in silence, and without that silence happiness would
be impossible. It's a case of general hypnotism. There ought to

be behind the door of every happy, contented man someone
standing with a hammer continually reminding him with a tap
that there are unhappy people; that however happy he may be,
life will show him her jaws sooner or later, trouble will come
for him—disease, poverty, losses, and no one will see or hear,
just as now he neither sees nor hears others. But there is no
man with a hammer; the happy man lives at his ease, the trivial
daily cares faintly agitate him like the wind in the aspen-tree—
and all goes well.

"That night I realized that I, too, was happy and contented,"
Ivan Ivanovich went on, getting up. "I, too, at dinner and at the
hunt liked to lay down the law on life and religion, and the
way to manage the peasantry. I, too, used to say that science
was light, that culture was essential, but for the simple people
reading and writing was enough for the time. Freedom is a
blessing, I used to say; we can no more do without it than without air, but we must wait a little. Yes, I used to talk like that,
and now I ask, 'For what reason are we to wait?'" asked Ivan
Ivanovich, looking angrily at Burkin. "Why wait, I ask you?
What grounds have we for waiting? I shall be told, it can't be
done all at once; every idea takes shape in life gradually, in its
due time. But who is it says that? Where is the proof that it's
right? You will fall back upon the natural order of things, the
uniformity of phenomena; but is there order and uniformity in
the fact that I, a living, thinking man, stand over a chasm and
wait for it to close of itself, or to fill up with mud at the very
time when perhaps I might leap over it or build a bridge across
it? And again, wait for the sake of what? Wait till there's no
strength to live? And meanwhile one must live, and one wants
to live!

"I went away from my brother's early in the morning, and
ever since then it has been unbearable for me to be among people.
I am oppressed by peace and quiet; I am afraid to look at the

windows, for there is no spectacle more painful to me now than the sight of a happy family sitting round the table drinking tea. I am old and am not fit for the struggle; I am not even capable of hatred; I can only grieve inwardly, feel irritated and vexed; but at night my head is hot from the rush of ideas, and I cannot sleep. . . . Ah, if I were young!"

Ivan Ivanovich walked backwards and forwards in excitement, and repeated: "If I were young!"

He suddenly went up to Alehin and began pressing first one of his hands and then the other.

"Pavel Konstantinovich," he said in an imploring voice, "don't be calm and contented, don't let yourself be put to sleep! While you are young, strong, confident, be not weary in well-doing! There is no happiness, and there ought not to be; but if there is a meaning and an object in life, that meaning and object is not our happiness, but something greater and more rational. Do good!"

And all this Ivan Ivanovich said with a pitiful, imploring smile, as though he were asking him a personal favor.

Then all three sat in armchairs at different ends of the drawing-room and were silent. Ivan Ivanovich's story had not satisfied either Burkin or Alehin. When the generals and ladies gazed down from their gilt frames, looking in the dusk as though they were alive, it was dreary to listen to the story of the poor clerk who ate gooseberries. They felt inclined for some reason to talk about elegant people, about women. And their sitting in the drawing-room where everything—the chandeliers in their covers, the armchairs, and the carpet under their feet—reminded them that those very people who were now looking down from their frames had once moved about, sat, drunk tea in this room, and the fact that lovely Pelageya was moving noiselessly about was better than any story.

Alehin was fearfully sleepy; he had got up early, before three o'clock in the morning, to look after his work, and now his eyes were closing; but he was afraid his visitors might tell some interesting story after he had gone, and he lingered on. He did not go into the question whether what Ivan Ivanovich had just said was right and true. His visitors did not talk of groats, nor of hay, nor of tar, but of something that had no direct bearing on his life, and he was glad and wanted them to go on.

"It's bedtime, though," said Burkin, getting up. "Allow me to wish you good night."

Alehin said good night and went downstairs to his own domain, while the visitors remained upstairs. They were both taken for the night to a big room where there stood two old wooden beds decorated with carvings, and in the corner was an ivory crucifix. The big cool beds, which had been made by the lovely Pelageya, smelt agreeably of clean linen.

Ivan Ivanovich undressed in silence and got into bed.

"Lord forgive us sinners!" he said, and put his head under the quilt.

His pipe lying on the table smelt strongly of stale tobacco, and Burkin could not sleep for a long while, and kept wondering where the oppressive smell came from.

The rain was pattering on the windowpanes all night.

A DILL PICKLE

by KATHERINE MANSFIELD

A<small>ND THEN</small>, after six years, she saw him again. He was seated at one of those little bamboo tables decorated with a Japanese vase of paper daffodils. There was a tall plate of fruit in front of him, and very carefully, in a way she recognized immediately as his "special" way, he was peeling an orange.

He must have felt that shock of recognition in her for he looked up and met her eyes. Incredible! He didn't know her! She smiled; he frowned. She came towards him. He closed his eyes an instant, but opening them his face lit up as though he had struck a match in a dark room. He laid down the orange and pushed back his chair, and she took her little warm hand out of her muff and gave it to him.

"Vera!" he exclaimed. "How strange. Really, for a moment I didn't know you. Won't you sit down? You've had lunch? Won't you have some coffee?"

She hesitated, but of course she meant to.

"Yes, I'd like some coffee." And she sat down opposite him.

"You've changed. You've changed very much," he said, staring at her with that eager, lighted look. "You look so well. I've never seen you look so well before."

"Really?" She raised her veil and unbuttoned her high fur collar. "I don't feel very well. I can't bear this weather, you know."

305

"Ah, no. You hate the cold. . . ."

"Loathe it." She shuddered. "And the worst of it is that the older one grows . . ."

He interrupted her. "Excuse me," and tapped on the table for the waitress. "Please bring some coffee and cream." To her: "You are sure you won't eat anything? Some fruit, perhaps. The fruit here is very good."

"No, thanks. Nothing."

"Then that's settled." And smiling just a hint too broadly he took up the orange again. "You were saying—the older one grows—"

"The colder," she laughed. But she was thinking how well she remembered that trick of his—the trick of interrupting her— and of how it used to exasperate her six years ago. She used to feel then as though he, quite suddenly, in the middle of what she was saying, put his hand over her lips, turned from her, attended to something different, and then took his hand away, and with just the same slightly too broad smile, gave her his attention again. . . . Now we are ready. That is settled.

"The colder!" He echoed her words, laughing too. "Ah, ah. You still say the same things. And there is another thing about you that is not changed at all—your beautiful voice—your beautiful way of speaking." Now he was very grave; he leaned towards her, and she smelled the warm, stinging scent of the orange peel. "You have only to say one word and I would know your voice among all other voices. I don't know what it is—I've often wondered—that makes your voice such a— haunting memory. . . . Do you remember that first afternoon we spent together at Kew Gardens? You were so surprised because I did not know the names of any flowers. I am still just as ignorant for all your telling me. But whenever it is very fine and warm, and I see some bright colors—it's awfully strange—I hear your voice saying: 'Geranium, marigold and

verbena.' And I feel those three words are all I recall of some
forgotten, heavenly language. . . . You remember that afternoon?"

"Oh, yes, very well." She drew a long, soft breath, as though
the paper daffodils between them were almost too sweet to bear.
Yet what had remained in her mind of that particular afternoon was an absurd scene over the tea table. A great many
people taking tea in a Chinese pagoda, and he behaving like a
maniac about the wasps—waving them away, flapping at them
with his straw hat, serious and infuriated out of all proportion
to the occasion. How delighted the sniggering tea drinkers had
been. And how she had suffered.

But now, as he spoke, that memory faded. His was the truer.
Yes, it had been a wonderful afternoon, full of geranium and
marigold and verbena, and—warm sunshine. Her thoughts
lingered over the last two words as though she sang them.

In the warmth, as it were, another memory unfolded. She
saw herself sitting on a lawn. He lay beside her, and suddenly,
after a long silence, he rolled over and put his head in her lap.

"I wish," he said, in a low, troubled voice, "I wish that I had
taken poison and were about to die—here now!"

At that moment a little girl in a white dress, holding a long,
dripping water lily, dodged from behind a bush, stared at them,
and dodged back again. But he did not see. She leaned over
him.

"Ah, why do you say that? I could not say that."

But he gave a kind of soft moan, and taking her hand he
held it to his cheek.

"Because I know I am going to love you too much—far too
much. And I shall suffer so terribly, Vera, because you never,
never will love me."

He was certainly far better looking now than he had been
then. He had lost all that dreamy vagueness and indecision.

Now he had the air of a man who has found his piace in life, and fills it with a confidence and an assurance which was, to say the least, impressive. He must have made money, too. His clothes were admirable, and at that moment he pulled a Russian cigarette case out of his pocket.

"Won't you smoke?"

"Yes, I will." She hovered over them. "They look very good."

"I think they are. I get them made for me by a little man in St. James's Street. I don't smoke very much. I'm not like you —but when I do, they must be delicious, very fresh cigarettes. Smoking isn't a habit with me; it's a luxury—like perfume. Are you still so fond of perfumes? Ah, when I was in Russia . . ."

She broke in: "You've really been to Russia?"

"Oh, yes. I was there for over a year. Have you forgotten how we used to talk of going there?"

"No, I've not forgotten."

He gave a strange half laugh and leaned back in his chair. "Isn't it curious. I have really carried out all those journeys that we planned. Yes, I have been to all those places that we talked of, and stayed in them long enough to—as you used to say, 'air oneself' in them. In fact, I have spent the last three years of my life traveling all the time. Spain, Corsica, Siberia, Russia, Egypt. The only country left is China, and I mean to go there, too, when the war is over."

As he spoke, so lightly, tapping the end of his cigarette against the ash-tray, she felt the strange beast that had slumbered so long within her bosom stir, stretch itself, yawn, prick up its ears, and suddenly bound to its feet, and fix its longing, hungry stare upon those far away places. But all she said was, smiling gently: "How I envy you."

He accepted that. "It has been," he said, "very wonderful—

especially Russia. Russia was all that we had imagined, and far, far more. I even spent some days on a river boat on the Volga. Do you remember that boatman's song that you used to play?"

"Yes." It began to play in her mind as she spoke.

"Do you ever play it now?"

"No, I've no piano."

He was amazed at that. "But what has become of your beautiful piano?"

She made a little grimace. "Sold. Ages ago."

"But you were so fond of music," he wondered.

"I've no time for it now," said she.

He let it go at that. "That river life," he went on, "is something quite special. After a day or two you cannot realize that you have ever known another. And it is not necessary to know the language—the life of the boat creates a bond between you and the people that's more than sufficient. You eat with them, pass the day with them, and in the evening there is that endless singing."

She shivered, hearing the boatman's song break out again loud and tragic, and seeing the boat floating on the darkening river with melancholy trees on either side. . . . "Yes, I should like that," said she, stroking her muff.

"You'd like almost everything about Russian life," he said warmly. "It's so informal, so impulsive, so free without question. And then the peasants are so splendid. They are such human beings—yes, that is it. Even the man who drives your carriage has—has some real part in what is happening. I remember the evening a party of us, two friends of mine and the wife of one of them, went for a picnic by the Black Sea. We took supper and champagne and ate and drank on the grass. And while we were eating the coachman came up. 'Have a

dill pickle,' he said. He wanted to share with us. That seemed
to me so right, so—you know what I mean?"

And she seemed at that moment to be sitting on the grass
beside the mysteriously Black Sea, black as velvet, and rippling
against the banks in silent, velvet waves. She saw the carriage
drawn up to one side of the road, and the little group on the
grass, their faces and hands white in the moonlight. She saw
the pale dress of the woman outspread and her folded parasol,
lying on the grass like a huge pearl crochet hook. Apart from
them, with his supper in a cloth on his knees, sat the coachman.
"Have a dill pickle," said he, and although she was not certain
what a dill pickle was, she saw the greenish glass jar with a
red chili like a parrot's beak glimmering through. She sucked
in her cheeks; the dill pickle was terribly sour. . . .

"Yes, I know perfectly what you mean," she said.

In the pause that followed they looked at each other. In the
past when they had looked at each other like that they had felt
such a boundless understanding between them that their souls
had, as it were, put their arms round each other and dropped
into the same sea, content to be drowned, like mournful lovers.
But now, the surprising thing was that it was he who held back.
He who said:

"What a marvelous listener you are. When you look at me
with those wild eyes I feel that I could tell you things that I
would never breathe to another human being."

Was there just a hint of mockery in his voice or was it her
fancy? She could not be sure.

"Before I met you," he said, "I had never spoken of myself
to anybody. How well I remember one night, the night that I
brought you the little Christmas tree, telling you all about my
childhood. And of how I was so miserable that I ran away and
lived under a cart in our yard for two days without being discovered. And you listened, and your eyes shone, and I felt that

you had even made the little Christmas tree listen too, as in a fairy story."

But of that evening she had remembered a little pot of caviare. It had cost seven and sixpence. He could not get over it. Think of it—a tiny jar like that costing seven and sixpence. While she ate it he watched her, delighted and shocked.

"No, really, that is eating money. You could not get seven shillings into a little pot that size. Only think of the profit they must make. . . ." And he had begun some immensely complicated calculations. . . . But now good-by to the caviare. The Christmas tree was on the table, and the little boy lay under the cart with his head pillowed on the yard dog.

"The dog was called Bosun," she cried delightedly.

But he did not follow. "Which dog? Had you a dog? I don't remember a dog at all."

"No, no. I mean the yard dog when you were a little boy." He laughed and snapped the cigarette case to.

"Was he? Do you know I had forgotten that. It seems such ages ago. I cannot believe that it is only six years. After I had recognized you today—I had to take such a leap—I had to take a leap over my whole life to get back to that time. I was such a kid then." He drummed on the table. "I've often thought how I must have bored you. And now I understand so perfectly why you wrote to me as you did—although at the time that letter nearly finished my life. I found it again the other day, and I couldn't help laughing as I read it. It was so clever—such a true picture of me." He glanced up. "You're not going?"

She had buttoned her collar again and drawn down her veil.

"Yes, I am afraid I must," she said, and managed a smile. Now she knew that he had been mocking.

"Ah, no, please," he pleaded. "Don't go just for a moment," and he caught up one of her gloves from the table and clutched at it as if that would hold her. "I see so few people to talk to nowadays, that I have turned into a sort of barbarian," he said. "Have I said something to hurt you?"

"Not a bit," she lied. But as she watched him draw her glove through his fingers, gently, gently, her anger really did die down, and besides, at the moment he looked more like himself of six years ago. . . .

"What I really wanted then," he said softly, "was to be a sort of carpet—to make myself into a sort of carpet for you to walk on so that you need not be hurt by the sharp stones and the mud that you hated so. It was nothing more positive than that —nothing more selfish. Only I did desire, eventually, to turn into a magic carpet and carry you away to all those lands you longed to see."

As he spoke she lifted her head as though she drank something; the strange beast in her bosom began to purr. . . .

"I felt that you were more lonely than anybody else in the world," he went on, "and yet, perhaps, that you were the only person in the world who was really, truly alive. Born out of your time," he murmured, stroking the glove, "fated."

Ah, God! What had she done! How had she dared to throw away her happiness like this. This was the only man who had ever understood her. Was it too late? Could it be too late? *She* was that glove that he held in his fingers. . . .

"And then the fact that you had no friends and never had made friends with people. How I understood that, for neither had I. Is it just the same now?"

"Yes," she breathed. "Just the same. I am as alone as ever."

"So am I," he laughed gently, "just the same."

Suddenly with a quick gesture he handed her back the glove and scraped his chair on the floor. "But what seemed to me so mysterious then is perfectly plain to me now. And to you, too, of course. . . . It simply was that we were such egoists so self-engrossed, so wrapped up in ourselves that we hadn't a corner in our hearts for anybody else. Do you know," he cried, naive and hearty, and dreadfully like another side of that old self again, "I began studying a Mind System when I was in Russia, and I found that we were not peculiar at all. It's quite a well-known form of . . ."

She had gone. He sat there, thunder-struck, astounded beyond words. . . . And then he asked the waitress for his bill.

"But the cream has not been touched," he said. "Please do not charge me for it."

THE BEAR

by WILLIAM FAULKNER

H E WAS ten. But it had already begun, long before that day when
at last he wrote his age in two
figures and he saw for the first time the camp where his father
and Major de Spain and old General Compson and the others
spent two weeks each November and two weeks again each
June. He had already inherited then, without ever having
seen it, the tremendous bear with one trap-ruined foot which,
in an area almost a hundred miles deep, had earned itself a
name, a definite designation like a living man.

He had listened to it for years: the long legend of corncribs
rifled, of shotes and grown pigs and even calves carried bodily
into the woods and devoured, of traps and deadfalls over-
thrown and dogs mangled and slain, and shotgun and even
rifle charges delivered at point-blank range and with no more
effect than so many peas blown through a tube by a boy—a
corridor of wreckage and destruction beginning back before he
was born, through which sped, not fast but rather with the ruthless and irresistible deliberation of a locomotive, the shaggy
tremendous shape.

It ran in his knowledge before he ever saw it. It looked
and towered in his dreams before he even saw the unaxed
woods where it left its crooked print, shaggy, huge, red-eyed,
not malevolent but just big—too big for the dogs which tried
to bay it, for the horses which tried to ride it down, for the

men and the bullets they fired into it, too big for the very country which was its constricting scope. He seemed to see it entire with a child's complete divination before he ever laid eyes on either—the doomed wilderness whose edges were being constantly and punily gnawed at by men with axes and plows who feared it because it was wilderness, men myriad and nameless even to one another in the land where the old bear had earned a name, through which ran not even a mortal animal but an anachronism, indomitable and invincible, out of an old dead time, a phantom, epitome and apotheosis of the old wild life at which the puny humans swarmed and hacked in a fury of abhorrence and fear, like pygmies about the ankles of a drowsing elephant: the old bear solitary, indomitable and alone, widowered, childless, and absolved of mortality—old Priam reft of his old wife and having outlived all his sons.

Until he was ten, each November he would watch the wagon containing the dogs and the bedding and food and guns and his father and Tennie's Jim, the Negro, and Sam Fathers, the Indian, son of a slave woman and a Chickasaw chief, depart on the road to town, to Jefferson, where Major de Spain and the others would join them. To the boy, at seven, eight, and nine, they were not going into the Big Bottom to hunt bear and deer, but to keep yearly rendezvous with the bear which they did not even intend to kill. Two weeks later they would return, with no trophy, no head and skin. He had not expected it. He had not even been afraid it would be in the wagon. He believed that even after he was ten and his father would let him go too, for those two weeks in November, he would merely make another one, along with his father and Major de Spain and General Compson and the others, the dogs which feared to bay at it and the rifles and shotguns which failed even to bleed it, in the yearly pageant of the old bear's furious immortality.

Then he heard the dogs. It was in the second week of his first time in the camp. He stood with Sam Fathers against a big oak beside the faint crossing where they had stood each dawn for nine days now, hearing the dogs. He had heard them once before, one morning last week—a murmur, sourceless, echoing through the wet woods, swelling presently into separate voices which he could recognize and call by name. He had raised and cocked the gun as Sam told him and stood motionless again while the uproar, the invisible course, swept up and past and faded; it seemed to him that he could actually see the deer, the buck, blond, smoke-colored, elongated with speed, fleeing, vanishing, the woods, the gray solitude, still ringing even when the cries of the dogs had died away.

"Now let the hammers down," Sam said.

"You knew they were not coming here too," he said.

"Yes," Sam said. "I want you to learn how to do when you didn't shoot. It's after the chance for the bear or the deer has done already come and gone that men and dogs get killed."

"Anyway," he said, "it was just a deer."

Then on the tenth morning he heard the dogs again. And he readied the too-long, too-heavy gun as Sam had taught him, before Sam even spoke. But this time it was no deer, no ringing chorus of dogs running strong on a free scent, but a moiling yapping an octave too high, with something more than indecision and even abjectness in it, not even moving very fast, taking a long time to pass completely out of hearing, leaving then somewhere in the air that echo, thin, slightly hysterical, abject, almost grieving, with no sense of a fleeing, unseen, smoke-colored, grass-eating shape ahead of it, and Sam, who had taught him first of all to cock the gun and take position where he could see everywhere and then never move again, had himself moved up beside him; he could hear Sam breathing at his shoulder, and he could see the arched curve of the old man's inhaling nostrils.

"Hah," Sam said. "Not even running. Walking."

"Old Ben!" the boy said. "But up here!" he cried. "Way up here!"

"He do it every year," Sam said. "Once. Maybe to see who in camp this time, if he can shoot or not. Whether we got the dog yet that can bay and hold him. He'll take them to the river, then he'll send them back home. We may as well go back too; see how they look when they come back to camp."

When they reached the camp the hounds were already there, ten of them crouching back under the kitchen, the boy and Sam squatting to peer back into the obscurity where they had huddled, quiet, the eyes luminous, glowing at them and vanishing, and no sound, only that effluvium of something more than dog, stronger than dog and not just animal, just beast, because still there had been nothing in front of that abject and almost painful yapping save the solitude, the wilderness, so that when the eleventh hound came in at noon and with all the others watching—even old Uncle Ash, who called himself first a cook—Sam daubed the tattered ear and the raked shoulder with turpentine and axle grease, to the boy it was still no living creature, but the wilderness which, leaning for the moment down, had patted lightly once the hound's temerity.

"Just like a man," Sam said. "Just like folks. Put off as long as she could having to be brave, knowing all the time that sooner or later she would have to be brave to keep on living with herself, and knowing all the time beforehand what was going to happen to her when she done it."

That afternoon, himself on the one-eyed wagon mule which did not mind the smell of blood nor, as they told him, of bear, and with Sam on the other one, they rode for more than three hours through the rapid, shortening winter day. They fol-

lowed no path, no trail even that he could see; almost at once
they were in a country which he had never seen before. Then
he knew why Sam had made him ride the mule which would
not spook. The sound one stopped short and tried to whirl
and bolt even as Sam got down, blowing its breath, jerking and
wrenching at the rein, while Sam held it, coaxing it forward
with his voice, since he could not risk tying it, drawing it forward while the boy got down from the marred one.

Then, standing beside Sam in the gloom of the dying afternoon, he looked down at the rotted over-turned log, gutted and
scored with claw marks and, in the wet earth beside it, the
print of the enormous warped two-toed foot. He knew now
what he had smelled when he peered under the kitchen where
the dogs huddled. He realized for the first time that the bear
which had run in his listening and loomed in his dreams since
before he could remember to the contrary, and which, therefore, must have existed in the listening and dreams of his father
and Major de Spain and even old General Compson, too, before they began to remember in their turn, was a mortal animal,
and that if they had departed for the camp each November
without any actual hope of bringing its trophy back, it was not
because it could not be slain, but because so far they had had
no actual hope to.

"Tomorrow," he said.

"We'll try tomorrow," Sam said. "We ain't got the dog
yet."

"We've got eleven. They ran him this morning."

"It won't need but one," Sam said. "He ain't here. Maybe
he ain't nowhere. The only other way will be for him to run
by accident over somebody that has a gun."

"That wouldn't be me," the boy said. "It will be Walter or
Major or—"

"It might," Sam said. "You watch close in the morning. Be-

cause he's smart. That's how come he has lived this long. If
he gets hemmed up and has to pick out somebody to run over,
he will pick out you."

"How?" the boy said. "How will he know—" He ceased.
"You mean he already knows me, that I ain't never been here
before, ain't had time to find out yet whether I—" He ceased
again, looking at Sam, the old man whose face revealed nothing
until it smiled. He said humbly, not even amazed, "It was me
he was watching. I don't reckon he did need to come but once."

The next morning they left the camp three hours before daylight. They rode this time because it was too far to walk, even
the dogs in the wagon; again the first gray light found him in
a place which he had never seen before, where Sam had placed
him and told him to stay and then departed. With the gun
which was too big for him, which did not even belong to him,
but to Major de Spain, and which he had fired only once—at a
stump on the first day, to learn the recoil and how to reload it
—he stood against a gum tree beside a little bayou whose black
still water crept without movement out of a canebrake and
crossed a small clearing and into cane again, where, invisible, a
bird—the big woodpecker called Lord-to-God by Negroes—clattered at a dead limb.

It was a stand like any other, dissimilar only in incidentals to
the one where he had stood each morning for ten days; a territory new to him, yet no less familiar than that other one which,
after almost two weeks, he had come to believe he knew a little
—the same solitude, the same loneliness through which human
beings had merely passed without altering it, leaving no mark,
no scar, which looked exactly as it must have looked when the
first ancestor of Sam Fathers' Chickasaw predecessors crept into
it and looked about, club or stone ax or bone arrow drawn and
poised; different only because, squatting at the edge of the
kitchen, he smelled the hounds huddled and cringing beneath it

and saw the raked ear and shoulder of the one who, Sam said, had had to be brave once in order to live with herself, and saw yesterday in the earth beside the gutted log the print of the living foot.

He heard no dogs at all. He never did hear them. He only heard the drumming of the woodpecker stop short off and knew that the bear was looking at him. He never saw it. He did not know whether it was in front of him or behind him. He did not move, holding the useless gun, which he had not even had warning to cock and which even now he did not cock, tasting in his saliva that taint as of brass which he knew now because he had smelled it when he peered under the kitchen at the huddled dogs.

Then it was gone. As abruptly as it had ceased, the wood-pecker's dry, monotonous clatter set up again, and after a while he even believed he could hear the dogs—a murmur, scarce a sound even, which he had probably been hearing for some time before he even remarked it, drifting into hearing and then out again, dying away. They came nowhere near him. If it was a bear they ran, it was another bear. It was Sam himself who came out of the cane and crossed the bayou, followed by the injured bitch of yesterday. She was almost at heel, like a bird dog, making no sound. She came and crouched against his leg, trembling, staring off into the cane.

"I didn't see him," he said. "I didn't, Sam!"

"I know it," Sam said. "He done the looking. You didn't hear him neither, did you?"

"No," the boy said. "I—"

"He's smart," Sam said. "Too smart." He looked down at the hound, trembling faintly and steadily against the boy's knee. From the raked shoulder a few drops of fresh blood oozed and clung. "Too big. We ain't got the dog yet. But maybe some-day. Maybe not next time. But someday."

So I must see him, he thought. *I must look at him.* Otherwise, it seemed to him that it would go on like this forever, as it had gone on with his father and Major de Spain, who was older than his father, and even with old General Compson, who had been old enough to be a brigade commander in 1865. Otherwise, it would go on so forever, next time and next time, after and after and after. It seemed to him that he could never see the two of them, himself and the bear, shadowy in the limbo from which time emerged, becoming time; the old bear absolved of mortality and himself partaking, sharing a little of it, enough of it. And he knew now what he had smelled in the huddled dogs and tasted in his saliva. He recognized fear. *So I will have to see him,* he thought, without dread or even hope. *I will have to look at him.*

It was in June of the next year. He was eleven. They were in camp again, celebrating Major de Spain's and General Compson's birthdays. Although the one had been born in September and the other in the depth of winter and in another decade, they had met for two weeks to fish and shoot squirrels and turkey and run coons and wildcats with the dogs at night. That is, he and Boon Hoggenbeck and the Negroes fished and shot squirrels and ran the coons and cats, because the proved hunters, not only Major de Spain and old General Compson, who spent those two weeks sitting in a rocking chair before a tremendous iron pot of Brunswick stew, stirring and tasting, with old Ash to quarrel with about how he was making it and Tennie's Jim to pour whiskey from the demijohn into the tin dipper from which he drank it, but even the boy's father and Walter Ewell, who were still young enough, scorned such, other than shooting the wild gobblers with pistols for wagers on their marksmanship.

Or, that is, his father and the others believed he was hunting squirrels. Until the third day, he thought that Sam Fathers be-

lieved that too. Each morning he would leave the camp right
after breakfast. He had his own gun now, a Christmas present.
He went back to the tree beside the bayou where he had stood
that morning. Using the compass which old General Compson
had given him, he ranged from that point; he was teaching himself to be a better-than-fair woodsman without knowing he was
doing it. On the second day he even found the gutted log
where he had first seen the crooked print. It was almost completely crumbled now, healing with unbelievable speed, a passionate and almost visible relinquishment, back into the earth
from which the tree had grown.

He ranged the summer woods now, green with gloom; if anything, actually dimmer than in November's gray dissolution,
where, even at noon, the sun fell only in intermittent dappling
upon the earth, which never completely dried out and which
crawled with snakes—moccasins and water snakes and rattlers,
themselves the color of the dappling gloom, so that he would
not always see them until they moved, returning later and later,
first day, second day, passing in the twilight of the third evening
the little log pen enclosing the log stable where Sam was putting
up the horses for the night.

"You ain't looked right yet," Sam said.

He stopped. For a moment he didn't answer. Then he said
peacefully, in a peaceful rushing burst as when a boy's miniature
dam in a little brook gives way, "All right. But how? I went
to the bayou. I even found that log again. I—"

"I reckon that was all right. Likely he's been watching you.
You never saw his foot?"

"I," the boy said—"I didn't—I never thought—"

"It's the gun," Sam said. He stood beside the fence motionless—the old man, the Indian, in the battered faded overalls and
the five-cent straw hat which in the Negro's race had been the
badge of his enslavement and was now the regalia of his freedom.

The camp—the clearing, the house, the barn and its tiny lot with which Major de Spain in his turn had scratched punily and evanescently at the wilderness—faded in the dusk, back into the immemorial darkness of the woods. *The gun,* the boy thought. *The gun.*

"Be scared," Sam said. "You can't help that. But don't be afraid. Ain't nothing in the woods going to hurt you unless you corner it, or it smells that you are afraid. A bear or a deer, too, has got to be scared of a coward the same as a brave man has got to be."

The gun, the boy thought.

"You will have to choose," Sam said.

He left the camp before daylight, long before Uncle Ash would wake in his quilts on the kitchen floor and start the fire for breakfast. He had only the compass and a stick for snakes. He could go almost a mile before he would begin to need the compass. He sat on a log, the invisible compass in his invisible hand, while the secret night sounds, fallen still at his movements, scurried again and then ceased for good, and the owls ceased and gave over to the waking of day birds, and he could see the compass. Then he went fast yet still quietly; he was becoming better and better as a woodsman, still without having yet realized it.

He jumped a doe and a fawn at sunrise, walked them out of the bed, close enough to see them—the crash of undergrowth, the white scut, the fawn scudding behind her faster than he had believed it could run. He was hunting right, upwind, as Sam had taught him; not that it mattered now. He had left the gun; of his own will and relinquishment he had accepted not a gambit, not a choice, but a condition in which not only the bear's heretofore inviolable anonymity but all the old rules and balances of hunter and hunted had been abrogated. He would not even be afraid, not even in the moment when the fear would take him completely—blood, skin, bowels, bones, memory from the long time before it became his memory—all save that thin, clear, immortal lucidity which alone differed him from this bear and from all the other bear and deer he would ever kill in the humility and pride of his skill and endurance, to which Sam had spoken when he leaned in the twilight on the lot fence yesterday.

By noon he was far beyond the little bayou, farther into the new and alien country than he had ever been. He was traveling now not only by the old, heavy, biscuit-thick silver watch which had belonged to his grandfather. When he stopped at last, it was for the first time since he had risen from the log at dawn when he could see the compass. It was far enough. He had left the camp nine hours ago; nine hours from now, dark would have already been an hour old. But he didn't think that. He thought, *All right. Yes. But what?* and stood for a moment, alien and small in the green and topless solitude, answering his own question before it had formed and ceased. It was the watch, the compass, the stick—the three lifeless mechanicals with which for nine hours he had fended the wilderness off; he hung the watch and compass carefully on a bush and leaned the stick beside them and relinquished completely to it.

He had not been going very fast for the last two or three hours. He went no faster now, since distance would not matter even if he could have gone fast. And he was trying to keep a bearing on the tree where he had left the compass, trying to complete a circle which would bring him back to it or at least intersect itself, since direction would not matter now either. But the tree was not there, and he did as Sam had schooled him— made the next circle in the opposite direction, so that the two patterns would bisect somewhere, but crossing no print of his own feet, finding the tree at last, but in the wrong place—no bush, no compass, no watch—and the tree not even the tree, because there was a down log beside it and he did what Sam Fathers had told him was the next thing and the last.

As he sat down on the log he saw the crooked print—the warped, tremendous, two-toed indentation which, even as he watched it, filled with water. As he looked up, the wilderness coalesced, solidified—the glade, the tree he sought, the bush, the watch and the compass glinting where a ray of sunshine touched them. Then he saw the bear. It did not emerge, appear; it was just there, immobile, solid, fixed in the hot dappling of the green and windless noon, not as big as he had dreamed it, but as big as he had expected it, bigger, dimensionless, against the dappled obscurity, looking at him where he sat quietly on the log and looked back at it.

Then it moved. It made no sound. It did not hurry. It crossed the glade, walking for an instant into the full glare of the sun; when it reached the other side it stopped again and looked back at him across one shoulder while his quiet breathing inhaled and exhaled three times.

Then it was gone. It didn't walk into the woods, the under-growth. It faded, sank back into the wilderness as he had watched a fish, a huge old bass, sink and vanish into the dark depths of its pool without even any movement of its fins.

He thought, *It will be next fall.* But it was not next fall, nor the next nor the next. He was fourteen then. He had killed his buck, and Sam Fathers had marked his face with the hot blood, and in the next year he killed a bear. But even before that accolade he had become as competent in the woods as many grown men with the same experience; by his four-teenth year he was a better woodsman than most grown men with more. There was no territory within thirty miles of the camp that he did not know—bayou, ridge, brake, landmark, tree and path. He could have led anyone to any point in it without deviation, and brought them out again. He knew the game trails that even Sam Fathers did not know; in his

thirteenth year he found a buck's bedding place, and unbeknown to his father he borrowed Walter Ewell's rifle and
lay in wait at dawn and killed the buck when it walked back
to the bed, as Sam had told him how the old Chickasaw
fathers did.

But not the old bear, although by now he knew its foot-
prints better than he did his own, and not only the crooked
one. He could see any one of the three sound ones and distinguish it from any other, and not only by its size. There
were other bears within these thirty miles which left tracks
almost as large, but this was more than that. If Sam Fathers
had been his mentor and the back-yard rabbits and squirrels
at home his kindergarten, then the wilderness the old bear
ran was his college, the old male bear itself, so long unwifed
and childless as to have become its own ungendered progeni-
tor, was his alma mater. But he never saw it.

He could find the crooked print now almost whenever he
liked, fifteen or ten or five miles, or sometimes nearer the
camp than that. Twice while on stand during the three
years he heard the dogs strike its trail by accident; on the second time they jumped it seemingly, the voices high, abject,
almost human in hysteria, as on that first morning two years
ago. But not the bear itself. He would remember that noon
three years ago, the glade, himself and the bear fixed during
that moment in the windless and dappled blaze, and it would
seem to him that it had never happened, that he had dreamed
that too. But it had happened. They had looked at each other,
they had emerged from the wilderness old as earth, synchronized
to the instant by something more than the blood that moved the
flesh and bones which bore them, and touched, pledged something, affirmed, something more lasting than the frail web of
bones and flesh which any accident could obliterate.

Then he saw it again. Because of the very fact that he thought of nothing else, he had forgotten to look for it. He was still hunting with Walter Ewell's rifle. He saw it cross the end of a long blow-down, a corridor where a tornado had swept, rushing through rather than over the tangle of trunks and branches as a locomotive would have, faster than he had ever believed it could move, almost as fast as a deer even, because a deer would have spent most of that time in the air, faster than he could bring the rifle sights up with it. And now he knew what had been wrong during all the three years. He sat on a log, shaking and trembling as if he had never seen the woods before nor anything that ran them, wondering with incredulous amazement how he could have forgotten the very thing which Sam Fathers had told him and which the bear itself had proved the next day and had now returned after three years to reaffirm.

And now he knew what Sam Fathers had meant about the right dog, a dog in which size would mean less than nothing. So when he returned alone in April—school was out then, so that the sons of farmers could help with the land's planting, and at last his father had granted him permission, on his promise to be back in four days—he had the dog. It was his own, a mongrel of the sort called by Negroes a fyce, a ratter, itself not much bigger than a rat and possessing that bravery which had long since stopped being courage and had become foolhardiness.

It did not take four days. Alone again, he found the trail on the first morning. It was not a stalk; it was an ambush. He timed the meeting almost as if it were an appointment with a human being. Himself holding the fyce muffled in a feed sack and Sam Fathers with two of the hounds on a piece of a plowline rope, they lay down wind of the trail at dawn of the second morning. They were so close that the bear turned without even running, as if in surprised amazement at the shrill and frantic uproar of the released fyce, turning at bay against the trunk of a tree, on its hind feet; it seemed to the boy that it would never stop rising, taller and taller, and even the two hounds seemed to take a desperate and despairing courage from the fyce, following it as it went in.

Then he realized that the fyce was actually not going to stop. He flung, threw the gun away, and ran; when he overtook and grasped the frantically pin-wheeling little dog, it seemed to him that he was directly under the bear.

He could smell it, strong and hot and rank. Sprawling, he looked up to where it loomed and towered over him like a cloudburst and colored like a thunderclap, quite familiar, peacefully and even lucidly familiar, until he remembered: This was the way he had used to dream about it. Then it was gone. He didn't see it go. He knelt, holding the frantic fyce with both hands, hearing the abashed wailing of the hounds drawing farther and farther away, until Sam came up. He carried the gun. He laid it down quietly beside the boy and stood looking down at him.

"You've done seed him twice now with a gun in your hands," he said. "This time you couldn't have missed him."

The boy rose. He still held the fyce. Even in his arms and clear of the ground, it yapped frantically, straining and surging after the fading uproar of the two hounds like a tangle of wire springs. He was panting a little, but he was neither shaking nor trembling now.

"Neither could you!" he said. "You had the gun! Neither did you!"

"And you didn't shoot," his father said. "How close were you?"

"I don't know, sir," he said. "There was a big wood tick inside his right hind leg. I saw that. But I didn't have the gun then."

"But you didn't shoot when you had the gun," his father said. "Why?"

But he didn't answer, and his father didn't wait for him to, rising and crossing the room, across the pelt of the bear which the boy had killed two years ago and the larger one which his father had killed before he was born, to the bookcase beneath the mounted head of the boy's first buck. It was the room which his father called the office, from which all the plantation business was transacted; in it for the fourteen years of his life he had heard the best of all talking. Major de Spain would be there and sometimes old General Compson, and Walter Ewell and Boon Hoggenback and Sam Fathers and Tennie's Jim, too, were hunters, knew the woods and what ran them.

He would hear it, not talking himself but listening—the wilderness, the big woods, bigger and older than any recorded document of white man fatuous enough to believe he had bought any fragment of it or Indian ruthless enough to pretend that any fragment of it had been his to convey. It was of the men, not white nor black nor red, but men, hunters with the will and hardihood to endure and the humility and skill to survive, and the dogs and the bear and deer juxtaposed and reliefed against it, ordered and compelled by and within the wilderness in the ancient and unremitting contest by the ancient and immitigable rules which voided all regrets and brooked no quarter, the voices quiet and weighty and deliberate for retrospection and recollection and exact remembering, while he squatted in the blazing firelight as Tennie's Jim squatted, who stirred only to put more wood on the fire and to pass the bottle from one glass to another. Because the bottle was always present, so that after a while it seemed to him that those fierce instants of heart and brain and courage and wiliness and speed were concentrated and distilled into that brown liquor which not women, not boys and children, but only hunters drank,

drinking not of the blood they had spilled but some con-
densation of the wild immortal spirit, drinking it moderately,
humbly even, not with the pagan's base hope of acquiring the
virtues of cunning and strength and speed, but in salute to them.

His father returned with the book and sat down again
and opened it. "Listen," he said. He read the five stanzas
aloud, his voice quiet and deliberate in the room where there
was no fire now because it was already spring. Then he
looked up. The boy watched him. "All right," his father
said. "Listen." He read again, but only the second stanza
this time, to the end of it, the last two lines, and closed the
book and put it on the table beside him. "She cannot fade,
though thou hast not thy bliss, forever wilt thou love, and
she be fair," he said.

"He's talking about a girl," the boy said.

"He had to talk about something," his father said. Then
he said, "He was talking about truth. Truth doesn't change.
Truth is one thing. It covers all things which touch the heart
—honor and pride and pity and justice and courage and love.
Do you see now?"

He didn't know. Somehow it was simpler than that. There
was an old bear, fierce and ruthless, not merely just to stay
alive, but with the fierce pride of liberty and freedom, proud
enough of the liberty and freedom to see it threatened without fear or even alarm; nay, who at times even seemed deliberately to put that freedom and liberty in jeopardy in order to
savor them, to remind his old strong bones and flesh to keep
supple and quick to defend and preserve them. There was an
old man, son of a Negro slave and an Indian king, inheritor
on the one side of the long chronicle of a people who had
learned humility through suffering, and pride through the endurance which survived the suffering and injustice, and on the
other side, the chronicle of a people even longer in the land

than the first, yet who no longer existed in the land at all save
in the solitary brotherhood of an old Negro's alien blood and
the wild and invincible spirit of an old bear. There was a
boy who wished to learn humility and pride in order to become
skillful and worthy in the woods, who suddenly found himself
becoming so skillful so rapidly that he feared he would never
become worthy because he had not learned humility and pride,
although he had tried to, until one day and as suddenly he
discovered that an old man who could not have defined either
had led him, as though by the hand, to that point where an
old bear and a little mongrel of a dog showed him that, by
possessing one thing other, he would possess them both.

And a little dog, nameless and mongrel and many-fathered,
grown, yet weighing less than six pounds, saying as if to itself,
"I can't be dangerous, because there's nothing much smaller
than I am; I can't be fierce, because they would call it just a
noise; I can't be humble, because I'm already too close to the
ground to genuflect; I can't be proud, because I wouldn't be
near enough to it for anyone to know who was casting the
shadow, and I don't even know that I'm not going to heaven,
because they have already decided that I don't possess an immortal soul. So all I can be is brave. But it's all right. I can
be that, even if they still call it just noise."

That was all. It was simple, much simpler than somebody
talking in a book about youth and a girl he would never need
to grieve over, because he could never approach any nearer her
and would never have to get any farther away. He had heard
about a bear, and finally got big enough to trail it, and he
trailed it four years and at last met it with a gun in his hands
and he didn't shoot. Because a little dog— But he could have
shot long before the little dog covered the twenty yards to
where the bear waited, and Sam Fathers could have shot at
any time during that interminable minute while Old Ben stood

on his hind feet over them. He stopped. His father was watching him gravely across the spring-rife twilight of the room; when he spoke, his words were as quiet as the twilight, too, not loud, because they did not need to be because they would last. "Courage, and honor, and pride," his father said, "and pity, and love of justice and of liberty. They all touch the heart, and what the heart holds to becomes truth, as far as we know the truth. Do you see now?"

Sam, and Old Ben, and Nip, he thought. And himself too. He had been all right too. His father had said so. "Yes, sir," he said.

THE PUPIL

by HENRY JAMES

THE POOR young man hesitated and procrastinated: it cost him such an effort to broach the subject of terms, to speak of money to a person who spoke only of feelings and, as it were, of the aristocracy. Yet he was unwilling to take leave, treating his engagement as settled, without some more conventional glance in that direction than he could find an opening for in the manner of the large affable lady who sat there drawing a pair of soiled *gants de Suède* through a fat jewelled hand and, at once pressing and gliding, repeated over and over everything but the thing he would have liked to hear. He would have liked to hear the figure of his salary; but just as he was nervously about to sound that note the little boy came back—the little boy Mrs. Moreen had sent out of the room to fetch her fan. He came back without the fan, only with the casual observation that he couldn't find it. As he dropped this cynical confession he looked straight and hard at the candidate for the honour of taking his education in hand. This personage reflected somewhat grimly that the first thing he should have to teach his little charge would be to appear to address himself to his mother when he spoke to her—especially not to make her such an improper answer as that.

When Mrs. Moreen bethought herself of this pretext for getting rid of their companion Pemberton supposed it was precisely to approach the delicate subject of his remuneration. But it

333

had been only to say some things about her son that it was
better a boy of eleven shouldn't catch. They were extravagantly
to his advantage save when she lowered her voice to sigh, tapping
her left side familiarly, "And all over-clouded by *this,* you know;
all at the mercy of a weakness—!" Pemberton gathered that the
weakness was in the region of the heart. He had known the
poor child was not robust: this was the basis on which he had
been invited to treat, through an English lady, an Oxford acquaintance, then at Nice, who happened to know both his needs
and those of the amiable American family looking out for something really superior in the way of a resident tutor.

The young man's impression of his prospective pupil, who
had come into the room as if to see for himself the moment
Pemberton was admitted, was not quite the soft solicitation the
visitor had taken for granted. Morgan Moreen was somehow
sickly without being "delicate," and that he looked intelligent—
it is true Pemberton wouldn't have enjoyed his being stupid—
only added to the suggestion that, as with his big mouth and big
ears he really couldn't be called pretty, he might too utterly fail
to please. Pemberton was modest, was even timid; and the
chance that his small scholar would prove cleverer than himself
had quite figured, to his anxiety, among the dangers of an un-
tried experiment. He reflected, however, that these were risks
one had to run when one accepted a position, as it was called, in
a private family; when as yet one's university honours had, pe-
cuniarily speaking, remained barren. At any rate when Mrs.
Moreen got up as to intimate that, since it was understood he
would enter upon his duties within the week she would let him
off now, he succeeded, in spite of the presence of the child, in
squeezing out a phrase about the rate of payment. It was not
the fault of the conscious smile which seemed a reference to the
lady's expensive identity, it was not the fault of this demonstration, which had, in a sort, both vagueness and point, if the allu-

sion didn't sound rather vulgar. This was exactly because she became still more gracious to reply: "Oh I can assure you that all that will be quite regular."

Pemberton only wondered, while he took up his hat, what "all that" was to amount to—people had such different ideas. Mrs. Moreen's words, however, seemed to commit the family to a pledge definite enough to elicit from the child a strange little comment in the shape of the mocking foreign ejaculation "Oh la-la!"

Pemberton, in some confusion, glanced at him as he walked slowly to the window with his back turned, his hands in his pockets and the air in his elderly shoulders of a boy who didn't play. The young man wondered if he should be able to teach him to play, though his mother had said it would never do and that this was why school was impossible. Mrs. Moreen exhibited no discomfiture; she only continued blandly: "Mr. Moreen will be delighted to meet your wishes. As I told you, he has been called to London for a week. As soon as he comes back you shall have it out with him."

This was so frank and friendly that the young man could only reply, laughing as his hostess laughed: "Oh I don't imagine we shall have much of a battle."

"They'll give you anything you like," the boy remarked unexpectedly, returning from the window. "We don't mind what anything costs—we live awfully well."

"My darling, you're too quaint!" his mother exclaimed, putting out to caress him a practised but ineffectual hand. He slipped out of it, but looked with intelligent innocent eyes at Pemberton, who had already had time to notice that from one moment to the other his small satiric face seemed to change its time of life. At this moment it was infantine, yet it appeared also to be under the influence of curious intuitions and knowledges. Pemberton rather disliked precocity and was disappointed

to find gleams of it in a disciple not yet in his teens. Nevertheless he divined on the spot that Morgan wouldn't prove a bore.
He would prove on the contrary a source of agitation. This
idea held the young man, in spite of a certain repulsion.

"You pompous little person! We're not extravagant!" Mrs.
Moreen gaily protested, making another unsuccessful attempt
to draw the boy to her side. "You must know what to expect,"
she went on to Pemberton.

"The less you expect the better!" her companion interposed.
"But we *are* people of fashion."

"Only so far as *you* make us so!" Mrs. Moreen tenderly
mocked. "Well then, on Friday—don't tell me you're superstitious—and mind you don't fail us. Then you'll see us all.
I'm so sorry the girls are out. I guess you'll like the girls. And,
you know, I've another son, quite different from this one."

"He tries to imitate me," Morgan said to their friend.

"He tries? Why he's twenty years old!" cried Mrs. Moreen.

"You're very witty," Pemberton remarked to the child—a
proposition his mother echoed with enthusiasm, declaring Morgan's sallies to be the delight of the house.

The boy paid no heed to this; he only enquired abruptly of
the visitor, who was surprised afterwards that he hadn't struck
him as offensively forward: "Do you *want* very much to come?"

"Can you doubt it after such a description of what I shall
hear?" Pemberton replied. Yet he didn't want to come at all;
he was coming because he had to go somewhere, thanks to
the collapse of his fortune at the end of a year abroad spent on
the system of putting his scant patrimony into a single full wave
of experience. He had had his full wave but couldn't pay the
score at his inn. Moreover he had caught in the boy's eyes the
glimpse of a far-off appeal.

"Well, I'll do the best I can for you," said Morgan; with which
he turned away again. He passed out of one of the long win-

dows; Pemberton saw him go and lean on the parapet of the
terrace. He remained there while the young man took leave of
his mother, who, on Pemberton's looking as if he expected a
farewell from him, interposed with: "Leave him, leave him; he's
so strange!" Pemberton supposed her to fear something he
might say. "He's a genius—you'll love him," she added. "He's
much the most interesting person in the family." And before
he could invent some civility to oppose to this she wound up
with: "But we're all good, you know!"

"He's a genius—you'll love him!" were words that recurred
to our aspirant before the Friday, suggesting among many
things that geniuses were not invariably lovable. However, it
was all the better if there was an element that would make
tutorship absorbing: he had perhaps taken too much for granted
it would only disgust him. As he left the villa after his interview he looked up at the balcony and saw the child leaning
over it. "We shall have great larks!" he called up.

Morgan hung fire a moment and then gaily returned: "By
the time you come back I shall have thought of something
witty!"

This made Pemberton say to himself "After all he's rather
nice."

II

On the Friday he saw them all, as Mrs. Moreen had promised,
for her husband had come back and the girls and the other son
were at home. Mr. Moreen had a white moustache, a confiding
manner and, in his buttonhole, the ribbon of a foreign order—
bestowed, as Pemberton eventually learned, for services. For
what services he never clearly ascertained: this was a point—one
of a large number—that Mr. Moreen's manner never confided.
What it emphatically did confide was that he was even more a
man of the world than you might first make out. Ulick, the

firstborn, was in visible training for the same profession—under the disadvantage as yet, however, of a buttonhole but feebly floral and a moustache with no pretensions to type. The girls had hair and figures and manners and small fat feet, but had never been out alone. As for Mrs. Moreen Pemberton saw on a nearer view that her elegance was intermittent and her parts didn't always match. Her husband, as she had promised, met with enthusiasm Pemberton's ideas in regard to a salary. The young man had endeavoured to keep these stammerings modest, and Mr. Moreen made it no secret that *he* found them wanting in "style." He further mentioned that he aspired to be intimate with his children, to be their best friend, and that he was always looking out for them. That was what he went off for, to London and other places—to look out; and this vigilance was the theory of life, as well as the real occupation, of the whole family. They all looked out, for they were very frank on the subject of its being necessary. They desired it to be understood that they were earnest people, and also that their fortune, though quite adequate for earnest people, required the most careful administration. Mr. Moreen, as the parent bird, sought sustenance for the nest. Ulick invoked support mainly at the club, where Pemberton guessed that it was usually served on green cloth. The girls used to do up their hair and their frocks themselves, and our young man felt appealed to to be glad, in regard to Morgan's education, that, though it must naturally be of the best, it didn't cost too much. After a little he *was* glad, forgetting at times his own needs in the interest inspired by the child's character and culture and the pleasure of making easy terms for him.

During the first weeks of their acquaintance Morgan had been as puzzling as a page in an unknown language—altogether different from the obvious little Anglo-Saxons who had misrepresented childhood to Pemberton. Indeed the whole mystic volume in which the boy had been amateurishly bound demanded some practice in translation. To-day, after a considerable interval, there is something phantasmagoric, like a prismatic reflexion or a serial novel, in Pemberton's memory of the queerness of the Moreens. If it were not for a few tangible tokens—a lock of Morgan's hair cut by his own hand, and the half-dozen letters received from him when they were disjoined—the whole episode and the figures peopling it would seem too inconsequent for anything but dreamland. Their supreme quaintness was their success—as it appeared to him for a while at the time; since he had never seen a family so brilliantly equipped for failure. Wasn't it success to have kept him so hatefully long? Wasn't it success to have drawn him in that first morning at déjeuner, the Friday he came—it was enough to *make* one superstitious—so that he utterly committed himself, and this not by calculation or on a signal, but from a happy instinct which made them, like a band of gipsies, work so neatly together? They amused him as much as if they had really been a band of gipsies. He was still young and had not seen much of the world—his English years had been properly arid; therefore the reversed conventions of the Moreens—for they had *their* desperate proprieties—struck him as topsy-turvy. He had encountered nothing like them at Oxford; still less had any such note been struck to his younger American ear during the four years at Yale in which he had richly supposed himself to be reacting against a Puritan strain. The reaction of the Moreens, at any rate, went ever so much further. He had thought himself very sharp that first day in hitting them all off in his mind with the "cosmopolite" label. Later it seemed feeble and colourless—confessedly helplessly provisional.

He yet when he first applied it felt a glow of joy—for an instructor he was still empirical—rise from the apprehension that living with them would really be to see life. Their sociable strangeness was an intimation of that—their chatter of tongues, their gaiety and good humour, their infinite dawdling (they were always getting themselves up, but it took for ever, and Pemberton had once found Mr. Moreen shaving in the drawing-room), their French, their Italian and, cropping up in the foreign fluencies, their cold tough slices of American. They lived on maccaroni and coffee—they had these articles prepared in perfection—but they knew recipes for a hundred other dishes. They overflowed with music and song, were always humming and catching each other up, and had a sort of professional acquaintance with Continental cities. They talked of "good places" as if they had been pickpockets or strolling players. They had at Nice a villa, a carriage, a piano and a banjo, and they went to official parties. They were a perfect calendar of the "days" of their friends, which Pemberton knew them, when they were indisposed, to get out of bed to go to, and which made the week larger than life when Mrs. Moreen talked of them with Paula and Amy. Their initiations gave their new inmate at first an almost dazzling sense of culture. Mrs. Moreen had translated something at some former period—an author whom it made Pemberton feel *borné* never to have heard of. They could imitate Venetian and sing Neapolitan, and when they wanted to say something very particular communicated with each other in an ingenious dialect of their own, an elastic spoken cipher which Pemberton at first took for some *patois* of one of their countries, but which he "caught on to" as he would not have grasped provincial development of Spanish or German.

"It's the family language—Ultramoreen," Morgan explained to him drolly enough; but the boy rarely condescended to use it himself, though he dealt in colloquial Latin as if he had been a little prelate.

Among all the "days" with which Mrs. Moreen's memory was taxed she managed to squeeze in one of her own, which her friends sometimes forgot. But the house drew a frequented air

from the number of fine people who were freely named there
and from several mysterious men with foreign titles and English
clothes whom Morgan called the Princes and who, on sofas with
the girls, talked French very loud—though sometimes with
some oddity of accent—as if to show they were saying nothing
improper. Pemberton wondered how the Princes could ever
propose in that tone and so publicly: he took for granted cyni-
cally that this was what was desired of them. Then he recognised that even for the chance of such an advantage Mrs.
Moreen would never allow Paula and Amy to receive alone.
These young ladies were not at all timid, but it was just the
safeguards that made them so candidly free. It was a household
of Bohemians who wanted tremendously to be Philistines.

In one respect, however, certainly, they achieved no rigour—
they were wonderfully amiable and ecstatic about Morgan. It
was a genuine tenderness, an artless admiration, equally strong
in each. They even praised his beauty, which was small, and
were as afraid of him as if they felt him of finer clay. They
spoke of him as a little angel and a prodigy—they touched on
his want of health with long, vague faces. Pemberton feared
at first an extravagance that might make him hate the boy, but
before this happened he had become extravagant himself. Later,
when he had grown rather to hate the others, it was a bribe to
patience for him that they were at any rate nice about Morgan,
going on tiptoe if they fancied he was showing symptoms, and
even giving up somebody's "day" to procure him a pleasure.
Mixed with this too was the oddest wish to make him independent, as if they had felt themselves not good enough for
him. They passed him over to the new members of their circle
very much as if wishing to force some charity of adoption on
so free an agent and get rid of their own charge. They were
delighted when they saw Morgan take so to his kind playfellow,
and could think of no higher praise for the young man. It was

strange how they contrived to reconcile the appearance, and indeed the essential fact, of adoring the child with their eagerness to wash their hands of him. Did they want to get rid of him before he should find them out? Pemberton was finding them out month by month. The boy's fond family, however this might be, turned their backs with exaggerated delicacy, as if to avoid the reproach of interfering. Seeing in time how little he had in common with them—it was by *them* he first observed it; they proclaimed it with complete humility—his companion was moved to speculate on the mysteries of transmission, the far jumps of heredity. Where his detachment from most of the things they represented had come from was more than an observer could say—it certainly had burrowed under two or three generations.

As for Pemberton's own estimate of his pupil, it was a good while before he got the point of view, so little had he been prepared for it by the smug young barbarians to whom the tradition of tutorship, as hitherto revealed to him, had been adjusted. Morgan was scrappy and surprising, deficient in many properties supposed common to the *genus* and abounding in others that were the portion only of the supernaturally clever. One day his friend made a great stride: it cleared up the question to perceive that Morgan *was* supernaturally clever and that, though the formula was temporarily meagre, this would be the only assumption on which one could successfully deal with him. He had the general quality of a child for whom life had not been simplified by school, a kind of home-bred sensibility which might have been bad for himself but was charming for others, and a whole range of refinement and perception—little musical vibrations as taking as picked-up airs—begotten by wandering about Europe at the tail of his migratory tribe. This might not have been an education to recommend in advance, but its results with so special a subject were as appreciable as the marks

on a piece of fine porcelain. There was at the same time in
him a small strain of stoicism, doubtless the fruit of having had
to begin early to bear pain, which counted for pluck and made
it of less consequence that he might have been thought at
school rather a polyglot little beast. Pemberton indeed quickly
found himself rejoicing that school was out of the question: in
any million of boys it was probably good for all but one, and
Morgan was that millionth. It would have made him comparative and superior—it might have made him really require kicking. Pemberton would try to be school himself—a bigger sem-
inary than five hundred grazing donkeys, so that, winning no
prizes, the boy would remain unconscious and irresponsible and
amusing—amusing, because, though life was already intense in
his childish nature, freshness still made there a strong draught
for jokes. It turned out that even in the still air of Morgan's
various disabilities jokes flourished greatly. He was a pale
lean acute undeveloped little cosmopolite, who liked intellectual
gymnastics and who also, as regards the behaviour of mankind,
had noticed more things than you might suppose, but who
nevertheless had his proper playroom of superstitions, where
he smashed a dozen toys a day.

III

At Nice once, toward evening, as the pair rested in the open
air after a walk, and looked over the sea at the pink western
lights, he said suddenly to his comrade: "Do you like it, you
know—being with us all in this intimate way?"

"My dear fellow, why should I stay if I didn't?"

"How do I know you'll stay? I'm almost sure you won't,
very long."

"I hope you don't mean to dismiss me," said Pemberton.

Morgan debated, looking at the sunset. "I think if I did right I ought to."

"Well, I know I'm supposed to instruct you in virtue; but in that case don't do right."

"You're very young—fortunately," Morgan went on, turning to him again.

"Oh yes, compared with you!"

"Therefore it won't matter so much if you do lose a lot of time."

"That's the way to look at it," said Pemberton accommodatingly.

They were silent a minute; after which the boy asked: "Do you like my father and my mother very much?"

"Dear me, yes. Charming people."

Morgan received this with another silence; then unexpectedly, familiarly, but at the same time affectionately, he remarked: "You're a jolly old humbug!"

For a particular reason the words made our young man change colour. The boy noticed in an instant that he had turned red, whereupon he turned red himself and pupil and master exchanged a longish glance in which there was a consciousness of many more things than are usually touched upon, even tacitly, in such a relation. It produced for Pemberton an embarrassment; it raised in a shadowy form a question—this was the first glimpse of it—destined to play a singular and, as he imagined, owing to the altogether peculiar conditions, an unprecedented part in his intercourse with his little companion. Later, when he found himself talking with the youngster in a way in which few youngsters could ever have been talked with, he thought of that clumsy moment on the bench at Nice as the dawn of an understanding that had broadened. What had added to the clumsiness then was that he thought it his duty to declare to Morgan that he might abuse him, Pemberton, as much as he

liked, but must never abuse his parents. To this Morgan had
the easy retort that he hadn't dreamed of abusing them; which
appeared to be true: it put Pemberton in the wrong.

"Then why am I a humbug for saying *I* think them charming?" the young man asked, conscious of a certain rashness.

"Well—they're not your parents."

"They love you better than anything in the world—never forget that," said Pemberton.

"Is that why you like them so much?"

"They're very kind to me," Pemberton replied evasively.

"You *are* a humbug!" laughed Morgan, passing an arm into
his tutor's. He leaned against him looking off at the sea again
and swinging his long thin legs.

"Don't kick my shins," said Pemberton while he reflected
"Hang it, I can't complain of them to the child!"

"There's another reason too," Morgan went on, keeping his
legs still.

"Another reason for what?"

"Besides their not being your parents."

"I don't understand you," said Pemberton.

"Well, you will before long. All right!"

He did understand fully before long, but he made a fight even
with himself before he confessed it. He thought it the oddest
thing to have a struggle with the child about. He wondered
he didn't hate the hope of the Moreens for bringing the struggle
on. But by the time it began any such sentiment for that scion
was closed to him. Morgan was a special case, and to know
him was to accept him on his own odd terms. Pemberton had
spent his aversion to special cases before arriving at knowledge.
When at last he did arrive his quandary was great. Against
every interest he had attached himself. They would have to
meet things together. Before they went home that evening at
Nice the boy had said, clinging to his arm:

"Well, at any rate you'll hang on to the last."

"To the last?"

"Till you're fairly beaten."

"*You* ought to be fairly beaten!" cried the young man, draw-ing him closer.

IV

A year after he had come to live with them Mr. and Mrs. Moreen suddenly gave up the villa at Nice. Pemberton had got used to suddenness, having seen it practised on a consid-erable scale during two jerky little tours—one in Switzerland the first summer, and the other late in the winter, when they all ran down to Florence and then, at the end of ten days, liking it much less than they had intended, straggled back in mys-terious depression. They had returned to Nice "for ever," as they said; but this didn't prevent their squeezing, one rainy muggy May night, into a second-class railway-carriage—you could never tell by which class they would travel—where Pem-berton helped them to stow away a wonderful collection of bundles and bags. The explanation of this manœuvre was that they had determined to spend the summer "in some bracing place"; but in Paris they dropped into a small furnished apart-ment—a fourth floor in a third-rate avenue, where there was a smell on the staircase and the *portier* was hateful—and passed the next four months in blank indigence.

The better part of this baffled sojourn was for the preceptor and his pupil, who, visiting the Invalides and Notre Dame, the Conciergerie and all the museums, took a hundred remunera-tive rambles. They learned to know their Paris, which was useful, for they came back another year for a longer stay, the general character of which in Pemberton's memory to-day mixes pitiably and confusedly with that of the first. He sees Morgan's shabby knickerbockers—the everlasting pair that didn't match his blouse and that as he grew longer could only grow faded. He remembers the particular holes in his three or four pair of coloured stockings.

Morgan was dear to his mother, but he never was better dressed than was absolutely necessary—partly, no doubt, by his own fault, for he was as indifferent to his appearance as a German philosopher. "My dear fellow, you *are* coming to pieces," Pemberton would say to him in sceptical remonstrance; to which the child would reply, looking at him serenely up and down: "My dear fellow, so are you! I don't want to cast you in the shade." Pemberton could have no rejoinder for this— the assertion so closely represented the fact. If however the deficiencies of his own wardrobe were a chapter by themselves he didn't like his little charge to look too poor. Later he used to say "Well, if we're poor, why, after all, shouldn't we look it?" and he consoled himself with thinking there was something rather elderly and gentlemanly in Morgan's disrepair—it differed from the untidiness of the urchin who plays and spoils his things. He could trace perfectly the degrees by which, in proportion as her little son confined himself to his tutor for society, Mrs. Moreen shrewdly forbore to renew his garments. She did nothing that didn't show, neglected him because he escaped notice, and then, as he illustrated this clever policy, discouraged at home his public appearances. Her position was logical enough—those members of her family who did show had to be showy.

During this period and several others Pemberton was quite aware of how he and his comrade might strike people; wandering languidly through the Jardin des Plantes as if they had nowhere to go, sitting on the winter days in the galleries of the Louvre, so splendidly ironical to the homeless, as if for the advantage of the *calorifère*. They joked about it sometimes: it was the sort of joke that was perfectly within the boy's compass.

They figured themselves as part of the vast vague hand-to-mouth multitude of the enormous city and pretended they were proud of their position in it—it showed them "such a lot of life" and made them conscious of a democratic brotherhood. If Pemberton couldn't feel a sympathy in destitution with his small companion—for after all Morgan's fond parents would never have let him really suffer—the boy would at least feel it with him, so it came to the same thing. He used sometimes to wonder what people would think they were—to fancy they were looked askance at, as if it might be a suspected case of kidnapping. Morgan wouldn't be taken for a young patrician with a preceptor—he wasn't smart enough; though he might pass for his companion's sickly little brother. Now and then he had a five-franc piece, and except once, when they bought a couple of lovely neckties, one of which he made Pemberton accept, they laid it out scientifically in old books. This was sure to be a great day, always spent on the quays, in a rummage of the dusty boxes that garnish the parapets. Such occasions helped them to live, for their books ran low very soon after the beginning of their acquaintance. Pemberton had a good many in England, but he was obliged to write to a friend and ask him kindly to get some fellow to give him something for them.

If they had to relinquish that summer the advantage of the bracing climate the young man couldn't but suspect this failure of the cup when at their very lips to have been the effect of a rude jostle of his own. This had represented his first blow-out, as he called it, with his patrons; his first successful attempt—though there was little other success about it—to bring them to a consideration of his impossible position. As the ostensible eve of a costly journey the moment had struck him as favourable to an earnest protest, the presentation of an ultimatum. Ridiculous as it sounded, he had never yet been able to compass an uninterrupted private interview with the elder pair or with either of them singly. They were always flanked by their elder children, and poor Pemberton usually had his own little charge at his side. He was conscious of its being a house in which the surface of one's delicacy got rather smudged; nevertheless he had preserved the bloom of his scruple against announcing to Mr. and Mrs. Moreen with publicity that he shouldn't be able to go on longer without a little money. He was still simple enough to suppose Ulick and Paula and Amy might not know that since his arrival he had only had a hundred and forty francs; and he was magnanimous enough to wish not to compromise their parents in their eyes. Mr. Moreen now listened to him, as he listened to every one and to every thing, like a man of the world, and seemed to appeal to him—though not of course too grossly— to try and be a little more of one himself. Pemberton recognised in fact the importance of the character—from the advantage it gave Mr. Moreen. He was not even confused or embarrassed, whereas the young man in his service was more so than there was any reason for. Neither was he surprised—at least any more than a gentleman had to be who freely confessed himself a little shocked—though not perhaps strictly at Pemberton.

"We must go into this, mustn't we, dear?" he said to his wife. He assured his young friend that the matter should have his very best attention; and he melted into space as elusively as if, at the door, he were taking an inevitable but deprecatory precedence. When, the next moment, Pemberton found himself alone with Mrs. Moreen it was to hear her say "I see, I see"—stroking the roundness of her chin and looking as if she were only hesitating between a dozen easy remedies. If they didn't make their push Mr. Moreen could at least disappear for several days. During his absence his wife took up the subject again spontaneously, but her contribution to it was merely that she had thought all the while they were getting on so beautifully. Pemberton's reply to this revelation was that unless they immediately put down something on account he would leave them on the spot and for ever. He knew she would wonder how he would get away, and for a moment expected her to enquire. She didn't, for which he was almost grateful to her, so little was he in a position to tell.

"You won't, you *know* you won't—you're too interested," she said. "You *are* interested, you know you are, you dear kind man!" She laughed with almost condemnatory archness, as if it were a reproach—though she wouldn't insist; and flirted a soiled pocket-handkerchief at him.

Pemberton's mind was fully made up to take his step the following week. This would give him time to get an answer to a letter he had dispatched to England. If he did in the event nothing of the sort—that is if he stayed another year and then went away only for three months—it was not merely because before the answer to his letter came (most unsatisfactory when it did arrive) Mr. Moreen generously counted out to him, and again with the sacrifice to "form" of a marked man of the world, three hundred francs in elegant ringing gold. He was irritated to find that Mrs. Moreen was right, that he couldn't at the pinch bear to leave the child. This stood out clearer for the very reason that, the night of his desperate appeal to his patrons, he had seen fully for the first time where he was. Wasn't it another proof of the success with which those patrons practised their arts that they had managed to avert for so long the illuminating flash? It descended on our friend with a breadth of effect which perhaps would have struck a spectator as comical, after he had returned to his little servile room, which looked into a close court where a bare dirty opposite wall took, with the sound of shrill clatter, the reflexion of lighted back windows. He had simply given himself away to a band of adventurers. The idea, the word itself, wore a romantic horror for him—he had always lived on such safe lines. Later it assumed a more interesting, almost a soothing, sense: it pointed a moral, and Pemberton could enjoy a moral. The Moreens were adventurers not merely because they didn't pay their debts, because they lived on society, but because their whole view of life, dim and confused and instinctive, like that of clever colour-blind animals, was speculative and rapacious and mean. Oh they were "respectable," and that only made them more *immondes!* The young man's analysis, while he brooded, put it at last very simply—they were adventurers because they were toadies and snobs. That was the completest account of them—it was the law of their being. Even when this truth became vivid to their ingenious inmate he remained unconscious of how much his mind had been prepared for it by the extraordinary little boy who had now become such a complication in his life. Much less could he then calculate on the information he was still to owe the extraordinary little boy.

v

But it was during the ensuing time that the real problem came up—the problem of how far it was excusable to discuss the turpitude of parents with a child of twelve, of thirteen, of fourteen. Absolutely inexcusable and quite impossible it of course at first appeared; and indeed the question didn't press for some time after Pemberton had received his three hundred francs. They produced a temporary lull, a relief from the sharpest pressure. The young man frugally amended his wardrobe and even had a few francs in his pocket. He thought the Moreens looked at him as if he were almost too smart, as if they ought to take care not to spoil him. If Mr. Moreen hadn't been such a man of the world he would perhaps have spoken of the freedom of such neckties on the part of a subordinate. But Mr. Moreen was always enough a man of the world to let things pass—he had certainly shown that. It was singular how Pemberton guessed that Morgan, though saying nothing about it, knew something had happened. But three hundred francs, especially when one owed money, couldn't last for ever; and when the treasure was gone—the boy knew when it had failed—Morgan did break ground. The party had returned to Nice at the beginning of the winter, but not to the charming villa. They went to an hotel, where they stayed three months, and then moved to another establishment, explaining that they had left the first because, after waiting and waiting, they couldn't get the rooms they wanted. These apartments, the rooms they wanted, were generally very splendid; but fortunately they never *could* get them—fortunately, I mean, for Pemberton, who reflected always that if they had got them there would have been a still scanter educational fund. What Morgan said at last was said suddenly, irrelevantly, when the moment came, in the middle of a lesson, and consisted of the apparently unfeeling words: "You ought to *filer,* you know—you really ought."

Pemberton stared. He had learnt enough French slang from Morgan to know that to *filer* meant to cut sticks. "Ah my dear fellow, don't turn me off!"

Morgan pulled a Greek lexicon toward him—he used a Greek-German—to look out a word, instead of asking it of Pemberton. "You can't go on like this, you know."

"Like what, my boy?"

"You know they don't pay you up," said Morgan, blushing and turning his leaves.

"Don't pay me?" Pemberton stared again and feigned amazement. "What on earth put that into your head?"

"It has been there a long time," the boy replied rummaging his book.

Pemberton was silent, then he went on: "I say, what are you hunting for? They pay me beautifully."

"I'm hunting for the Greek for awful whopper," Morgan dropped.

"Find that rather for gross impertinence and disabuse your mind. What do I want of money?"

"Oh that's another question!"

Pemberton wavered—he was drawn in different ways. The severely correct thing would have been to tell the boy that such a matter was none of his business and bid him go on with his lines. But they were really too intimate for that; it was not the way he was in the habit of treating him; there had been no reason it should be. On the other hand Morgan had quite lighted on the truth—he really shouldn't be able to keep it up much longer; therefore why not let him know one's real motive for forsaking him? At the same time it wasn't decent to abuse to one's pupil the family of one's pupil; it was better to misrepresent than to do that. So in reply to his comrade's last exclamation he just declared, to dismiss the subject, that he had received several payments.

"I say—I say!" the boy ejaculated, laughing.

"That's all right," Pemberton insisted. "Give me your written rendering."

Morgan pushed a copybook across the table, and he began to read the page, but with something running in his head that made it no sense. Looking up after a minute or two he found the child's eyes fixed on him and felt in them something strange. Then Morgan said: "I'm not afraid of the stern reality."

"I haven't yet seen the thing you *are* afraid of—I'll do you that justice!"

This came out with a jump—it was perfectly true—and evidently gave Morgan pleasure. "I've thought of it a long time," he presently resumed.

"Well, don't think of it any more."

The boy appeared to comply, and they had a comfortable

and even an amusing hour. They had a theory that they were very thorough, and yet they seemed always to be in the amusing part of lessons, the intervals between the dull dark tunnels, where there were waysides and jolly views. Yet the morning was brought to a violent end by Morgan's suddenly leaning his arms on the table, burying his head in them and bursting into tears: at which Pemberton was the more startled that, as it then came over him, it was the first time he had ever seen the boy cry and that the impression was consequently quite awful.

The next day, after much thought, he took a decision and, believing it to be just, immediately acted on it. He cornered Mr. and Mrs. Moreen again and let them know that if on the spot they didn't pay him all they owed him he wouldn't only leave their house but would tell Morgan exactly what had brought him to it.

"Oh you *haven't* told him?" cried Mrs. Moreen with a pacifying hand on her well-dressed bosom.

"Without warning you? For what do you take me?" the young man returned.

Mr. and Mrs. Moreen looked at each other; he could see that they appreciated, as tending to their security, his superstition of delicacy, and yet that there was a certain alarm in their relief. "My dear fellow," Mr. Moreen demanded, "what use *can* you have, leading the quiet life we all do, for such a lot of money?" —a question to which Pemberton made no answer, occupied as he was in noting that what passed in the mind of his patrons was something like: "Oh then, if we've felt that the child, dear little angel, has judged us and how he regards us, and we haven't been betrayed, he must have guessed—and in short it's *general!*" an inference that rather stirred up Mr. and Mrs. Moreen, as Pemberton had desired it should. At the same time, if he had supposed his threat would do something towards bring- ing them round, he was disappointed to find them taking for granted—how vulgar their perception *had* been!—that he had already given them away. There was a mystic uneasiness in their parental breasts, and that had been the inferior sense of it. None the less, however, his threat did touch them; for if they had escaped it was only to meet a new danger. Mr. Moreen appealed to him, on every precedent, as a man of the world; but his wife had recourse, for the first time since his domestication with them, to a fine *hauteur,* reminding him that a devoted mother, with her child, had arts that protected her against gross misrepresentation.

"I should misrepresent you grossly if I accused you of common honesty!" our friend replied; but as he closed the door behind him sharply, thinking he had not done himself much good, while Mr. Moreen lighted another cigarette, he heard his hostess shout after him more touchingly:

"Oh you do, you *do,* put the knife to one's throat!"

The next morning, very early, she came to his room. He recognised her knock, but had no hope she brought him money; as to which he was wrong, for she had fifty francs in her hand. She squeezed forward in her dressing-gown, and he received her in his own, between his bath-tub and his bed. He had been tolerably schooled by this time to the "foreign ways" of his hosts. Mrs. Moreen was ardent, and when she was ardent she didn't care what she did; so she now sat down on his bed, his clothes being on the chairs, and, in her preoccupation, forgot, as she glanced round, to be ashamed of giving him such a horrid room. What Mrs. Moreen's ardour now bore upon was the design of persuading him that in the first place she was very good-natured to bring him fifty francs, and that in the second, if he would only see it, he was really too absurd to expect to be *paid.* . Wasn't he paid enough without perpetual money—wasn't he paid by the comfortable luxurious home he enjoyed with them all, without a care, an anxiety, a solitary want? Wasn't he sure of his position, and wasn't that everything to a young man like him, quite unknown, with singularly little to show, the ground of whose exorbitant pretensions it had never been easy to discover? Wasn't he paid above all by the sweet relation he had established with Morgan—quite ideal as from master to pupil—and by the simple privilege of knowing and living with so amazingly gifted a child; than whom really (and she meant literally what she said) there was no better company in Europe? Mrs. Moreen herself took to appealing to him as a man of the world; she said, "Voyons, mon cher," and "My dear man, look here now"; and urged him to be reasonable, putting it before him that it was truly a chance for him. She spoke as if, according as he *should* be reasonable, he would prove himself worthy to be her son's tutor and of the extraordinary confidence they had placed in him.

After all, Pemberton reflected, it was only a difference of theory and the theory didn't matter much. They had hitherto gone on that of remunerated, as now they would go on that of gratuitous, service; but why should they have so many words about it? Mrs. Moreen at all events continued to be convincing; sitting there with her fifty francs she talked and reiterated, as women reiterate, and bored and irritated him, while he leaned against the wall with his hands in the pockets of his wrapper, drawing it together round his legs and looking over the head of his visitor at the grey negations of his window. She wound up with saying: "You see I bring you a definite proposal."

"A definite proposal?"

"To make our relations regular, as it were—to put them on a comfortable footing."

"I see—it's a system," said Pemberton. "A kind of organised blackmail."

Mrs. Moreen bounded up, which was exactly what he wanted. "What do you mean by that?"

"You practise on one's fears—one's fears about the child if one should go away."

"And pray what would happen to him in that event?" she demanded with majesty.

"Why he'd be alone with *you*."

"And pray with whom *should* a child be but with those whom he loves most?"

"If you think that, why don't you dismiss me?"

"Do you pretend he loves you more than he loves *us?*" cried Mrs. Moreen.

"I think he ought to. I make sacrifices for him. Though I've heard of those *you* make I don't see them."

Mrs. Moreen stared a moment; then with emotion she grasped her inmate's hand. *"Will* you make it—the sacrifice?"

He burst out laughing. "I'll see. I'll do what I can. I'll stay a little longer. Your calculation's just—I *do* hate intensely to give him up; I'm fond of him and he thoroughly interests me, in spite of the inconvenience I suffer. You know my situation perfectly. I haven't a penny in the world and, occupied as you see me with Morgan, am unable to earn money."

Mrs. Moreen tapped her undressed arm with her folded bank-note. "Can't you write articles? Can't you translate as *I* do?"

"I don't know about translating; it's wretchedly paid."

"I'm glad to earn what I can," said Mrs. Moreen with prodigious virtue.

"You ought to tell me who you do it for." Pemberton paused a moment, and she said nothing; so he added: "I've tried to turn off some little sketches, but the magazines won't have them—they're declined with thanks."

"You see then you're not such a phœnix," his visitor pointedly smiled—"to pretend to abilities you're sacrificing for our sake."

"I haven't time to do things properly," he ruefully went on. Then as it came over him that he was almost abjectly good-natured to give these explanations he added: "If I stay on longer it must be on one condition—that Morgan shall know distinctly on what footing I am."

Mrs. Moreen demurred. "Surely you don't want to show off to a child?"

"To show *you* off, do you mean?"

Again she cast about, but this time it was to produce a still finer flower. "And *you* talk of blackmail!"

"You can easily prevent it," said Pemberton.

"And *you* talk of practising on fears!" she bravely pushed on.

"Yes, there's no doubt I'm a great scoundrel."

His patroness met his eyes—it was clear she was in straits. Then she thrust out her money at him. "Mr. Moreen desired me to give you this on account."

"I'm much obliged to Mr. Moreen, but we *have* no account."

"You won't take it?"

"That leaves me more free," said Pemberton.

"To poison my darling's mind?" goaned Mrs. Moreen.

"Oh your darling's mind—!" the young man laughed.

She fixed him a moment, and he thought she was going to break out tormentedly, pleadingly: "For God's sake, tell me what *is* in it!" But she checked this impulse—another was stronger. She pocketed the money—the crudity of the alternative was comical—and swept out of the room with the desperate concession: "You may tell him any horror you like!"

VI

A couple of days after this, during which he had failed to profit by so free a permission, he had been for a quarter of an hour walking with his charge in silence when the boy became sociable again with the remark: "I'll tell you how I know it; I know it through Zénobie."

"Zénobie? Who in the world is *she?*"

"A nurse I used to have—ever so many years ago. A charming woman. I liked her awfully, and she liked me."

"There's no accounting for tastes. What is it you know through her?"

"Why what their idea is. She went away because they didn't fork out. She did like me awfully, and she stayed two years. She told me all about it—that at last she could never get her wages. As soon as they saw how much she liked me they stopped giving her anything. They thought she'd stay for nothing—just *because,* don't you know?" And Morgan had a queer little conscious lucid look. "She did stay ever so long—as long as she could. She was only a poor girl. She used to send money to her mother. At last she couldn't afford it any longer, and went away in a fearful rage one night—I mean of course in a rage against *them.* She cried over me tremendously, she hugged me nearly to death. She told me all about it," the boy repeated. "She told me it was their idea. So I guessed, ever so long ago, that they have had the same idea with you."

"Zénobie was very sharp," said Pemberton. "And she made you so."

"Oh that wasn't Zénobie; that was nature. And experience!" Morgan laughed.

"Well, Zénobie was a part of your experience."

"Certainly I was a part of hers, poor dear!" the boy wisely sighed. "And I'm part of yours."

"A very important part. But I don't see how you know I've been treated like Zénobie."

"Do you take me for the biggest dunce you've known?" Morgan asked. "Haven't I been conscious of what we've been through together?"

"What we've been through?"

"Our privations—our dark days."

"Oh our days have been bright enough."

Morgan went on in silence for a moment. Then he said: "My dear chap, you're a hero!"

"Well, you're another!" Pemberton retorted.

"No I'm not, but I ain't a baby. I won't stand it any longer. You must get some occupation that pays. I'm ashamed, I'm ashamed!" quavered the boy with a ring of passion, like some high silver note from a small cathedral chorister, that deeply touched his friend.

"We ought to go off and live somewhere together," the young man said.

"I'll go like a shot if you'll take me."

"I'd get some work that would keep us both afloat," Pemberton continued.

"So would I. Why shouldn't *I* work? I ain't such a beastly little muff as *that* comes to."

"The difficulty is that your parents wouldn't hear of it. They'd never part with you; they worship the ground you tread on. Don't you see the proof of it?" Pemberton developed. "They don't dislike me; they wish me no harm; they're very amiable people; but they're perfectly ready to expose me to any awkwardness in life for your sake."

The silence in which Morgan received his fond sophistry struck Pemberton somehow as expressive. After a moment the child repeated: "You *are* a hero!" Then he added: "They leave me with you altogether. You've all the responsibility. They put me off on you from morning till night. Why then should they object to my taking up with you completely? I'd help you."

"They're not particularly keen about my being helped, and they delight in thinking of you as *theirs*. They're tremendously proud of you."

"I'm not proud of *them*. But you know that," Morgan returned.

"Except for the little matter we speak of they're charming people," said Pemberton, not taking up the point made for his intelligence, but wondering greatly at the boy's own, and especially at this fresh reminder of something he had been conscious of from the first—the strangest thing in his friend's large little composition, a temper, a sensibility, even a private ideal, which made him as privately disown the stuff his people were made of. Morgan had in secret a small loftiness which made him acute about betrayed meanness; as well as a critical sense for the manners immediately surrounding him that was quite without precedent in a juvenile nature, especially when one noted that it had not made this nature "old-fashioned," as the word is of children—quaint or wizened or offensive. It was as if he had been a little gentleman and had paid the penalty by discovering that he was the only such person in his family. This comparison didn't make him vain, but it could make him melancholy and a trifle austere. While Pemberton guessed at these dim young things, shadows of shadows, he was partly drawn on and partly checked, as for a scruple, by the charm of attempting to sound the little cool shallows that were so quickly growing deeper. When he tried to figure to himself the morning twilight of childhood, so as to deal with it safely, he saw it was never fixed, never arrested, that ignorance, at the instant he touched it, was already flushing faintly into knowledge, that there was nothing that at a given moment you could say an intelligent child didn't know. It seemed to him that he himself knew too much to imagine Morgan's simplicity and too little to disembroil his tangle.

The boy paid no heed to his last remark; he only went on: "I'd have spoken to them about their idea, as I call it, long ago, if I hadn't been sure what they'd say."

"And what would they say?"

"Just what they said about what poor Zénobie told me—that it was a horrid dreadful story, that they had paid her every penny they owed her."

"Well, perhaps they had," said Pemberton.

"Perhaps they've paid you!"

"Let us pretend they have, and *n'en parlons plus.*"

"They accused her of lying and cheating"—Morgan stuck to historic truth. "That's why I don't want to speak to them."

"Lest they should accuse me too?" To this Morgan made no answer, and his companion, looking down at him—the boy turned away his eyes, which had filled—saw that he couldn't have trusted himself to utter. "You're right. Don't worry them," Pemberton pursued. "Except for that, they *are* charming people."

"Except for *their* lying and *their* cheating?"

"I say—I say!" cried Pemberton, imitating a little tone of the lad's which was itself an imitation.

"We must be frank, at the last; we *must* come to an understanding," said Morgan with the importance of the small boy who lets himself think he is arranging great affairs—almost playing at shipwreck or at Indians. "I know all about everything."

"I dare say your father has his reasons," Pemberton replied, but too vaguely, as he was aware.

"For lying and cheating?"

"For saving and managing and turning his means to the best account. He has plenty to do with his money. You're an expensive family."

"Yes, I'm very expensive," Morgan concurred in a manner that made his preceptor burst out laughing.

"He's saving for *you,*" said Pemberton. "They think of you in everything they do."

"He might, while he's about it, save a little—" The boy

paused, and his friend waited to hear what. Then Morgan brought out oddly: "A little reputation."

"Oh there's plenty of that. That's all right!"

"Enough of it for the people they know, no doubt. The people they know are awful."

"Do you mean the princes? We mustn't abuse the princes."

"Why not? They haven't married Paula—they haven't married Amy. They only clean out Ulick."

"You *do* know everything!" Pemberton declared.

"No I don't after all. I don't know what they live on, or how they live, or *why* they live! What have they got and how did they get it? Are they rich, are they poor, or have they a *modeste aisance?* Why are they always chiveying me about —living one year like ambassadors and the next like paupers? Who are they, anyway, and what are they? I've thought of all that—I've thought of a lot of things. They're so beastly worldly. That's what I hate most—oh I've *seen* it! All they care about is to make an appearance and to pass for something or other. What the dickens do they want to pass for? What *do* they, Mr. Pemberton?"

"You pause for a reply," said Pemberton, treating the question as a joke, yet wondering too and greatly struck with his mate's intense if imperfect vision. "I haven't the least idea."

"And what good does it do? Haven't I seen the way people treat them—the 'nice' people, the ones they want to know? They'll take anything from them—they'll lie down and be trampled on. The nice ones hate that—they just sicken them. You're the only really nice person we know."

"Are you sure? They don't lie down for me!"

"Well, you shan't lie down for them. You've got to go— that's what you've got to do," said Morgan.

"And what will become of you?"

"Oh I'm growing up. I shall get off before long. I'll see you later."

"You had better let me finish you," Pemberton urged, lending himself to the child's strange superiority.

Morgan stopped in their walk, looking up at him. He had to look up much less than a couple of years before—he had grown, in his loose leanness, so long and high. "Finish me?" he echoed.

"There are such a lot of jolly things we can do together yet. I want to turn you out—I want you to do me credit."

Morgan continued to look at him. "To give you credit—do you mean?"

"My dear fellow, you're too clever to live."

"That's just what I'm afraid you think. No, no; it isn't fair —I can't endure it. We'll separate next week. The sooner it's over the sooner to sleep."

"If I hear of anything—any other chance—I promise to go," Pemberton said.

Morgan consented to consider this. "But you'll be honest," he demanded; "you won't pretend you haven't heard?"

"I'm much more likely to pretend I have."

"But what can you hear of, this way, stuck in a hole with us? You ought to be on the spot, to go to England—you ought to go to America."

"One would think you were *my* tutor!" said Pemberton.

Morgan walked on and after a little had begun again: "Well, now that you know I know and that we look at the facts and keep nothing back—it's much more comfortable, isn't it?"

"My dear boy, it's so amusing, so interesting, that it will surely be quite impossible for me to forego such hours as these."

This made Morgan stop once more. "You *do* keep something back. Oh you're not straight—*I* am!"

"How am I not straight?"

"Oh you've got your idea!"

"My idea?"

"Why that I probably shan't make old—make older—bones, and that you can stick it out till I'm removed."

"You *are* too clever to live!" Pemberton repeated.

"I call it a mean idea," Morgan pursued. "But I shall punish you by the way I hang on."

"Look out or I'll poison you!" Pemberton laughed.

"I'm stronger and better every year. Haven't you noticed that there hasn't been a doctor near me since you came?"

"*I'm* your doctor," said the young man, taking his arm and drawing him tenderly on again.

Morgan proceeded and after a few steps gave a sigh of mingled weariness and relief. "Ah now that we look at the facts it's all right!"

VII

They looked at the facts a good deal after this; and one of the first consequences of their doing so was that Pemberton stuck it out, in his friend's parlance, for the purpose. Morgan made the facts so vivid and so droll, and at the same time so bald and so ugly, that there was fascination in talking them over with him, just as there would have been heartlessness in leaving him alone with them. Now that the pair had such perceptions in common it was useless for them to pretend they didn't judge such people; but the very judgment and the exchange of perceptions created another tie. Morgan had never been so interesting as now that he himself was made plainer by the sidelight of these confidences. What came out in it most was the small fine passion of his pride. He had plenty of that, Pemberton felt—so much that one might perhaps wisely wish for it some early bruises. He would have liked his people to have a spirit and had waked up to the sense of their perpetually eating humble-pie. His mother would consume any amount, and his father would consume even more than his mother. He had a theory that Ulick had wriggled out of an "affair" at Nice: there had once been a flurry at home, a regular panic, after which they all went to bed and took medicine, not to be accounted for on any other supposition. Morgan had a romantic imagination, fed by poetry and history, and he would have liked those who "bore his name"—as he used to say to Pemberton with the humour that made his queer delicacies manly—to carry themselves with an air. But their one idea was to get in with people who didn't want them and to take snubs as if they were honourable scars. Why people didn't want them more he didn't know—that was people's own affair; after all they weren't superficially repulsive, they were a hundred times cleverer than most of the dreary grandees, the "poor swells" they rushed about Europe to catch up with. "After all they *are* amusing—they are!" he used to pronounce with the wisdom of the ages. To which Pemberton always replied: "Amusing—the great Moreen troupe? Why they're altogether delightful; and if it weren't for the hitch that you and I (feeble performers!) make in the *ensemble* they'd carry everything before them."

What the boy couldn't get over was the fact that this particular blight seemed, in a tradition of self-respect, so undeserved and so arbitrary. No doubt people had a right to take the line they liked; but why should *his* people have liked the line of pushing and toadying and lying and cheating? What had their forefathers—all decent folk, so far as he knew—done to them, or what had *he* done to them? Who had poisoned their blood with the fifth-rate social ideal, the fixed idea of making smart acquaintances and getting into the *monde chic,* especially when it was foredoomed to failure and exposure? They showed so what they were after; that was what made the people they wanted not want *them.* And never a wince for dignity, never a throb of shame at looking each other in the face, never any

independence or resentment or disgust. If his father or his
brother would only knock some one down once or twice a year!
Clever as they were they never guessed the impression they
made. They were good-natured, yes—as good-natured as Jews
at the doors of clothing-shops! But was that the model one
wanted one's family to follow? Morgan had dim memories of
an old grandfather, the maternal, in New York, whom he had
been taken across the ocean at the age of five to see: a gentleman with a high neck-cloth and a good deal of pronunciation,
who wore a dress-coat in the morning, which made one wonder
what he wore in the evening, and had, or was supposed to have,
"property" and something to do with the Bible Society. It
couldn't have been but that *he* was a good type. Pemberton
himself remembered Mrs. Clancy, a widowed sister of Mr.
Moreen's, who was as irritating as a moral tale and had paid a
fortnight's visit to the family at Nice shortly after he came to
live with them. She was "pure and refined," as Amy said over
the banjo, and had the air of not knowing what they meant
when they talked, and of keeping something rather important
back. Pemberton judged that what she kept back was an approval of many of their ways; therefore it was to be supposed
that she too was of a good type, and that Mr. and Mrs. Moreen
and Ulick and Paula and Amy might easily have been of a
better one if they would.

But that they wouldn't was more and more perceptible from
day to day. They continued to "chivey," as Morgan called it,
and in due time became aware of a variety of reasons for proceeding to Venice. They mentioned a great many of them—
they were always strikingly frank and had the brightest friendly
chatter, at the late foreign breakfast in especial, before the ladies
had made up their faces, when they leaned their arms on the
table, had something to follow the *demi-tasse,* and, in the heat
of familiar discussion as to what they "really ought" to do, fell

inevitably into the languages in which they could *tutoyer*. Even
Pemberton liked them then; he could endure even Ulick when
he heard him give his little flat voice for the "sweet sea-city."
That was what made him have a sneaking kindness for them—
that they were so out of the workaday world and kept him so
out of it. The summer had waned when, with cries of ecstasy,
they all passed out on the balcony that overhung the Grand
Canal. The sunsets then were splendid and the Dorringtons
had arrived. The Dorringtons were the only reason they hadn't
talked of at breakfast; but the reasons they didn't talk of at
breakfast always came out in the end. The Dorringtons on the
other hand came out very little; or else when they did they
stayed—as was natural—for hours, during which periods Mrs.
Moreen and the girls sometimes called at their hotel (to see if
they had returned) as many as three times running. The gon-
dola was for the ladies, as in Venice too there were "days,"
which Mrs. Moreen knew in their order an hour after she
arrived. She immediately took one herself, to which the Dorringtons never came, though on a certain occasion when Pemberton and his pupil were together at Saint Mark's—where,
taking the best walks they had ever had and haunting a hundred
churches, they spent a great deal of time—they saw the old lord
turn up with Mr. Moreen and Ulick, who showed him the dim
basilica as if it belonged to them. Pemberton noted how much
less, among its curiosities, Lord Dorrington carried himself as
a man of the world; wondering too whether, for such services,
his companions took a fee from him. The autumn at any rate
waned, the Dorringtons departed, and Lord Verschoyle, the
eldest son, had proposed neither for Amy nor for Paula.

One sad November day, while the wind roared round the old
palace and the rain lashed the lagoon, Pemberton, for exercise
and even somewhat for warmth—the Moreens were horribly
frugal about fires; it was a cause of suffering to their inmate—

walked up and down the big bare *sala* with his pupil. The
scagliola floor was cold, the high battered casements shook in the
storm, and the stately decay of the place was unrelieved by a
particle of furniture. Pemberton's spirits were low, and it
came over him that the fortune of the Moreens was now even
lower. A blast of desolation, a portent of disgrace and disaster,
seemed to draw through the comfortless hall. Mr. Moreen and
Ulick were in the Piazza, looking out for something, strolling
drearily, in mackintoshes, under the arcades; but still, in spite
of mackintoshes, unmistakeable men of the world. Paula and
Amy were in bed—it might have been thought they were staying there to keep warm. Pemberton looked askance at the boy
at his side, to see to what extent he was conscious of these dark
omens. But Morgan, luckily for him, was now mainly conscious
of growing taller and stronger and indeed of being in his
fifteenth year. This fact was intensely interesting to him and
the basis of a private theory—which, however, he had imparted
to his tutor—that in a little while he should stand on his own
feet. He considered that the situation would change—that in
short he should be "finished," grown up, producible in the world
of affairs and ready to prove himself of sterling ability. Sharply
as he was capable at times of analysing, as he called it, his life,
there were happy hours when he remained, as he also called it
—and as the name, really, of their right ideal—"jolly" superficial; the proof of which was his fundamental assumption that
he should presently go to Oxford, to Pemberton's college, and
aided and abetted by Pemberton, do the most wonderful things.
It depressed the young man to see how little in such a project
he took account of ways and means: in other connexions he
mostly kept to the measure. Pemberton tried to imagine the
Moreens at Oxford and fortunately failed; yet unless they were
to adopt it as a residence there would be no *modus vivendi* for
Morgan. How could he live without an allowance, and where

was the allowance to come from? He, Pemberton, might live on Morgan; but how could Morgan live on *him?* What was to become of him anyhow? Somehow the fact that he was a big boy now, with better prospects of health, made the question of his future more difficult. So long as he was markedly frail the great consideration he inspired seemed enough of an answer to it. But at the bottom of Pemberton's heart was the recognition of his probably being strong enough to live and not yet strong enough to struggle or to thrive. Morgan himself at any rate was in the first flush of the rosiest consciousness of adolescence, so that the beating of the tempest seemed to him after all but the voice of life and the challenge of fate. He had on his shabby little overcoat, with the collar up, but was enjoying his walk.

It was interrupted at last by the appearance of his mother at the end of the *sala.* She beckoned him to come to her, and while Pemberton saw him, complaisant, pass down the long vista and over the damp false marble, he wondered what was in the air. Mrs. Moreen said a word to the boy and made him go into the room she had quitted. Then, having closed the door after him, she directed her steps swiftly to Pemberton. There *was* something in the air, but his wildest flight of fancy wouldn't have suggested what it proved to be. She signified that she had made a pretext to get Morgan out of the way, and then she enquired—without hesitation—if the young man could favour her with the loan of three louis. While, before bursting into a laugh, he stared at her with surprise, she declared that she was awfully pressed for the money; she was desperate for it—it would save her life.

"Dear lady, *c'est trop fort!*" Pemberton laughed in the manner and with the borrowed grace of idiom that marked the best colloquial, the best anecdotic, moments of his friends themselves.

"Where in the world do you suppose I should get three louis, *du train dont vous allez?*"

"I thought you worked—wrote things. Don't they pay you?"

"Not a penny."

"Are you such a fool as to work for nothing?"

"You ought surely to know that."

Mrs. Moreen stared; then she coloured a little. Pemberton saw she had quite forgotten the terms—if "terms" they could be called—that he had ended by accepting from herself; they had burdened her memory as little as her conscience. "Oh yes, I see what you mean—you've been very nice about that; but why drag it in so often?" She had been perfectly urbane with him ever since the rough scene of explanation in his room the morning he made her accept *his* "terms"—the necessity of his making his case known to Morgan. She had felt no resentment after seeing there was no danger Morgan would take the matter up with her. Indeed, attributing this immunity to the good taste of his influence with the boy, she had once said to Pemberton "My dear fellow, it's an immense comfort you're a gentleman." She repeated this in substance now. "Of course you're a gentleman—that's a bother the less!" Pemberton reminded her that he had not "dragged in" anything that wasn't already in as much as his foot was in his shoe; and she also repeated her prayer that, somewhere and somehow, he would find her sixty francs. He took the liberty of hinting that if he could find them it wouldn't be to lend them to *her*—as to which he consciously did himself injustice, knowing that if he had them he would certainly put them at her disposal. He accused himself, at bottom and not unveraciously, of a fantastic, a demoralised sympathy with her. If misery made strange bedfellows it also made strange sympathies. It was moreover a part of the abasement of living with such people that one had to make vulgar retorts, quite out of one's own tradition of good manners. "Mor-

gan, Morgan, to what pass have I come for you?" he groaned
while Mrs. Moreen floated voluminously down the *sala* again
to liberate the boy, wailing as she went that everything was too
odious.

Before their young friend was liberated there came a thump
at the door communicating with the staircase, followed by the
apparition of a dripping youth who poked in his head. Pemberton recognised him as the bearer of a telegram and recognised the
telegram as addressed to himself. Morgan came back as, after
glancing at the signature—that of a relative in London—he was
reading the words: "Found jolly job for you, engagement to
coach opulent youth on own terms. Come at once." The
answer happily was paid and the messenger waited. Morgan,
who had drawn near, waited too and looked hard at Pemberton; and Pemberton, after a moment, having met his look,
handed him the telegram. It was really by wise looks—they
knew each other so well now—that, while the telegraph-boy, in
his waterproof cape, made a great puddle on the floor, the thing
was settled between them. Pemberton wrote the answer with
a pencil against the frescoed wall, and the messenger departed.
When he had gone the young man explained himself.

"I'll make a tremendous charge; I'll earn a lot of money in a
short time, and we'll live on it."

"Well, I hope the opulent youth will be a dismal dunce—he
probably will," Morgan parenthesised—"and keep you a long
time a-hammering of it in."

"Of course the longer he keeps me the more we shall have
for our old age."

"But suppose *they* don't pay you!" Morgan awfully suggested.

"Oh there are not two such—!" But Pemberton pulled up;
he had been on the point of using too invidious a term. Instead
of this he said "Two such fatalities."

Morgan flushed—the tears came to his eyes. *"Dites toujours*

two such rascally crews!" Then in a different tone he added:
"Happy opulent youth!"

"Not if he's a dismal dunce."

"Oh they're happier then. But you can't have everything,
can you?" the boy smiled.

Pemberton held him fast, hands on his shoulders—he had
never loved him so. "What will become of *you,* what will you
do?" He thought of Mrs. Moreen, desperate for sixty francs.

"I shall become an *homme fait.*" And then as if he recognised
all the bearings of Pemberton's allusion: "I shall get on with
them better when you're not here."

"Ah don't say that—it sounds as if I set you against them!"

"You do—the sight of you. It's all right; you know what I
mean. I shall be beautiful. I'll take their affairs in hand; I'll
marry my sisters."

"You'll marry yourself!" joked Pemberton; as high, rather
tense pleasantry would evidently be the right, or the safest, tone
for their separation.

It was, however, not purely in this strain that Morgan suddenly asked: "But I say—how will you get to your jolly job?
You'll have to telegraph to the opulent youth for money to come
on."

Pemberton bethought himself. "They won't like that, will
they?"

"Oh look out for them!"

Then Pemberton brought out his remedy. "I'll go to the
American Consul; I'll borrow some money of him—just for the
few days, on the strength of the telegram."

Morgan was hilarious. "Show him the telegram—then collar the money and stay!"

Pemberton entered into the joke sufficiently to reply that for
Morgan he was really capable of that; but the boy, growing
more serious, and to prove he hadn't meant what he said, not

only hurried him off to the Consulate—since he was to start that evening, as he had wired to his friend—but made sure of their affair by going with him. They splashed through the tortuous perforations and over the humpbacked bridges, and they passed through the Piazza, where they saw Mr. Moreen and Ulick go into a jeweller's shop. The Consul proved accommodating— Pemberton said it wasn't the letter, but Morgan's grand air— and on their way back they went into Saint Mark's for a hushed ten minutes. Later they took up and kept up the fun of it to the very end; and it seemed to Pemberton a part of that fun that Mrs. Moreen, who was very angry when he had announced her his intention, should charge him, grotesquely and vulgarly and in reference to the loan she had vainly endeavoured to effect, with bolting lest they should "get something out" of him. On the other hand he had to do Mr. Moreen and Ulick the justice to recognise that when on coming in *they* heard the cruel news they took it like perfect men of the world.

VIII

When he got at work with the opulent youth, who was to be taken in hand for Balliol, he found himself unable to say if this aspirant had really such poor parts or if the appearance were only begotten of his own long association with an intensely living little mind. From Morgan he heard half a dozen times: the boy wrote charming young letters, a patchwork of tongues, with indulgent postscripts in the family Volapuk and, in little squares and rounds and crannies of the text, the drollest illustrations—letters that he was divided between the impulse to show his present charge as a vain, a wasted incentive, and the sense of something in them that publicity would profane. The opulent youth went up in due course and failed to pass; but it seemed to add to the presumption that brilliancy was not ex-

pected of him all at once that his parents, condoning the lapse,
which they good-naturedly treated as little as possible as if it
were Pemberton's, should have sounded the rally again, begged
the young coach to renew the siege.

The young coach was now in a position to lend Mrs. Moreen
three louis, and he sent her a post-office order even for a larger
amount. In return for this favour he received a frantic scribbled
line from her: "Implore you to come back instantly—Morgan
dreadfully ill." They were on the rebound, once more in Paris
—often as Pemberton had seen them depressed he had never
seen them crushed—and communication was therefore rapid.
He wrote to the boy to ascertain the state of his health, but
awaited the answer in vain. He accordingly, after three days,
took an abrupt leave of the opulent youth and, crossing the
Channel, alighted at the small hotel, in the quarter of the
Champs Elysées, of which Mrs. Moreen had given him the
address. A deep if dumb dissatisfaction with this lady and her
companions bore him company: they couldn't be vulgarly honest, but they could live at hotels, in velvety *entresols,* amid a
smell of burnt pastilles, surrounded by the most expensive city
in Europe. When he had left them in Venice it was with an
irrepressible suspicion that something was going to happen; but
the only thing that could have taken place was again their masterly retreat. "How is he? where is he?" he asked of Mrs.
Moreen; but before she could speak these questions were answered by the pressure round his neck of a pair of arms, in
shrunken sleeves, which still were perfectly capable of an ef-
fusive young foreign squeeze.

"Dreadfully ill—I don't see it!" the young man cried. And
then to Morgan: "Why on earth didn't you relieve me? Why
didn't you answer my letter?"

Mrs. Moreen declared that when she wrote he was very bad,
and Pemberton learned at the same time from the boy that he

had answered every letter he had received. This led to the clear
inference that Pemberton's note had been kept from him so that
the game to be practised should not be interfered with. Mrs.
Moreen was prepared to see the fact exposed, as Pemberton
saw the moment he faced her that she was prepared for a good
many other things. She was prepared above all to maintain that
she had acted from a sense of duty, that she was enchanted she
had got him over, whatever they might say, and that it was useless of him to pretend he didn't know in all his bones that his
place at such a time was with Morgan. He had taken the boy
away from them and now had no right to abandon him. He
had created for himself the gravest responsibilities and must at
least abide by what he had done.

"Taken him away from you?" Pemberton exclaimed indignantly.

"Do it—do it for pity's sake; that's just what I want. I
can't stand *this*—and such scenes. They're awful frauds—poor
dears!" These words broke from Morgan, who had intermitted
his embrace, in a key which made Pemberton turn quickly to
him and see that he had suddenly seated himself, was breathing
in great pain and was very pale.

"*Now* do you say he's not in a state, my precious pet?" shouted
his mother, dropping on her knees before him with clasped hands,
but touching him no more than if he had been a gilded idol.
"It will pass—it's only for an instant; but don't say such dreadful things!"

"I'm all right—all right," Morgan panted to Pemberton,
whom he sat looking up at with a strange smile, his hands resting on either side on the sofa.

"Now do you pretend I've been dishonest, that I've deceived?"
Mrs. Moreen flashed at Pemberton as she got up.

"It isn't *he* says it, it's I!" the boy returned, apparently easier
but sinking back against the wall; while his restored friend,

who had sat down beside him, took his hand and bent over him.

"Darling child, one does what one can; there are so many things to consider," urged Mrs. Moreen. "It's his *place*—his only place. You see *you* think it is now."

"Take me away—take me away," Morgan went on, smiling to Pemberton with his white face.

"Where shall I take you, and how—oh *how,* my boy?" the young man stammered, thinking of the rude way in which his friends in London held that, for his convenience, with no assurance of prompt return, he had thrown them over; of the just resentment with which they would already have called in a successor, and of the scant help to finding fresh employment that resided for him in the grossness of his having failed to pass his pupil.

"Oh we'll settle that. You used to talk about it," said Morgan. "If we can only go all the rest's a detail."

"Talk about it as much as you like, but don't think you can attempt it. Mr. Moreen would never consent—it would be so *very* hand-to-mouth," Pemberton's hostess beautifully explained to him. Then to Morgan she made it clearer: "It would destroy our peace, it would break our hearts. Now that he's back it will be all the same again. You'll have your life, your work and your freedom, and we'll all be happy as we used to be. You'll bloom and grow perfectly well, and we won't have any more silly experiments, will we? They're too absurd. It's Mr. Pemberton's place—every one in his place. You in yours, your papa in his, me in mine—*n'est-ce pas, chéri?* We'll all forget how foolish we've been and have lovely times."

She continued to talk and to surge vaguely about the little draped stuffy salon while Pemberton sat with the boy, whose colour gradually came back; and she mixed up her reasons, hinting that there were going to be changes, that the other

children might scatter (who knew?—Paula had her ideas) and
that then it might be fancied how much the poor old parent-
birds would want the little nestling. Morgan looked at Pemberton, who wouldn't let him move; and Pemberton knew exactly
how he felt at hearing himself called a little nestling. He admitted that he had had one or two bad days, but he protested
afresh against the wrong of his mother's having made them
the ground of an appeal to poor Pemberton. Poor Pemberton
could laugh now, apart from the comicality of Mrs. Moreen's
mustering so much philosophy for her defence—she seemed to
shake it out of her agitated petticoats, which knocked over the
light gilt chairs—so little did their young companion, *marked,*
unmistakeably marked at the best, strike him as qualified to
repudiate any advantage.

He himself was in for it at any rate. He should have Morgan
on his hands again indefinitely; though indeed he saw the lad
had a private theory to produce which would be intended to
smooth this down. He was obliged to him for it in advance; but
the suggested amendment didn't keep his heart rather from
sinking, any more than it prevented him from accepting the
prospect on the spot, with some confidence moreover that he
should do so even better if he could have a little supper. Mrs.
Moreen threw out more hints about the changes that were to be
looked for, but she was such a mixture of smiles and shudders—
she confessed she was very nervous—that he couldn't tell if
she were in high feather or only in hysterics. If the family was
really at last going to pieces why shouldn't she recognise the
necessity of pitching Morgan into some sort of lifeboat? This
presumption was fostered by the fact that they were established
in luxurious quarters in the capital of pleasure; that was exactly
where they naturally *would* be established in view of going to
pieces. Moreover didn't she mention that Mr. Moreen and the
others were enjoying themselves at the opera with Mr. Granger,

and wasn't *that* also precisely where one would look for them on
the eve of a smash? Pemberton gathered that Mr. Granger was
a rich vacant American—a big bill with a flourishy heading and
no items; so that one of Paula's "ideas" was probably that this
time she hadn't missed fire—by which straight shot indeed she
would have shattered the general cohesion. And if the cohesion was to crumble what would become of poor Pemberton?
He felt quite enough bound up with them to figure to his alarm
as a dislodged block in the edifice.

It was Morgan who eventually asked if no supper had been
ordered for him; sitting with him below, later, at the dim delayed meal, in the presence of a great deal of corded green plush,
a plate of ornamental biscuit and an aloofness marked on the
part of the waiter. Mrs. Moreen had explained that they had
been obliged to secure a room for the visitor out of the house;
and Morgan's consolation—he offered it while Pemberton reflected on the nastiness of lukewarm sauces—proved to be,
largely, that this circumstance would facilitate their escape. He
talked of their escape—recurring to it often afterwards—as if
they were making up a "boy's book" together. But he likewise
expressed his sense that there was something in the air, that
the Moreens couldn't keep it up much longer. In point of fact,
as Pemberton was to see, they kept it up for five or six months.
All the while, however, Morgan's contention was designed to
cheer him. Mr. Moreen and Ulick, whom he had met the day
after his return, accepted that return like perfect men of the
world. If Paula and Amy treated it even with less formality
an allowance was to be made for them, inasmuch as Mr.
Granger hadn't come to the opera after all. He had only placed
his box at their service, with a bouquet for each of the party;
there was even one apiece, embittering the thought of his profusion, for Mr. Moreen and Ulick. "They're all like that," was

Morgan's comment; "at the very last, just when we think we've landed them they're back in the deep sea!"

Morgan's comments in these days were more and more free; they even included a large recognition of the extraordinary tenderness with which he had been treated while Pemberton was away. Oh yes, they couldn't do enough to be nice to him, to show him they had him on their mind and make up for his loss. That was just what made the whole thing so sad and caused him to rejoice after all in Pemberton's return—he had to keep thinking of their affection less, had less sense of obligation. Pemberton laughed out at this last reason, and Morgan blushed and said "Well, dash it, you know what I mean." Pemberton knew perfectly what he meant; but there were a good many things that—dash it too!—it didn't make any clearer. This episode of his second sojourn in Paris stretched itself out wearily, with their resumed readings and wanderings and maunderings, their potterings on the quays, their hauntings of the museums, their occasional lingerings in the Palais Royal when the first sharp weather came on and there was a comfort in warm emanations, before Chevet's wonderful succulent window. Morgan wanted to hear all about the opulent youth—he took an immense interest in him. Some of the details of his opulence—Pemberton could spare him none of them—evidently fed the boy's appreciation of all his friend had given up to come back to him; but in addition to the greater reciprocity established by that heroism he had always his little brooding theory, in which there was a frivolous gaiety too, that their long probation was drawing to a close. Morgan's conviction that the Moreens couldn't go on much longer kept pace with the unexpended impetus with which, from month to month, they did go on. Three weeks after Pemberton had rejoined them they went on to another hotel, a dingier one than the first; but Morgan rejoiced that his tutor had at least still not sacrificed the advantage of a room outside. He

clung to the romantic utility of this when the day, or rather the
night, should arrive for their escape.

For the first time, in this complicated connexion, our friend
felt his collar gall him. It was, as he had said to Mrs. Moreen in
Venice, *trop fort*—everything was *trop fort*. He could neither
really throw off his blighting burden nor find in it the benefit of
a pacified conscience or of a rewarded affection. He had spent
all the money accruing to him in England, and he saw his youth
going and that he was getting nothing back for it. It was all
very well of Morgan to count it for reparation that he should
now settle on him permanently—there was an irritating flaw in
such a view. He saw what the boy had in his mind; the conception that as his friend had had the generosity to come back
he must show his gratitude by giving him his life. But the poor
friend didn't desire the gift—what could he do with Morgan's
dreadful little life? Of course at the same time that Pemberton
was irritated he remembered the reason, which was very honourable to Morgan and which dwelt simply in his making one
so forget that he was no more than a patched urchin. If one
dealt with him on a different basis one's misadventures were
one's own fault. So Pemberton waited in a queer confusion of
yearning and alarm for the catastrophe which was held to
hang over the house of Moreen, of which he certainly at moments felt the symptoms brush his cheek and as to which he
wondered much in what form it would find its liveliest effect.

Perhaps it would take the form of sudden dispersal—a frightened *sauve qui peut,* a scuttling into selfish corners. Certainly
they were less elastic than of yore; they were evidently looking
for something they didn't find. The Dorringtons hadn't re-
appeared, the princes had scattered; wasn't that the beginning
of the end? Mrs. Moreen had lost her reckoning of the famous
"days"; her social calendar was blurred—it had turned its face
to the wall. Pemberton suspected that the great, the cruel dis-

comfiture had been the unspeakable behaviour of Mr. Granger, who seemed not to know what he wanted, or, what was much worse, what *they* wanted. He kept sending flowers, as if to bestrew the path of his retreat, which was never the path of a return. Flowers were all very well, but—Pemberton could complete the proposition. It was not positively conspicuous that in the long run the Moreens were a social failure; so that the young man was almost grateful the run had not been short. Mr. Moreen indeed was still occasionally able to get away on business and, what was more surprising, was likewise able to get back. Ulick had no club, but you couldn't have discovered it from his appearance, which was as much as ever that of a person looking at life from the window of such an institution; therefore Pemberton was doubly surprised at an answer he once heard him make his mother in the desperate tone of a man familiar with the worst privations. Her question Pemberton had not quite caught; it appeared to be an appeal for a suggestion as to whom they might get to take Amy. "Let the Devil take her!" Ulick snapped; so that Pemberton could see that they had not only lost their amiability but had ceased to believe in themselves. He could also see that if Mrs. Moreen was trying to get people to take her children she might be regarded as closing the hatches for the storm. But Morgan would be the last she would part with.

One winter afternoon—it was a Sunday—he and the boy walked far together in the Bois de Boulogne. The evening was so splendid, the cold lemon-coloured sunset so clear, the stream of carriages and pedestrians so amusing and the fascination of Paris so great, that they stayed out later than usual and became aware that they should have to hurry home to arrive in time for dinner. They hurried accordingly, arm-in-arm, good-humoured and hungry, agreeing that there was nothing like Paris after all and that after everything too that had come and gone they were not yet sated with innocent pleasures. When they reached the hotel they found that, though scandalously late, they were in time for all the dinner they were likely to sit down to. Confusion reigned in the apartments of the Moreens—very shabby ones this time, but the best in the house—and before the interrupted service of the table, with objects displaced almost as if there had been a scuffle and a great wine-stain from an over-turned bottle, Pemberton couldn't blink the fact that there had been a scene of the last proprietary firmness. The storm had come—they were all seeking refuge. The hatches were down, Paula and Amy were invisible—they had never tried the most casual art upon Pemberton, but he felt they had enough of an eye to him not to wish to meet him as young ladies whose frocks had been confiscated—and Ulick appeared to have jumped overboard. The host and his staff, in a word, had ceased to "go on" at the pace of their guests, and the air of embarrassed detention, thanks to a pile of gaping trunks in the passage, was strangely commingled with the air of indignant withdrawal.

When Morgan took all this in—and he took it in very quickly —he coloured to the roots of his hair. He had walked from his infancy among difficulties and dangers, but he had never seen a public exposure. Pemberton noticed in a second glance at him that the tears had rushed into his eyes and that they were tears of a new and untasted bitterness. He wondered an instant, for the boy's sake, whether he might successfully pretend not to understand. Not successfully, he felt, as Mr. and Mrs. Moreen, dinnerless by their extinguished hearth, rose before him in their little dishonoured salon, casting about with glassy eyes for the nearest port in such a storm. They were not prostrate but were horribly white, and Mrs. Moreen had evidently been crying. Pemberton quickly learned however that her grief was not for the loss of her dinner, much as she usually enjoyed it, but the fruit of a blow that struck even deeper, as she made all haste to explain. He would see for himself, so far as that went, how the great change had come, the dreadful bolt had fallen, and how they would now all have to turn themselves about. Therefore cruel as it was to them to part with their darling she must look to him to carry a little further the influence he had so fortunately acquired with the boy—to induce his young charge to follow him into some modest retreat. They depended on him—that was the fact—to take their delightful child temporarily under his protection: it would leave Mr. Moreen and herself so much more free to give the proper attention (too little, alas! had been given) to the readjustment of their affairs.

"We trust you—we feel we *can*," said Mrs. Moreen, slowly rubbing her plump white hands and looking with compunction hard at Morgan, whose chin, not to take liberties, her husband stroked with a tentative paternal forefinger.

"Oh yes—we feel that we *can*. We trust Mr. Pemberton fully, Morgan," Mr. Moreen pursued.

Pemberton wondered again if he might pretend not to understand; but everything good gave way to the intensity of Morgan's understanding. "Do you mean he may take me to live with him for ever and ever?" cried the boy. "May take me away, away, anywhere he likes?"

"For ever and ever? *Comme vous-y-allez!*" Mr. Moreen laughed indulgently. "For as long as Mr. Pemberton may be so good."

"We've struggled, we've suffered," his wife went on; "but you've made him so your own that we've already been through the worst of the sacrifice."

Morgan had turned away from his father—he stood looking at Pemberton with a light in his face. His sense of shame for their common humiliated state had dropped; the case had another side—the thing was to clutch at *that*. He had a moment of boyish joy, scarcely mitigated by the reflexion that with this unexpected consecration of his hope—too sudden and too violent; the turn taken was away from a *good* boy's book—the "escape" was left on their hands. The boyish joy was there an instant, and Pemberton was almost scared at the rush of gratitude and affection that broke through his first abasement. When he stammered, "My dear fellow, what do you say to *that?*" how could one not say something enthusiastic? But there was more need for courage at something else that immediately followed and that made the lad sit down quickly on the nearest chair. He had turned quite livid and had raised his hand to his left side. They were all three looking at him, but Mrs. Moreen suddenly bounded forward. "Ah his darling little heart!" she broke out; and this time, on her knees before him and without respect for the idol, she caught him ardently in her arms. "You walked him too far, you hurried him too fast!" she hurled over her shoulder at Pemberton. Her son made no protest, and the next instant, still holding him, she sprang up with her face convulsed and with the terrified cry "Help, help! he's going, he's gone!" Pemberton saw with equal horror, by Morgan's own stricken face, that he was beyond their wildest recall. He pulled him half out of his mother's hands, and for a moment, while they held him together, they looked all their dismay into each other's eyes. "He couldn't stand it with his weak organ," said Pemberton— "the shock, the whole scene, the violent emotion."

"But I thought he *wanted* to go to you!" wailed Mrs. Moreen.

"I *told* you he didn't, my dear," her husband made answer. Mr. Moreen was trembling all over and was in his way as deeply affected as his wife. But after the very first he took his bereavement as a man of the world.

THE GREAT WALL OF CHINA

by FRANZ KAFKA

T HE Great Wall of China was finished off at its northernmost corner.
From the southeast and the south-
west it came up in two sections that finally converged there.
This principle of piecemeal construction was also applied on a
smaller scale by both of the two great armies of labor, the
eastern and the western. It was done in this way: gangs of
some twenty workers were formed who had to accomplish a
length, say, of five hundred yards of wall, while a similar gang
built another stretch of the same length to meet the first. But
after the junction had been made the construction of the wall
was not carried on from the point, let us say, where this thousand yards ended; instead the two groups of workers were
transferred to begin building again in quite different neighbor-
hoods. Naturally in this way many great gaps were left, which
were only filled in gradually and bit by bit, some, indeed, not
till after the official announcement that the wall was finished.
In fact it is said that there are gaps which have never been filled
in at all, an assertion, however, which is probably merely one
of the many legends to which the building of the wall gave rise,
and which cannot be verified, at least by any single man with
his own eyes and judgment, on account of the extent of the
structure.

Now on first thoughts one might conceive that it would have
been more advantageous in every way to build the wall continu-

ously, or at least continuously within the two main divisions. After all, the wall was intended, as was universally proclaimed and known, to be a protection against the peoples of the north. But how can a wall protect if it is not a continuous structure? Not only cannot such a wall protect, but what there is of it is in perpetual danger. These blocks of wall left standing in deserted regions could be easily pulled down again and again by the nomads, especially as these tribes, rendered apprehensive by the building operations, kept changing their encampments with incredible rapidity, like locusts, and so perhaps had a better general view of the progress of the wall than we, the builders. Nevertheless the task of construction probably could not have been carried out in any other way. To understand this we must take into account the following: The wall was to be a protection for centuries; accordingly the most scrupulous care in the building, the application of the architectural wisdom of all known ages and peoples, and an unremitting sense of personal responsibility in the builders, were indispensable prerequisites for the work. True, for the more purely manual tasks, ignorant day laborers from the populace, men, women, and children who offered their services for good money, could be employed; but for the supervision even of every four day laborers, an expert versed in the art of building was required, a man who was capable of entering into and feeling with all his heart what was involved. And the higher the task, the greater the responsibility. And such men were actually to be had, if not indeed so abundantly as the work of construction could have absorbed, yet in great numbers.

For the work had not been undertaken without thought. Fifty years before the first stone was laid, the art of architecture, and especially that of masonry, had been proclaimed as the most important branch of knowledge throughout the whole area of a China that was to be walled round, and all other arts gained recognition only in so far as they had reference to it. I can still remember quite well us standing as small children, scarcely sure on our feet, in our teacher's garden, and being ordered to build a sort of wall out of pebbles; and then the teacher, girding up his robe, ran full tilt against the wall, of course knocking it down, and scolded us so terribly for the shoddiness of our work that we ran weeping in all directions to our parents. A trivial incident, but significant of the spirit of the time.

I was lucky inasmuch as the building of the wall was just beginning when, at twenty, I had passed the last examination of the lowest grade school. I say lucky, for many who before my time had achieved the highest degree of culture available to them could find nothing year after year to do with their knowledge, and drifted uselessly about with the most splendid architectural plans in their heads, and sank by thousands into hopelessness. But those who finally came to be employed in the work as supervisors, even though it might be of the lowest rank, were truly worthy of their task. They were masons who had reflected much, and did not cease to reflect, on the building of the wall, men who with the first stone which they sank in the ground felt themselves a part of the wall. Masons of that kind, of course, had not only a desire to perform their work in the most thorough manner, but were also impatient to see the wall finished in its complete perfection. Day laborers have not this impatience, for they look only to their wages, and the higher supervisors, indeed even the supervisors of middle rank, could see enough of the manifold growth of the construction to keep their spirits confident and high. But to encourage the subordinate supervisors, intellectually so vastly superior to their apparently petty tasks, other measures must be taken. One could not, for instance, expect them to lay one stone on another for months or even years on end, in an uninhabited mountainous region, hundreds of miles from their homes; the hopelessness of such hard toil, which yet could not reach completion even in the longest lifetime, would have cast them into despair and above all made them less capable for the work. It was for this reason that the system of piecemeal building was decided on. Five hundred yards could be accomplished in about five years; by that time, however, the supervisors were as a rule quite exhausted and had lost all faith in themselves, in the wall, in the world. Accordingly, while they were still exalted by the jubilant celebrations marking the completion of the thousand yards of wall, they were sent far, far away, saw on their journey finished sections of the wall rising here and there, came past the quarters of the high command and were presented with badges of honor, heard the rejoicings of new armies of labor streaming past from the depths of the land, saw forests being cut down to become supports for the wall, saw mountains being hewn into stones for the wall, heard at the holy shrines hymns rising in which the pious prayed for the completion of the wall. All this assuaged their impatience. The quiet life of their homes, where they rested some time, strengthened them; the humble credulity with which their reports were listened to, the confidence with which the simple and peaceful burgher believed in the eventual completion of the wall, all this tightened up again the cords of the soul. Like eternally hopeful children they then said farewell to their homes; the desire once more to labor on the wall of the nation became irresistible. They set off earlier than they needed; half the village accompanied them for long distances. Groups of people with banners and scarves waving were on all the roads; never before had they seen how great and rich and beautiful and worthy of love their country was. Every fellow-countryman was a brother for whom one was building a wall of protection, and who would return life-long thanks for it with all he had and did. Unity! Unity! Shoulder to shoulder, a ring of brothers, a current of blood no longer confined within the narrow circulation of one body, but sweetly rolling and yet ever returning throughout the endless leagues of China.

Thus, then, the system of piecemeal construction becomes comprehensible; but there were still other reasons for it as well. Nor is there anything odd in my pausing over this question for so long; it is one of the crucial problems in the whole building of the wall, unimportant as it may appear at first glance. If I am to convey and make understandable the ideas and feelings of that time I cannot go deeply enough into this very question.

First, then, it must be said that in those days things were achieved scarcely inferior to the construction of the Tower of Babel, although as regards divine approval, at least according to human reckoning, strongly at variance with that work. I say this because during the early days of building a scholar wrote a book in which he drew the comparison in the most exhaustive way. In it he tried to prove that the Tower of Babel failed to reach its goal, not because of the reasons universally advanced, or at least that among those recognized reasons the most important of all was not to be found. His proofs were drawn not merely from written documents and reports; he also claimed to have made enquiries on the spot, and to have discovered that the tower failed and was bound to fail because of the weakness of the foundation. In this respect at any rate our age was vastly superior to that ancient one. Almost every educated man of our time was a mason by profession and infallible in the matter of laying foundations. That, however, was not what our scholar was concerned to prove; for he maintained that the Great Wall alone would provide for the first time in the history of mankind a secure foundation for a new Tower of Babel. First the wall, therefore, and then the tower. His book was in everybody's hands at that time, but I admit that even today I cannot quite make out how he conceived this tower. How could the wall, which did not form even a circle, but only a sort of quarter or half-circle, provide the foundation for a tower? That could obviously be meant only in a spiritual sense. But in that case why build the actual wall, which after all was something concrete, the result of the lifelong labor of multitudes of people? And why were there in the book plans, somewhat nebulous plans, it must be admitted, of the tower, and proposals worked out in detail for mobilizing the people's energies for the stupendous new work?

There were many wild ideas in people's heads at that time—this scholar's book is only one example—perhaps simply because so many were trying to join forces as far as they could for the achievement of a single aim. Human nature, essentially changeable, unstable as the dust, can endure no restraint; if it binds itself it soon begins to tear madly at its bonds, until it rends everything asunder, the wall, the bonds, and its very self.

It is possible that these very considerations, which militated against the building of the wall at all, were not left out of account by the high command when the system of piecemeal construction was decided on. We—and here I speak in the name of many people—did not really know ourselves until we had carefully scrutinised the decrees of the high command, when we discovered that without the high command neither our book learning nor our human understanding would have sufficed for the humble tasks which we performed in the great whole. In the office of the command—where it was and who sat there no one whom I have asked knew then or knows now—in that office one may be certain that all human thoughts and desires were revolved, and counter to them all human aims and fulfillments. And through the window the reflected splendors of divine worlds fell on the hands of the leaders as they traced their plans.

And for that reason the incorruptible observer must hold that the command, if it had seriously desired it, could also have overcome those difficulties which prevented a system of continuous construction. There remains, therefore, nothing but the conclusion that the command deliberately chose the system of piecemeal construction. But the piecemeal construction was only a makeshift and therefore inexpedient. Remains the conclusion that the command willed something inexpedient.—Strange conclusion!—True, and yet in one respect it has much to be said for it. One can perhaps safely discuss it now. In those days many people, and among them the best, had a secret maxim which ran: Try with all your might to comprehend the decrees of the high command, but only up to a certain point; then avoid further meditation. A very wise maxim, which moreover was elaborated in a parable that was later often quoted: Avoid further meditation, but not because it might be harmful; it is not at all certain that it would be harmful. What is harmful or not harmful has nothing to do with the question. Consider rather the river in spring. It rises until it grows mightier and nourishes more richly the soil on the long stretch of its banks, still maintaining its own course until it reaches the sea, where it is all the more welcome because it is a worthier ally.—Thus far may you urge your meditations on the decrees of the high command.—But after that the river overflows its banks, loses outline and shape, slows down the speed of its current, tries to ignore its destiny by forming little seas in the interior of the land, damages the fields, and yet cannot maintain itself for long in its new expanse, but must run back between its banks again, must even dry up wretchedly in the hot season that presently follows.—Thus far may you not urge your meditations on the decrees of the high command.

Now though this parable may have had extraordinary point and force during the building of the wall, it has at most only a restricted relevance for my present essay. My enquiry is purely historical; no lightning flashes any longer from the long-since-

vanished thunderclouds, and so I may venture to seek for an
explanation of the system of piecemeal construction which goes
farther than the one that contented people then. The limits
which my capacity for thought imposes upon me are narrow
enough, but the province to be traversed here is infinite. Against
whom was the Great Wall to serve as a protection? Against
the people of the north. Now, I come from the southeast of
China. No northern people can menace us there. We read of
them in the books of the ancients; the cruelties which they
commit in accordance with their nature make us sigh beneath
our peaceful trees. The faithful representations of the artist
show us these faces of the damned, their gaping mouths, their
jaws furnished with great pointed teeth, their half-shut eyes that
already seem to be seeking out the victim which their jaws will
rend and devour. When our children are unruly we show them
these pictures, and at once they fly weeping into our arms. But
nothing more than that do we know about these northerners.
We have not seen them, and if we remain in our villages we
shall never see them, even if on their wild horses they should
ride as hard as they can straight towards us—the land is too
vast and would not let them reach us, they would end their
course in the empty air.

Why, then, since that is so, did we leave our homes, the stream
with its bridges, our mothers and fathers, our weeping wives,
our children who needed our care, and depart for the distant
city to be trained there, while our thoughts journeyed still farther
away to the wall in the north? Why? A question for the high
command. Our leaders know us. They, absorbed in gigantic
anxieties, know of us, know our petty pursuits, see us sitting
together in our humble huts, and approve or disapprove the evening prayer which the father of the house recites in the midst
of his family. And if I may be allowed to express such ideas
about the high command, then I must say that in my opinion

the high command has existed from old time, and was not assembled, say, like a gathering of mandarins summoned hastily to discuss somebody's fine dream in a conference as hastily terminated, so that that very evening the people are drummed out of their beds to carry out what has been decided, even if it should be nothing but an illumination in honor of a god who may have shown great favor to their masters the day before, only to drive them into some dark corner with cudgel blows tomorrow, almost before the illuminations have died down. Far rather do I believe that the high command has existed from all eternity, and the decision to build the wall likewise. Unwitting peoples of the north, who imagined they were the cause of it! Honest, unwitting Emperor, who imagined he decreed it! We builders of the wall know that it was not so and hold our tongues.

During the building of the wall and ever since, to this very day, I have occupied myself almost exclusively with the comparative history of races—there are certain questions which one can probe to the marrow, as it were, only by this method—and I have discovered that we Chinese possess certain folk and political institutions that are unique in their clarity, others again unique in their obscurity. The desire to trace the causes of these phenomena, especially the latter, has always teased me and teases me still, and the building of the wall is itself essentially involved with these problems.

Now one of the most obscure of our institutions is that of the empire itself. In Pekin, naturally, at the imperial court, there is some clarity to be found on this subject, though even that is more illusive than real. Also the teachers of political law and history in the high schools claim to be exactly informed on these matters, and to be capable of passing on their knowledge to their students. The farther one descends among the lower schools the more, naturally enough, does one find teachers' and pupils' doubts of their own knowledge vanishing, and superficial culture mounting sky-high round a few precepts that have been drilled into people's minds for centuries, precepts which, though they have lost nothing of their eternal truth, remain eternally invisible in this fog of confusion.

But it is precisely this question of the empire which in my opinion the common people should be asked to answer, since after all they are the empire's final support. Here, I must confess, I can only speak once more for my native place. Except for the nature gods and their ritual, which fills the whole year in such beautiful and rich alternation, we think only about the Emperor. But not about the present one; or rather we would think about the present one if we knew who he was or knew anything definite about him. True—and it is the sole curiosity that fills us—we are always trying to get information on this subject, but, strange as it may sound, it is almost impossible to discover anything, either from pilgrims, though they have wandered through many lands, or from near or distant villages, or from sailors, though they have navigated not only our little stream, but also the sacred rivers. One hears a great many things, true, but can gather nothing definite.

So vast is our land that no fable could do justice to its vastness—the heavens can scarcely span it—and Pekin is only a dot in it, and the imperial palace less than a dot. The Emperor as such, on the other hand, is mighty throughout all the hierarchies of the world: admitted. But the existent Emperor, a man like us, lies much like us on a couch which is of generous proportions, perhaps, and yet very possibly may be quite narrow and short. Like us he sometimes stretches himself and when he is very tired yawns with his delicately cut mouth. But how should we know anything about that—thousands of miles away in the south—almost on the borders of the Tibetan Highlands? And besides, any tidings, even if they did reach us, would arrive far too late, would have become obsolete long before they reached

us. The Emperor is always surrounded by a brilliant and yet
ambiguous throng of nobles and courtiers—malice and enmity
in the guise of servants and friends—who form a counterweight
to the Imperial power and perpetually labor to unseat the ruler
from his place with poisoned arrows. The Empire is immortal,
but the Emperor himself totters and falls from his throne, yes,
whole dynasties sink in the end and breathe their last in one
death-rattle. Of these struggles and sufferings the people will
never know; like tardy arrivals, like strangers in a city, they
stand at the end of some densely thronged side street peacefully
munching the food they have brought with them, while far
away in front, in the market square at the heart of the city, the
execution of their ruler is proceeding.

There is a parable that describes this situation very well: The
Emperor, so it runs, has sent a message to you, the humble
subject, the insignificant shadow cowering in the remotest distance before the imperial sun; the Emperor from his deathbed
has sent a message to you alone. He has commanded the messenger to kneel down by the bed, and has whispered the message
to him; so much store did he lay on it that he ordered the
messenger to whisper it back into his ear again. Then by a nod
of the head he has confirmed that it is right. Yes, before the
assembled spectators of his death—all the obstructing walls have
been broken down, and on the spacious and loftily-mounting
open staircases stand in a ring the great princes of the Empire—
before all these he has delivered his message. The messenger
immediately sets out on his journey; a powerful, an indefatigable
man; now pushing with his right arm, now with his left, he
cleaves a way for himself through the throng; if he encounters
resistance he points to his breast, where the symbol of the sun
glitters; the way, too, is made easier for him than it would
be for any other man. But the multitudes are so vast; their
numbers have no end. If he could reach the open fields how
fast he would fly, and soon doubtless you would hear the wel-

come hammering of his fists on your door. But instead, how vainly does he wear out his strength; still he is only making his way through the chambers of the innermost palace; never will he get to the end of them; and if he succeeded in that, nothing would be gained; he must fight his way next down the stair; and if he succeeded in that, nothing would be gained; the courts would still have to be crossed; and after the courts the second outer palace; and once more stairs and courts; and once more another palace; and so on for thousands of years; and if at last he should burst through the outermost gate—but never, never can that happen—the imperial capital would lie before him, the centre of the world, crammed to bursting with its own refuse. Nobody could fight his way through here even with a message from a dead man.—But you sit at your window when evening falls and dream it to yourself.

Just so, as hopelessly and as hopefully, do our people regard the Emperor. They do not know what emperor is reigning, and there exist doubts regarding even the name of the dynasty. In school a great deal is taught about the dynasties with the dates of succession, but the universal uncertainty in this matter is so great that even the best scholars are drawn into it. Long-dead emperors are set on the throne in our villages, and one that only lives in song recently had a proclamation of his read out by the priest before the altar. Battles that are old history are new to us, and one's neighbor rushes in with a jubilant face to tell the news. The wives of the emperors, pampered and overweening, seduced from noble custom by wily courtiers, swelling with ambition, vehement in their greed, uncontrollable in their lust, practise their abominations ever anew. The more deeply they are buried in time the more glaring are the colors in which their deeds are painted, and with a loud cry of woe our village eventually hears how an Empress drank her husband's blood in long draughts thousands of years ago.

Thus, then, do our people deal with departed emperors, but

the living ruler they confuse among the dead. If once, only once in a man's lifetime, an imperial official on his tour of the provinces should arrive by chance at our village, make certain announcements in the name of the government, scrutinize the tax lists, examine the school children, enquire of the priest regarding our doings and affairs, and then, before he steps into his litter, should sum up his impressions in verbose admonitions to the assembled commune—then a smile flits over every face, each man throws a stolen glance at his neighbor, and bends over his children so as not to be observed by the official. Why, they think to themselves, he's speaking of a dead man as if he were alive, this Emperor of his died long ago, the dynasty is blotted out, the good official is having his joke with us, but we will behave as if we did not notice it, so as not to offend him. But we shall obey in earnest no one but our present ruler, for not to do so would be a crime. And behind the departing litter of the official there rises in might as ruler of the village some figure fortuitously exalted from an urn already crumbled to dust.

Similarly our people are but little affected by revolutions in the state or contemporary wars. I recall an incident in my youth. A revolt had broken out in a neighboring, but yet quite distant, province. What caused it I can no longer remember, nor is it of any importance now; occasions for revolt can be found there any day, the people are an excitable people. Well, one day a leaflet published by the rebels was brought to my father's house by a beggar who had crossed that province. It happened to be a feast day, our rooms were filled with guests, the priest sat in the chief place and studied the sheet. Suddenly everybody started to laugh, in the confusion the sheet was torn, the beggar, who however had already received abundant alms, was driven out of the room with blows, the guests dispersed to enjoy the beautiful day. Why? The dialect of this neighboring province differs in some essential respects from ours, and this difference occurs also in certain turns of the written speech, which for us have an archaic character. Hardly had the priest read out two lines before we had already come to our decision. Ancient history told long ago, old sorrows long since healed. And though—so it seems to me in recollection—the gruesomeness of the living present was irrefutably conveyed by the beggar's words, we laughed and shook our heads and refused to listen any longer. So eager are our people to obliterate the present.

If from such appearances any one should draw the conclusion that in reality we have no Emperor, he would not be far from the truth. Over and over again it must be repeated: There is perhaps no people more faithful to the Emperor than ours in the south, but the Emperor derives no advantage from our fidelity. True, the sacred dragon stands on the little column at the end of our village, and ever since the beginning of human memory it has breathed out its fiery breath in the direction of Pekin in token of homage—but Pekin itself is far stranger to the people in our village than the next world. Can there really be a village where the houses stand side by side, covering all the fields for a greater distance than one can see from our hills, and can there be dense crowds of people packed between these houses day and night? We find it more difficult to picture such a city than to believe that Pekin and its Emperor are one, a cloud, say, peacefully voyaging beneath the sun in the course of the ages.

Now the result of holding such opinions is a life on the whole free and unconstrained. By no means immoral, however; hardly ever have I found in my travels such pure morals as in my native village. But yet a life that is subject to no contemporary law, and attends only to the exhortations and warnings which come to us from olden times.

I guard against large generalizations and do not assert that in all the countless villages in my province it is so, far less in all the five hundred provinces of China. Yet perhaps I may venture to assert on the basis of the many writings on this subject which I have read, as well as from my own observation —the building of the wall in particular, with its abundance of human material, provided a man of sensibility with the opportunity of traversing the souls of almost all the provinces—on the basis of all this, then, perhaps I may venture to assert that the prevailing attitude to the Emperor shows persistently and universally something fundamentally in common with that of our village. Now I have no wish whatever to represent this attitude as a virtue; on the contrary. True, the essential responsibility for it lies with the government, which in the most ancient empire in the world has not yet succeeded in developing, or has neglected to develop, the institution of the empire to such precision that its workings extend directly and unceasingly to the farthest frontiers of the land. On the other hand, however, there is also involved a certain feebleness of faith and imaginative power on the part of the people, that prevents them from raising the empire out of its stagnation in Pekin and clasping it in all its palpable living reality to their own breasts, which yet desire nothing better than but once to feel that touch and then to die.

This attitude then is certainly no virtue. All the more remarkable is it that this very weakness should seem to be one of the greatest unifying influences among our people; indeed, if one may dare to use the expression, the very ground on which we live. To set about establishing a fundamental defect here would mean undermining not only our consciences, but, what is far worse, our feet. And for that reason I shall not proceed any further at this stage with my inquiry into these questions.

BARTLEBY THE SCRIVENER

A Story of Wall Street

by HERMAN MELVILLE

I AM a rather elderly man. The nature of my avocations, for the last thirty years, has brought me into more than ordinary contact with what would seem an interesting and somewhat singular set of men, of whom, as yet, nothing, that I know of, has ever been written—I mean, the law-copyists, or scriveners. I have known very many of them, professionally and privately, and, if I pleased, could relate divers histories, at which good-natured gentlemen might smile, and sentimental souls might weep. But I waive the biographies of all other scriveners, for a few passages in the life of Bartleby, who was a scrivener, the strangest I ever saw, or heard of. While, of other law-copyists, I might write the complete life, of Bartleby nothing of that sort can be done. I believe that no materials exist for a full and satisfactory biography of this man. It is an irreparable loss to literature. Bartleby was one of those beings of whom nothing is ascertainable, except from the original sources, and, in his case, those are very small. What my own astonished eyes saw of Bartleby, *that* is all I know of him, except, indeed, one vague report, which will appear in the sequel.

Ere introducing the scrivener, as he first appeared to me, it is fit I make some mention of myself, my *employés*, my business, my chambers, and general surroundings; because some such description is indispensable to an adequate understanding of the chief character about to be presented. Imprimis: I am a man who, from his youth upwards, has been filled with a profound conviction that the easiest way of life is the best. Hence, though I belong to a profession proverbially energetic and nervous, even to turbulence, at times, yet nothing of that sort have I ever suffered to invade my peace. I am one of those unambitious lawyers who never addresses a jury, or in any way draws down public applause; but, in the cool tranquillity of a snug retreat, do a snug business among rich men's bonds, and mortgages, and title-deeds. All who know me consider me an eminently *safe* man. The late John Jacob Astor, a personage little given to poetic enthusiasm, had no hesitation in pronouncing my first grand point to be prudence; my next, method. I do not speak it in vanity, but simply record the fact, that I was not unemployed in my profession by the late John Jacob Astor; a name which, I admit, I love to repeat; for it hath a rounded and orbicular sound to it, and rings like unto bullion. I will freely add, that I was not insensible to the late John Jacob Astor's good opinion.

Some time prior to the period at which this little history begins, my avocations had been largely increased. The good old office, now extinct in the State of New York, of a Master in Chancery, had been conferred upon me. It was not a very arduous office, but very pleasantly remunerative. I seldom lose my temper; much more seldom indulge in dangerous indignation at wrongs and outrages; but, I must be permitted to be rash here, and declare, that I consider the sudden and violent abrogation of the office of Master in Chancery, by the new Constitution, as a—premature act; inasmuch as I had counted upon a life-lease of the profits, whereas I only received those of a few short years. But this is by the way.

My chambers were upstairs, at No. — Wall Street. At one

end, they looked upon the white wall of the interior of a spacious sky-light shaft, penetrating the building from top to bottom.

This view might have been considered rather tame than otherwise, deficient in what landscape painters call "life." But, if so, the view from the other end of my chambers offered, at least, a contrast, if nothing more. In that direction, my windows commanded an unobstructed view of a lofty brick wall, black by age and everlasting shade; which wall required no spyglass to bring out its lurking beauties, but, for the benefit of all nearsighted spectators, was pushed up to within ten feet of my window panes. Owing to the great height of the surrounding buildings, and my chambers being on the second floor, the interval between this wall and mine not a little resembled a huge square cistern.

At the period just preceding the advent of Bartleby, I had two persons as copyists in my employment, and a promising lad as an office-boy. First, Turkey; second, Nippers; third, Ginger Nut. These may seem names, the like of which are not usually found in the Directory. In truth, they were nicknames, mutually conferred upon each other by my three clerks, and were deemed expressive of their respective persons or characters. Turkey was a short, pursy Englishman, of about my own age—that is, somewhere not far from sixty. In the morning, one might say, his face was of a fine florid hue, but after twelve o'clock, meridian—his dinner hour—it blazed like a grate full of Christmas coals; and continued blazing—but, as it were, with a gradual wane—till six o'clock P.M., or thereabouts; after which, I saw no more of the proprietor of the face, which, gaining its meridian with the sun, seemed to set with it, to rise, culminate, and decline the following day, with the like regularity and undiminished glory. There are many singular coincidences I have known in the course of my life, not the least among which was the fact, that, exactly when Turkey displayed his fullest beams from his red and radiant countenance, just then, too, at that critical moment, began the daily period when I considered his business capacities as seriously disturbed for the remainder of the twenty-four hours. Not that he was absolutely idle, or averse to business, then; far from it. The difficulty was, he was apt to be altogether too energetic. There was a strange, inflamed, flurried, flighty recklessness of activity about him. He would be incautious in dipping his pen into his inkstand. All his blots upon my documents were dropped there after twelve o'clock meridian. Indeed, not only would he be reckless, and sadly given to making blots in the afternoon, but, some days, he went further, and was rather noisy. At such times, too, his face flamed with augmented blazonry, as if cannel coal had been heaped on anthracite. He made an unpleasant racket with his chair; spilled his sand-box; in mending his pens, impatiently split them all to pieces, and threw them on the floor in a sudden passion; stood up, and leaned over his table, boxing his papers about in a most indecorous manner, very sad to behold in an elderly man like him. Nevertheless, as he was in many ways a most valuable person to me, and all the time before twelve o'clock meridian, was the quickest, steadiest creature, too, accomplishing a great deal of work in a style not easily to be matched—for these reasons, I was willing to overlook his eccentricities, though, indeed, occasionally, I remonstrated with him. I did this very gently, however, because, though the civilest, nay, the blandest and most reverential of men in the morning, yet, in the afternoon, he was disposed, upon provocation, to be slightly rash with his tongue—in fact, insolent. Now, valuing his morning services as I did, and resolved not to lose them— yet, at the same time, made uncomfortable by his inflamed ways after twelve o'clock—and being a man of peace, unwilling by my admonitions to call forth unseemly retorts from him, I took upon me, one Saturday noon (he was always worse on Saturdays) to hint to him, very kindly, that, perhaps, now that he was growing old, it might be well to abridge his labors; in short, he need not come to my chambers after twelve o'clock, but, dinner over, had best go home to his lodgings, and rest himself till tea-time. But no; he insisted upon his afternoon devotions. His countenance became intolerably fervid, as he oratorically assured me—gesticulating with a long ruler at the other end of the room—that if his services in the morning were useful, how indispensable, then, in the afternoon?

"With submission, sir," said Turkey, on this occasion, "I consider myself your right-hand man. In the morning I but marshal and deploy my columns; but in the afternoon I put myself at their head, and gallantly charge the foe, thus"—and he made a violent thrust with the ruler.

"But the blots, Turkey," intimated I.

"True; but, with submission, sir, behold these hairs! I am getting old. Surely, sir, a blot or two of a warm afternoon is not to be severely urged against gray hairs. Old age—even if it blot the page—is honorable. With submission, sir, we *both* are getting old."

This appeal to my fellow-feeling was hardly to be resisted. At all events, I saw that go he would not. So, I made up my mind to let him stay, resolving, nevertheless, to see to it that, during the afternoon, he had to do with my less important papers.

Nippers, the second on my list, was a whiskered, sallow, and, upon the whole, rather piratical-looking young man, of about five and twenty. I always deemed him the victim of two evil powers—ambition and indigestion. The ambition was evinced by a certain impatience of the duties of a mere copyist, an unwarrantable usurpation of strictly professional affairs, such as the original drawing up of legal documents. The indigestion seemed betokened in an occasional nervous testiness and grinning irritability, causing the teeth to audibly grind together over mistakes committed in copying; unnecessary maledictions, hissed, rather than spoken, in the heat of business; and especially by a continual discontent with the height of the table where he worked. Though of a very ingenious, mechanical turn, Nippers could never get this table to suit him. He put chips under it, blocks of various sorts, bits of pasteboard, and at last went so far as to attempt an exquisite adjustment, by final pieces of folded blotting-paper. But no invention would answer. If, for the sake of easing his back, he brought the table lid at a sharp angle well up towards his chin, and wrote there like a man using the steep roof of a Dutch house for his desk, then he declared that it stopped the circulation in his arms. If now he lowered the table to his waistbands, and stooped over it in writing, then there was a sore aching in his back. In short, the truth of the matter was, Nippers knew not what he wanted. Or, if he wanted anything, it was to be rid of a scrivener's table altogether. Among the manifestations of his diseased ambition was a fondness he had for receiving visits from certain ambiguous-looking fellows in seedy coats, whom he called his clients. Indeed, I was aware that not only was he, at times, considerable of a ward-politician, but he occasionally did a little business at the Justices' courts, and was not unknown on the steps of the Tombs. I have good reason to believe, however, that one individual who called upon him at my chambers, and who, with a grand air, he insisted was his client, was no other than a dun, and the alleged title-deed, a bill. But, with all his failings, and the annoyances he caused me, Nippers, like his compatriot Turkey, was a very useful man to me; wrote a neat, swift hand; and, when he chose, was not deficient in a gentlemanly sort of deportment. Added to this, he always dressed in a gentlemanly sort of way; and so, incidentally, reflected credit upon my chambers. Whereas, with respect to Turkey, I had much ado to keep him from being a reproach to me. His clothes were apt to look oily, and smell of eating-houses. He wore his pantaloons very loose and baggy in summer. His coats were execrable; his hat not to be handled. But while the hat was a thing of indifference to me, inasmuch as his natural civility and deference, as a dependent Englishman, always led him to doff it the moment he entered the room, yet his coat was another matter. Concerning his coats, I reasoned with him; but with no effect. The truth was, I suppose, that a man with so small an income could not afford to sport such a lustrous face and a lustrous coat at one and the same time. As Nippers once observed, Turkey's money went chiefly for red ink. One winter day, I presented Turkey with a highly respectable-looking coat of my own—a padded gray coat, of a most comfortable warmth, and which buttoned straight up from the knee to the neck. I thought Turkey would appreciate the favor, and abate his rashness and obstreperousness of afternoons. But no; I verily believe that buttoning himself up in so downy and blanket-like a coat had a pernicious effect upon him—upon the same principle that too much oats are bad for horses. In fact, precisely as a rash, restive horse is said to feel his oats, so Turkey felt his coat. It made him insolent. He was a man whom prosperity harmed.

Though, concerning the self-indulgent habits of Turkey, I had my own private surmises, yet, touching Nippers, I was well persuaded that, whatever might be his faults in other respects, he was, at least, a temperate young man. But, indeed, nature herself seemed to have been his vintner, and, at his birth, charged him so thoroughly with an irritable, brandylike disposition, that all subsequent potations were needless. When I consider how, amid the stillness of my chambers, Nippers would sometimes impatiently rise from his seat, and stooping over his table, spread his arms wide apart, seize the whole desk, and move it, and jerk it, with a grim, grinding motion on the floor, as if the table were a perverse voluntary agent and vexing him, I plainly perceive that, for Nippers, brandy-and-water were altogether superfluous.

It was fortunate for me that, owing to its peculiar cause—indigestion—the irritability and consequent nervousness of Nippers were mainly observable in the morning, while in the afternoon he was comparatively mild. So that, Turkey's paroxysms only coming on about twelve o'clock, I never had to do with their eccentricities at one time. Their fits relieved each other, like guards. When Nippers's was on, Turkey's was off; and *vice versa.* This was a good natural arrangement, under the circumstances.

Ginger Nut, the third on my list, was a lad some twelve years old. His father was a car-man, ambitious of seeing his son on the bench instead of a cart, before he died. So he sent him to my office, as student at law, errand-boy, cleaner and sweeper, at the rate of one dollar a week. He had a little desk to himself; but he did not use it much. Upon inspection, the drawer exhibited a great array of the shells of various sorts of nuts. Indeed, to this quick-witted youth, the whole noble science of the law was contained in a nutshell. Not the least among the employments of Ginger Nut, as well as one which he discharged with the most alacrity, was his duty as cake and apple purveyor for Turkey and Nippers. Copying law-papers being proverbially a dry, husky sort of business, my two scriveners were fain to moisten their mouths very often with Spitzenbergs, to be had at the numerous stalls nigh the Custom House and Post Office. Also, they sent Ginger Nut very frequently for that peculiar cake—small, flat, round, and very spicy—after which he had been named by them. Of a cold morning, when business was but dull, Turkey would gobble up scores of these cakes, as if they were mere wafers—indeed, they sell them at the rate of six or eight for a penny—the scrape of his pen blending with the crunching of the crisp particles in his mouth. Rashest of all the fiery afternoon blunders and flurried rashnesses of Turkey was his once moistening a ginger-cake between his lips and clapping it on to a mortgage for a seal. I came within an ace of dismissing him then. But he mollified me by making an oriental bow, and saying—

"With submission, sir, it was generous of me to find you in stationery on my own account."

Now my original business—that of a conveyancer and title hunter, and drawer-up of recondite documents of all sorts—was considerably increased by receiving the master's office. There was now great work for scriveners. Not only must I push the clerks already with me, but I must have additional help.

In answer to my advertisement, a motionless young man one morning stood upon my office threshold, the door being open, for it was summer. I can see that figure now—pallidly neat, pitiably respectable, incurably forlorn! It was Bartleby.

After a few words touching his qualifications, I engaged him, glad to have among my corps of copyists a man of so singularly sedate an aspect, which I thought might operate beneficially upon the flighty temper of Turkey, and the fiery one of Nippers.

I should have stated before that ground glass folding doors divided my premises into two parts, one of which was occupied by my scriveners, the other by myself. According to my humor, I threw open these doors, or closed them. I resolved to assign Bartleby a corner by the folding doors, but on my side of them, so as to have this quiet man within easy call, in case any trifling thing was to be done. I placed his desk close up to a small side-window in that part of the room, a window which originally had afforded a lateral view of certain grimy back-yards and bricks, but which, owing to subsequent erections, commanded at present no view at all, though it gave some light. Within three feet of the panes was a wall, and the light came down from far above, between two lofty buildings, as from a very small opening in a dome. Still further to a satisfactory arrangement, I procured a high green folding screen, which might entirely isolate Bartleby from my sight, though not remove him from my voice. And thus, in a manner, privacy and society were conjoined.

At first, Bartleby did an extraordinary quantity of writing. As if long famishing for something to copy, he seemed to gorge himself on my documents. There was no pause for digestion. He ran a day and night line, copying by sunlight and by candle-light. I should have been quite delighted with his application, had he been cheerfully industrious. But he wrote on silently, palely, mechanically.

It is, of course, an indispensable part of a scrivener's business to verify the accuracy of his copy, word by word. Where there are two or more scriveners in an office, they assist each other in this examination, one reading from the copy, the other holding the original. It is a very dull, wearisome, and lethargic affair. I can readily imagine that, to some sanguine temperaments, it would be altogether intolerable. For example, I cannot credit that the mettlesome poet, Byron, would have contentedly sat down with Bartleby to examine a law document of, say five hundred pages, closely written in a crimpy hand.

Now and then, in the haste of business, it had been my habit to assist in comparing some brief document myself, calling Turkey or Nippers for this purpose. One object I had, in placing Bartleby so handy to me behind the screen, was to avail myself of his services on such trivial occasions. It was on the third day, I think, of his being with me, and before any necessity had arisen for having his own writing examined, that, being much hurried to complete a small affair I had in hand, I abruptly called to Bartleby. In my haste and natural expectancy of instant compliance, I sat with my head bent over the original on

my desk, and my right hand sideways, and somewhat nervously
extended with the copy, so that, immediately upon emerging
from his retreat, Bartleby might snatch it and proceed to business without the least delay.

In this very attitude did I sit when I called to him, rapidly
stating what it was I wanted him to do—namely, to examine
a small paper with me. Imagine my surprise, nay, my consternation, when, without moving from his privacy, Bartleby, in a
singularly mild, firm voice, replied, "I would prefer not to."

I sat awhile in perfect silence, rallying my stunned faculties.
Immediately it occurred to me that my ears had deceived me,
or Bartleby had entirely misunderstood my meaning. I repeated
my request in the clearest tone I could assume; but in quite as
clear a one came the previous reply, "I would prefer not to."

"Prefer not to," echoed I, rising in high excitement, and crossing the room with a stride. "What do you mean? Are you
moon-struck? I want you to help me compare this sheet here—
take it," and I thrust it towards him.

"I would prefer not to," said he.

I looked at him steadfastly. His face was leanly composed;
his gray eye dimly calm. Not a wrinkle of agitation rippled
him. Had there been the least uneasiness, anger, impatience,
or impertinence in his manner; in other words, had there been
anything ordinarily human about him, doubtless I should have
violently dismissed him from the premises. But as it was, I
should have as soon thought of turning my pale plaster-of-paris
bust of Cicero out of doors. I stood gazing at him awhile, as
he went on with his own writing, and then reseated myself at
my desk. This is very strange, thought I. What had one best
do? But my business hurried me. I concluded to forget the
matter for the present, reserving it for my future leisure. So
calling Nippers from the other room, the paper was speedily
examined.

A few days after this, Bartleby concluded four lengthy documents, being quadruplicates of a week's testimony taken before me in my High Court of Chancery. It became necessary to examine them. It was an important suit, and great accuracy was imperative. Having all things arranged, I called Turkey, Nippers, and Ginger Nut from the next room, meaning to place the four copies in the hands of my four clerks, while I should read from the original. Accordingly, Turkey, Nippers, and Ginger Nut had taken their seats in a row, each with his document in his hand, when I called to Bartleby to join this interesting group.

"Bartleby! quick, I am waiting."

I heard a slow scrape of his chair legs on the uncarpeted floor, and soon he appeared standing at the entrance of his hermitage.

"What is wanted?" said he, mildly.

"The copies, the copies," said I, hurriedly. "We are going to examine them. There—" and I held towards him the fourth quadruplicate.

"I would prefer not to," he said, and gently disappeared behind the screen.

For a few moments I was turned into a pillar of salt, standing at the head of my seated column of clerks. Recovering myself, I advanced towards the screen, and demanded the reason for such extraordinary conduct.

"*Why* do you refuse?"

"I would prefer not to."

With any other man I should have flown outright into a dreadful passion, scorned all further words, and thrust him ignominiously from my presence. But there was something about Bartleby that not only strangely disarmed me, but in a wonderful manner, touched and disconcerted me. I began to reason with him.

"These are your own copies we are about to examine. It is labor saving to you, because one examination will answer for your four papers. It is common usage. Every copyist is bound to help examine his copy. Is it not so? Will you not speak? Answer!"

"I prefer not to," he replied in a flutelike tone. It seemed to me that, while I had been addressing him, he carefully revolved every statement that I made; fully comprehended the meaning; could not gainsay the irresistible conclusion; but, at the same time, some paramount consideration prevailed with him to reply as he did.

"You are decided, then, not to comply with my request—a request made according to common usage and common sense?"

He briefly gave me to understand, that on that point my judgment was sound. Yes: his decision was irreversible.

It is not seldom the case that, when a man is browbeaten in some unprecedented and violently unreasonable way, he begins to stagger in his own plainest faith. He begins, as it were, vaguely to surmise that, wonderful as it may be, all the justice and all the reason is on the other side. Accordingly, if any disinterested persons are present, he turns to them for some reinforcement of his own faltering mind.

"Turkey," said I, "what do you think of this? Am I not right?"

"With submission, sir," said Turkey, in his blandest tone, "I think that you are."

"Nippers," said I, "what do *you* think of it?"

"I think I should kick him out of the office."

(The reader, of nice perceptions, will here perceive that, it being morning, Turkey's answer is couched in polite and tranquil terms, but Nippers replies in ill-tempered ones. Or, to repeat a previous sentence, Nippers's ugly mood was on duty, and Turkey's off.)

"Ginger Nut," said I, willing to enlist the smallest suffrage in my behalf, "what do *you* think of it?"

"I think, sir, he's a little *luny*," replied Ginger Nut, with a grin.

"You hear what they say," said I, turning towards the screen, "come forth and do your duty."

But he vouchsafed no reply. I pondered a moment in sore perplexity. But once more business hurried me. I determined again to postpone the consideration of this dilemma to my future leisure. With a little trouble we made out to examine the papers without Bartleby, though at every page or two Turkey deferentially dropped his opinion, that this proceeding was quite out of the common; while Nippers, twitching in his chair with a dyspeptic nervousness, ground out, between his set teeth, occasional hissing maledictions against the stubborn oaf behind the screen. And for his (Nippers's) part, this was the first and the last time he would do another man's business without pay.

Meanwhile Bartleby sat in his hermitage, oblivious to everything but his own peculiar business there.

Some days passed, the scrivener being employed upon another lengthy work. His late remarkable conduct led me to regard his ways narrowly. I observed that he never went to dinner; indeed, that he never went anywhere. As yet I had never, of my personal knowledge, known him to be outside of my office. He was a perpetual sentry in the corner. At about eleven o'clock though, in the morning, I noticed that Ginger Nut would advance toward the opening in Bartleby's screen, as if silently beckoned thither by a gesture invisible to me where I sat. The boy would then leave the office, jingling a few pence, and reappear with a handful of ginger-nuts, which he delivered in the hermitage, receiving two of the cakes for his trouble.

He lives, then, on ginger-nuts, thought I; never eats a dinner, properly speaking; he must be a vegetarian, then; but no; he never eats even vegetables; he eats nothing but ginger-nuts. My mind then ran on in reveries concerning the probable effects upon the human constitution of living entirely on ginger-nuts.

Ginger-nuts are so called, because they contain ginger as one of their peculiar constituents, and the final flavoring one. Now, what was ginger? A hot, spicy thing. Was Bartleby hot and spicy? Not at all. Ginger, then, had no effect upon Bartleby. Probably he preferred it should have none.

Nothing so aggravates an earnest person as a passive resistance. If the individual so resisted be of a not inhumane temper, and the resisting one perfectly harmless in his passivity, then, in the better moods of the former, he will endeavor charitably to construe to his imagination what proves impossible to be solved by his judgment. Even so, for the most part, I regarded Bartleby and his ways. Poor fellow! thought I, he means no mischief; it is plain he intends no insolence; his aspect sufficiently evinces that his eccentricities are involuntary. He is useful to me. I can get along with him. If I turn him away, the chances are he will fall in with some less indulgent employer, and then he will be rudely treated, and perhaps driven forth miserably to starve. Yes. Here I can cheaply purchase a delicious self-approval. To befriend Bartleby; to humor him in his strange willfulness, will cost me little or nothing, while I lay up in my soul what will eventually prove a sweet morsel for my conscience. But this mood was not invariable with me. The passiveness of Bartleby sometimes irritated me. I felt strangely goaded on to encounter him in new opposition—to elicit some angry spark from him answerable to my own. But, indeed, I might as well have essayed to strike fire with my knuckles against a bit of Windsor soap. But one afternoon the evil impulse in me mastered me, and the following little scene ensued:

"Bartleby," said I, "when those papers are all copied, I will compare them with you."

"I would prefer not to."

"How? Surely you do not mean to persist in that mulish vagary?"

No answer.

I threw open the folding-doors near by, and, turning upon Turkey and Nippers, exclaimed:

"Bartleby a second time says he won't examine his papers. What do you think of it, Turkey?"

It was afternoon, be it remembered. Turkey sat glowing like a brass boiler; his bald head steaming; his hands reeling among his blotted papers.

"Think of it?" roared Turkey; "I think I'll just step behind his screen, and black his eyes for him!"

So saying, Turkey rose to his feet and threw his arms into a pugilistic position. He was hurrying away to make good his promise, when I detained him, alarmed at the effect of incautiously rousing Turkey's combativeness after dinner.

"Sit down, Turkey," said I, "and hear what Nippers has to say. What do you think of it, Nippers? Would I not be justified in immediately dismissing Bartleby?"

"Excuse me, that is for you to decide, sir. I think his conduct quite unusual, and, indeed, unjust, as regards Turkey and myself. But it may only be a passing whim."

"Ah," exclaimed I, "you have strangely changed your mind, then—you speak very gently of him now."

"All beer," cried Turkey; "gentleness is effects of beer—Nippers and I dined together today. You see how gentle *I* am, sir. Shall I go and black his eyes?"

"You refer to Bartleby, I suppose. No, not today, Turkey," I replied; "pray, put up your fists."

I closed the doors, and again advanced towards Bartleby. I felt additional incentives tempting me to my fate. I burned to be rebelled against again. I remembered that Bartleby never left the office.

"Bartleby," said I, "Ginger Nut is away; just step around to the Post Office, won't you? (it was but a three minutes' walk), and see if there is anything for me."

"I would prefer not to."

"You *will* not?"

"I *prefer* not."

I staggered to my desk, and sat there in a deep study. My blind inveteracy returned. Was there any other thing in which I could procure myself to be ignominiously repulsed by this lean, penniless wight?—my hired clerk? What added thing is there, perfectly reasonable, that he will be sure to refuse to do?

"Bartleby!"

No answer.

"Bartleby," in a louder tone.

No answer.

"Bartleby," I roared.

Like a very ghost, agreeably to the laws of magical invocation, at the third summons, he appeared at the entrance of his hermitage.

"Go to the next room, and tell Nippers to come to me."

"I prefer not to," he respectfully and slowly said, and mildly disappeared.

"Very good, Bartleby," said I, in a quiet sort of serenely-severe, self-possessed tone, intimating the unalterable purpose of some terrible retribution very close at hand. At the moment I half intended something of the kind. But upon the whole, as it was drawing towards my dinner-hour, I thought it best to put on my hat and walk home for the day, suffering much from perplexity and distress of mind.

Shall I acknowledge it? The conclusion of this whole business was, that it soon became a fixed fact of my chambers, that a pale young scrivener, by the name of Bartleby, had a desk there; that he copied for me at the usual rate of four cents a folio (one hundred words); but he was permanently exempt from examining the work done by him, that duty being transferred to Turkey and Nippers, out of compliment, doubtless, to their superior acuteness; moreover, said Bartleby was never, on any account, to be dispatched on the most trivial errand of any sort; and that even if entreated to take upon him such a matter, it was generally understood that he would "prefer not to"—in other words, that he would refuse point-blank.

As days passed on, I became considerably reconciled to Bartleby. His steadiness, his freedom from all dissipation, his incessant industry (except when he chose to throw himself into a standing revery behind his screen), his great stillness, his unalterableness of demeanor under all circumstances, made him a valuable acquisition. One prime thing was this—*he was always there*—first in the morning, continually through the day, and the last at night. I had a singular confidence in his honesty. I felt my most precious papers perfectly safe in his hands. Sometimes, to be sure, I could not, for the very soul of me, avoid falling into sudden spasmodic passions with him. For it was exceeding difficult to bear in mind all the time those strange peculiarities, privileges, and unheard of exemptions, forming the tacit stipulations on Bartleby's part under which he remained in my office. Now and then, in the eagerness of dispatching pressing business, I would inadvertently summon Bartleby, in a short, rapid tone, to put his finger, say, on the incipient tie of a bit of red tape with which I was about compressing some papers. Of course, from behind the screen the usual answer, "I prefer not to," was sure to come; and then, how could a human creature, with the common infirmities of our nature, refrain from bitterly exclaiming upon such perverseness—such unreasonableness. However, every added repulse of this sort which I received only tended to lessen the probability of my repeating the inadvertence.

Here it must be said that according to the custom of most legal gentlemen occupying chambers in densely-populated law buildings, there were several keys to my door. One was kept by a woman residing in the attic, which person weekly scrubbed and daily swept and dusted my apartments. Another was kept by Turkey for convenience sake. The third I sometimes carried in my own pocket. The fourth I knew not who had.

Now, one Sunday morning I happened to go to Trinity Church, to hear a celebrated preacher, and finding myself rather early on the ground I thought I would walk around to my chambers for a while. Luckily I had my key with me; but upon applying it to the lock, I found it resisted by something inserted from the inside. Quite surprised, I called out; when to my consternation a key was turned from within; and thrusting his lean visage at me, and holding the door ajar, the apparition of Bartleby appeared, in his shirt sleeves, and otherwise in a strangely tattered *déshabillé,* saying quietly that he was sorry, but he was deeply engaged just then, and—preferred not admitting me at present. In a brief word or two, he moreover added, that perhaps I had better walk around the block two or three times, and by that time he would probably have concluded his affairs.

Now, the utterly unsurmised appearance of Bartleby, tenanting my law-chambers of a Sunday morning, with his cadaverously gentlemanly *nonchalance,* yet withal firm and self-possessed, had such a strange effect upon me, that incontinently I slunk away from my own door, and did as desired. But not without sundry twinges of impotent rebellion against the mild effrontery of this unaccountable scrivener. Indeed, it was his wonderful mildness chiefly, which not only disarmed me, but unmanned me, as it were. For I consider that one, for the time, is somehow unmanned when he tranquilly permits his hired clerk to dictate to him, and order him away from his own premises. Furthermore, I was full of uneasiness as to what Bartleby could possibly be doing in my office in his shirt sleeves, and in an otherwise dismantled condition of a Sunday morning. Was anything amiss going on? Nay, that was out of the question. It was not to be thought of for a moment that Bartleby was an immoral person. But what could he be doing there?—copying? Nay again, whatever might be his eccentricities, Bartleby was an eminently decorous person. He would be the last man to sit down to his desk in any state approaching to nudity. Besides, it was Sunday; and there was something about Bartleby that forbade the supposition that he would by any secular occupation violate the proprieties of the day.

Nevertheless, my mind was not pacified; and full of a restless curiosity, at last I returned to the door. Without hindrance I inserted my key, opened it, and entered. Bartleby was not to be seen. I looked round anxiously, peeped behind his screen; but it was very plain that he was gone. Upon more closely examining the place, I surmised that for an indefinite period Bartleby must have eaten, dressed, and slept in my office, and that, too, without plate, mirror, or bed. The cushioned seat of a ricketty old sofa in one corner bore the faint impress of a lean, reclining form. Rolled away under his desk, I found a blanket; under the empty grate, a blacking box and brush; on a chair, a tin basin, with soap and a ragged towel; in a newspaper a few crumbs of ginger-nuts and a morsel of cheese. Yes, thought I, it is evident enough that Bartleby has been making his home here, keeping bachelor's hall all by himself. Immediately then the thought came sweeping across me, what miserable friendlessness and loneliness are here revealed! His poverty is great; but his solitude, how horrible! Think of it. Of a Sunday, Wall Street is deserted as Petra; and every night of every day it is an emptiness. This building, too, which of weekdays hums with industry and life, at nightfall echoes with sheer vacancy, and all through Sunday is forlorn. And here Bartleby makes his home; sole spectator of a solitude which he has seen all populous—a sort of innocent and transformed Marius brooding among the ruins of Carthage!

For the first time in my life a feeling of over-powering sting-ing melancholy seized me. Before, I had never experienced aught but a not unpleasing sadness. The bond of a common humanity now drew me irresistibly to gloom. A fraternal mel-ancholy! For both I and Bartleby were sons of Adam. I re-membered the bright silks and sparkling faces I had seen that day, in gala trim, swan-like sailing down the Mississippi of Broadway; and I contrasted them with the pallid copyist, and thought to myself, Ah, happiness courts the light, so we deem the world is gay; but misery hides aloof, so we deem that mis-ery there is none. These sad fancyings—chimeras, doubtless, of a sick and silly brain—led on to other and more special thoughts, concerning the eccentricities of Bartleby. Presenti-ments of strange discoveries hovered round me. The scrive-ner's pale form appeared to me laid out, among uncaring strangers, in its shivering winding sheet.

Suddenly I was attracted by Bartleby's closed desk, the key in open sight left in the lock.

I mean no mischief, seek the gratification of no heartless curiosity, thought I; besides, the desk is mine, and its contents, too, so I will make bold to look within. Everything was me-thodically arranged, the papers smoothly placed. The pigeon holes were deep, and removing the files of documents, I groped into their recesses. Presently I felt something there, and dragged it out. It was an old bandanna handkerchief, heavy and knotted. I opened it, and saw it was a savings bank.

I now recalled all the quiet mysteries which I had noted in the man. I remembered that he never spoke but to answer; that, though at intervals he had considerable time to himself, yet I had never seen him reading—no, not even a newspaper; that for long periods he would stand looking out, at his pale window behind the screen, upon the dead brick wall; I was quite sure he never visited any refectory or eating house; while his pale face clearly indicated that he never drank beer like

Turkey, or tea and coffee even, like other men; that he never
went anywhere in particular that I could learn; never went out
for a walk, unless, indeed, that was the case at present; that
he had declined telling who he was, or whence he came, or
whether he had any relatives in the world; that though so thin
and pale, he never complained of ill health. And more than
all, I remembered a certain unconscious air of pallid—how shall
I call it?—of pallid haughtiness, say, or rather an austere reserve about him, which had positively awed me into my tame
compliance with his eccentricities, when I had feared to ask
him to do the slightest incidental thing for me, even though I
might know, from his long-continued motionlessness, that behind his screen he must be standing in one of those dead-wall
reveries of his.

Revolving all these things, and coupling them with the recently discovered fact that he made my office his constant abiding place and home, and not forgetful of his morbid moodi-
ness; revolving all these things, a prudential feeling began to
steal over me. My first emotions had been those of pure melancholy and sincerest pity; but just in proportion as the for-
lornness of Bartleby grew and grew to my imagination, did
that same melancholy merge into fear, that pity into repulsion.
So true it is, and so terrible, too, that up to a certain point the
thought or sight of misery enlists our best affections; but, in
certain special cases, beyond that point it does not. They err
who would assert that invariably this is owing to the inherent
selfishness of the human heart. It rather proceeds from a certain hopelessness of remedying excessive and organic ill. To a
sensitive being, pity is not seldom pain. And when at last it
is perceived that such pity cannot lead to effectual succor, common sense bids the soul be rid of it. What I saw that morning persuaded me that the scrivener was the victim of innate
and incurable disorder. I might give alms to his body; but his

body did not pain him; it was his soul that suffered, and his soul I could not reach.

I did not accomplish the purpose of going to Trinity Church that morning. Somehow, the things I had seen disqualified me for the time from church-going. I walked homeward, thinking what I would do with Bartleby. Finally, I resolved upon this —I would put certain calm questions to him the next morning, touching his history, etc., and if he declined to answer them openly and unreservedly (and I supposed he would prefer not), then to give him a twenty dollar bill over and above whatever I might owe him, and tell him his services were no longer required; but that if in any other way I could assist him, I would be happy to do so, especially if he desired to return to his native place, wherever that might be, I would willingly help to defray the expenses. Moreover, if, after reaching home, he found himself at any time in want of aid, a letter from him would be sure of a reply.

The next morning came.

"Bartleby," said I, gently calling to him behind his screen. No reply.

"Bartleby," said I, in a still gentler tone, "come here; I am not going to ask you to do anything you would prefer not to do—I simply wish to speak to you."

Upon this he noiselessly slid into view.

"Will you tell me, Bartleby, where you were born?"

"I would prefer not to."

"Will you tell me *anything* about yourself?"

"I would prefer not to."

"But what reasonable objection can you have to speak to me? I feel friendly towards you."

He did not look at me while I spoke, but kept his glance fixed upon my bust of Cicero, which, as I then sat, was directly behind me, some six inches above my head.

"What is your answer, Bartleby," said I, after waiting a considerable time for a reply, during which his countenance remained immovable, only there was the faintest conceivable
tremor of the white attenuated mouth.

"At present I prefer to give no answer," he said, and retired
into his hermitage.

It was rather weak in me I confess, but his manner, on this
occasion, nettled me. Not only did there seem to lurk in it a
certain calm disdain, but his perverseness seemed ungrateful,
considering the undeniable good usage and indulgence he had
received from me.

Again I sat ruminating what I should do. Mortified as I was
at his behavior, and resolved as I had been to dismiss him when
I entered my office, nevertheless I strangely felt something superstitious knocking at my heart, and forbidding me to carry out
my purpose, and denouncing me for a villain if I dared to
breathe one bitter word against this forlornest of mankind. At
last, familiarly drawing my chair behind his screen, I sat down
and said: "Bartleby, never mind, then, about revealing your
history; but let me entreat you, as a friend, to comply as far as
may be with the usages of this office. Say now, you will help
to examine papers tomorrow or next day: in short, say now,
that in a day or two you will begin to be a little reasonable:
—say so, Bartleby."

"At present I would prefer not to be a little reasonable," was
his mildly cadaverous reply.

Just then the folding doors opened, and Nippers approached.
He seemed suffering from an unusually bad night's rest, induced by severer indigestion than common. He overheard those
final words of Bartleby.

"*Prefer not,* eh?" gritted Nippers—"I'd *prefer* him, if I were
you, sir," addressing me—"I'd *prefer* him; I'd give him preferences, the stubborn mule! What is it, sir, pray, that he *prefers*
not to do now?"

Bartleby moved not a limb.

"Mr. Nippers," said I, "I'd prefer that you would withdraw for the present."

Somehow, of late, I had got into the way of involuntarily using this word "prefer" upon all sorts of not exactly suitable occasions. And I trembled to think that my contact with the scrivener had already and seriously affected me in a mental way. And what further and deeper aberration might it not yet produce? This apprehension had not been without efficacy in determining me to summary measures.

As Nippers, looking very sour and sulky, was departing, Turkey blandly and deferentially approached.

"With submission, sir," said he, "yesterday I was thinking about Bartleby here, and I think that if he would but prefer to take a quart of good ale every day, it would do much towards mending him, and enabling him to assist in examining his papers."

"So you have got the word, too," said I, slightly excited.

"With submission, what word, sir," asked Turkey, respectfully crowding himself into the contracted space behind the screen, and by so doing, making me jostle the scrivener. "What word, sir?"

"I would prefer to be left alone here," said Bartleby, as if offended at being mobbed in his privacy.

"*That's* the word, Turkey," said I—"*that's* it."

"Oh, *prefer?* oh yes—queer word. I never use it myself. But, sir, as I was saying, if he would but prefer—"

"Turkey," interrupted I, "you will please withdraw."

"Oh certainly, sir, if you prefer that I should."

As he opened the folding door to retire, Nippers at his desk caught a glimpse of me, and asked whether I would prefer to have a certain paper copied on blue paper or white. He did not in the least roguishly accent the word prefer. It was plain that it involuntarily rolled from his tongue. I thought to myself, surely I must get rid of a demented man, who already has in some degree turned the tongues, if not the heads of myself and clerks. But I thought it prudent not to break the dismission at once.

The next day I noticed that Bartleby did nothing but stand at his window in his dead-wall revery. Upon asking him why he did not write, he said that he had decided upon doing no more writing.

"Why, how now? what next?" exclaimed I, "do no more writing?"

"No more."

"And what is the reason?"

"Do you not see the reason for yourself," he indifferently replied.

I looked steadfastly at him, and perceived that his eyes looked dull and glazed. Instantly it occurred to me, that his unexampled diligence in copying by his dim window for the first few weeks of his stay with me might have temporarily impaired his vision.

I was touched. I said something in condolence with him. I hinted that of course he did wisely in abstaining from writing for a while; and urged him to embrace that opportunity of taking wholesome exercise in the open air. This, however, he did not do. A few days after this, my other clerks being absent, and being in a great hurry to dispatch certain letters by the mail, I thought that, having nothing else earthly to do, Bartleby would surely be less inflexible than usual, and carry these letters to the post-office. But he blankly declined. So, much to my inconvenience, I went myself.

Still added days went by. Whether Bartleby's eyes improved or not, I could not say. To all appearance I thought they did. But when I asked him if they did, he vouchsafed no answer. At all events, he would do no copying. At last, in reply to my urgings, he informed me that he had permanently given up copying.

"What!" exclaimed I; "suppose your eyes should get entirely well—better than ever before—would you not copy then?"

"I have given up copying," he answered, and slid aside.

He remained as ever, a fixture in my chamber. Nay—if that were possible—he became still more of a fixture than before. What was to be done? He would do nothing in the office; why should he stay there? In plain fact, he had now become a millstone to me, not only useless as a necklace, but afflictive to bear. Yet I was sorry for him. I speak less than truth when I say that, on his own account, he occasioned me uneasiness. If he would but have named a single relative or friend, I would instantly have written, and urged their taking the poor fellow away to some convenient retreat. But he seemed alone, absolutely alone in the universe. A bit of wreck in the mid-Atlantic. At length, necessities connected with my business tyrannized over all other considerations. Decently as I could, I told Bartleby that in six days' time he must unconditionally leave the office. I warned him to take measures, in the interval, for procuring some other abode. I offered to assist him in his endeavor, if he himself would but take the first step towards a removal. "And when you finally quit me, Bartleby," added I, "I shall see that you go not away entirely unprovided. Six days from this hour, remember."

At the expiration of that period, I peeped behind the screen, and lo! Bartleby was there.

I buttoned up my coat, balanced myself; advanced slowly towards him, touched his shoulder, and said, "The time has come; you must quit this place; I am sorry for you; here is money; but you must go."

"I would prefer not," he replied, with his back still towards me.

"You *must.*"

He remained silent.

Now I had an unbounded confidence in this man's common honesty. He had frequently restored to me sixpences and shillings carelessly dropped upon the floor, for I am apt to be very reckless in such shirt-button affairs. The proceeding, then, which followed will not be deemed extraordinary.

"Bartleby," said I, "I owe you twelve dollars on account; here are thirty-two; the odd twenty are yours— Will you take it?" and I handed the bills towards him.

But he made no motion.

"I will leave them here, then," putting them under a weight on the table. Then taking my hat and cane and going to the door, I tranquilly turned and added—"After you have removed your things from these offices, Bartleby, you will of course lock the door—since every one is now gone for the day but you— and if you please, slip your key underneath the mat, so that I may have it in the morning. I shall not see you again; so good-by to you. If, hereafter, in your new place of abode, I can be of any service to you, do not fail to advise me by letter. Good-by, Bartleby, and fare you well."

But he answered not a word; like the last column of some ruined temple, he remained standing mute and solitary in the middle of the otherwise deserted room.

As I walked home in a pensive mood, my vanity got the better of my pity. I could not but highly plume myself on my masterly management in getting rid of Bartleby. Masterly I call it, and such it must appear to any dispassionate thinker. The beauty of my procedure seemed to consist in its perfect quietness. There was no vulgar bullying, no bravado of any sort, no choleric hectoring, and striding to and fro across the apartment, jerking out vehement commands for Bartleby to bundle himself off with his beggarly traps. Nothing of the kind. Without loudly bidding Bartleby depart—as an inferior genius might have done—I *assumed* the ground that depart he must; and upon that assumption built all I had to say. The more I thought over my procedure, the more I was charmed with it. Nevertheless, next morning, upon awakening, I had my doubts—I had somehow slept off the fumes of vanity. One of the coolest and wisest hours a man has, is just after he awakes in the morning. My procedure seemed as sagacious as ever—but only in theory. How it would prove in practice—there was the rub. It was truly a beautiful thought to have assumed Bartleby's departure; but, after all, that assumption was simply my own, and none of Bartleby's. The great point was, not whether I had assumed that he would quit me, but whether he would prefer so to do. He was more a man of preferences than assumptions.

After breakfast, I walked downtown, arguing the probabilities *pro* and *con*. One moment I thought it would prove a miserable failure, and Bartleby would be found all alive at my office as usual; the next moment it seemed certain that I should find his chair empty. And so I kept veering about. At the corner of Broadway and Canal Street, I saw quite an excited group of people standing in earnest conversation.

"I'll take odds he doesn't," said a voice as I passed.

"Doesn't go?—done!" said I; "put up your money."

I was instinctively putting my hand in my pocket to produce my own, when I remembered that this was an election day. The words I had overheard bore no reference to Bartleby, but to the success or nonsuccess of some candidate for the mayoralty. In my intent frame of mind, I had, as it were, imagined that all Broadway shared in my excitement, and were debating the same question with me. I passed on, very thankful that the uproar of the street screened my momentary absent-mindedness.

As I had intended, I was earlier than usual at my office door.

I stood listening for a moment. All was still. He must be gone. I tried the knob. The door was locked. Yes, my procedure had worked to a charm; he indeed must be vanished. Yet a certain melancholy mixed with this: I was almost sorry for my brilliant success. I was fumbling under the door mat for the key, which Bartleby was to have left there for me, when accidentally my knee knocked against a panel, producing a summoning sound, and in response a voice came to me from within —"Not yet; I am occupied."

It was Bartleby.

I was thunderstruck. For an instant I stood like the man who, pipe in mouth, was killed one cloudless afternoon long ago in Virginia, by summer lightning; at his own warm open window he was killed, and remained leaning out there upon the dreamy afternoon, till some one touched him, when he fell.

"Not gone!" I murmured at last. But again obeying that wondrous ascendancy which the inscrutable scrivener had over me, and from which ascendancy, for all my chafing, I could not completely escape, I slowly went downstairs and out into the street, and while walking round the block, considered what I should next do in this unheard-of perplexity. Turn the man out by an actual thrusting I could not; to drive him away by calling him hard names would not do; calling in the police was an unpleasant idea; and yet, permit him to enjoy his cadaverous triumph over me—this, too, I could not think of. What was to be done? or, if nothing could be done, was there anything further that I could *assume* in the matter? Yes, as before I had prospectively assumed that Bartleby would depart, so now I might retrospectively assume that departed he was. In the legitimate carrying out of this assumption, I might enter my office in a great hurry, and pretending not to see Bartleby at all, walk straight against him as if he were air. Such a proceeding would in a singular degree have the appearance of a home-thrust. It was hardly possible that Bartleby could withstand such an application of the doctrine of assumptions. But upon second thoughts the success of the plan seemed rather dubious. I resolved to argue the matter over with him again.

"Bartleby," said I, entering the office, with a quietly severe expression, "I am seriously displeased. I am pained, Bartleby. I had thought better of you. I had imagined you of such a gentlemanly organization, that in any delicate dilemma a slight hint would suffice—in short, an assumption. But it appears I am deceived. Why," I added, unaffectedly starting, "you have not even touched that money yet," pointing to it, just where I had left it the evening previous.

He answered nothing.

"Will you, or will you not, quit me?" I now demanded in a sudden passion, advancing close to him.

"I would prefer *not* to quit you," he replied, gently emphasizing the *not*.

"What earthly right have you to stay here? Do you pay any rent? Do you pay my taxes? Or is this property yours?"

He answered nothing.

"Are you ready to go on and write now? Are your eyes recovered? Could you copy a small paper for me this morning? or help examine a few lines? or step round to the post-office? In a word, will you do anything at all, to give a coloring to your refusal to depart the premises?"

He silently retired into his hermitage.

I was now in such a state of nervous resentment that I thought it but prudent to check myself at present from further demonstrations. Bartleby and I were alone. I remembered the tragedy of the unfortunate Adams and the still more unfortunate Colt in the solitary office of the latter; and how poor Colt, being dreadfully incensed by Adams, and imprudently permitting himself to get wildly excited, was at unawares hurried into his fatal act—an act which certainly no man could possibly deplore more than the actor himself. Often it had occurred to me in my ponderings upon the subject, that had that altercation taken place in the public street, or at a private residence, it would not have terminated as it did. It was the circumstance of being alone in a solitary office, upstairs, of a building entirely unhallowed by humanizing domestic associations—an uncarpeted office, doubtless, of a dusty, haggard sort of appearance—this it must have been, which greatly helped to enhance the irritable desperation of the hapless Colt.

But when this old Adam of resentment rose in me and tempted me concerning Bartleby, I grappled him and threw him. How? Why, simply by recalling the divine injunction: "A new commandment give I unto you, that ye love one another." Yes, this it was that saved me. Aside from higher considerations, charity often operates as a vastly wise and prudent principle—a great safeguard to its possessor. Men have committed murder for jealousy's sake, and anger's sake, and hatred's sake, and selfishness' sake, and spiritual pride's sake; but no man, that ever I heard of, ever committed a diabolical murder for sweet charity's sake. Mere self-interest, then, if no better motive can be enlisted, should, especially with high-tempered men, prompt all beings to charity and philanthropy. At any rate, upon the occasion in question, I strove to drown my exasperated feelings towards the scrivener by benevolently construing his conduct. Poor fellow, poor fellow! thought I, he don't mean anything; and besides, he has seen hard times, and ought to be indulged.

I endeavored, also, immediately to occupy myself, and at the same time to comfort my despondency. I tried to fancy, that in the course of the morning, at such time as might prove agreeable to him, Bartleby, of his own free accord, would emerge from his hermitage and take up some decided line of march in the direction of the door. But no. Half-past twelve o'clock came; Turkey began to glow in the face, overturn his inkstand, and become generally obstreperous; Nippers abated down into quietude and courtesy; Ginger Nut munched his noon apple; and Bartleby remained standing at his window in one of his profoundest dead-wall reveries. Will it be credited? Ought I to acknowledge it? That afternoon I left the office without saying one further word to him.

Some days now passed, during which, at leisure intervals I looked a little into "Edwards on the Will" and "Priestley on Necessity." Under the circumstances, those books induced a salutary feeling. Gradually I slid into the persuasion that these troubles of mine, touching the scrivener, had been all predestinated from eternity, and Bartleby was billeted upon me for some mysterious purpose of an all-wise Providence, which it was not for a mere mortal like me to fathom. Yes, Bartleby, stay there behind your screen, thought I; I shall persecute you no more; you are harmless and noiseless as any of these old chairs; in short, I never feel so private as when I know you are here. At last I see it, I feel it; I penetrate to the predestinated purpose of my life. I am content. Others may have loftier parts to enact; but my mission in this world, Bartleby, is to furnish you with office-room for such period as you may see fit to remain.

I believe that this wise and blessed frame of mind would have continued with me, had it not been for the unsolicited and uncharitable remarks obtruded upon me by my professional friends who visited the rooms. But thus it often is, that the constant friction of illiberal minds wears out at last the best resolves of the more generous. Though to be sure, when I reflected upon it, it was not strange that people entering my office should be struck by the peculiar aspect of the unaccountable Bartleby, and so be tempted to throw out some sinister observations concerning him. Sometimes an attorney, having business with me, and calling at my office, and finding no one but the scrivener there, would undertake to obtain some sort of precise information from him touching my whereabouts; but without heeding his idle talk, Bartleby would remain standing immovable in the middle of the room. So after contemplating him in that position for a time, the attorney would depart, no wiser than he came.

Also, when a reference was going on, and the room full of lawyers and witnesses, and business driving fast, some deeply occupied legal gentleman present, seeing Bartleby wholly un-employed, would request him to run round to his (the legal gentleman's) office and fetch some papers for him. Thereupon, Bartleby would tranquilly decline, and yet remain idle as be-fore. Then the lawyer would give a great stare, and turn to me. And what could I say? At last I was made aware that all through the circle of my professional acquaintance, a whis-per of wonder was running round, having reference to the strange creature I kept at my office. This worried me very much. And as the idea came upon me of his possibly turning out a long-lived man, and keep occupying my chambers, and denying my authority; and perplexing my visitors; and scandal-izing my professional reputation; and casting a general gloom over the premises; keeping soul and body together to the last upon his savings (for doubtless he spent but half a dime a day), and in the end perhaps outlive me, and claim possession of my office by right of his perpetual occupancy: as all these dark anticipations crowded upon me more and more, and my friends continually intruded their relentless remarks upon the apparition in my room; a great change was wrought in me. I resolved to gather all my faculties together, and forever rid me of this intolerable incubus.

Ere revolving any complicated project, however, adapted to this end, I first simply suggested to Bartleby the propriety of his permanent departure. In a calm and serious tone, I com-mended the idea to his careful and mature consideration. But, having taken three days to meditate upon it, he apprised me, that his original determination remained the same; in short, that he still preferred to abide with me.

What shall I do? I now said to myself, buttoning up my coat to the last button. What shall I do? what ought I to do? what does conscience say I *should* do with this man, or, rather, ghost. Rid myself of him, I must; go, he shall. But how? You will not thrust him, the poor, pale, passive mortal—you will not thrust such a helpless creature out of your door? you will not dishonor yourself by such cruelty? No, I will not, I cannot do that. Rather would I let him live and die here, and then mason up his remains in the wall. What, then, will you do? For all your coaxing, he will not budge. Bribes he leaves under your own paper-weight on your table; in short, it is quite plain that he prefers to cling to you.

Then something severe, something unusual must be done. What! surely you will not have him collared by a constable, and commit his innocent pallor to the common jail? And upon what ground could you procure such a thing to be done?—a vagrant, is he? What! he a vagrant, a wanderer, who refuses to budge? It is because he will *not* be a vagrant, then, that you seek to count him *as* a vagrant. That is too absurd. No visible means of support: there I have him. Wrong again: for indubitably he *does* support himself, and that is the only un-answerable proof that any man can show of his possessing the means so to do. No more, then. Since he will not quit me, I must quit him. I will change my offices; I will move else-where, and give him fair notice, that if I find him on my new premises I will then proceed against him as a common tres-passer.

Acting accordingly, next day I thus addressed him: "I find these chambers too far from the City Hall; the air is unwhole-some. In a word, I propose to remove my offices next week, and shall no longer require your services. I tell you this now, in order that you may seek another place."

He made no reply; and nothing more was said.

On the appointed day I engaged carts and men, proceeded to my chambers, and, having but little furniture, everything was removed in a few hours. Throughout, the scrivener remained standing behind the screen, which I directed to be removed the last thing. It was withdrawn; and, being folded up like a huge folio, left him the motionless occupant of a naked room. I stood in the entry watching him a moment, while something from within me upbraided me.

I re-entered, with my hand in my pocket—and—and my heart in my mouth.

"Good-by, Bartleby; I am going—good-by, and God some way bless you; and take that," slipping something in his hand. But it dropped upon the floor, and then—strange to say—I tore myself from him whom I had so longed to be rid of.

Established in my new quarters, for a day or two I kept the door locked, and started at every footfall in the passages. When I returned to my rooms, after any little absence, I would pause at the threshold for an instant, and attentively listen, ere applying my key. But these fears were needless. Bartleby never came nigh me.

I thought all was going well, when a perturbed-looking stranger visited me, inquiring whether I was the person who had recently occupied rooms at No. — Wall Street.

Full of forebodings, I replied that I was.

"Then, sir," said the stranger, who proved a lawyer, "you are responsible for the man you left there. He refuses to do any copying; he refuses to do anything; he says he prefers not to; and he refuses to quit the premises."

"I am very sorry, sir," said I, with assumed tranquillity, but an inward tremor, "but, really, the man you allude to is nothing to me—he is no relation or apprentice of mine, that you should hold me responsible for him."

"In mercy's name, who is he?"

"I certainly cannot inform you. I know nothing about him. Formerly I employed him as a copyist; but he has done nothing for me now for some time past."

"I shall settle him, then—good morning, sir."

Several days passed, and I heard nothing more; and, though I often felt a charitable prompting to call at the place and see poor Bartleby, yet a certain squeamishness, of I know not what, withheld me.

All is over with him, by this time, thought I, at last, when, through another week, no further intelligence reached me. But, coming to my room the day after, I found several persons waiting at my door in a high state of nervous excitement.

"That's the man—here he comes," cried the foremost one, whom I recognized as the lawyer who had previously called upon me alone.

"You must take him away, sir, at once," cried a portly person among them, advancing upon me, and whom I knew to be the landlord of No. — Wall Street. "These gentlemen, my tenants, cannot stand it any longer; Mr. B——," pointing to the lawyer, "has turned him out of his room, and he now persists in haunting the building generally, sitting upon the banisters of the stairs by day, and sleeping in the entry by night. Everybody is concerned; clients are leaving the offices; some fears are entertained of a mob; something you must do, and that without delay."

Aghast at this torrent, I fell back before it, and would fain have locked myself in my new quarters. In vain I persisted that Bartleby was nothing to me—no more than to any one else. In vain—I was the last person known to have anything to do with him, and they held me to the terrible account. Fearful, then, of being exposed in the papers (as one person present obscurely threatened), I considered the matter, and, at length, said, that if the lawyer would give me a confidential interview with the scrivener, in his (the lawyer's) own room, I would, that afternoon, strive my best to rid them of the nuisance they complained of.

Going upstairs to my old haunt, there was Bartleby silently sitting upon the banister at the landing.

"What are you doing here, Bartleby?" said I.

"Sitting upon the banister," he mildly replied.

I motioned him into the lawyer's room, who then left us.

"Bartleby," said I, "are you aware that you are the cause of great tribulation to me, by persisting in occupying the entry after being dismissed from the office?"

No answer.

"Now one of two things must take place. Either you must do something, or something must be done to you. Now what sort of business would you like to engage in? Would you like to re-engage in copying for some one?"

"No; I would prefer not to make any change."

"Would you like a clerkship in a dry-goods store?"

"There is too much confinement about that. No, I would not like a clerkship; but I am not particular."

"Too much confinement," I cried, "why you keep yourself confined all the time!"

"I would prefer not to take a clerkship," he rejoined, as if to settle that little item at once.

"How would a bar-tender's business suit you? There is no trying of the eye-sight in that."

"I would not like it at all; though, as I said before, I am not particular."

His unwonted wordiness inspirited me. I returned to the charge.

"Well, then, would you like to travel through the country collecting bills for the merchants? That would improve your health."

"No, I would prefer to be doing something else."

"How, then, would going as a companion to Europe, to entertain some young gentleman with your conversation—how would that suit you?"

"Not at all. It does not strike me that there is anything definite about that. I like to be stationary. But I am not particular."

"Stationary you shall be, then," I cried, now losing all patience, and, for the first time in all my exasperating connection with him, fairly flying into a passion. "If you do not go away from these premises before night, I shall feel bound—indeed, I *am* bound—to—to—to quit the premises myself!" I rather absurdly concluded, knowing not with what possible threat to try to frighten his immobility into compliance. Despairing of all further efforts, I was precipitately leaving him, when a final thought occurred to me—one which had not been wholly unindulged before.

"Bartleby," said I, in the kindest tone I could assume under such exciting circumstances, "will you go home with me now —not to my office, but my dwelling—and remain there till we can conclude upon some convenient arrangement for you at our leisure? Come, let us start now, right away."

"No: at present I would prefer not to make any change at all."

I answered nothing; but, effectually dodging every one by the suddenness and rapidity of my flight, rushed from the building, ran up Wall Street towards Broadway, and, jumping into the first omnibus, was soon removed from pursuit. As soon as tranquillity returned, I distinctly perceived that I had now done all that I possibly could, both in respect to the demands of the landlord and his tenants, and with regard to my own desire and sense of duty, to benefit Bartleby, and shield him from rude persecution. I now strove to be entirely carefree and quiescent; and my conscience justified me in the attempt; though, indeed, it was not so successful as I could have wished. So

fearful was I of being again hunted out by the incensed landlord and his exasperated tenants, that, surrendering my business
to Nippers, for a few days, I drove about the upper part of the
town and through the suburbs, in my rockaway; crossed over
to Jersey City and Hoboken, and paid fugitive visits to Manhat-
tanville and Astoria. In fact, I almost lived in my rockaway
for the time.

When again I entered my office, lo, a note from the landlord
lay upon the desk. I opened it with trembling hands. It informed me that the writer had sent to the police, and had
Bartleby removed to the Tombs as a vagrant. Moreover, since
I knew more about him than any one else, he wished me to
appear at that place, and make a suitable statement of the facts.
These tidings had a conflicting effect upon me. At first I was
indignant; but, at last, almost approved. The landlord's energetic, summary disposition, had led him to adopt a procedure
which I do not think I would have decided upon myself; and
yet, as a last resort, under such peculiar circumstances, it seemed
the only plan.

As I afterwards learned, the poor scrivener, when told that
he must be conducted to the Tombs, offered not the slightest
obstacle, but, in his pale, unmoving way, silently acquiesced.

Some of the compassionate and curious bystanders joined the
party; and headed by one of the constables arm in arm with
Bartleby, the silent procession filed its way through all the noise,
and heat, and joy of the roaring thoroughfares at noon.

The same day I received the note, I went to the Tombs, or,
to speak more properly, the Halls of Justice. Seeking the right
officer, I stated the purpose of my call, and was informed that
the individual I described was, indeed, within. I then assured
the functionary that Bartleby was a perfectly honest man, and
greatly to be compassionated, however unaccountably eccentric.
I narrated all I knew, and closed by suggesting the idea of letting him remain in as indulgent confinement as possible, till

something less harsh might be done—though, indeed, I hardly knew what. At all events, if nothing else could be decided upon, the almshouse must receive him. I then begged to have an interview.

Being under no disgraceful charge, and quite serene and harmless in all his ways, they had permitted him freely to wander about the prison, and, especially, in the inclosed grass-platted yards thereof. And so I found him there, standing all alone in the quietest of the yards, his face towards a high wall, while all around, from the narrow slits of the jail windows, I thought I saw peering out upon him the eyes of murderers and thieves.

"Bartleby!"

"I know you," he said, without looking round—"and I want nothing to say to you."

"It was not I that brought you here, Bartleby," said I, keenly pained at his implied suspicion. "And to you, this should not be so vile a place. Nothing reproachful attaches to you by being here. And see, it is not so sad a place as one might think. Look, there is the sky, and here is the grass."

"I know where I am," he replied, but would say nothing more, and so I left him.

As I entered the corridor again, a broad meatlike man, in an apron, accosted me, and, jerking his thumb over his shoulder, said—"Is that your friend?"

"Yes."

"Does he want to starve? If he does, let him live on the prison fare, that's all."

"Who are you?" asked I, not knowing what to make of such an unofficially speaking person in such a place.

"I am the grub-man. Such gentlemen as have friends here, hire me to provide them with something good to eat."

"Is this so?" said I, turning to the turnkey.

He said it was.

"Well, then," said I, slipping some silver into the grub-man's hands (for so they called him), "I want you to give particular attention to my friend there; let him have the best dinner you can get. And you must be as polite to him as possible."

"Introduce me, will you?" said the grub-man, looking at me with an expression which seemed to say he was all impatience for an opportunity to give a specimen of his breeding.

Thinking it would prove of benefit to the scrivener, I acquiesced; and, asking the grub-man his name, went up with him to Bartleby.

"Bartleby, this is a friend; you will find him very useful to you."

"Your sarvant, sir, your sarvant," said the grub-man, making a low salutation behind his apron. "Hope you find it pleasant here, sir; nice grounds—cool apartments—hope you'll stay with us sometime—try to make it agreeable. What will you have for dinner today?"

"I prefer not to dine today," said Bartleby, turning away. "It would disagree with me; I am unused to dinners." So saying, he slowly moved to the other side of the inclosure, and took up a position fronting the dead-wall.

"How's this?" said the grub-man, addressing me with a stare of astonishment. "He's odd, ain't he?"

"I think he is a little deranged," said I, sadly.

"Deranged? deranged, is it? Well, now, upon my word, I thought that friend of yourn was a gentleman forger; they are always pale and genteel-like, them forgers. I can't help pity 'em—can't help it, sir. Did you know Monroe Edwards?" he added, touchingly, and paused. Then, laying his hand piteously on my shoulder, sighed, "he died of consumption at Sing-Sing. So you weren't acquainted with Monroe?"

"No, I was never socially acquainted with any forgers. But I cannot stop longer. Look to my friend yonder. You will not lose by it. I will see you again."

Some few days after this, I again obtained admission to the Tombs, and went through the corridors in quest of Bartleby; but without finding him.

"I saw him coming from his cell not long ago," said a turnkey, "maybe he's gone to loiter in the yards."

So I went in that direction.

"Are you looking for the silent man?" said another turnkey, passing me. "Yonder he lies—sleeping in the yard there. 'Tis not twenty minutes since I saw him lie down."

The yard was entirely quiet. It was not accessible to the common prisoners. The surrounding walls, of amazing thickness, kept off all sounds behind them. The Egyptian character of the masonry weighed upon me with its gloom. But a soft imprisoned turf grew underfoot. The heart of the eternal pyramids, it seemed, wherein, by some strange magic, through the clefts, grass seed, dropped by birds, had sprung.

Strangely huddled at the base of the wall, his knees drawn up, and lying on his side, his head touching the cold stones, I saw the wasted Bartleby. But nothing stirred. I paused; then went close up to him; stooped over, and saw that his dim eyes were open; otherwise he seemed profoundly sleeping. Something prompted me to touch him. I felt his hand, when a tingling shiver ran up my arm and down my spine to my feet.

The round face of the grub-man peered upon me now. "His dinner is ready. Won't he dine today, either? Or does he live without dining?"

"Lives without dining," said I, and closed the eyes.

"Eh!—He's asleep, ain't he?"

"With kings and counselors," murmured I.

There would seem little need for proceeding further in this history. Imagination will readily supply the meagre recital of poor Bartleby's interment. But, ere parting with the reader, let me say, that if this little narrative has sufficiently interested him, to awaken curiosity as to who Bartleby was, and what manner of life he led prior to the present narrator's making his acquaintance, I can only reply, that in such curiosity I fully share, but am wholly unable to gratify it. Yet here I hardly know whether I should divulge one little item of rumor, which came to my ear a few months after the scrivener's decease. Upon what basis it rested, I could never ascertain; and hence, how true it is I cannot now tell. But, inasmuch as this vague report has not been without a certain suggestive interest to me, however sad, it may prove the same with some others; and so I will briefly mention it. The report was this: that Bartleby had been a subordinate clerk in the Dead Letter Office at Washington, from which he had been suddenly removed by a change in the administration. When I think over this rumor, hardly can I express the emotions which seize me. Dead letters! does it not sound like dead men? Conceive a man by nature and misfortune prone to a pallid hopelessness, can any business seem more fitted to heighten it than that of continually handling these dead letters, and assorting them for the flames? For by the cartload they are annually burned. Sometimes from out the folded paper the pale clerk takes a ring—the finger it was meant for, perhaps, moulders in the grave; a bank-note sent in swiftest charity—he whom it would relieve, nor eats nor hungers any more; pardon for those who died despairing; hope for those who died unhoping; good tidings for those who died stifled by unrelieved calamities. On errands of life, these letters speed to death.

Ah, Bartleby! Ah, humanity!

MARIO AND THE MAGICIAN

by THOMAS MANN

THE ATMOSPHERE of Torre di Venere remains unpleasant in the memory. From the first moment the air of the place made us uneasy, we felt irritable, on edge; then at the end came the shocking business of Cipolla, that dreadful being who seemed to incorporate, in so fateful and so humanly impressive a way, all the peculiar evilness of the situation as a whole. Looking back, we had the feeling that the horrible end of the affair had been preordained and lay in the nature of things; that the children had to be present at it was an added impropriety, due to the false colors in which the weird creature presented himself. Luckily for them, they did not know where the comedy left off and the tragedy began; and we let them remain in their happy belief that the whole thing had been a play up till the end.

Torre di Venere lies some fifteen kilometers from Portoclemente, one of the most popular summer resorts on the Tyrrhenian Sea. Portoclemente is urban and elegant and full to overflowing for months on end. Its gay and busy main street of shops and hotels runs down to a wide sandy beach covered with tents and pennanted sand-castles and sunburnt humanity, where at all times a lively social bustle reigns, and much noise. But this same spacious and inviting fine-sanded beach, this same border of pine grove and near, presiding mountains, continues all the way along the coast. No wonder then that some competition of a quiet kind should have sprung up further on. Torre di Venere—the tower that gave the town its name is gone long since, one looks for it in vain—is an offshoot of the larger resort, and for some years remained an idyll for the few, a refuge for more unworldly spirits. But the usual history of such places repeated itself: peace has had to retire further along the coast, to Marina Petriera and dear knows where else. We' all know how the world at once seeks peace and puts her to flight —rushing upon her in the fond idea that they two will wed, and where she is, there it can be at home. It will even set up its Vanity Fair in a spot and be capable of thinking that peace is still by its side. Thus Torre—though its atmosphere so far is more modest and contemplative than that of Portoclemente— has been quite taken up, by both Italians and foreigners. It is no longer the thing to go to Portoclemente—though still so much the thing that it is as noisy and crowded as ever. One goes next door, so to speak: to Torre. So much more refined, even, and cheaper to boot. And the attractiveness of these qualities persists, though the qualities themselves long ago ceased to be evident. Torre has got a Grand Hotel. Numerous pensions have sprung up, some modest, some pretentious. The people who own or rent the villas and pinetas overlooking the sea no longer have it all their own way on the beach. In July and August it looks just like the beach at Portoclemente: it swarms with a screaming, squabbling, merrymaking crowd, and the sun, blazing down like mad, peels the skin off their necks. Garish little flat-bottomed boats rock on the glittering blue, manned by children, whose mothers hover afar and fill the air with anxious cries of Nino! and Sandro! and Bice! and Maria! Peddlers step across the legs of recumbent sun-bathers, selling flowers and corals, oysters, lemonade, and *cornetti al burro,* and crying their wares in the breathy, full-throated southern voice.

Such was the scene that greeted our arrival in Torre: pleasant

enough, but after all, we thought, we had come too soon. It was
the middle of August, the Italian season was still at its height,
scarcely the moment for strangers to learn to love the special
charms of the place. What an afternoon crowd in the cafés on
the front! For instance, in the Esquisito, where we sometimes
sat and were served by Mario, that very Mario of whom I shall
have presently to tell. It is well-nigh impossible to find a table;
and the various orchestras contend together in the midst of one's
conversation with bewildering effect. Of course, it is in the
afternoon that people come over from Portoclemente. The ex-
cursion is a favorite one for the restless denizens of that pleasure
resort, and a Fiat motor-bus plies to and fro, coating inch-thick
with dust the oleander and laurel hedges along the highroad—
a notable if repulsive sight.

Yes, decidedly one should go to Torre in September, when
the great public has left. Or else in May, before the water is
warm enough to tempt the Southerner to bathe. Even in the
before and after seasons Torre is not empty, but life is less
national and more subdued. English, French, and German pre-
vail under the tent-awnings and in the pension dining-rooms;
whereas in August—in the Grand Hotel, at least, where, in de-
fault of private addresses, we had engaged rooms—the stranger
finds the field so occupied by Florentine and Roman society that
he feels quite isolated and even temporarily *déclassé*.

We had, rather to our annoyance, this experience on the evening we arrived, when we went in to dinner and were shown
to our table by the waiter in charge. As a table, it had nothing
against it, save that we had already fixed our eyes upon those
on the veranda beyond, built out over the water, where little
red-shaded lamps glowed—and there were still some tables
empty, though it was as full as the dining-room within. The
children went into raptures at the festive sight, and without
more ado we announced our intention to take our meals by

preference in the veranda. Our words, it appeared, were prompted by ignorance; for we were informed, with somewhat embarrassed politeness, that the cozy nook outside was reserved for the clients of the hotel: *ai nostri clienti*. Their clients? But we were their clients. We were not tourists or trippers, but boarders for a stay of some three or four weeks. However, we forbore to press for an explanation of the difference between the likes of us and that clientèle to whom it was vouchsafed to eat out there in the glow of the red lamps, and took our dinner by the prosaic common light of the dining-room chandelier—a thoroughly ordinary and monotonous hotel bill of fare, be it said. In Pensione Eleonora, a few steps landward, the table, as we were to discover, was much better.

And thither it was that we moved, three or four days later, before we had had time to settle in properly at the Grand Hotel. Not on account of the veranda and the lamps. The children, straightway on the best of terms with waiters and pages, absorbed in the joys of life on the beach, promptly forgot those colorful seductions. But now there arose, between ourselves and the veranda clientèle—or perhaps more correctly with the compliant management—one of those little unpleasantnesses which can quite spoil the pleasure of a holiday. Among the guests were some high Roman aristocracy, a Principe X and his family. These grand folk occupied rooms close to our own, and the Principessa, a great and a passionately maternal lady, was thrown into a panic by the vestiges of a whooping-cough which our little ones had lately got over, but which now and then still faintly troubled the unshatterable slumbers of our youngest-born. The nature of this illness is not clear, leaving some play for the imagination. So we took no offense at our elegant neighbor for clinging to the widely held view that whooping-cough is acoustically contagious and quite simply fearing lest her children yield to the bad example set by ours. In the fullness of her feminine self-confidence she protested to the management, which then, in the person of the proverbial frock-coated manager, hastened to represent to us, with many expressions of regret, that under the circumstances they were obliged to transfer us to the annexe. We did our best to assure him that the disease was in its very last stages, that it was actually over, and presented no danger of infection to anybody. All that we gained was permission to bring the case before the hotel physician—not one chosen by us—by whose verdict we must then abide. We agreed, convinced that thus we should at once pacify the Princess and escape the trouble of moving. The doctor appeared, and behaved like a faithful and honest servant of science. He examined the child and gave his opinion: the disease was quite over, no danger of contagion was present. We drew a long breath and considered the incident closed—until the manager announced that despite the doctor's verdict it would still be necessary for us to give up our rooms and retire to the *dépendance*. Byzantinism like this outraged us. It is not likely that the Principessa was responsible for the willful breach of faith. Very likely the fawning management had not even dared to tell her what the physician said. Anyhow, we made it clear to his understanding that we preferred to leave the hotel altogether and at once—and packed our trunks. We could do so with a light heart, having already set up casual friendly relations with Casa Eleonora. We had noticed its pleasant exterior and formed the acquaintance of its proprietor, Signora Angiolieri, and her husband: she slender and black-haired, Tuscan in type, probably at the beginning of the thirties, with the dead ivory complexion of the southern woman, he quiet and bald and carefully dressed. They owned a larger establishment in Florence and presided only in summer and early autumn over the branch in Torre di Venere. But earlier, before her marriage, our new landlady had been companion, fellow-traveler, wardrobe mistress, yes, friend, of Eleonora Duse and manifestly regarded that period as the crown of her career. Even at our first visit she spoke of it with animation. Numerous photographs of the great actress, with affectionate inscriptions, were displayed about the drawing-room, and other souvenirs of their life together adorned the little tables and étagères. This cult of a so interesting past was calculated, of course, to heighten the advantages of the signora's present business. Nevertheless our pleasure and interest were quite genuine as we were conducted through the house by its owner and listened to her sonorous and staccato Tuscan voice relating anecdotes of that immortal mistress, depicting her suffering saintliness, her genius, her profound delicacy of feeling.

Thither, then, we moved our effects, to the dismay of the staff of the Grand Hotel, who, like all Italians, were very good to children. Our new quarters were retired and pleasant, we were within easy reach of the sea through the avenue of young plane trees that ran down to the esplanade. In the clean, cool dining-room Signora Angiolieri daily served the soup with her own hands, the service was attentive and good, the table capital. We even discovered some Viennese acquaintances, and enjoyed chatting with them after luncheon, in front of the house. They, in their turn, were the means of our finding others—in short, all seemed for the best, and we were heartily glad of the change we had made. Nothing was now wanting to a holiday of the most gratifying kind.

And yet no proper gratification ensued. Perhaps the stupid occasion of our change of quarters pursued us to the new ones we had found. Personally, I admit that I do not easily forget these collisions with ordinary humanity, the naïve misuse of power, the injustice, the sycophantic corruption. I dwelt upon the incident too much, it irritated me in retrospect—quite futilely, of course, since such phenomena are only all too natural and all too much the rule. And we had not broken off relations with the Grand Hotel. The children were as friendly as ever there, the porter mended their toys, and we sometimes took tea in the garden. We even saw the Principessa. She would come out, with her firm and delicate tread, her lips emphatically corallined, to look after her children, playing under the supervision of their English governess. She did not dream that we were anywhere near, for so soon as she appeared in the offing we sternly forbade our little one even to clear his throat.

The heat—if I may bring it in evidence—was extreme. It was African. The power of the sun, directly one left the border of the indigo-blue wave, was so frightful, so relentless, that the mere thought of the few steps between the beach and luncheon was a burden, clad though one might be only in pajamas. Do you care for that sort of thing? Weeks on end? Yes, of course, it is proper to the south, it is classic weather, the sun of Homer, the climate wherein human culture came to flower—and all the rest of it. But after a while it is too much for me, I reach a point where I begin to find it dull. The burning void of the sky, day after day, weighs one down; the high coloration, the enormous naïveté of the unrefracted light—they do, I dare say, induce light-heartedness, a care-free mood born of immunity from downpours and other meteorological caprices. But slowly, slowly, there makes itself felt a lack: the deeper, more complex needs of the northern soul remain unsatisfied. You are left barren—even, it may be, in time, a little contemptuous. True, without that stupid business of the whooping-cough I might not have been feeling these things. I was annoyed, very likely I wanted to feel them and so half-unconsciously seized upon an idea lying ready to hand to induce, or if not to induce, at least to justify and strengthen, my attitude. Up to this point, then, if you like, let us grant some ill will on our part. But the sea; and the mornings spent extended upon the fine sand in face of its eternal splendors—no, the sea could not conceivably induce such feelings. Yet it was none the less true that, despite all previous experience, we were not at home on the beach, we were not happy.

It was too soon, too soon. The beach, as I have said, was still in the hands of the middle-class native. It is a pleasing breed to look at, and among the young we saw much shapeliness and charm. Still, we were necessarily surrounded by a great deal of very average humanity—a middle-class mob, which, you will admit, is not more charming under this sun than under one's own native sky. The voices these women have! It was sometimes hard to believe that we were in the land which is the western cradle of the art of song. *"Fuggièro!"* I can still hear that cry, as for twenty mornings long I heard it close behind me, breathy, full-throated, hideously stressed, with a harsh open *e,* uttered in accents of mechanical despair. *"Fuggièro! Rispondi almeno!"* Answer when I call you! The *sp* in *rispondi* was pronounced like *shp,* as Germans pronounce it; and this, on top of what I felt already, vexed my sensitive soul. The cry was addressed to a repulsive youngster whose sunburn had made disgusting raw sores on his shoulders. He outdid anything I have ever seen for ill-breeding, refractoriness, and temper and was a great coward to boot, putting the whole beach in an uproar, one day, because of his outrageous sensitiveness to the slightest pain. A sand-crab had pinched his toe in the water, and the minute injury made him set up a cry of heroic proportions—the shout of an antique hero in his agony—that pierced one to the marrow and called up visions of some frightful tragedy. Evidently he considered himself not only wounded, but poisoned as well; he crawled out on the sand and lay in apparently intolerable anguish, groaning *"Ohi!"* and *"Ohimè!"* and threshing about with arms and legs to ward off his mother's tragic appeals and the questions of the bystanders. An audience gathered round. A doctor was fetched ‑‑the same who had pronounced objective judgment on our whooping-cough—and here again acquitted himself like a man of science. Good-naturedly he reassured the boy, telling him that he was not hurt at all, he should simply go into the water again to relieve the smart. Instead of which, Fuggièro was borne off the beach, followed by a concourse of people. But he did not fail to appear next morning, nor did he leave off spoiling our children's sand-castles. Of course, always by accident. In short, a perfect terror.

And this twelve-year-old lad was prominent among the influences that, imperceptibly at first, combined to spoil our holiday and render it unwholesome. Somehow or other, there was a stiffness, a lack of innocent enjoyment. These people stood on their dignity—just why, and in what spirit, it was not easy at first to tell. They displayed much self-respectingness; towards each other and towards the foreigner their bearing was that of a person newly conscious of a sense of honor. And wherefore? Gradually we realized the political implications and understood that we were in the presence of a national ideal. The beach, in fact, was alive with patriotic children—a phenomenon as unnatural as it was depressing. Children are a human species and a society apart, a nation of their own, so to speak. On the basis of their common form of life, they find each other out with the greatest ease, no matter how different their small vocabularies. Ours soon played with natives and foreigners alike. Yet they were plainly both puzzled and disappointed at times. There were wounded sensibilities, displays of assertiveness—or rather hardly assertiveness, for it was too self-conscious and too didactic to deserve the name. There were quarrels over flags, disputes about authority and precedence. Grown-ups joined in, not so much to pacify as to render judgment and enunciate principles. Phrases were dropped about the greatness and dignity of Italy, solemn phrases that spoilt the fun. We saw our two little ones retreat, puzzled and hurt, and were put to it to explain the situation. These people, we told them, were just passing through a certain stage, something rather like an illness, perhaps; not very pleasant, but probably unavoidable.

We had only our own carelessness to thank that we came to blows in the end with this "stage"—which, after all, we had seen and sized up long before now. Yes, it came to another "cross-purposes," so evidently the earlier ones had not been sheer accident. In a word, we became an offense to the public morals. Our small daughter—eight years old, but in physical development a good year younger and thin as a chicken—had had a good long bathe and gone playing in the warm sun in her wet costume. We told her that she might take off her bathing-suit, which was stiff with sand, rinse it in the sea, and put it on again, after which she must take care to keep it cleaner. Off goes the costume and she runs down naked to the sea, rinses her little jersey, and comes back. Ought we to have foreseen the outburst of anger and resentment which her conduct, and thus our conduct, called forth? Without delivering a homily on the subject, I may say that in the last decade our attitude towards the nude body and our feelings regarding it have undergone, all over the world, a fundamental change. There are things we "never think about" any more, and among them is the freedom we had permitted to this by no means provocative little childish body. But in these parts it was taken as a challenge. The patriotic children hooted. Fuggièro whistled on his fingers. The sudden buzz of conversation among the grown people in our neighborhood boded no good. A gentleman in city togs, with a not very apropos bowler hat on the back of his head, was assuring his outraged womenfolk that he proposed to take punitive measures; he stepped up to us, and a philippic descended on our unworthy heads, in which all the emotionalism of the sense-loving south spoke in the service of morality and discipline. The offense against decency of which we had been guilty was, he said, the more to be condemned because it was also a gross ingratitude and an insulting breach of his country's hospitality. We had criminally injured not only the letter and spirit of the public bathing regulations, but also the honor of Italy; he, the gentleman in the city togs, knew how to defend that honor and proposed to see to it that our offense against the national dignity should not go unpunished.

We did our best, bowing respectfully, to give ear to this eloquence. To contradict the man, overheated as he was, would probably be to fall from one error into another. On the tips of our tongues we had various answers: as, that the word "hospitality," in its strictest sense, was not quite the right one, taking all the circumstances into consideration. We were not literally the guests of Italy, but of Signora Angiolieri, who had assumed the role of dispenser of hospitality some years ago on laying down that of familiar friend to Eleonora Duse. We longed to say that surely this beautiful country had not sunk so low as to be reduced to a state of hypersensitive prudishness. But we confined ourselves to assuring the gentleman that any lack of respect, any provocation on our parts, had been the furthest from our thoughts. And as a mitigating circumstance we pointed out the tender age and physical slightness of the little culprit. In vain. Our protests were waved away, he did not believe in them; our defense would not hold water. We must be made an example of. The authorities were notified, by telephone, I believe, and their representative appeared on the beach. He said the case was *"molto grave."* We had to go with him to the Municipio up in the Piazza, where a higher official confirmed the previous verdict of *"molto grave,"* launched into a stream of the usual didactic phrases—the selfsame tune and words as the man in the bowler hat—and levied a fine and ransom of fifty lire. We felt that the adventure must willy-nilly be worth to us this much of a contribution to the economy of the Italian government;

paid, and left. Ought we not at this point to have left Torre as well?

If we only had! We should thus have escaped that fatal Cipolla. But circumstances combined to prevent us from making up our minds to a change. A certain poet says that it is indolence that makes us endure uncomfortable situations. The *aperçu* may serve as an explanation for our inaction. Anyhow, one dislikes voiding the field immediately upon such an event. Especially if sympathy from other quarters encourages one to defy it. And in the Villa Eleonora they pronounced as with one voice upon the injustice of our punishment. Some Italian after-dinner acquaintances found that the episode put their country in a very bad light, and proposed taking the man in the bowler hat to task, as one fellow-citizen to another. But the next day he and his party had vanished from the beach. Not on our account, of course. Though it might be that the consciousness of his impending departure had added energy to his rebuke; in any case his going was a relief. And, furthermore, we stayed because our stay had by now become remarkable in our own eyes, which is worth something in itself, quite apart from the comfort or discomfort involved. Shall we strike sail, avoid a certain experience so soon as it seems not expressly calculated to increase our enjoyment or our self-esteem? Shall we go away whenever life looks like turning in the slightest uncanny, or not quite normal, or even rather painful and mortifying? No, surely not. Rather stay and look matters in the face, brave them out; perhaps precisely in so doing lies a lesson for us to learn. We stayed on and reaped as the awful reward of our constancy the unholy and staggering experience with Cipolla.

I have not mentioned that the after season had begun, almost on the very day we were disciplined by the city authorities. The worshipful gentleman in the bowler hat, our denouncer, was not the only person to leave the resort. There was a regular exodus, on every hand you saw luggage-carts on their way to the station. The beach denationalized itself. Life in Torre, in the cafés and the pinetas, became more homelike and more European. Very likely we might even have eaten at a table in the glass veranda, but we refrained, being content at Signora Angiolieri's—as content, that is, as our evil star would let us be. But at the same time with this turn for the better came a change in the weather: almost to an hour it showed itself in harmony with the holiday calendar of the general public. The sky was overcast; not that it grew any cooler, but the unclouded heat of the entire eighteen days since our arrival, and probably long before that, gave place to a stifling sirocco air, while from time to time a little ineffectual rain sprinkled the velvety surface of the beach. Add to which, that two-thirds of our intended stay at Torre had passed. The colorless, lazy sea, with sluggish jellyfish floating in its shallows, was at least a change. And it would have been silly to feel retrospective longings after a sun that had caused us so many sighs when it burned down in all its arrogant power.

At this juncture, then, it was that Cipolla announced himself. Cavaliere Cipolla he was called on the posters that appeared one day stuck up everywhere, even in the dining-room of Pensione Eleonora. A traveling virtuoso, an entertainer, *"forzatore, illusionista, prestidigitatore,"* as he called himself, who proposed to wait upon the highly respectable population of Torre di Venere with a display of extraordinary phenomena of a mysterious and staggering kind. A conjuror! The bare announcement was enough to turn our children's heads. They had never seen anything of the sort, and now our present holiday was to afford them this new excitement. From that moment on they besieged us with prayers to take tickets for the performance. We had doubts, from the first, on the score of the lateness of the hour, nine o'clock; but gave way, in the idea that we might see a little of what Cipolla had to offer, probably no great matter, and then go home. Besides, of course, the children could sleep late next day. We bought four tickets of Signora Angiolieri herself, she having taken a number of the stalls on commission to sell them to her guests. She could not vouch for the man's performance, and we had no great expectations. But we were conscious of a need for diversion, and the children's violent curiosity proved catching.

The Cavaliere's performance was to take place in a hall where during the season there had been a cinema with a weekly program. We had never been there. You reached it by following the main street under the wall of the *"palazzo,"* a ruin with a "For sale" sign, that suggested a castle and had obviously been built in lordlier days. In the same street were the chemist, the hairdresser, and all the better shops; it led, so to speak, from the feudal past the bourgeois into the proletarian, for it ended off between two rows of poor fishing-huts, where old women sat mending nets before the doors. And here, among the proletariat, was the hall, not much more, actually, than a wooden shed, though a large one, with a turreted entrance, plastered on either side with layers of gay placards. Some while after dinner, then, on the appointed evening, we wended our way thither in the dark, the children dressed in their best and blissful with the sense of so much irregularity. It was sultry, as it had been for days; there was heat lightning now and then, and a little rain; we proceeded under umbrellas. It took us a quarter of an hour.

Our tickets were collected at the entrance, our places we had to find ourselves. They were in the third row left, and as we sat down we saw that, late though the hour was for the performance, it was to be interpreted with even more laxity. Only very slowly did an audience—who seemed to be relied upon to come late—begin to fill the stalls. These comprised the whole auditorium; there were no boxes. This tardiness gave us some concern. The children's cheeks were already flushed as much with fatigue as with excitement. But even when we entered, the standing-room at the back and in the side aisles was already well occupied. There stood the manhood of Torre di Venere, all and sundry, fisherfolk, rough-and-ready youths with bare forearms crossed over their striped jerseys. We were well pleased with the presence of this native assemblage, which always adds color and animation to occasions like the present; and the children were frankly delighted. For they had friends among these people—acquaintances picked up on afternoon strolls to the further ends of the beach. We would be turning homeward, at the hour when the sun dropped into the sea, spent with the huge effort it had made and gilding with reddish gold the oncoming surf; and we would come upon bare-legged fisherfolk standing in rows, bracing and hauling with long-drawn cries as they drew in the nets and harvested in dripping baskets their catch, often so scanty, of *frutta di mare*. The children looked on, helped to pull, brought out their little stock of Italian words, made friends. So now they exchanged nods with the "standing-room" clientèle: there was Guiscardo, there Antonio, they knew them by name and waved and called across in half-whispers, getting answering nods and smiles that displayed rows of healthy white teeth. Look, there is even Mario, Mario from the Esquisito, who brings us the chocolate. He wants to see the conjuror, too, and he must have come early, for he is almost in front; but he does not see us, he is not paying attention; that is a way he has, even though he is a waiter. So we wave instead to the man who lets out the little boats on the beach; he is there too, standing at the back.

It had got to a quarter past nine, it got to almost half past. It was natural that we should be nervous. When would the children get to bed? It had been a mistake to bring them, for now it would be very hard to suggest breaking off their enjoyment before it had got well under way. The stalls had filled in time; all Torre, apparently, was there: the guests of the Grand Hotel, the guests of Villa Eleonora, familiar faces from the beach. We heard English and German and the sort of French that Rumanians speak with Italians. Madame Angiolieri herself sat two rows behind us, with her quiet, bald-headed spouse, who kept stroking his mustache with the two middle fingers of his right hand. Everybody had come late, but nobody too late. Cipolla made us wait for him.

He made us wait. That is probably the way to put it. He heightened the suspense by his delay in appearing. And we could see the point of this, too—only not when it was carried to extremes. Towards half past nine the audience began to clap— an amiable way of expressing justifiable impatience, evincing as it does an eagerness to applaud. For the little ones, this was a joy in itself—all children love to clap. From the popular sphere came loud cries of *"Pronti!"* *"Cominciamo!"* And lo, it seemed now as easy to begin as before it had been hard. A gong sounded, greeted by the standing rows with a many-voiced "Ah-h!" and the curtains parted. They revealed a platform furnished more like a schoolroom than like the theater of a conjuring performance—largely because of the blackboard in the left foreground. There was a common yellow hat-stand, a few ordinary straw-bottomed chairs, and further back a little round table holding a water carafe and glass, also a tray with a liqueur glass and a flask of pale yellow liquid. We had still a few seconds of time to let these things sink in. Then, with no darkening of the house, Cavaliere Cipolla made his entry.

He came forward with a rapid step that expressed his eagerness to appear before his public and gave rise to the illusion that he had already come a long way to put himself at their service —whereas, of course, he had only been standing in the wings. His costume supported the fiction. A man of an age hard to determine, but by no means young; with a sharp, ravaged face, piercing eyes, compressed lips, small black waxed mustache, and a so-called imperial in the curve between mouth and chin. He was dressed for the street with a sort of complicated evening elegance, in a wide black pelerine with velvet collar and satin lining; which, in the hampered state of his arms, he held together in front with his white-gloved hands. He had a white scarf round his neck; a top hat with a curving brim sat far back on his head. Perhaps more than anywhere else the eighteenth century is still alive in Italy, and with it the charlatan and mountebank type so characteristic of the period. Only there, at any rate, does one still encounter really well-preserved specimens. Cipolla had in his whole appearance much of the historic type; his very clothes helped to conjure up the traditional figure with its blatantly, fantastically foppish air. His pretentious costume sat upon him, or rather hung upon him, most curiously, being in one place drawn too tight, in another a mass of awkward folds. There was something not quite in order about his figure, both front and back—that was plain later on. But I must emphasize the fact that there was not a trace of personal jocularity or clownishness in his pose, manner, or behavior. On the contrary, there was complete seriousness, an absence of any humorous appeal; occasionally even a cross-grained pride, along with that curious, self-satisfied air so characteristic of the deformed. None of all this, however, prevented his appearance from being greeted with laughter from more than one quarter of the hall.

All the eagerness had left his manner. The swift entry had been merely an expression of energy, not of zeal. Standing at the footlights he negligently drew off his gloves, to display long yellow hands, one of them adorned with a seal ring with a lapis-lazuli in a high setting. As he stood there, his small hard eyes, with flabby pouches beneath them, roved appraisingly about the hall, not quickly, rather in a considered examination, pausing here and there upon a face with his lips clipped together, not

speaking a word. Then with a display of skill as surprising as
it was casual, he rolled his gloves into a ball and tossed them
across a considerable distance into the glass on the table. Next
from an inner pocket he drew forth a packet of cigarettes; you
could see by the wrapper that they were the cheapest sort the
government sells. With his fingertips he pulled out a cigarette
and lighted it, without looking, from a quick-firing benzine
lighter. He drew the smoke deep into his lungs and let it out
again, tapping his foot, with both lips drawn in an arrogant
grimace and the gray smoke streaming out between broken and
saw-edged teeth.

With a keenness equal to his own his audience eyed him. The
youths at the rear scowled as they peered at this cocksure creature
to search out his secret weaknesses. He betrayed none. In fetch-
ing out and putting back the cigarettes his clothes got in his
way. He had to turn back his pelerine, and in so doing revealed
a riding-whip with a silver claw-handle that hung by a leather
thong from his left forearm and looked decidedly out of place.
You could see that he had on not evening clothes but a frock-
coat, and under this, as he lifted it to get at his pocket, could
be seen a striped sash worn about the body. Somebody behind
me whispered that this sash went with his title of Cavaliere. I
give the information for what it may be worth—personally, I
never heard that the title carried such insignia with it. Perhaps
the sash was sheer pose, like the way he stood there, without a
word, casually and arrogantly puffing smoke into his audience's
face.

People laughed, as I said. The merriment had become almost
general when somebody in the "standing seats," in a loud, dry
voice, remarked: *"Buona sera."*

Cipolla cocked his head. "Who was that?" asked he, as
though he had been dared. "Who was that just spoke? Well?
First so bold and now so modest? *Paura,* eh?" He spoke with

a rather high, asthmatic voice, which yet had a metallic quality. He waited.

"That was me," a youth at the rear broke into the stillness, seeing himself thus challenged. He was not far from us, a handsome fellow in a woolen shirt, with his coat hanging over one shoulder. He wore his curly, wiry hair in a high, disheveled mop, the style affected by the youth of the awakened Fatherland; it gave him an African appearance that rather spoiled his looks. *"Bè!* That was me. It was your business to say it first, but I was trying to be friendly."

More laughter. The chap had a tongue in his head. *"Ha sciolto lo scilinguágnolo,"* I heard near me. After all, the retort was deserved.

"Ah, bravo!" answered Cipolla. "I like you, *giovanotto.* Trust me, I've had my eye on you for some time. People like you are just in my line. I can use them. And you are the pick of the lot, that's plain to see. You do what you like. Or is it possible you have ever not done what you liked—or even, maybe, what you didn't like? What somebody else liked, in short? Hark ye, my friend, that might be a pleasant change for you, to divide up the willing and the doing and stop tackling both jobs at once. Division of labor, *sistema americano, sa'!* For instance, suppose you were to show your tongue to this select and honorable audience here—your whole tongue, right down to the roots?"

"No, I won't," said the youth, hostilely. "Sticking out your tongue shows a bad bringing-up."

"Nothing of the sort," retorted Cipolla. "You would only be *doing* it. With all due respect to your bringing-up, I suggest that before I count ten, you will perform a right turn and stick out your tongue at the company here further than you knew yourself that you could stick it out."

He gazed at the youth, and his piercing eyes seemed to sink deeper into their sockets. *"Uno!"* said he. He had let his riding-whip slide down his arm and made it whistle once through the air. The boy faced about and put out his tongue, so long, so extendedly, that you could see it was the very uttermost in tongue which he had to offer. Then turned back, stony-faced, to his former position.

"That was me," mocked Cipolla, with a jerk of his head towards the youth. *"Bè!* That was me." Leaving the audience to enjoy its sensations, he turned towards the little round table, lifted the bottle, poured out a small glass of what was obviously cognac, and tipped it up with a practiced hand.

The children laughed with all their hearts. They had understood practically nothing of what had been said, but it pleased them hugely that something so funny should happen, straightaway, between that queer man up there and somebody out of the audience. They had no preconception of what an "evening" would be like and were quite ready to find this a priceless beginning. As for us, we exchanged a glance and I remember that involuntarily I made with my lips the sound that Cipolla's whip had made when it cut the air. For the rest, it was plain that people did not know what to make of a preposterous beginning like this to a sleight-of-hand performance. They could not see why the *giovanotto,* who after all in a way had been their spokesman, should suddenly have turned on them to vent his incivility. They felt that he had behaved like a silly ass and withdrew their countenances from him in favor of the artist, who now came back from his refreshment table and addressed them as follows:

"Ladies and gentleman," said he, in his wheezing, metallic voice, "you saw just now that I was rather sensitive on the score of the rebuke this hopeful young linguist saw fit to give me"— *"questo linguista di belle speranze"* was what he said, and we all laughed at the pun. "I am a man who sets some store by himself, you may take it from me. And I see no point in being wished a good-evening unless it is done courteously and in all seriousness. For anything else there is no occasion. When a man wishes me a good-evening he wishes himself one, for the audience will have one only if I do. So this lady-killer of Torre di Venere" (another thrust) "did well to testify that I have one tonight and that I can dispense with any wishes of his in the matter. I can boast of having good evenings almost without exception. One not so good does come my way now and again, but very seldom. My calling is hard and my health not of the best. I have a little physical defect which prevented me from doing my bit in the war for the greater glory of the Fatherland. It is perforce with my mental and spiritual parts that I conquer life—which after all only means conquering oneself. And I flat-ter myself that my achievements have aroused interest and re-spect among the educated public. The leading newspapers have lauded me, the *Corriere della Sera* did me the courtesy of calling me a phenomenon, and in Rome the brother of the *Duce* hon-ored me by his presence at one of my evenings. I should not have thought that in a relatively less important place" (laughter here, at the expense of poor little Torre) "I should have to give up the small personal habits which brilliant and elevated audi-ences had been ready to overlook. Nor did I think I had to stand being heckled by a person who seems to have been rather spoilt by the favors of the fair sex." All this of course at the expense of the youth whom Cipolla never tired of presenting in the guise of *donnaiuolo* and rustic Don Juan. His persistent thin-skinnedness and animosity were in striking contrast to the self-confidence and the worldly success he boasted of. One might have assumed that the *giovanotto* was merely the chosen butt of Cipolla's customary professional sallies, had not the very pointed witticisms betrayed a genuine antagonism. No one looking at the physical parts of the two men need have been at a loss for the explanation, even if the deformed man had not constantly played on the other's supposed success with the fair sex. "Well," Cipolla went on, "before beginning our entertainment this evening, perhaps you will permit me to make myself comfortable."

And he went towards the hat-stand to take off his things.

"Parla benissimo," asserted somebody in our neighborhood. So far, the man had done nothing; but what he had said was accepted as an achievement, by means of that he had made an impression. Among southern peoples speech is a constituent part of the pleasure of living, it enjoys far livelier social esteem than in the north. That national cement, the mother tongue, is paid symbolic honors down here, and there is something blithely symbolical in the pleasure people take in their respect for its forms and phonetics. They enjoy speaking, they enjoy listening; and they listen with discrimination. For the way a man speaks serves as a measure of his personal rank; carelessness and clumsiness are greeted with scorn, elegance and mastery are rewarded with social éclat. Wherefore the small man too, where it is a question of getting his effect, chooses his phrase nicely and turns it with care. On this count, then, at least, Cipolla had won his audience; though he by no means belonged to the class of men which the Italian, in a singular mixture of moral and esthetic judgments, labels *"simpatico."*

After removing his hat, scarf, and mantle he came to the front of the stage, settling his coat, pulling down his cuffs with their large cuff-buttons, adjusting his absurd sash. He had very ugly hair; the top of his head, that is, was almost bald, while a narrow, black-varnished frizz of curls ran from front to back as though stuck on; the side hair, likewise blackened, was brushed forward to the corners of the eyes—it was, in short, the hairdressing of an old-fashioned circus-director, fantastic, but entirely suited to his outmoded personal type and worn with so much assurance as to take the edge off the public's sense of humor.

The little physical defect of which he had warned us was now all too visible, though the nature of it was even now not very clear: the chest was too high, as is usual in such cases; but the corresponding malformation of the back did not sit between the shoulders, it took the form of a sort of hips or buttocks hump, which did not indeed hinder his movements but gave him a grotesque and dipping stride at every step he took. However, by mentioning his deformity beforehand he had broken the shock of it, and a delicate propriety of feeling appeared to reign throughout the hall.

"At your service," said Cipolla. "With your kind permission, we will begin the evening with some arithmetical tests."

Arithmetic? That did not sound much like sleight-of-hand. We began to have our suspicions that the man was sailing under a false flag, only we did not yet know which was the right one. I felt sorry on the children's account; but for the moment they were content simply to be there.

The numerical test which Cipolla now introduced was as simple as it was baffling. He began by fastening a piece of paper to the upper right-hand corner of the blackboard; then lifting it up, he wrote something underneath. He talked all the while, relieving the dryness of his offering by a constant flow of words, and showed himself a practiced speaker, never at a loss for conversational turns of phrase. It was in keeping with the nature of his performance, and at the same time vastly entertained the children, that he went on to eliminate the gap between stage and audience, which had already been bridged over by the curious skirmish with the fisher lad: he had representatives from the audience mount the stage, and himself descended the wooden steps to seek personal contact with his public. And again, with individuals, he fell into his former taunting tone. I do not know how far that was a deliberate feature of his system; he preserved a serious, even a peevish air, but his audience, at least the more popular section, seemed convinced that that was all part of the game. So then, after he had written something and covered the writing by the paper, he desired that two persons should come up on the platform and help to perform the calculations. They would not be difficult, even for people not clever at figures. As usual, nobody volunteered, and Cipolla took care not to molest the more select portion of his audience. He kept to the populace. Turning to two sturdy young louts standing behind us, he beckoned them to the front, encouraging and scolding by turns. They should not stand there gaping, he said, unwilling to oblige the company. Actually, he got them in motion; with clumsy tread they came down the middle aisle, climbed the steps, and stood in front of the blackboard, grinning sheepishly at their comrades' shouts and applause. Cipolla joked with them for a few minutes, praised their heroic firmness of limb and the size of their hands, so well calculated to do this service for the public. Then he handed one of them the chalk and told him to write down the numbers as they were called out. But now the creature declared that he could not write! *"Non so scrivere,"* said he in his gruff voice, and his companion added that neither did he.

God knows whether they told the truth or whether they wanted to make game of Cipolla. Anyhow, the latter was far from sharing the general merriment which their confession aroused. He was insulted and disgusted. He sat there on a straw-bottomed chair in the center of the stage with his legs crossed, smoking a fresh cigarette out of his cheap packet; obviously it tasted the better for the cognac he had indulged in while the yokels were stumping up the steps. Again he inhaled the smoke and let it stream out between curling lips. Swinging his leg, with his gaze sternly averted from the two shamelessly chuckling creatures and from the audience as well, he stared

into space as one who withdraws himself and his dignity from
the contemplation of an utterly despicable phenomenon.

"Scandalous," said he, in a sort of icy snarl. "Go back to
your places! In Italy everybody can write—in all her greatness
there is no room for ignorance and unenlightenment. To accuse
her of them, in the hearing of this international company, is a
cheap joke, in which you yourselves cut a very poor figure and
humiliate the government and the whole country as well. If it
is true that Torre di Venere is indeed the last refuge of such
ignorance, then I must blush to have visited the place—being, as
I already was, aware of its inferiority to Rome in more than one
respect—"

Here Cipolla was interrupted by the youth with the Nubian
coiffure and his jacket across his shoulder. His fighting spirit,
as we now saw, had only abdicated temporarily, and he now
flung himself into the breach in defense of his native heath.
"That will do," said he loudly. "That's enough jokes about
Torre. We all come from the place and we won't stand
strangers making fun of it. These two chaps are our friends.
Maybe they are no scholars, but even so they may be straighter
than some folks in the room who are so free with their boasts
about Rome, though they did not build it either."

That was capital. The young man had certainly cut his eye-
teeth. And this sort of spectacle was good fun, even though it
still further delayed the regular performance. It is always fascinating to listen to an altercation. Some people it simply amuses,
they take a sort of kill-joy pleasure in not being principals.
Others feel upset and uneasy, and my sympathies are with these
latter, although on the present occasion I was under the impression that all this was part of the show—the analphabetic yokels
no less than the *giovanotto* with the jacket. The children
listened well pleased. They understood not at all, but the sound
of the voices made them hold their breath. So this was a

"magic evening"—at least it was the kind they have in Italy. They expressly found it "lovely."

Cipolla had stood up and with two of his scooping strides was at the footlights.

"Well, well, see who's here!" said he with grim cordiality. "An old acquaintance! A young man with his heart at the end of his tongue" (he used the word *linguaccia,* which means a coated tongue, and gave rise to much hilarity). "That will do, my friends," he turned to the yokels. "I do not need you now, I have business with this deserving young man here, *con questo torregiano di Venere,* this tower of Venus, who no doubt expects the gratitude of the fair as a reward for his prowess—"

"*Ah, non scherziamo!* We're talking earnest," cried out the youth. His eyes flashed, and he actually made as though to pull off his jacket and proceed to direct methods of settlement.

Cipolla did not take him too seriously. We had exchanged apprehensive glances; but he was dealing with a fellow-countryman and had his native soil beneath his feet. He kept quite cool and showed complete mastery of the situation. He looked at his audience, smiled, and made a sideways motion of the head towards the young cockerel as though calling the public to witness how the man's bumptiousness only served to betray the simplicity of his mind. And then, for the second time, something strange happened, which set Cipolla's calm superiority in an uncanny light, and in some mysterious and irritating way turned all the explosiveness latent in the air into matter for laughter.

Cipolla drew still nearer to the fellow, looking him in the eye with a peculiar gaze. He even came half-way down the steps that led into the auditorium on our left, so that he stood directly in front of the trouble-maker, on slightly higher ground. The riding-whip hung from his arm.

"My son, you do not feel much like joking," he said. "It is

only too natural, for anyone can see that you are not feeling too well. Even your tongue, which leaves something to be desired on the score of cleanliness, indicates acute disorder of the gastric system. An evening entertainment is no place for people in your state; you yourself, I can tell, were of several minds whether you would not do better to put on a flannel bandage and go to bed. It was not good judgment to drink so much of that very sour white wine this afternoon. Now you have such a colic you would like to double up with the pain. Go ahead, don't be embarrassed. There is a distinct relief that comes from bending over, in cases of intestinal cramp."

He spoke thus, word for word, with quiet impressiveness and a kind of stern sympathy, and his eyes, plunged the while deep in the young man's, seemed to grow very tired and at the same time burning above their enlarged tear-ducts—they were the strangest eyes, you could tell that not manly pride alone was preventing the young adversary from withdrawing his gaze. And presently, indeed, all trace of its former arrogance was gone from the bronzed young face. He looked open-mouthed at the Cavaliere and the open mouth was drawn in a rueful smile.

"Double over," repeated Cipolla. "What else can you do? With a colic like that you *must* bend. Surely you will not struggle against the performance of a perfectly natural action just because somebody suggests it to you?"

Slowly the youth lifted his forearms, folded and squeezed them across his body; it turned a little sideways, then bent, lower and lower, the feet shifted, the knees turned inward, until he had become a picture of writhing pain, until he all but groveled upon the ground. Cipolla let him stand for some seconds thus, then made a short cut through the air with his whip and went with his scooping stride back to the little table, where he poured himself out a cognac.

"*Il boit beaucoup,*" asserted a lady behind us. Was that the only thing that struck her? We could not tell how far the audience grasped the situation. The fellow was standing upright again, with a sheepish grin—he looked as though he scarcely knew how it had all happened. The scene had been followed with tense interest and applauded at the end; there were shouts of *"Bravo, Cipolla!"* and *"Bravo, giovanotto!"* Apparently the issue of the duel was not looked upon as a personal defeat for the young man. Rather the audience encouraged him as one does an actor who succeeds in an unsympathetic role. Certainly his way of screwing himself up with cramp had been highly picturesque, its appeal was directly calculated to impress the gallery—in short, a fine dramatic performance. But I am not sure how far the audience were moved by that natural tactfulness in which the south excels, or how far it penetrated into the nature of what was going on.

The Cavaliere, refreshed, had lighted another cigarette. The numerical tests might now proceed. A young man was easily found in the back row who was willing to write down on the blackboard the numbers as they were dictated to him. Him too we knew; the whole entertainment had taken on an intimate character through our acquaintance with so many of the actors. This was the man who worked at the greengrocer's in the main street; he had served us several times, with neatness and dispatch. He wielded the chalk with clerkly confidence, while Cipolla descended to our level and walked with his deformed gait through the audience, collecting numbers as they were given, in two, three, and four places, and calling them out to the grocer's assistant, who wrote them down in a column. In all this, everything on both sides was calculated to amuse, with its jokes and its oratorical asides. The artist could not fail to hit on foreigners, who were not ready with their figures, and with them he was elaborately patient and chivalrous, to the great amusement of the natives, whom he reduced to confusion in their turn, by making them translate numbers that were given in English or French. Some people gave dates concerned with great events in Italian history. Cipolla took them up at once and made patriotic comments. Somebody shouted "Number one!" The Cavaliere, incensed at this as at every attempt to make game of him, retorted over his shoulder that he could not take less than two-place figures. Whereupon another joker cried out "Number two!" and was greeted with the applause and laughter which every reference to natural functions is sure to win among southerners.

When fifteen numbers stood in a long straggling row on the board, Cipolla called for a general adding-match. Ready reckoners might add in their heads, but pencil and paper were not forbidden. Cipolla, while the work went on, sat on his chair near the blackboard, smoked and grimaced, with the complacent, pompous air cripples so often have. The five-place addition was soon done. Somebody announced the answer, somebody else confirmed it, a third had arrived at a slightly different result, but the fourth agreed with the first and second. Cipolla got up, tapped some ash from his coat, and lifted the paper at the upper right-hand corner of the board to display the writing. The correct answer, a sum close on a million, stood there; he had written it down beforehand.

Astonishment, and loud applause. The children were overwhelmed. How had he done that, they wanted to know. We told them it was a trick, not easily explainable offhand. In short, the man was a conjuror. This was what a sleight-of-hand evening was like, so now they knew. First the fisherman had cramp, and then the right answer was written down beforehand —it was all simply glorious, and we saw with dismay that despite the hot eyes and the hand of the clock at almost half past ten, it would be very hard to get them away. There would be tears. And yet it was plain that this magician did not "magick"—at least not in the accepted sense, of manual dexterity—and that the entertainment was not at all suitable for children. Again, I do not know, either, what the audience really thought. Obviously there was grave doubt whether its answers had been given of "free choice"; here and there an individual might have answered of his own motion, but on the whole Cipolla certainly selected his people and thus kept the whole procedure in his own hands and directed it towards the given result. Even so, one had to admire the quickness of his calculations, however much one felt disinclined to admire anything else about the performance. Then his patriotism, his irritable sense of dignity—the Cavaliere's own countrymen might feel in their element with all that and continue in a laughing mood; but the combination certainly gave us outsiders food for thought.

Cipolla himself saw to it—though without giving them a name —that the nature of his powers should be clear beyond a doubt to even the least-instructed person. He alluded to them, of course, in his talk—and he talked without stopping—but only in vague, boastful, self-advertising phrases. He went on awhile with experiments on the same lines as the first, merely making them more complicated by introducing operations in multiplying, subtracting, and dividing; then he simplified them to the last degree in order to bring out the method. He simply had numbers "guessed" which were previously written under the paper; and the guess was nearly always right. One guesser admitted that he had had in mind to give a certain number, when Cipolla's whip went whistling through the air, and a quite different one slipped out, which proved to be the "right" one. Cipolla's shoulders shook. He pretended admiration for the powers of the people he questioned. But in all his compliments there was something fleering and derogatory; the victims could scarcely have relished them much, although they smiled, and although they might easily have set down some part of the applause to their own credit. Moreover, I had not the impression that the artist was popular with his public. A certain ill will and reluctance were in the air, but courtesy kept such feelings in check, as did Cipolla's competency and his stern self-confidence. Even the riding-whip, I think, did much to keep rebellion from becoming overt.

From tricks with numbers he passed to tricks with cards. There were two packs, which he drew out of his pockets, and so much I still remember, that the basis of the tricks he played with them was as follows: from the first pack he drew three cards and thrust them without looking at them inside his coat. Another person then drew three out of the second pack, and these turned out to be the same as the first three—not invariably all the three, for it did happen that only two were the same. But in the majority of cases Cipolla triumphed, showing his three cards with a little bow in acknowledgment of the applause with which his audience conceded his possession of strange powers—strange whether for good or evil. A young man in the front row, to our right, an Italian, with proud, finely chiseled features, rose up and said that he intended to assert his own will in his choice and consciously to resist any influence, of whatever sort. Under these circumstances, what did Cipolla think would be the result? "You will," answered the Cavaliere, "make my task somewhat more difficult thereby. As for the result, your resistance will not alter it in the least. Freedom exists, and also the will exists; but freedom of the will does not exist, for a will that aims at its own freedom aims at the unknown. You are free to draw or not to draw. But if you draw, you will draw the right cards—the more certainly, the more willfully obstinate your behavior."

One must admit that he could not have chosen his words better, to trouble the waters and confuse the mind. The refractory youth hesitated before drawing. Then he pulled out a card and at once demanded to see if it was among the chosen three. "But why?" queried Cipolla. "Why do things by halves?" Then, as the other defiantly insisted, *"E servito,"* said the juggler, with a gesture of exaggerated servility; and held out the three cards fanwise, without looking at them himself. The left-hand card was the one drawn.

Amid general applause, the apostle of freedom sat down. How far Cipolla employed small tricks and manual dexterity to help out his natural talents, the deuce only knew. But even without them the result would have been the same: the curiosity of the entire audience was unbounded and universal, everybody both enjoyed the amazing character of the entertainment and unanimously conceded the professional skill of the performer. *"Lavora bene,"* we heard, here and there in our neighborhood; it signified the triumph of objective judgment over antipathy and repressed resentment.

After his last, incomplete, yet so much the more telling success, Cipolla had at once fortified himself with another cognac. Truly he did "drink a lot," and the fact made a bad impression. But obviously he needed the liquor and the cigarettes for the replenishment of his energy, upon which, as he himself said, heavy demands were made in all directions. Certainly in the intervals he looked very ill, exhausted and hollow-eyed. Then the little glassful would redress the balance, and the flow of lively, self-confident chatter run on, while the smoke he inhaled gushed out gray from his lungs. I clearly recall that he passed from the card-tricks to parlor games—the kind based on certain powers which in human nature are higher or else lower than human reason: on intuition and "magnetic" transmission; in short, upon a low type of manifestation. What I do not remember is the precise order things came in. And I will not bore you with a description of these experiments; everybody knows them, everybody has at one time or another taken part in this finding of hidden articles, this blind carrying out of a series of acts, directed by a force that proceeds from organism to organism by unexplored paths. Everybody has had his little glimpse into the equivocal, impure, inexplicable nature of the occult, has been conscious of both curiosity and contempt, has shaken his head over the human tendency of those who deal in it to help themselves out with humbuggery, though, after all, the humbuggery is no disproof whatever of the genuineness of the other elements in the dubious amalgam. I can only say here that each single circumstance gains in weight and the whole greatly in impressiveness when it is a man like Cipolla who is the chief actor and guiding spirit in the sinister business. He sat smoking at the rear of the stage, his back to the audience while they conferred. The object passed from hand to hand which it was his task to find, with which he was to perform some action agreed upon beforehand. Then he would start to move zigzag through the hall, with his head thrown back and one hand outstretched, the other clasped in that of a guide who was in the secret but enjoined to keep himself perfectly passive, with his thoughts directed upon the agreed goal. Cipolla moved with the bearing typical in these experiments: now groping upon a false start, now with a quick forward thrust, now pausing as though to listen and by sudden inspiration correcting his course. The roles seemed reversed, the stream of influence was moving in the contrary direction, as the artist himself pointed out, in his ceaseless flow of discourse. The suffering, receptive, performing part was now his, the will he had before imposed on others was shut out, he acted in obedience to a voiceless common will which was in the air. But he made it perfectly clear that it all came to the same thing. The capacity for self-surrender, he said, for becoming a tool, for the most unconditional and utter self-abnegation, was but the reverse side of that other power to will and to command. Commanding and obeying formed together one single principle, one indissoluble unity; he who knew how to obey knew also how to command, and conversely; the one idea was comprehended in the other, as people and leader were comprehended in one another. But that which was *done,* the highly exacting and exhausting performance, was in every case his, the leader's and mover's, in whom the will became obedience, the obedience will, whose person was the cradle and womb of both, and who thus suffered enormous hardship. Repeatedly he emphasized the fact that his lot was a hard one—presumably to account for his need of stimulant and his frequent recourse to the little glass.

Thus he groped his way forward, like a blind seer, led and sustained by the mysterious common will. He drew a pin set with a stone out of its hiding-place in an Englishwoman's shoe, carried it, halting and pressing on by turns, to another lady—Signora Angiolieri—and handed it to her on bended knee, with the words it had been agreed he was to utter. "I present you with this in token of my respect," was the sentence. Their sense was obvious, but the words themselves not easy to hit upon, for the reason that they had been agreed on in French; the language complication seemed to us a little malicious, implying as it did a conflict between the audience's natural interest in the success of the miracle, and their desire to witness the humiliation of this presumptuous man. It was a strange sight: Cipolla on his knees before the signora, wrestling, amid efforts at speech, after knowledge of the preordained words. "I must say something," he said, "and I feel clearly what it is I must say. But I also feel that if it passed my lips it would be wrong. Be careful not to help me unintentionally!" he cried out, though very likely that was precisely what he was hoping for. *"Pensez très fort,"* he cried all at once, in bad French, and then burst out with the required words—in Italian, indeed, but with the final substantive pronounced in the sister tongue, in which he was probably far from fluent: he said *vénération* instead of *venerazione,* with an impossible nasal. And this partial success, after the complete success before it, the finding of the pin, the presentation of it on his knees to the right person—was almost more impressive than if he had got the sentence exactly right, and evoked bursts of admiring applause.

Cipolla got up from his knees and wiped the perspiration from his brow. You understand that this experiment with the pin was a single case, which I describe because it sticks in my memory. But he changed his method several times and improvised a number of variations suggested by his contact with his audience; a good deal of time thus went by. He seemed to get particular inspiration from the person of our landlady; she drew him on to the most extraordinary displays of clairvoyance. "It does not escape me, madame," he said to her, "that there is something unusual about you, some special and honorable distinction. He who has eyes to see descries about your lovely brow an aureola—if I mistake not, it once was stronger than now—a slowly paling radiance . . . hush, not a word! Don't help me. Beside you sits your husband—yes?" He turned towards the silent Signor Angiolieri. "You are the husband of this lady, and your happiness is complete. But in the midst of this happiness memories rise . . . the past, signora, so it seems to me, plays an important part in your present. You knew a king . . . has not a king crossed your path in bygone days?"

"No," breathed the dispenser of our midday soup, her golden-brown eyes gleaming in the noble pallor of her face.

"No? No, not a king; I meant that generally, I did not mean literally a king. Not a king, not a prince, and a prince after all, a king of a loftier realm; it was a great artist, at whose side you once—you would contradict me, and yet I am not wholly wrong. Well, then! It was a woman, a great, a world-renowned woman artist, whose friendship you enjoyed in your tender years, whose sacred memory overshadows and transfigures your whole existence. Her name? Need I utter it, whose fame has long been bound up with the Fatherland's, immortal as its own? Eleonora Duse," he finished, softly and with much solemnity.

The little woman bowed her head, overcome. The applause was like a patriotic demonstration. Nearly everyone there knew about Signora Angiolieri's wonderful past; they were all able to confirm the Cavaliere's intuition—not least the present guests of Casa Eleonora. But we wondered how much of the truth he had learned as the result of professional inquiries made on his arrival. Yet I see no reason at all to cast doubt, on rational grounds, upon powers which, before our very eyes, became fatal to their possessor.

At this point there was an intermission. Our lord and master withdrew. Now I confess that almost ever since the beginning of my tale I have looked forward with dread to this moment in it. The thoughts of men are mostly not hard to read; in this case they are very easy. You are sure to ask why we did not choose this moment to go away—and I must continue to owe you an answer. I do not know why. I cannot defend myself. By this time it was certainly eleven, probably later. The children were asleep. The last series of tests had been too long, nature had had her way. They were sleeping in our laps, the little one on mine, the boy on his mother's. That was, in a way, a consolation; but at the same time it was also ground for compassion and a clear leading to take them home to bed. And I give you my word that we wanted to obey this touching admonition, we seriously wanted to. We roused the poor things and told them it was now high time to go. But they were no sooner conscious than they began to resist and implore—you know how horrified children are at the thought of leaving before the end of a thing. No cajoling has any effect, you have to use force.

It was so lovely, they wailed. How did we know what was coming next? Surely we could not leave until after the intermission; they liked a little nap now and again—only not go home, only not go to bed, while the beautiful evening was still going on!

We yielded, but only for the moment, of course—so far as we knew—only for a little while, just a few minutes longer. I cannot excuse our staying, scarcely can I even understand it. Did we think, having once said A, we had to say B—having once brought the children hither we had to let them stay? No, it is not good enough. Were we ourselves so highly entertained? Yes, and no. Our feelings for Cavaliere Cipolla were of a very mixed kind, but so were the feelings of the whole audience, if I mistake not, and nobody left. Were we under the sway of a fascination which emanated from this man who took so strange a way to earn his bread; a fascination which he gave out independently of the program and even between the tricks and which paralyzed our resolve? Again, sheer curiosity may account for something. One was curious to know how such an evening turned out; Cipolla in his remarks having all along hinted that he had tricks in his bag stranger than any he had yet produced.

But all that is not it—or at least it is not all of it. More correct it would be to answer the first question with another. Why had we not left Torre di Venere itself before now? To me the two questions are one and the same, and in order to get out of the impasse I might simply say that I had answered it already. For, as things had been in Torre in general: queer, uncomfortable, troublesome, tense, oppressive, so precisely they were here in this hall tonight. Yes, more than precisely. For it seemed to be the fountainhead of all the uncanniness and all the strained feelings which had oppressed the atmosphere of our holiday. This man whose return to the stage we were awaiting was the personification of all that; and, as we had not gone away in general, so to speak, it would have been inconsistent to do it in the particular case. You may call this an explanation, you may call it inertia, as you see fit. Any argument more to the purpose I simply do not know how to adduce.

Well, there was an interval of ten minutes, which grew into nearly twenty. The children remained awake. They were enchanted by our compliance, and filled the break to their own satisfaction by renewing relations with the popular sphere, with Antonio, Guiscardo, and the canoe man. They put their hands to their mouths and called messages across, appealing to us for the Italian words. "Hope you have a good catch tomorrow, a whole netful!" They called to Mario, Esquisito Mario: "*Mario, una cioccolata e biscotti!*". And this time he heeded and answered with a smile: "*Subito, signorini!*" Later we had reason to recall this kindly, if rather absent and pensive smile.

Thus the interval passed, the gong sounded. The audience, which had scattered in conversation, took their places again, the children sat up straight in their chairs with their hands in their laps. The curtain had not been dropped. Cipolla came forward again, with his dipping stride, and began to introduce the second half of the program with a lecture.

Let me state once for all that this self-confident cripple was the most powerful hypnotist I have ever seen in my life. It was pretty plain now that he threw dust in the public eye and advertised himself as a prestidigitator on account of police regulations which would have prevented him from making his living by the exercise of his powers. Perhaps this eye-wash is the usual thing in Italy; it may be permitted or even connived at by the authorities. Certainly the man had from the beginning made little concealment of the actual nature of his operations; and this second half of the program was quite frankly and exclusively devoted to one sort of experiment. While he still practiced some rhetorical circumlocutions, the tests themselves were one long series of attacks upon the will-power, the loss or compulsion of volition. Comic, exciting, amazing by turns, by midnight they were still in full swing; we ran the gamut of all the phenomena this natural-unnatural field has to show, from the unimpressive at one end of the scale to the monstrous at the other. The audience laughed and applauded as they followed the grotesque details; shook their heads, clapped their knees, fell very frankly under the spell of this stern, self-assured personality. At the same time I saw signs that they were not quite complacent, not quite unconscious of the peculiar ignominy which lay, for the individual and for the general, in Cipolla's triumphs.

Two main features were constant in all the experiments: the liquor glass and the claw-handled riding-whip. The first was always invoked to add fuel to his demoniac fires; without it, apparently, they might have burned out. On this score we might even have felt pity for the man; but the whistle of his scourge, the insulting symbol of his domination, before which we all cowered, drowned out every sensation save a dazed and outbraved submission to his power. Did he then lay claim to our sympathy to boot? I was struck by a remark he made—it suggested no less. At the climax of his experiments, by stroking and breathing upon a certain young man who had offered himself as a subject and already proved himself a particularly susceptible one, he had not only put him into the condition known as deep trance and extended his insensible body by neck and feet across the backs of two chairs, but had actually sat down on the rigid form as on a bench, without making it yield. The sight of this unholy figure in a frock-coat squatted on the stiff body was horrible and incredible; the audience, convinced that the victim of this scientific diversion must be suffering, expressed its sympathy: *"Ah, poveretto!"* Poor soul, poor soul! *"Poor soul!"* Cipolla mocked them, with some bitterness. "Ladies and gentlemen, you are barking up the wrong tree. *Sono io il poveretto.* I am the person who is suffering, I am the one to be pitied." We pocketed the information. Very good. Maybe the experiment was at his expense, maybe it was he who had suffered the cramp when the *giovanotto* over there had made the faces. But appearances were all against it; and one does not feel like saying *poveretto* to a man who is suffering to bring about the humiliation of others.

I have got ahead of my story and lost sight of the sequence of events. To this day my mind is full of the Cavaliere's feats of endurance; only I do not recall them in their order—which does not matter. So much I do know: that the longer and more circumstantial tests, which got the most applause, impressed me less than some of the small ones which passed quickly over. I remember the young man whose body Cipolla converted into a board, only because of the accompanying remarks which I have quoted. An elderly lady in a cane-seated chair was lulled by Cipolla in the delusion that she was on a voyage to India and gave a voluble account of her adventures by land and sea. But I found this phenomenon less impressive than one which followed immediately after the intermission. A tall, well-built, soldierly man was unable to lift his arm, after the hunchback had told him that he could not and given a cut through the air with his whip. I can still see the face of that stately, mustachioed colonel smiling and clenching his teeth as he struggled to regain his lost freedom of action. A staggering performance! He seemed to be exerting his will, and in vain; the trouble, however, was probably simply that he could not will. There was involved here that recoil of the will upon itself which paralyzes choice—as our tyrant had previously explained to the Roman gentleman.

Still less can I forget the touching scene, at once comic and horrible, with Signora Angiolieri. The Cavaliere, probably in his first bold survey of the room, had spied out her ethereal lack of resistance to his power. For actually he bewitched her, literally drew her out of her seat, out of her row, and away with him whither he willed. And in order to enhance his effect, he bade Signor Angiolieri call upon his wife by her name, to throw, as it were, all the weight of his existence and his rights in her into the scale, to rouse by the voice of her husband everything in his spouse's soul which could shield her virtue against the evil assaults of magic. And how vain it all was! Cipolla was standing at some distance from the couple, when he made a single cut with his whip through the air. It caused our landlady to shudder violently and turn her face towards him. "Sofronia!" cried Signor Angiolieri—we had not known that Signora Angiolieri's name was Sofronia. And he did well to call, everybody saw that there was no time to lose. His wife kept her face turned in the direction of the diabolical Cavaliere, who with his ten long yellow fingers was making passes at his victim, moving backwards as he did so, step by step. Then Signora Angiolieri, her pale face gleaming, rose up from her seat, turned right round, and began to glide after him. Fatal and forbidding sight! Her face as though moonstruck, stiff-armed, her lovely hands lifted a little at the wrists, the feet as it were together, she seemed to float slowly out of her row and after the tempter. "Call her, sir, keep on calling," prompted the redoubtable man. And Signor Angiolieri, in a weak voice, called: "Sofronia!" Ah, again and again he called; as his wife went further off he even curved one hand round his lips and beckoned with the other as he called. But the poor voice of love and duty echoed unheard, in vain, behind the lost one's back; the signora swayed along, moonstruck, deaf, enslaved; she glided into the middle aisle and down it towards the fingering hunchback, towards the door. We were convinced, we were driven to the conviction, that she would have followed her master, had he so willed it, to the ends of the earth.

"*Accidente!*" cried out Signor Angiolieri, in genuine affright, springing up as the exit was reached. But at the same moment the Cavaliere put aside, as it were, the triumphal crown and broke off. "Enough, signora, I thank you," he said, and offered his arm to lead her back to her husband. "Signor," he greeted the latter, "here is your wife. Unharmed, with my compliments, I give her into your hands. Cherish with all the strength of your manhood a treasure which is so wholly yours, and let your zeal be quickened by knowing that there are powers stronger than reason or virtue, and not always so magnanimously ready to relinquish their prey!"

Poor Signor Angiolieri, so quiet, so bald! He did not look as though he would know how to defend his happiness, even against powers much less demoniac than these which were now adding mockery to frightfulness. Solemnly and pompously the Cavaliere retired to the stage, amid applause to which his elo- quence gave double strength. It was this particular episode, I feel sure, that set the seal upon his ascendancy. For now he made them dance, yes, literally; and the dancing lent a dissolute, abandoned, topsy-turvy air to the scene, a drunken abdication of the critical spirit which had so long resisted the spell of this man. Yes, he had had to fight to get the upper hand—for in- stance against the animosity of the young Roman gentleman, whose rebellious spirit threatened to serve others as a rallying- point. But it was precisely upon the importance of example that the Cavaliere was so strong. He had the wit to make his attack at the weakest point and to choose as his first victim that feeble, ecstatic youth whom he had previously made into a board. The master had but to look at him, when this young man would fling himself back as though struck by lightning, place his hands rigidly at his sides, and fall into a state of military somnambu- lism, in which it was plain to any eye that he was open to the most absurd suggestion that might be made to him. He seemed quite content in his abject state, quite pleased to be relieved of the burden of voluntary choice. Again and again he offered himself as a subject and gloried in the model facility he had in losing consciousness. So now he mounted the platform, and a single cut of the whip was enough to make him dance to the Cavaliere's orders, in a kind of complacent ecstasy, eyes closed, head nodding, lank limbs flying in all directions.

It looked unmistakably like enjoyment, and other recruits were not long in coming forward: two other young men, one humbly and one well dressed, were soon jigging alongside the first. But now the gentleman from Rome bobbed up again, asking defiantly if the Cavaliere would engage to make him dance too, even against his will.

"Even against your will," answered Cipolla, in unforgettable accents. That frightful *"anche se non vuole"* still rings in my ears. The struggle began. After Cipolla had taken another little glass and lighted a fresh cigarette he stationed the Roman at a point in the middle aisle and himself took up a position some distance behind him, making his whip whistle through the air as he gave the order: *"Balla!"* His opponent did not stir. *"Balla!"* repeated the Cavaliere incisively, and snapped his whip. You saw the young man move his neck round in his collar; at the same time one hand lifted slightly at the wrist, one ankle turned outward. But that was all, for the time at least; merely a tendency to twitch, now sternly repressed, now seeming about to get the upper hand. It escaped nobody that here a heroic obstinacy, a fixed resolve to resist, must needs be conquered; we were beholding a gallant effort to strike out and save the honor of the human race. He twitched but danced not; and the struggle was so prolonged that the Cavaliere had to divide his attention between it and the stage, turning now and then to make his riding-whip whistle in the direction of the dancers, as it were to keep them in leash. At the same time he advised

the audience that no fatigue was involved in such activities, however long they went on, since it was not the automatons up there
who danced, but himself. Then once more his eye would bore
itself into the back of the Roman's neck and lay siege to the
strength of purpose which defied him.

One saw it waver, that strength of purpose, beneath the repeated summons and whip-crackings. Saw with an objective
interest which yet was not quite free from traces of sympathetic
emotion—from pity, even from a cruel kind of pleasure. If I
understand what was going on, it was the negative character of
the young man's fighting position which was his undoing. It is
likely that *not* willing is not a practicable state of mind; *not* to
want to do something may be in the long run a mental content
impossible to subsist on. Between not willing a certain thing
and not willing at all—in other words, yielding to another
person's will—there may lie too small a space for the idea of
freedom to squeeze into. Again, there were the Cavaliere's persuasive words, woven in among the whip-crackings and commands, as he mingled effects that were his own secret with
others of a bewilderingly psychological kind. *"Balla!"* said he.
"Who wants to torture himself like that? Is forcing yourself
your idea of freedom? *Una ballatina!* Why, your arms and
legs are aching for it. What a relief to give way to them—there,
you are dancing already! That is no struggle any more, it is a
pleasure!" And so it was. The jerking and twitching of the
refractory youth's limbs had at last got the upper hand; he lifted
his arms, then his knees, his joints quite suddenly relaxed, he
flung his legs and danced, and amid bursts of applause the
Cavaliere led him to join the row of puppets on the stage. Up
there we could see his face as he "enjoyed" himself; it was
clothed in a broad grin and the eyes were half-shut. In a way,
it was consoling to see that he was having a better time than
he had had in the hour of his pride.

His "fall" was, I may say, an epoch. The ice was completely broken, Cipolla's triumph had reached its height. The Circe's wand, that whistling leather whip with the claw handle, held absolute sway. At one time—it must have been well after midnight—not only were there eight or ten persons dancing on the little stage, but in the hall below a varied animation reigned, and a long-toothed Anglo-Saxoness in a pince-nez left her seat of her own motion to perform a tarantella in the center aisle. Cipolla was lounging in a cane-seated chair at the left of the stage, gulping down the smoke of a cigarette and breathing it impudently out through his bad teeth. He tapped his foot and shrugged his shoulders, looking down upon the abandoned scene in the hall; now and then he snapped his whip backwards at a laggard upon the stage. The children were awake at the moment. With shame I speak of them. For it was not good to be here, least of all for them; that we had not taken them away can only be explained by saying that we had caught the general devil-may-careness of the hour. By that time it was all one. Anyhow, thank goodness, they lacked understanding for the disreputable side of the entertainment, and in their innocence were perpetually charmed by the unheard-of indulgence which permitted them to be present at such a thing as a magician's "evening." Whole quarter-hours at a time they drowsed on our laps, waking refreshed and rosy-cheeked, with sleep-drunken eyes, to laugh to bursting at the leaps and jumps the magician made those people up there make. They had not thought it would be so jolly; they joined with their clumsy little hands in every round of applause. And jumped for joy upon their chairs, as was their wont, when Cipolla beckoned to their friend Mario from the Esquisito, beckoned to him just like a picture in a book, holding his hand in front of his nose and bending and straightening the forefinger by turns.

Mario obeyed. I can see him now going up the stairs to

Cipolla, who continued to beckon him, in that droll, picture-book sort of way. He hesitated for a moment at first; that, too, I recall quite clearly. During the whole evening he had lounged against a wooden pillar at the side entrance, with his arms folded, or else with his hands thrust into his jacket pockets. He was on our left, near the youth with the militant hair, and had followed the performance attentively, so far as we had seen, if with no particular animation and God knows how much comprehension. He could not much relish being summoned thus, at the end of the evening. But it was only too easy to see why he obeyed. After all, obedience was his calling in life; and then, how should a simple lad like him find it within his human capacity to refuse compliance to a man so throned and crowned as Cipolla at that hour? Willy-nilly he left his column and with a word of thanks to those making way for him he mounted the steps with a doubtful smile on his full lips.

Picture a thickset youth of twenty years, with clipt hair, a low forehead, and heavy-lidded eyes of an indefinite gray, shot with green and yellow. These things I knew from having spoken with him, as we often had. There was a saddle of freckles on the flat nose, the whole upper half of the face retreated behind the lower, and that again was dominated by thick lips that parted to show the salivated teeth. These thick lips and the veiled look of the eyes lent the whole face a primitive melan-choly—it was that which had drawn us to him from the first. In it was not the faintest trace of brutality—indeed, his hands would have given the lie to such an idea, being unusually slender and delicate even for a southerner. They were hands by which one liked being served.

We knew him humanly without knowing him personally, if I may make that distinction. We saw him nearly every day, and felt a certain kindness for his dreamy ways, which might at times be actual inattentiveness, suddenly transformed into a redeeming zeal to serve. His mien was serious, only the children could bring a smile to his face. It was not sulky, but uningratiating, without intentional effort to please—or, rather, it seemed to give up being pleasant in the conviction that it could not succeed. We should have remembered Mario in any case, as one of those homely recollections of travel which often stick in the mind better than more important ones. But of his circumstances we knew no more than that his father was a petty clerk in the Municipio and his mother took in washing.

His white waiter's-coat became him better than the faded striped suit he wore, with a gay colored scarf instead of a collar, the ends tucked into his jacket. He neared Cipolla, who however did not leave off that motion of his finger before his nose, so that Mario had to come still closer, right up to the chair-seat and the master's legs. Whereupon the latter spread out his elbows and seized the lad, turning him so that we had a view of his face. Then gazed him briskly up and down, with a careless, commanding eye.

"Well, *ragazzo mio,* how comes it we make acquaintance so late in the day? But believe me, I made yours long ago. Yes, yes, I've had you in my eye this long while and known what good stuff you were made of. How could I go and forget you again? Well, I've had a good deal to think about. . . . Now tell me, what is your name? The first name, that's all I want."

"My name is Mario," the young man answered, in a low voice.

"Ah, Mario. Very good. Yes, yes, there is such a name, quite a common name, a classic name too, one of those which preserve the heroic traditions of the Fatherland. *Bravo! Salve!*" And he flung up his arm slantingly above his crooked shoulder, palm outward, in the Roman salute. He may have been slightly tipsy by now, and no wonder; but he spoke as before, clearly, fluently, and with emphasis. Though about this time there had crept into his voice a gross, autocratic note, and a kind of arrogance was in his sprawl.

"Well, now, Mario *mio*," he went on, "it's a good thing you came this evening, and that's a pretty scarf you've got on; it is becoming to your style of beauty. It must stand you in good stead with the girls, the pretty pretty girls of Torre—"

From the row of youths, close by the place where Mario had been standing, sounded a laugh. It came from the youth with the militant hair. He stood there, his jacket over his shoulder, and laughed outright, rudely and scornfully.

Mario gave a start. I think it was a shrug, but he may have started and then hastened to cover the movement by shrugging his shoulders, as much as to say that the neckerchief and the fair sex were matters of equal indifference to him.

The Cavaliere gave a downward glance.

"We needn't trouble about him," he said. "He is jealous, because your scarf is so popular with the girls, maybe partly because you and I are so friendly up here. Perhaps he'd like me to put him in mind of his colic—I could do it free of charge. Tell me, Mario. You've come here this evening for a bit of fun —and in the daytime you work in an ironmonger's shop?"

"In a café," corrected the youth.

"Oh, in a café. That's where Cipolla nearly came a cropper! What you are is a cup-bearer, a Ganymede—I like that, it is another classical allusion—*Salvietta!*" Again the Cavaliere saluted, to the huge gratification of his audience.

Mario smiled too. "But before that," he interpolated, in the interest of accuracy, "I worked for a while in a shop in Porto-clemente." He seemed visited by a natural desire to assist the prophecy by dredging out its essential features.

"There, didn't I say so? In an ironmonger's shop?"

"They kept combs and brushes," Mario got round it.

"Didn't I say that you were not always a Ganymede? Not

always at the sign of the serviette? Even when Cipolla makes a mistake, it is a kind that makes you believe in him. Now tell me: Do you believe in me?"

An indefinite gesture.

"A half-way answer," commented the Cavaliere. "Probably it is not easy to win your confidence. Even for me, I can see, it is not so easy. I see in your features a reserve, a sadness, *un tratto di malinconia* . . . tell me" (he seized Mario's hand persuasively) "have you troubles?"

"*Nossignore,*" answered Mario, promptly and decidedly.

"You *have* troubles," insisted the Cavaliere, bearing down the denial by the weight of his authority. "Can't I see? Trying to pull the wool over Cipolla's eyes, are you? Of course, about the girls—it is a girl, isn't it? You have love troubles?"

Mario gave a vigorous head-shake. And again the *giovanotto's* brutal laugh rang out. The Cavaliere gave heed. His eyes were roving about somewhere in the air; but he cocked an ear to the sound, then swung his whip backwards, as he had once or twice before in his conversation with Mario, that none of his puppets might flag in their zeal. The gesture had nearly cost him his new prey: Mario gave a sudden start in the direction of the steps. But Cipolla had him in his clutch.

"Not so fast," said he. "That would be fine, wouldn't it? So you want to skip, do you, Ganymede, right in the middle of the fun, or, rather, when it is just beginning? Stay with me, I'll show you something nice. I'll convince you. You have no reason to worry, I promise you. This girl—you know her and others know her too—what's her name? Wait! I read the name in your eyes, it is on the tip of my tongue and yours too—"

"Silvestra!" shouted the *giovanotto* from below.

The Cavaliere's face did not change.

"Aren't there the forward people?" he asked, not looking down, more as in undisturbed converse with Mario. "Aren't there the young fighting-cocks that crow in season and out? Takes the word out of your mouth, the conceited fool, and seems to think he has some special right to it. Let him be. But Silvestra, your Silvestra—ah, what a girl that is! What a prize! Brings your heart into your mouth to see her walk or laugh or breathe, she is so lovely. And her round arms when she washes, and tosses her head back to get the hair out of her eyes! An angel from paradise!"

Mario stared at him, his head thrust forward. He seemed to have forgotten the audience, forgotten where he was. The red rings round his eyes had got larger, they looked as though they were painted on. His thick lips parted.

"And she makes you suffer, this angel," went on Cipolla, "or, rather, you make yourself suffer for her—there is a difference, my lad, a most important difference, let me tell you. There are misunderstandings in love, maybe nowhere else in the world are there so many. I know what you are thinking: what does this Cipolla, with his little physical defect, know about love? Wrong, all wrong, he knows a lot. He has a wide and powerful understanding of its workings, and it pays to listen to his advice. But let's leave Cipolla out, cut him out altogether and think only of Silvestra, your peerless Silvestra! What! Is she to give any young gamecock the preference, so that he can laugh while you cry? To prefer him to a chap like you, so full of feeling and so sympathetic? Not very likely, is it? It is impossible—we know better, Cipolla and she. If I were to put myself in her place and choose between the two of you, a tarry lout like that—a codfish, a sea-urchin—and a Mario, a knight of the serviette, who moves among gentlefolk and hands round refreshments with an air— my word, but my heart would speak in no uncertain tones—it knows to whom I gave it long ago. It is time that he should see and understand, my chosen one! It is time that you see me and recognize me, Mario, my beloved! Tell me, who am I?"

It was grisly, the way the betrayer made himself irresistible, wreathed and coquetted with his crooked shoulder, languished with the puffy eyes, and showed his splintered teeth in a sickly smile. And alas, at his beguiling words, what was come of our Mario? It is hard for me to tell, hard as it was for me to see; for here was nothing less than an utter abandonment of the inmost soul, a public exposure of timid and deluded passion and rapture. He put his hands across his mouth, his shoulders rose and fell with his pantings. He could not, it was plain, trust his eyes and ears for joy, and the one thing he forgot was precisely that he could not trust them. "Silvestra!" he breathed, from the very depths of his vanquished heart.

"Kiss me!" said the hunchback. "Trust me, I love thee. Kiss me here." And with the tip of his index finger, hand, arm, and little finger outspread, he pointed to his cheek, near the mouth. And Mario bent and kissed him.

It had grown very still in the room. That was a monstrous moment, grotesque and thrilling, the moment of Mario's bliss. In that evil span of time, crowded with a sense of the illusiveness of all joy, one sound became audible, and that not quite at once, but on the instant of the melancholy and ribald meeting between Mario's lips and the repulsive flesh which thrust itself forward for his caress. It was the sound of a laugh, from the *giovanotto* on our left. It broke into the dramatic suspense of the moment, coarse, mocking, and yet—or I must have been grossly mistaken—with an undertone of compassion for the poor bewildered, victimized creature. It had a faint ring of that *"Poveretto"* which Cipolla had declared was wasted on the wrong person, when he claimed the pity for his own.

The laugh still rang in the air when the recipient of the caress gave his whip a little swish, low down, close to his chair-leg, and Mario started up and flung himself back. He stood in that posture staring, his hands one over the other on those desecrated lips. Then he beat his temples with his clenched fists, over and over; turned and staggered down the steps, while the audience applauded, and Cipolla sat there with his hands in his lap, his shoulders shaking. Once below, and even while in full retreat, Mario hurled himself round with legs flung wide apart; one arm flew up, and two flat shattering detonations crashed through applause and laughter.

There was instant silence. Even the dancers came to a full stop and stared about, struck dumb. Cipolla bounded from his seat. He stood with his arms spread out, slanting as though to ward everybody off, as though next moment he would cry out: "Stop! Keep back! Silence! What was that?" Then, in that instant, he sank back in his seat, his head rolling on his chest; in the next he had fallen sideways to the floor, where he lay motionless, a huddled heap of clothing, with limbs awry.

The commotion was indescribable. Ladies hid their faces, shuddering, on the breasts of their escorts. There were shouts for a doctor, for the police. People flung themselves on Mario in a mob, to disarm him, to take away the weapon that hung from his fingers—that small, dull-metal, scarcely pistol-shaped tool with hardly any barrel—in how strange and unexpected a direction had fate leveled it!

And now—now finally, at last—we took the children and led them towards the exit, past the pair of *carabinieri* just entering. Was that the end, they wanted to know, that they might go in peace? Yes, we assured them, that was the end. An end of horror, a fatal end. And yet a liberation—for I could not, and I cannot, but find it so!

HEART OF DARKNESS

by JOSEPH CONRAD

THE *Nellie,* a cruising yawl, swung to her anchor without a flutter of the sails, and was at rest. The flood had made, the wind was nearly calm, and being bound down the river, the only thing for it was to come to and wait for the turn of the tide.

The sea-reach of the Thames stretched before us like the beginning of an interminable waterway. In the offing the sea and the sky were welded together without a joint, and in the luminous space the tanned sails of the barges drifting up with the tide seemed to stand still in red clusters of canvas sharply peaked, with gleams of varnished sprits. A haze rested on the low shores that ran out to sea in vanishing flatness. The air was dark above Gravesend, and farther back still seemed condensed into a mournful gloom, brooding motionless over the biggest, and the greatest, town on earth.

The Director of Companies was our captain and our host. We four affectionately watched his back as he stood in the bows looking to seaward. On the whole river there was nothing that looked half so nautical. He resembled a pilot, which to a seaman is trustworthiness personified. It was difficult to realize his work was not out there in the luminous estuary, but behind him, within the brooding gloom.

Between us there was, as I have already said somewhere, the bond of the sea. Besides holding our hearts together through

long periods of separation, it had the effect of making us tolerant
of each other's yarns—and even convictions. The Lawyer—
the best of old fellows—had, because of his many years and many
virtues, the only cushion on deck, and was lying on the only
rug. The Accountant had brought out already a box of dominoes, and was toying architecturally with the bones. Marlow sat
cross-legged right aft, leaning against the mizzen-mast. He had
sunken cheeks, a yellow complexion, a straight back, an ascetic
aspect, and, with his arms dropped, the palms of hands outwards, resembled an idol. The director, satisfied the anchor
had good hold, made his way aft and sat down amongst us.
We exchanged a few words lazily. Afterwards there was silence
on board the yacht. For some reason or other we did not begin
that game of dominoes. We felt meditative, and fit for nothing
but placid staring. The day was ending in a serenity of still
and exquisite brilliance. The water shone pacifically; the sky,
without a speck, was a benign immensity of unstained light;
the very mist on the Essex marshes was like a gauzy and radiant
fabric, hung from the wooded rises inland, and draping the low
shores in diaphanous folds. Only the gloom to the west, brooding over the upper reaches, became more somber every minute,
as if angered by the approach of the sun.

And at last, in its curved and imperceptible fall, the sun sank
low, and from glowing white changed to a dull red without
rays and without heat, as if about to go out suddenly, stricken
to death by the touch of that gloom brooding over a crowd of
men.

Forthwith a change came over the waters, and the serenity
became less brilliant but more profound. The old river in its
broad reach rested unruffled at the decline of day, after ages of
good service done to the race that peopled its banks, spread out
in the tranquil dignity of a waterway leading to the uttermost
ends of the earth. We looked at the venerable stream not in the

vivid flush of a short day that comes and departs forever, but in the august light of abiding memories. And indeed nothing is easier for a man who has, as the phrase goes, "followed the sea" with reverence and affection, than to evoke the great spirit of the past upon the lower reaches of the Thames. The tidal current runs to and fro in its unceasing service, crowded with memories of men and ships it had borne to the rest of home or to the battles of the sea. It had known and served all the men of whom the nation is proud, from Sir Francis Drake to Sir John Franklin, knights all, titled and untitled—the knights-errant of the sea. It had borne all the ships whose names are like jewels flashing in the night of time, from the *Golden Hind* returning with her round flanks full of treasure, to be visited by the Queen's Highness and thus pass out of the gigantic tale, to the *Erebus* and *Terror,* bound on other conquests—and that never returned. It had known the ships and the men. They had sailed from Deptford, from Greenwich, from Erith—the adventurers and the settlers; kings' ships and the ships of men on 'Change; captains, admirals, the dark "interlopers" of the Eastern trade, and the commissioned "generals" of East India fleets. Hunters for gold or pursuers of fame, they all had gone out on that stream, bearing the sword, and often the torch, messengers of the might within the land, bearers of a spark from the sacred fire. What greatness had not floated on the ebb of that river into the mystery of an unknown earth! . . . The dreams of men, the seed of commonwealths, the germs of empires.

The sun set; the dusk fell on the stream, and lights began to appear along the shore. The Chapman lighthouse, a three-legged thing erect on a mud-flat, shone strongly. Lights of ships moved in the fairway—a great stir of lights going up and going down. And farther west on the upper reaches the place of the

monstrous town was still marked ominously on the sky, a brooding gloom in sunshine, a lurid glare under the stars.

"And this also," said Marlow suddenly, "has been one of the
dark places on the earth."

He was the only man of us who still "followed the sea." The
worst that could be said of him was that he did not represent
his class. He was a seaman, but he was a wanderer, too, while
most seamen lead, if one may so express it, a sedentary life.
Their minds are of the stay-at-home order, and their home is
always with them—the ship; and so is their country—the sea.
One ship is very much like another, and the sea is always the
same. In the immutability of their surroundings the foreign
shores, the foreign faces, the changing immensity of life, glide
past, veiled not by a sense of mystery but by a slightly disdainful
ignorance; for there is nothing mysterious to a seaman unless it
be the sea itself, which is the mistress of his existence and as inscrutable as Destiny. For the rest, after his hours of work, a
casual stroll or a casual spree on shore suffices to unfold for him
the secret of a whole continent, and generally he finds the secret
not worth knowing. The yarns of seamen have a direct simplicity, the whole meaning of which lies within the shell of a
cracked nut. But Marlow was not typical (if his propensity to
spin yarns be excepted), and to him the meaning of an episode
was not inside like a kernel but outside, enveloping the tale
which brought it out only as a glow brings out a haze, in the
likeness of one of these misty halos that sometimes are made
visible by the spectral illumination of moonshine.

His remark did not seem at all surprising. It was just like
Marlow. It was accepted in silence. No one took the trouble
to grunt even; and presently he said, very slow—

"I was thinking of very old times, when the Romans first
came here, nineteen hundred years ago—the other day. . . .
Light came out of this river since—you say Knights? Yes;

but it is like a running blaze on a plain, like a flash of lightning in the clouds. We live in the flicker—may it last as long
as the old earth keeps rolling! But darkness was here yesterday. Imagine the feelings of a commander of a fine—what d'ye
call 'em?—trireme in the Mediterranean, ordered suddenly to
the north; run overland across the Gauls in a hurry; put in
charge of one of these craft the legionaries—a wonderful lot of
handy men they must have been, too—used to build, apparently
by the hundred, in a month or two, if we may believe what we
read. Imagine him here—the very end of the world, a sea the
color of lead, a sky the color of smoke, a kind of ship about as
rigid as a concertina—and going up this river with stores, or
orders, or what you like. Sand-banks, marshes, forests, savages,
—precious little to eat fit for a civilized man, nothing but
Thames water to drink. No Falernian wine here, no going
ashore. Here and there a military camp lost in a wilderness,
like a needle in a bundle of hay—cold, fog, tempests, disease,
exile, and death,—death skulking in the air, in the water, in
the bush. They must have been dying like flies here. Oh, yes—
he did it. Did it very well, too, no doubt, and without thinking much about it either, except afterwards to brag of what he
had gone through in his time, perhaps. They were men enough
to face the darkness. And perhaps he was cheered by keeping
his eye on a chance of promotion to the fleet at Ravenna by and
by, if he had good friends in Rome and survived the awful
climate. Or think of a decent young citizen in a toga—perhaps
too much dice, you know—coming out here in the train of some
prefect, or tax-gatherer, or trader even, to mend his fortunes.
Land in a swamp, march through the woods, and in some inland
post feel the savagery, the utter savagery, had closed round him,
—all that mysterious life of the wilderness that stirs in the forest,
in the jungles, in the hearts of wild men. There's no initiation either into such mysteries. He has to live in the midst of

the incomprehensible, which is also detestable. And it has a
fascination, too, that goes to work upon him. The fascination of
the abomination—you know, imagine the growing regrets, the
longing to escape, the powerless disgust, the surrender, the hate."
  He paused.

  "Mind," he began again, lifting one arm from the elbow, the
palm of the hand outwards, so that, with his legs folded before
him, he had the pose of a Buddha preaching in European clothes
and without a lotus-flower—"Mind, none of us would feel exactly
like this. What saves us is efficiency—the devotion to efficiency.
But these chaps were not much account, really. They were no
colonists; their administration was merely a squeeze, and
nothing more, I suspect. They were conquerors, and for that
you want only brute force—nothing to boast of, when you have
it, since your strength is just an accident arising from the weakness of others. They grabbed what they could get for the sake
of what was to be got. It was just robbery with violence, aggravated murder on a great scale, and men going at it blind—
as is very proper for those who tackle a darkness. The conquest
of the earth, which mostly means the taking it away from those
who have a different complexion or slightly flatter noses than
ourselves, is not a pretty thing when you look into it too much.
What redeems it is the idea only. An idea at the back of it; not
a sentimental pretense but an idea; and an unselfish belief in the
idea—something you can set up, and bow down before, and offer
a sacrifice to. . . ."

  He broke off. Flames glided in the river, small green flames,
red flames, white flames, pursuing, overtaking, joining, crossing
each other—then separating slowly or hastily. The traffic of the
great city went on in the deepening night upon the sleepless
river. We looked on, waiting patiently—there was nothing else
to do till the end of the flood; but it was only after a long
silence, when he said, in a hesitating voice, "I suppose you fel-

lows remember I did once turn fresh-water sailor for a bit," that we knew we were fated, before the ebb began to run, to hear one of Marlow's inconclusive experiences.

"I don't want to bother you much with what happened to me personally," he began, showing in this remark the weakness of many tellers of tales who seem so often unaware of what their audience would best like to hear; "yet to understand the effect of it on me you ought to know how I got out there, what I saw, how I went up that river to the place where I first met the poor chap. It was the farthest point of navigation and the culminating point of my experience. It seemed somehow to throw a kind of light on everything about me—and into my thoughts. It was somber enough, too—and pitiful—not extraordinary in any way—not very clear either. No, not very clear. And yet it seemed to throw a kind of light.

"I had then, as you remember, just returned to London after a lot of Indian Ocean, Pacific, China Seas—a regular dose of the East—six years or so, and I was loafing about, hindering you fellows in your work and invading your homes, just as though I had got a heavenly mission to civilize you. It was very fine for a time, but after a bit I did get tired of resting. Then I began to look for a ship—I should think the hardest work on earth. But the ships wouldn't even look at me. And I got tired of that game, too.

"Now when I was a little chap I had a passion for maps. I would look for hours at South America, or Africa, or Australia, and lose myself in all the glories of exploration. At that time there were many blank spaces on the earth, and when I saw one that looked particularly inviting on a map (but they all look that) I would put my finger on it and say, When I grow up I will go there. The North Pole was one of these places, I remember. Well, I haven't been there yet, and shall not try now. The glamour's off. Other places were scattered about the Equator, and in every sort of latitude all over the two hemispheres. I have been in some of them, and . . . well, we won't talk about that. But there was one yet—the biggest, the most blank, so to speak—that I had a hankering after.

"True, by this time it was not a blank space any more. It had got filled since my childhood with rivers and lakes and names. It had ceased to be a blank space of delightful mystery—a white patch for a boy to dream gloriously over. It had become a place of darkness. But there was in it one river especially, a mighty big river, that you could see on the map, resembling an immense snake uncoiled, with its head in the sea, its body at rest curving afar over a vast country, and its tail lost in the depths of the land. And as I looked at the map of it in a shop-window, it fascinated me as a snake would a bird—a silly little bird. Then I remembered there was a big concern, a Company for trade on that river. Dash it all! I thought to myself, they can't trade without using some kind of craft on that lot of fresh water—steamboats! Why shouldn't I try to get charge of one? I went on along Fleet Street, but could not shake off the idea. The snake had charmed me.

"You understand it was a Continental concern, that Trading society; but I have a lot of relations living on the Continent, because it's cheap and not so nasty as it looks, they say.

"I am sorry to own I began to worry them. This was already a fresh departure for me. I was not used to getting things that way, you know. I always went my own road and on my own legs where I had a mind to go. I wouldn't have believed it of myself; but, then—you see—I felt somehow I must get there by hook or by crook. So I worried them. The men said 'My dear fellow,' and did nothing. Then—would you believe it?—I tried the women. I, Charlie Marlow, set the women to work—to get a job. Heavens! Well, you see, the notion drove me. I had an aunt, a dear enthusiastic soul. She wrote: 'It will be delightful.

I am ready to do anything, anything for you. It is a glorious idea. I know the wife of a very high personage in the Administration, and also a man who has lots of influence with,' etc., etc. She was determined to make no end of fuss to get me appointed skipper of a river steamboat, if such was my fancy.

"I got my appointment—of course; and I got it very quick. It appears the Company had received news that one of their captains had been killed in a scuffle with the natives. This was my chance, and it made me the more anxious to go. It was only months and months afterwards, when I made the attempt to recover what was left of the body, that I heard the original quarrel arose from a misunderstanding about some hens. Yes, two black hens. Fresleven—that was the fellow's name, a Dane—thought himself wronged somehow in the bargain, so he went ashore and started to hammer the chief of the village with a stick. Oh, it didn't surprise me in the least to hear this, and at the same time to be told that Fresleven was the gentlest, quietest creature that ever walked on two legs. No doubt he was; but he had been a couple of years already out there engaged in the noble cause, you know, and he probably felt the need at last of asserting his self-respect in some way. Therefore he whacked the old nigger mercilessly, while a big crowd of his people watched him, thunderstruck, till some man—I was told the chief's son—in desperation at hearing the old chap yell, made a tentative jab with a spear at the white man—and of course it went quite easy between the shoulder blades. Then the whole population cleared into the forest, expecting all kinds of calamities to happen, while, on the other hand, the steamer Fresleven commanded left also in a bad panic, in charge of the engineer, I believe. Afterwards nobody seemed to trouble much about Fresleven's remains, till I got out and stepped into his shoes. I couldn't let it rest, though; but when an opportunity offered at last to meet my predecessor, the grass growing through his ribs was tall enough to hide his bones. They were all there. The supernatural being had not been touched after he fell. And the village was deserted, the huts gaped black, rotting, all askew within the fallen enclosures. A calamity had come to it, sure enough. The people had vanished. Mad terror had scattered them, men, women, and children, through the bush, and they had never returned. What became of the hens I don't know either. I should think the cause of progress got them, anyhow. However, through this glorious affair I got my appointment, before I had fairly begun to hope for it.

"I flew around like mad to get ready, and before forty-eight hours I was crossing the Channel to show myself to my employers, and sign the contract. In a very few hours I arrived in a city that always makes me think of a whited sepulcher. Prejudice no doubt. I had no difficulty in finding the Company's offices. It was the biggest thing in the town, and everybody I met was full of it. They were going to run an over-sea empire, and make no end of coin by trade.

"A narrow and deserted street in deep shadow, high houses, innumerable windows with venetian blinds, a dead silence, grass sprouting between the stones, imposing carriage archways right and left, immense double doors standing ponderously ajar. I slipped through one of these cracks, went up a swept and ungarnished staircase, as arid as a desert, and opened the first door I came to. Two women, one fat and the other slim, sat on straw-bottomed chairs, knitting black wool. The slim one got up and walked straight at me—still knitting with downcast eyes—and only just as I began to think of getting out of her way, as you would for a somnambulist, stood still, and looked up. Her dress was as plain as an umbrella-cover, and she turned round without out a word and preceded me into a waiting-room. I gave my name, and looked about. Deal table in the middle, plain chairs all around the walls, on one end a large shining map, marked

with all the colors of a rainbow. There was a vast amount of
red—good to see at any time, because one knows that some real
work is done in there, a deuce of a lot of blue, a little green,
smears of orange, and, on the East Coast, a purple patch, to show
where the jolly pioneers of progress drink the jolly lager-beer.
However, I wasn't going into any of these. I was going into the
yellow. Dead in the center. And the river was there—fascinating—deadly—like a snake. Ough! A door opened, a white-
haired secretarial head, but wearing a compassionate expression,
appeared, and a skinny forefinger beckoned me into the sanctu-
ary. Its light was dim, and a heavy writing-desk squatted in
the middle. From behind that structure came out an impression
of pale plumpness in a frock-coat. The great man himself. He
was five feet six, I should judge, and had his grip on the handle-
end of ever so many millions. He shook hands, I fancy, murmured vaguely, was satisfied with my French. *Bon voyage.*

"In about forty-five seconds I found myself again in the
waiting-room with the compassionate secretary, who, full of desolation and sympathy, made me sign some document. I believe
I undertook amongst other things not to disclose any trade secrets. Well, I am not going to.

"I began to feel slightly uneasy. You know I am not used to
such ceremonies, and there was something ominous in the atmosphere. It was just as though I had been let into some con-
spiracy—I don't know—something not quite right; and I was
glad to get out. In the outer room the two women knitted black
wool feverishly. People were arriving, and the younger one was
walking back and forth introducing them. The old one sat on
her chair. Her flat cloth slippers were propped up on a foot-
warmer, and a cat reposed on her lap. She wore a starched
white affair on her head, had a wart on one cheek, and silver-
rimmed spectacles hung on the tip of her nose. She glanced at
me above the glasses. The swift and indifferent placidity of that

look troubled me. Two youths with foolish and cheery countenances were being piloted over, and she threw at them the
same quick glance of unconcerned wisdom. She seemed to
know all about them and about me, too. An eerie feeling came
over me. She seemed uncanny and fateful. Often far away
there I thought of these two, guarding the door of Darkness,
knitting black wool as for a warm pall, one introducing, introducing continuously to the unknown, the other scrutinizing the
cheery and foolish faces with unconcerned old eyes. *Ave!* Old
knitter of black wool. *Morituri te salutant.* Not many of those
she looked at ever saw her again—not half, by a long way.

"There was yet a visit to the doctor. 'A simple formality,'
assured me the secretary, with an air of taking an immense part
in all my sorrows. Accordingly a young chap wearing his hat
over the left eyebrow, some clerk I suppose,—there must have
been clerks in the business, though the house was as still as a
house in a city of the dead—came from somewhere upstairs, and
led me forth. He was shabby and careless, with inkstains on
the sleeves of his jacket, and his cravat was large and billowy,
under a chin shaped like the toe of an old boot. It was a little
too early for the doctor, so I proposed a drink, and thereupon
he developed a vein of joviality. As we sat over our vermouths
he glorified the Company's business, and by and by I expressed
casually my surprise at him not going out there. He became
very cool and collected all at once. 'I am not such a fool as I
look, quoth Plato to his disciples,' he said sententiously, emptied
his glass with great resolution, and we rose.

"The old doctor felt my pulse, evidently thinking of something else the while. 'Good, good for there,' he mumbled, and
then with a certain eagerness asked me whether I would let
him measure my head. Rather surprised, I said Yes, when he
produced a thing like calipers and got the dimensions back and
front and every way, taking notes carefully. He was an un-

shaven little man in a threadbare coat like a gaberdine, with his
feet in slippers, and I thought him a harmless fool. 'I always
ask leave, in the interests of science, to measure the crania of
those going out there,' he said. 'And when they come back,
too?' I asked. 'Oh, I never see them,' he remarked; 'and,
moreover, the changes take place inside, you know.' He smiled,
as if at some quiet joke. 'So you are going out there. Famous.
Interesting, too.' He gave me a searching glance, and made another note. 'Ever any madness in your family?' he asked, in a
matter-of-fact tone. I felt very annoyed. 'Is that question in
the interests of science, too?' 'It would be,' he said, without
taking notice of my irritation, 'interesting for science to watch
the mental changes of individuals, on the spot, but . . .' 'Are
you an alienist?' I interrupted. 'Every doctor should be—a
little,' answered that original, imperturbably. 'I have a little
theory which you Messieurs who go out there must help me to
prove. This is my share in the advantages my country shall
reap from the possession of such a magnificent dependency. The
mere wealth I leave to others. Pardon my questions, but you are
the first Englishman coming under my observation . . .' I hastened to assure him I was not in the least typical. 'If I were,'
said I, 'I wouldn't be talking like this with you.' 'What you
say is rather profound, and probably erroneous,' he said, with a
laugh. 'Avoid irritation more than exposure to the sun. Adieu.
How do you English say, eh? Good-by. Ah! Good-by. Adieu.
In the tropics one must before everything keep calm.' . . . He
lifted a warning forefinger. . . . *'Du calme, du calme. Adieu.'*

"One thing more remained to do—say good-by to my excellent
aunt. I found her triumphant. I had a cup of tea—the last
decent cup of tea for many days—and in a room that most
soothingly looked just as you would expect a lady's drawing-room
to look, we had a long quiet chat by the fireside. In the course
of these confidences it became quite plain to me I had been rep-

resented to the wife of the high dignitary, and goodness knows
to how many more people besides, as an exceptional and gifted
creature—a piece of good fortune for the Company—a man you
don't get hold of every day. Good heavens! and I was going to
take charge of a two-penny-half-penny river-steamboat with a
penny whistle attached! It appeared, however, I was also one
of the Workers, with a capital—you know. Something like an
emissary of light, something like a lower sort of apostle. There
had been a lot of such rot let loose in print and talk just about
that time, and the excellent woman, living right in the rush of
all that humbug, got carried off her feet. She talked about
'weaning those ignorant millions from their horrid ways,' till,
upon my word, she made me quite uncomfortable. I ventured
to hint that the Company was run for profit.

"'You forget, dear Charlie, that the laborer is worthy of his
hire,' she said, brightly. It's queer how out of touch with truth
women are. They live in a world of their own, and there has
never been anything like it, and never can be. It is too beautiful
altogether, and if they were to set it up it would go to pieces
before the first sunset. Some confounded fact we men have been
living contentedly with ever since the day of creation would start
up and knock the whole thing over.

"After this I got embraced, told to wear flannel, be sure to
write often, and so on—and I left. In the street—I don't know
why—a queer feeling came to me that I was an impostor. Odd
thing that I, who used to clear out for any part of the world
at twenty-four hours' notice, with less thought than most men
give to the crossing of a street, had a moment—I won't say of
hesitation, but of startled pause, before this commonplace affair.
The best way I can explain it to you is by saying that, for a
second or two, I felt as though, instead of going to the center
of a continent, I were about to set off for the center of the earth.

"I left in a French steamer, and she called in every blamed

port they have out there, for, as far as I could see, the sole purpose of landing soldiers and custom-house officers. I watched
the coast. Watching a coast as it slips by the ship is like thinking about an enigma. There it is before you—smiling, frowning, inviting, grand, mean, insipid, or savage, and always mute
with an air of whispering, Come and find out. This one was
almost featureless, as if still in the making, with an aspect of
monotonous grimness. The edge of a colossal jungle, so dark-
green as to be almost black, fringed with white surf, ran straight,
like a ruled line, far, far away along a blue sea whose glitter
was blurred by a creeping mist. The sun was fierce, the land
seemed to glisten and drip with steam. Here and there grayish-
whitish specks showed up clustered inside the white surf, with
a flag flying above them perhaps. Settlements some centuries
old, and still no bigger than pinheads on the untouched expanse
of their background. We pounded along, stopped, landed soldiers; went on, landed custom-house clerks to levy toll in what
looked like a God-forsaken wilderness, with a tin shed and a
flag-pole lost in it; landed more soldiers—to take care of the
custom-house clerks, presumably. Some, I heard, got drowned
in the surf; but whether they did or not, nobody seemed particularly to care. They were just flung out there, and on we
went. Every day the coast looked the same, as though we had
not moved; but we passed various places—trading places—with
names like Gran' Bassam, Little Popo; names that seemed to
belong to some sordid farce acted in front of a sinister back-
cloth. The idleness of a passenger, my isolation amongst all
these men with whom I had no point of contact, the oily and
languid sea, the uniform somberness of the coast, seemed to keep
me away from the truth of things, within the toil of a mournful
and senseless delusion. The voice of the surf heard now and
then was a positive pleasure, like the speech of a brother. It was
something natural, that had its reason, that had a meaning.

Now and then a boat from the shore gave one a momentary contact with reality. It was paddled by black fellows. You could see from afar the white of their eyeballs glistening. They shouted, sang; their bodies streamed with perspiration; they had faces like grotesque masks—these chaps; but they had bone, muscle, a wild vitality, an intense energy of movement, that was as natural and true as the surf along their coast. They wanted no excuse for being there. They were a great comfort to look at. For a time I would feel I belonged still to a world of straightforward facts; but the feeling would not last long. Something would turn up to scare it away. Once, I remember, we came upon a man-of-war anchored off the coast. There wasn't even a shed there, and she was shelling the bush. It appears the French had one of their wars going on thereabouts. Her ensign dropped limp like a rag; the muzzles of the long six-inch guns stuck out all over the low hull; the greasy, slimy swell swung her up lazily and let her down, swaying her thin masts. In the empty immensity of earth, sky, and water, there she was, incomprehensible, firing into a continent. Pop, would go one of the six-inch guns; a small flame would dart and vanish, a little white smoke would disappear, a tiny projectile would give a feeble screech—and nothing happened. Nothing could happen. There was a touch of insanity in the proceeding, a sense of lugubrious drollery in the sight; and it was not dissipated by somebody on board assuring me earnestly there was a camp of natives—he called them enemies!—hidden out of sight somewhere.

"We gave her her letters (I heard the men in that lonely ship were dying of fever at the rate of three a day) and went on. We called at some more places with farcical names, where the merry dance of death and trade goes on in a still and earthy atmosphere as of an overheated catacomb; all along the formless coast bordered by dangerous surf, as if Nature herself had tried to ward off intruders; in and out of rivers, streams of death in life, whose banks were rotting into mud, whose waters, thickened into slime, invaded the contorted mangroves, that seemed to writhe at us in the extremity of an impotent despair. Nowhere did we stop long enough to get a particularized impression, but the general sense of vague and oppressive wonder grew upon me. It was like a weary pilgrimage amongst hints for nightmares.

"It was upward of thirty days before I saw the mouth of the big river. We anchored off the seat of the government. But my work would not begin till some two hundred miles farther on. So as soon as I could I made a start for a place thirty miles higher up.

"I had my passage on a little sea-going steamer. Her captain was a Swede, and knowing me for a seaman, invited me on the bridge. He was a young man, lean, fair, and morose, with lanky hair and a shuffling gait. As we left the miserable little wharf, he tossed his head contemptuously at the shore. 'Been living there?' he asked. I said, 'Yes.' 'Fine lot these government chaps —are they not?' he went on, speaking English with great precision and considerable bitterness. 'It is funny what some people will do for a few francs a month. I wonder what becomes of that kind when it goes up-country?' I said to him I expected to see that soon. 'So-o-o!' he exclaimed. He shuffled athwart, keeping one eye ahead vigilantly. 'Don't be too sure,' he continued. 'The other day I took up a man who hanged himself on the road. He was a Swede, too.' 'Hanged himself! Why, in God's name?' I cried. He kept on looking out watchfully. 'Who knows? The sun was too much for him, or the country perhaps.'

"At last we opened a reach. A rocky cliff appeared, mounds of turned-up earth by the shore, houses on a hill, others with iron roofs, amongst a waste of excavations, or hanging to the declivity. A continuous noise of the rapids above hovered over this scene of inhabited devastation. A lot of people, mostly

black and naked, moved about like ants. A jetty projected into
the river. A blinding sunlight drowned all this at times in a
sudden recrudescence of glare. 'There's your Company's station,' said the Swede, pointing to three wooden barrack-like
structures on the rocky slope. 'I will send your things up. Four
boxes did you say? So. Farewell.'

"I came upon a boiler wallowing in the grass, then found a
path leading up the hill. It turned aside for the boulders, and
also for an undersized railway-truck lying there on its back with
its wheels in the air. One was off. The thing looked as dead
as the carcass of some animal. I came upon more pieces of decaying machinery, a stack of rusty rails. To the left a clump of
trees made a shady spot, where dark things seemed to stir feebly.
I blinked, the path was steep. A horn tooted to the right, and I
saw the black people run. A heavy and dull detonation shook
the ground, a puff of smoke came out of the cliff, and that was
all. No change appeared on the face of the rock. They were
building a railway. The cliff was not in the way or anything;
but this objectless blasting was all the work going on.

"A slight clinking behind me made me turn my head. Six
black men advanced in a file, toiling up the path. They walked
erect and slow, balancing small baskets full of earth on their
heads, and the clink kept time with their footsteps. Black rags
were wound round their loins, and the short ends behind wag-
gled to and fro like tails. I could see every rib, the joints of
their limbs were like knots in a rope; each had an iron collar
on his neck, and all were connected together with a chain whose
bights swung between them, rhythmically clinking. Another
report from the cliff made me think suddenly of that ship of
war I had seen firing into a continent. It was the same kind
of ominous voice; but these men could by no stretch of imagination be called enemies. They were called criminals, and the outraged law, like the bursting shells, had come to them, an insol-

uble mystery from the sea. All their meager breasts panted together, the violently dilated nostrils quivered, the eyes stared
stonily up-hill. They passed me within six inches, without a
glance, with that complete, deathlike indifference of unhappy
savages. Behind this raw matter one of the reclaimed, the prod-
uct of the new forces at work, strolled despondently, carrying a
rifle by its middle. He had a uniform jacket with one button
off, and seeing a white man on the path, hoisted his weapon to
his shoulder with alacrity. This was simple prudence, white
men being so much alike at a distance that he could not tell who
I might be. He was speedily reassured, and with a large, white,
rascally grin, and a glance at his charge, seemed to take me into
partnership in his exalted trust. After all, I also was a part of
the great cause of these high and just proceedings.

"Instead of going up, I turned and descended to the left. My
idea was to let that chain-gang get out of sight before I climbed
the hill. You know I am not particularly tender; I've had to
strike and to fend off. I've had to resist and to attack sometimes
—that's only one way of resisting—without counting the exact
cost, according to the demands of such sort of life as I had blundered into. I've seen the devil of violence, and the devil of
greed, and the devil of hot desire; but, by all the stars! these
were strong, lusty, red-eyed devils, that swayed and drove men
—men, I tell you. But as I stood on this hillside, I foresaw that
in the blinding sunshine of that land I would become acquainted
with a flabby, pretending, weak-eyed devil of a rapacious and
pitiless folly. How insidious he could be, too, I was only to find
out several months later and a thousand miles farther. For a
moment I stood appalled, as though by a warning. Finally I
descended the hill, obliquely, towards the trees I had seen.

"I avoided a vast artificial hole somebody had been digging
on the slope, the purpose of which I found it impossible to
divine. It wasn't a quarry or a sandpit, anyhow. It was just a

hole. It might have been connected with the philanthropic desire of giving the criminals something to do. I don't know.
Then I nearly fell into a very narrow ravine, almost no more
than a scar in the hillside. I discovered that a lot of imported
drainage-pipes for the settlement had been tumbled in there.
There wasn't one that was not broken. It was a wanton smash-
up. At last I got under the trees. My purpose was to stroll into
the shade for a moment; but no sooner within than it seemed
to me I had stepped into the gloomy circle of some Inferno. The
rapids were near, and an uninterrupted, uniform, headlong,
rushing noise filled the mournful stillness of the grove, where
not a breath stirred, not a leaf moved, with a mysterious sound—
as though the tearing pace of the launched earth had suddenly
become audible.

"Black shapes crouched, lay, sat between the trees leaning
against the trunks, clinging to the earth, half coming out, half
effaced within the dim light, in all the attitudes of pain, abandonment, and despair. Another mine on the cliff went off, followed by a slight shudder of the soil under my feet. The work
was going on. The work! And this was the place where some
of the helpers had withdrawn to die.

"They were dying slowly—it was very clear. They were not
enemies, they were not criminals, they were nothing earthly
now,— nothing but black shadows of disease and starvation, lying confusedly in the greenish gloom. Brought from all the
recesses of the coast in all the legality of time contracts, lost in
uncongenial surroundings, fed on unfamiliar food, they sick-
ened, became inefficient, and were then allowed to crawl away
and rest. These moribund shapes were free as air—and nearly
as thin. I began to distinguish the gleam of the eyes under the
trees. Then, glancing down, I saw a face near my hand. The
black bones reclined at full length with one shoulder against the
tree, and slowly the eyelids rose and the sunken eyes looked up

at me, enormous and vacant, a kind of blind, white flicker in
the depths of the orbs, which died out slowly. The man seemed
young—almost a boy—but you know with them it's hard to tell.
I found nothing else to do but to offer him one of my good
Swede's ship's biscuits I had in my pocket. The fingers closed
slowly on it and held—there was no other movement and no
other glance. He had tied a bit of white worsted round his
neck— Why? Where did he get it? Was it a badge—an
ornament—a charm—a propitiatory act? Was there any idea at
all connected with it? It looked startling round his black neck,
this bit of white thread from beyond the seas.

"Near the same tree two more bundles of acute angles sat
with their legs drawn up. One, with his chin propped on his
knees, stared at nothing, in an intolerable and appalling manner: his brother phantom rested its forehead, as if overcome
with a great weariness; and all about others were scattered in
every pose of contorted collapse, as in some picture of a massacre
or a pestilence. While I stood horror-struck, one of these creatures rose to his hands and knees, and went off on all-fours towards the river to drink. He lapped out of his hand, then sat
up in the sunlight, crossing his shins in front of him, and after
a time let his wooly head fall on his breastbone.

"I didn't want any more loitering in the shade, and I made
haste towards the station. When near the buildings I met a
white man, in such an unexpected elegance of get-up that in the
first moment I took him for a sort of vision. I saw a high
starched collar, white cuffs, a light alpaca jacket, snowy trousers,
a clean necktie, and varnished boots. No hat. Hair parted,
brushed, oiled, under a green-lined parasol held in a big white
hand. He was amazing, and had a penholder behind his ear.

"I shook hands with this miracle, and I learned he was the
Company's chief accountant, and that all the bookkeeping was
done at this station. He had come out for a moment, he said,

'to get a breath of fresh air.' The expression sounded wonderfully odd, with its suggestion of sedentary desk-life. I wouldn't have mentioned the fellow to you at all, only it was from his lips that I first heard the name of the man who is so indissolubly connected with the memories of that time. Moreover, I respected the fellow. Yes; I respected his collars, his vast cuffs, his brushed hair. His appearance was certainly that of a hairdresser's dummy; but in the great demoralization of the land he kept up his appearance. That's backbone. His starched collars and got-up shirt-fronts were achievements of character. He had been out nearly three years; and, later, I could not help asking him how he managed to sport such linen. He had just the faintest blush, and said modestly, 'I've been teaching one of the native women about the station. It was difficult. She had a distaste for the work.' Thus this man had verily accomplished something. And he was devoted to his books, which were in apple-pie order.

"Everything else in the station was in a muddle,—heads, things, buildings. Strings of dusty niggers with splay feet arrived and departed; a stream of manufactured goods, rubbishy cottons, beads, and brass-wire set into the depths of darkness, and in return came a precious trickle of ivory.

"I had to wait in the station for ten days—an eternity. I lived in a hut in the yard, but to be out of the chaos I would sometimes get into the accountant's office. It was built of horizontal planks, and so badly put together that, as he bent over his high desk, he was barred from neck to heels with narrow strips of sunlight. There was no need to open the big shutter to see. It was hot there, too; big flies buzzed fiendishly, and did not sting, but stabbed. I sat generally on the floor, while, of faultless appearance (and even slightly scented), perching on a high stool, he wrote, he wrote. Sometimes he stood up for exercise. When a trucklebed with a sick man (some invalid agent from up-country) was put in there, he exhibited a gentle annoyance. 'The groans of this sick person,' he said, 'distract my attention. And without that it is extremely difficult to guard against clerical errors in this climate.'

"One day he remarked, without lifting his head, 'In the interior you will no doubt meet Mr. Kurtz.' On my asking who Mr. Kurtz was, he said he was a first-class agent; and seeing my disappointment at this information, he added slowly, laying down his pen, 'He is a very remarkable person.' Further questions elicited from him that Mr. Kurtz was at present in charge of a trading post, a very important one, in the true ivory-country, at 'the very bottom of there. Sends in as much ivory as all the others put together. . . .' He began to write again. The sick man was too ill to groan. The flies buzzed in a great peace.

"Suddenly there was a growing murmur of voices and a great tramping of feet. A caravan had come in. A violent babble of uncouth sounds burst out on the other side of the planks. All the carriers were speaking together, and in the midst of the uproar the lamentable voice of the chief agent was heard 'giving it up' tearfully for the twentieth time that day. . . . He rose slowly. 'What a frightful row,' he said. He crossed the room gently to look at the sick man, and returning, said to me, 'He does not hear.' 'What! Dead?' I asked, startled. 'No, not yet,' he answered, with great composure. Then, alluding with a toss of the head to the tumult in the station-yard, 'When one has got to make correct entries, one comes to hate those savages—hate them to the death.' He remained thoughtful for a moment. 'When you see Mr. Kurtz,' he went on, 'tell him for me that everything here'—he glanced at the desk—'is very satisfactory. I don't like to write to him—with those messengers of ours you never know who may get hold of your letter—at that Central Station.' He stared at me for a moment with his

mild, bulging eyes. 'Oh, he will go far, very far,' he began
again. 'He will be a somebody in the Administration before
long. They, above—the Council in Europe, you know—mean
him to be.'

"He turned to his work. The noise outside had ceased, and
presently in going out I stopped at the door. In the steady buzz
of flies the homeward-bound agent was lying flushed and insensible; the other, bent over his books, was making correct entries of perfectly correct transactions; and fifty feet below the
doorstep I could see the still tree-tops of the grove of death.

"Next day I left that station at last, with a caravan of sixty
men, for a two-hundred-mile tramp.

"No use telling you much about that. Paths, paths, everywhere; a stamped-in network of paths spreading over the empty
land, through long grass, through burnt grass, through thickets,
down and up chilly ravines, up and down stony hills ablaze
with heat; and a solitude, a solitude, nobody, not a hut. The
population had cleared out a long time ago. Well, if a lot of
mysterious niggers armed with all kinds of fearful weapons suddenly took to traveling on the road between Deal and Gravesend,
catching the yokels right and left to carry heavy loads for them,
I fancy every farm and cottage thereabouts would get empty
very soon. Only here the dwellings were gone, too. Still I
passed through several abandoned villages. There's something
pathetically childish in the ruins of grass walls. Day after day,
with the stamp and shuffle of sixty pair of bare feet behind me,
each pair under a sixty-pound load. Camp, cook, sleep, strike
camp, march. Now and then a carrier dead in harness, at rest
in the long grass near the path, with an empty water-gourd and
his long staff lying by his side. A great silence around and
above. Perhaps on some quiet night the tremor of far-off
drums, sinking, swelling, a tremor vast, faint; a sound weird,
appealing, suggestive, and wild—and perhaps with as profound

a meaning as the sound of bells in a Christian country. Once
a white man in an unbuttoned uniform, camping on the path
with an armed escort of lank Zanzibaris, very hospitable and
festive—not to say drunk. Was looking after the upkeep of the
road, he declared. Can't say I saw any road or any upkeep,
unless the body of a middle-aged Negro, with a bullet-hole in
the forehead, upon which I absolutely stumbled three miles
farther on, may be considered as a permanent improvement. I
had a white companion, too, not a bad chap, but rather too fleshy
and with the exasperating habit of fainting on the hot hillsides,
miles away from the least bit of shade and water. Annoying,
you know, to hold your own coat like a parasol over a man's
head while he is coming-to. I couldn't help asking him once
what he meant by coming there at all. 'To make money, of
course. What do you think?' he said, scornfully. Then he got
fever, and had to be carried in a hammock slung under a pole.
As he weighed sixteen stone I had no end of rows with the
carriers. They jibbed, ran away, sneaked off with their loads in
the night—quite a mutiny. So, one evening, I made a speech
in English with gestures, not one of which was lost to the sixty
pairs of eyes before me, and the next morning I started the
hammock off in front all right. An hour afterwards I came
upon the whole concern wrecked in a bush—man, hammock,
groans, blankets, horrors. The heavy pole had skinned his poor
nose. He was very anxious for me to kill somebody, but there
wasn't the shadow of a carrier near. I remembered the old
doctor—'It would be interesting for science to watch the mental
changes of individuals, on the spot.' I felt I was becoming
scientifically interesting. However, all that is to no purpose. On
the fifteenth day I came in sight of the big river again, and
hobbled into the Central Station. It was on a backwater surrounded by scrub and forest, with a pretty border of smelly mud
on one side, and on the three others enclosed by a crazy fence of

rushes. A neglected gap was all the gate it had, and the first glance at the place was enough to let you see the flabby devil was running that show. White men with long staves in their hands appeared languidly from amongst the buildings, strolling up to take a look at me, and then retired out of sight somewhere. One of them, a stout, excitable chap with black mustaches, informed me with great volubility and many digressions, as soon as I told him who I was, that my steamer was at the bottom of the river. I was thunderstruck. What, how, why? Oh, it was 'all right.' The 'manager himself' was there. All quite correct. 'Everybody had behaved splendidly! splendidly!' —'you must,' he said in agitation, 'go and see the general manager at once. He is waiting!'

"I did not see the real significance of that wreck at once. I fancy I see it now, but I am not sure—not at all. Certainly the affair was too stupid—when I think of it—to be altogether natural. Still. . . . But at the moment it presented itself simply as a confounded nuisance. The steamer was sunk. They had started two days before in a sudden hurry up the river with the manager on board, in charge of some volunteer skipper, and before they had been out three hours they tore the bottom out of her on stones, and she sank near the south bank. I asked myself what I was to do there, now my boat was lost. As a matter of fact, I had plenty to do in fishing my command out of the river. I had to set about it the very next day. That, and the repairs when I brought the pieces to the station, took some months.

"My first interview with the manager was curious. He did not ask me to sit down after my twenty-mile walk that morning. He was commonplace in complexion, in feature, in manners, and in voice. He was of middle size and of ordinary build. His eyes, of the usual blue, were perhaps remarkably cold, and he certainly could make his glance fall on one as trenchant and heavy as an ax. But even at these times the rest of his person seemed to disclaim the intention. Otherwise there was only an indefinable, faint expression of his lips, something stealthy—a smile—not a smile—I remember it, but I can't explain. It was unconscious, this smile was, though just after he had said something it got intensified for an instant. It came at the end of his speeches like a seal applied on the words to make the meaning of the commonest phrase appear absolutely inscrutable. He was a common trader, from his youth up employed in these parts—nothing more. He was obeyed, yet he inspired neither love nor fear, nor even respect. He inspired uneasiness. That was it! Uneasiness. Not a definite mistrust—just uneasiness— nothing more. You have no idea how effective such a . . . a . . . faculty can be. He had no genius for organizing, for initiative, or for order even. That was evident in such things as the deplorable state of the station. He had no learning, and no intelligence. His position had come to him—why? Perhaps because he was never ill. . . . He had served three terms of three years out there. . . . Because triumphant health in the general rout of constitutions is a kind of power in itself. When he went home on leave he rioted on a large scale—pompously. Jack ashore—with a difference—in externals only. This one could gather from his casual talk. He originated nothing, he could keep the routine going—that's all. But he was great. He was great by this little thing that it was impossible to tell what could control such a man. He never gave that secret away. Perhaps there was nothing within him. Such a suspicion made one pause—for out there there were no external checks. Once when various tropical diseases had laid low almost every 'agent' in the station, he was heard to say, 'Men who come out here should have no entrails.' He sealed the utterance with that smile of his, as though it had been a door opening into a darkness he had in his keeping. You fancied you had seen things—but the seal was on. When annoyed at meal-times by the constant quarrels of the white men about precedence, he ordered an immense round table to be made, for which a special house had to be built. This was the station's mess-room. Where he sat was the first place—the rest were nowhere. One felt this to be his unalterable conviction. He was neither civil nor uncivil. He was quiet. He allowed his 'boy'—an overfed young Negro from the coast—to treat the white men, under his very eyes, with provoking insolence.

"He began to speak as soon as he saw me. I had been very long on the road. He could not wait. Had to start without me. The up-river stations had to be relieved. There had been so many delays already that he did not know who was dead and who was alive, and how they got on—and so on, and so on. He paid no attention to my explanations, and, playing with a stick of sealing-wax, repeated several times that the situation was 'very grave, very grave.' There were rumors that a very important station was in jeopardy, and its chief, Mr. Kurtz, was ill. Hoped it was not true. Mr. Kurtz was . . . I felt weary and irritable. Hang Kurtz, I thought. I interrupted him by saying I had heard of Mr. Kurtz on the coast. 'Ah! So they talk of him down there,' he murmured to himself. Then he began again, assuring me Mr. Kurtz was the best agent he had, an exceptional man, of the greatest importance to the Company; therefore I could understand his anxiety. He was, he said, 'very, very uneasy.' Certainly he fidgeted on his chair a good deal, exclaimed, 'Ah, Mr. Kurtz!' broke the stick of sealing-wax and seemed dumfounded by the accident. Next thing he wanted to know 'how long it would take to . . .' I interrupted him again. Being hungry, you know, and kept on my feet too, I was getting savage. 'How can I tell?' I said. 'I haven't even seen the wreck yet—some months, no doubt.' All this talk seemed to me so futile. 'Some months,' he said. 'Well, let us say three months before we can

make a start. Yes. That ought to do the affair.' I flung out
of his hut (he lived all alone in a clay hut with a sort of
veranda) muttering to myself my opinion of him. He was a
chattering idiot. Afterwards I took it back when it was borne
in upon me startlingly with what extreme nicety he had esti-
mated the time requisite for the 'affair.'

"I went to work the next day, turning, so to speak, my back
on that station. In that way only it seemed to me I could keep
my hold on the redeeming facts of life. Still, one must look
about sometimes; and then I saw this station, these men strolling
aimlessly about in the sunshine of the yard. I asked myself
sometimes what it all meant. They wandered here and there
with their absurd long staves in their hands, like a lot of faith-
less pilgrims bewitched inside a rotten fence. The word 'ivory'
rang in the air, was whispered, was sighed. You would think
they were praying to it. A taint of imbecile rapacity blew
through it all, like a whiff from some corpse. By Jove! I've
never seen anything so unreal in my life. And outside, the
silent wilderness surrounding this cleared speck on the earth
struck me as something great and invincible, like evil or truth,
waiting patiently for the passing away of this fantastic invasion.

"Oh, these months! Well, never mind. Various things happened. One evening a grass shed full of calico, cotton prints,
beads, and I don't know what else, burst into a blaze so suddenly
that you would have thought the earth had opened to let an
avenging fire consume all that trash. I was smoking my pipe
quietly by my dismantled steamer, and saw them all cutting
capers in the light, with their arms lifted high, when the stout
man with mustaches came tearing down to the river, a tin pail
in his hand, assured me that everybody was 'behaving splendidly,
splendidly,' dipped about a quart of water and tore back again.
I noticed there was a hole in the bottom of his pail.

"I strolled up. There was no hurry. You see the thing had

gone off like a box of matches. It had been hopeless from the very first. The flame had leaped high, driven everybody back, lighted up everything—and collapsed. The shed was already a heap of embers glowing fiercely. A nigger was being beaten near by. They said he had caused the fire in some way; be that as it may, he was screeching most horribly. I saw him, later, for several days, sitting in a bit of shade looking very sick and trying to recover himself: afterwards he arose and went out— and the wilderness without a sound took him into its bosom again. As I approached the glow from the dark I found myself at the back of two men, talking. I heard the name of Kurtz pronounced, then the words, 'take advantage of this unfortunate accident.' One of the men was the manager. I wished him a good evening. 'Did you ever see anything like it—eh? it is incredible,' he said, and walked off. The other man remained. He was a first-class agent, young, gentlemanly, a bit reserved, with a forked little beard and a hooked nose. He was standoffish with the other agents, and they on their side said he was the manager's spy upon them. As to me, I had hardly ever spoken to him before. We got into talk, and by and by we strolled away from the hissing ruins. Then he asked me to his room, which was in the main building of the station. He struck a match, and I perceived that this young aristocrat had not only a silver-mounted dressing-case but also a whole candle all to himself. Just at that time the manager was the only man supposed to have any right to candles. Native mats covered the clay walls; a collection of spears, assegais, shields, knives was hung up in trophies. The business intrusted to this fellow was the making of bricks—so I had been informed; but there wasn't a fragment of a brick anywhere in the station, and he had been there more than a year—waiting. It seems he could not make bricks without something, I don't know what—straw, maybe. Anyway, it could not be found there, and as it was not likely

to be sent from Europe, it did not appear clear to me what he
was waiting for. An act of special creation perhaps. However,
they were all waiting—all the sixteen or twenty pilgrims of
them—for something; and upon my word it did not seem an
uncongenial occupation, from the way they took it, though the
only thing that ever came to them was disease—as far as I could
see. They beguiled the time by back-biting and intriguing
against each other in a foolish kind of way. There was an air
of plotting about that station, but nothing came of it, of course.
It was as unreal as everything else—as the philanthropic pretense of the whole concern, as their talk, as their government,
as their show of work. The only real feeling was a desire to
get appointed to a trading-post where ivory was to be had, so
that they could earn percentages. They intrigued and slandered
and hated each other only on that account,—but as to effectually
lifting a little finger—oh, no. By heavens! there is something
after all in the world allowing one man to steal a horse while
another must not look at a halter. Steal a horse straight out.
Very well. He has done it. Perhaps he can ride. But there
is a way of looking at a halter that would provoke the most
charitable of saints into a kick.

"I had no idea why he wanted to be sociable, but as we
chatted in there it suddenly occurred to me the fellow was trying to get at something—in fact, pumping me. He alluded constantly to Europe, to the people I was supposed to know there—
putting leading questions as to my acquaintances in the sepulchral city, and so on. His little eyes glittered like mica discs—
with curiosity—though he tried to keep up a bit of supercilious-
ness. At first I was astonished, but very soon I became awfully
curious to see what he would find out from me. I couldn't possibly imagine what I had in me to make it worth his while. It
was very pretty to see how he baffled himself, for in truth my
body was full only of chills, and my head had nothing in it but

that wretched steamboat business. It was evident he took me for a perfectly shameless prevaricator. At last he got angry, and, to conceal a movement of furious annoyance, he yawned. I rose. Then I noticed a small sketch in oils, on a panel, representing a woman, draped and blindfolded, carrying a lighted torch. The background was somber—almost black. The movement of the woman was stately, and the effect of the torch-light on the face was sinister.

"It arrested me, and he stood by civilly, holding an empty half-pint champagne bottle (medical comforts) with the candle stuck in it. To my question he said Mr. Kurtz had painted this—in this very station more than a year ago—while waiting for means to go to his trading-post. 'Tell me, pray,' said I, 'who is this Mr. Kurtz?'

" 'The chief of the Inner Station,' he answered in a short tone, looking away. 'Much obliged,' I said, laughing. 'And you are the brickmaker of the Central Station. Everyone knows that.' He was silent for a while. 'He is a prodigy,' he said at last. 'He is an emissary of pity, and science, and progress, and devil knows what else. We want,' he began to declaim suddenly, 'for the guidance of the cause intrusted to us by Europe, so to speak, higher intelligence, wide sympathies, a singleness of purpose.' 'Who says that?' I asked. 'Lots of them,' he replied. 'Some even write that; and so *he* comes here, a special being, as you ought to know.' 'Why ought I to know?' I interrupted, really surprised. He paid no attention. 'Yes. Today he is chief of the best station, next year he will be assistant-manager, two years more and . . . but I daresay you know what he will be in two years' time. You are of the new gang—the gang of virtue. The same people who sent him specially also recommended you. Oh, don't say no. I've my own eyes to trust.' Light dawned upon me. My dear aunt's influential acquaintances were producing an unexpected effect upon that young man. I nearly burst into a laugh. 'Do you read the Company's confidential correspondence?' I asked. He hadn't a word to say. It was great fun. 'When Mr. Kurtz,' I continued, severely, 'is General Manager, you won't have the opportunity.'

"He blew the candle out suddenly, and we went outside. The moon had risen. Black figures strolled about listlessly, pouring water on the glow, whence proceeded a sound of hissing; steam ascended in the moonlight, the beaten nigger groaned somewhere. 'What a row the brute makes!' said the indefatigable man with the mustaches, appearing near us. 'Serves him right. Transgression—punishment—bang! Pitiless, pitiless. That's the only way. This will prevent all conflagrations for the future. I was just telling the manager. . . .' He noticed my companion, and became crestfallen all at once. 'Not in bed yet,' he said, with a kind of servile heartiness; 'it's so natural. Ha! Danger—agitation.' He vanished. I went on to the river-side, and the other followed me. I heard a scathing murmur at my ear, 'Heap of muffs—go to.' The pilgrims could be seen in knots gesticulating, discussing. Several had still their staves in their hands. I verily believe they took these sticks to bed with them. Beyond the fence the forest stood up spectrally in the moonlight, and through the dim stir, through the faint sounds of that lamentable courtyard, the silence of the land went home to one's very heart—its mystery, its greatness, the amazing reality of its concealed life. The hurt nigger moaned feebly somewhere near by, and then fetched a deep sigh that made me mend my pace away from there. I felt a hand introducing itself under my arm. 'My dear sir,' said the fellow, 'I don't want to be misunderstood, and especially by you, who will see Mr. Kurtz long before I can have that pleasure. I wouldn't like him to get a false idea of my disposition. . . .'

"I let him run on, this papier-mâché Mephistopheles, and it seemed to me that if I tried I could poke my forefinger through him, and would find nothing inside but a little loose dirt, maybe. He, don't you see, had been planning to be assistant-manager by and by under the present man, and I could see that the coming of that Kurtz had upset them both not a little. He talked precipitately, and I did not try to stop him. I had my shoulders against the wreck of my steamer, hauled up on the slope like a carcass of some big river animal. The smell of mud, of primeval mud, by Jove! was in my nostrils, the high stillness of primeval forest was before my eyes; there were shiny patches on the black creek. The moon had spread over everything a thin layer of silver—over the rank grass, over the mud, upon the wall of matted vegetation standing higher than the wall of a temple, over the great river I could see through a somber gap glittering, glittering, as it flowed broadly by without a murmur. All this was great, expectant, mute, while the man jabbered about himself. I wondered whether the stillness on the face of the immensity looking at us two were meant as an appeal or as a menace. What were we who had strayed in here? Could we handle that dumb thing, or would it handle us? I felt how big, how confoundedly big, was that thing that couldn't talk, and perhaps was deaf as well. What was in there? I could see a little ivory coming out from there, and I had heard Mr. Kurtz was in there. I had heard enough about it, too—God knows! Yet somehow it didn't bring any image with it—no more than if I had been told an angel or a fiend was in there. I believed it in the same way one of you might believe there are inhabitants in the planet Mars. I knew once a Scotch sailmaker who was certain, dead sure, there were people in Mars. If you asked him for some idea how they looked and behaved, he would get shy and mutter something about 'walking on all-fours.' If you as much as smiled, he would—though a man of sixty—offer to fight you. I would not have gone so far as to fight for Kurtz, but I went for him near enough to a lie. You know I hate,

detest, and can't bear a lie, not because I am straighter than the
rest of us, but simply because it appalls me. There is a taint of
death, a flavor of mortality in lies—which is exactly what I hate
and detest in the world—what I want to forget. It makes me
miserable and sick, like biting something rotten would do.
Temperament, I suppose. Well, I went near enough to it by
letting the young fool there believe anything he liked to imagine
as to my influence in Europe. I became in an instant as much
of a pretense as the rest of the bewitched pilgrims. This simply
because I had a notion it somehow would be of help to that
Kurtz whom at the time I did not see—you understand. He
was just a word for me. I did not see the man in the name any
more than you do. Do you see him? Do you see the story?
Do you see anything? It seems to me I am trying to tell you
a dream—making a vain attempt, because no relation of a dream
can convey the dream-sensation, that commingling of absurdity,
surprise, and bewilderment in a tremor of struggling revolt, that
notion of being captured by the incredible which is of the very
essence of dreams. . . ."

He was silent for a while.

". . . No, it is impossible; it is impossible to convey the life-
sensation of any given epoch of one's existence—that which
makes its truth, its meaning—its subtle and penetrating essence.
It is impossible. We live, as we dream—alone. . . ."

He paused again as if reflecting, then added—

"Of course in this you fellows see more than I could then.
You see me, whom you know. . . ."

It had become so pitch dark that we listeners could hardly see
one another. For a long time already he, sitting apart, had been
no more to us than a voice. There was not a word from anybody. The others might have been asleep, but I was awake.
I listened, I listened on the watch for the sentence, for the word,
that would give me the clew to the faint uneasiness inspired by

this narrative that seemed to shape itself without human lips in
the heavy night-air of the river.

"... Yes—I let him run on," Marlow began again, "and think
what he pleased about the powers that were behind me. I did!
And there was nothing behind me! There was nothing but
that wretched, old, mangled steamboat I was leaning against,
while he talked fluently about 'the necessity for every man to
get on.' 'And when one comes out here, you conceive, it is not
to gaze at the moon.' Mr. Kurtz was a 'universal genius,' but
even a genius would find it easier to work with 'adequate tools
—intelligent men.' He did not make bricks—why, there was a
physical impossibility in the way—as I was well aware; and if
he did secretarial work for the manager, it was because 'no
sensible man rejects wantonly the confidence of his superiors.'
Did I see it? I saw it. What more did I want? What I really
wanted was rivets, by heaven! Rivets. To get on with the work
—to stop the hole. Rivets I wanted. There were cases of them
down at the coast—cases—piled up—burst—split! You kicked a
loose rivet at every second step in that station yard on the hill-
side. Rivets had rolled into the grove of death. You could fill
your pockets with rivets for the trouble of stooping down—and
there wasn't one rivet to be found where it was wanted. We
had plates that would do, but nothing to fasten them with. And
every week the messenger, a lone Negro, letter-bag on shoulder
and staff in hand, left our station for the coast. And several
times a week a coast caravan came in with trade goods—ghastly
glazed calico that made you shudder only to look at it; glass
beads, valued about a penny a quart, confounded spotted cotton
handkerchiefs. And no rivets. Three carriers could have
brought all that was wanted to set that steamboat afloat.

"He was becoming confidential now, but I fancy my un-
responsive attitude must have exasperated him at last, for he
judged it necessary to inform me he feared neither God nor

devil, let alone any mere man. I said I could see that very well, but what I wanted was a certain quantity of rivets—and rivets were what really Mr. Kurtz wanted, if he had only known it. Now letters went to the coast every week. . . . 'My dear sir,' he cried, 'I write from dictation.' I demanded rivets. There was a way—for an intelligent man. He changed his manner; became very cold, and suddenly began to talk about a hippopotamus; wondered whether sleeping on board the steamer (I stuck to my salvage night and day) I wasn't disturbed. There was an old hippo that had the bad habit of getting out on the bank and roaming at night over the station grounds. The pilgrims used to turn out in a body and empty every rifle they could lay hands on at him. Some even had sat up o' nights for him. All this energy was wasted, though. 'That animal has a charmed life,' he said; 'but you can say this only of brutes in this country. No man—you apprehend me?—no man here bears a charmed life.' He stood there for a moment in the moonlight with his delicate hooked nose set a little askew, and his mica eyes glittering without a wink, then, with a curt good night, he strode off. I could see he was disturbed and considerably puzzled, which made me feel more hopeful than I had been for days. It was a great comfort to turn from that chap to my influential friend, the battered, twisted, ruined, tin-pot steamboat. I clambered on board. She rang under my feet like an empty Huntley & Palmer biscuit-tin kicked along a gutter; she was nothing so solid in make, and rather less pretty in shape, but I had expended enough hard work on her to make me love her. No influential friend would have served me better. She had given me a chance to come out a bit—to find out what I could do. No, I don't like work. I had rather laze about and think of all the fine things that can be done. I don't like work—no man does—but I like what is in the work,—the chance to find yourself. Your own reality—for yourself, not for others—what no other man can

ever know. They can only see the mere show, and never can
tell what it really means.

"I was not surprised to see somebody sitting aft, on the deck,
with his legs dangling over the mud. You see I rather chummed
with the few mechanics there were in that station, whom the
other pilgrims naturally despised—on account of their imperfect
manners, I suppose. This was the foreman—a boiler-maker by
trade—a good worker. He was a lank, bony, yellow-faced man,
with big intense eyes. His aspect was worried, and his head
was as bald as the palm of my hand; but his hair in falling
seemed to have stuck to his chin, and had prospered in the new
locality, for his beard hung down to his waist. He was a
widower with six young children (he had left them in charge of
a sister of his to come out there), and the passion of his life was
pigeon-flying. He was an enthusiast and a connoisseur. He
would rave about pigeons. After work hours he used sometimes to come over from his hut for a talk about his children
and his pigeons; at work, when he had to crawl in the mud
under the bottom of the steamboat, he would tie up that beard
of his in a kind of white serviette he brought for the purpose.
It had loops to go over his ears. In the evening he could be
seen squatted on the bank rinsing that wrapper in the creek with
great care, then spreading it solemnly on a bush to dry.

"I slapped him on the back and shouted, 'We shall have
rivets!' He scrambled to his feet exclaiming, 'No! Rivets!' as
though he couldn't believe his ears. Then in a low voice, 'You
. . . eh?' I don't know why we behaved like lunatics. I put
my finger to the side of my nose and nodded mysteriously.
'Good for you!' he cried, snapped his fingers above his head,
lifting one foot. I tried a jig. We capered on the iron deck. A
frightful clatter came out of that hulk, and the virgin forest on
the other bank of the creek sent it back in a thundering roll
upon the sleeping station. It must have made some of the

pilgrims sit up in their hovels. A dark figure obscured the lighted doorway of the manager's hut, vanished, then, a second or so after, the doorway itself vanished, too. We stopped, and the silence driven away by the stamping of our feet flowed back again from the recesses of the land. The great wall of vegetation, an exuberant and entangled mass of trunks, branches, leaves, boughs, festoons, motionless in the moonlight, was like a rioting invasion of soundless life, a rolling wave of plants, piled up, crested, ready to topple over the creek, to sweep every little man of us out of his little existence. And it moved not. A deadened burst of mighty splashes and snorts reached us from afar, as though an ichthyosaurus had been taking a bath of glitter in the great river. 'After all,' said the boiler-maker in a reasonable tone, 'why shouldn't we get the rivets?' Why not, indeed! I did not know of any reason why we shouldn't. 'They'll come in three weeks,' I said, confidently.

"But they didn't. Instead of rivets there came an invasion, an infliction, a visitation. It came in sections during the next three weeks, each section headed by a donkey carrying a white man in new clothes and tan shoes, bowing from that elevation right and left to the impressed pilgrims. A quarrelsome band of foot-sore sulky niggers trod on the heels of the donkeys; a lot of tents, campstools, tin boxes, white cases, brown bales would be shot down in the courtyard, and the air of mystery would deepen a little over the muddle of the station. Five such installments came, with their absurd air of disorderly flight with the loot of innumerable outfit shops and provision stores, that, one would think, they were lugging, after a raid, into the wilderness for equitable division. It was an inextricable mess of things decent in themselves but that human folly made look like the spoils of thieving.

"This devoted band called itself the Eldorado Exploring Expedition, and I believe they were sworn to secrecy. Their talk,

however, was the talk of sordid buccaneers: it was reckless without hardihood, greedy without audacity, and cruel without courage; there was not an atom of foresight or of serious intention
in the whole batch of them, and they did not seem aware these
things are wanted for the work of the world. To tear treasure
out of the bowels of the land was their desire, with no more
moral purpose at the back of it than there is in burglars breaking into a safe. Who paid the expenses of the noble enterprise
I don't know; but the uncle of our manager was leader of that
lot.

"In exterior he resembled a butcher in a poor neighborhood,
and his eyes had a look of sleepy cunning. He carried his fat
paunch with ostentation on his short legs, and during the time
his gang infested the station spoke to no one but his nephew.
You could see these two roaming about all day long with their
heads close together in an everlasting confab.

"I had given up worrying myself about the rivets. One's capacity for that kind of folly is more limited than you would
suppose. I said Hang!—and let things slide. I had plenty of
time for meditation, and now and then I would give some
thought to Kurtz. I wasn't very interested in him. No. Still,
I was curious to see whether this man, who had come out
equipped with moral ideas of some sort, would climb to the top
after all and how he would set about his work when there."

II

"One evening as I was lying flat on the deck of my steamboat,
I heard voices approaching—and there were the nephew and the
uncle strolling along the bank. I laid my head on my arm
again, and had nearly lost myself in a doze, when somebody said
in my ear, as it were: 'I am as harmless as a little child, but I
don't like to be dictated to. Am I the manager—or am I not?

I was ordered to send him there. It's incredible.' . . . I became
aware that the two were standing on the shore alongside the
forepart of the steamboat, just below my head. I did not move;
it did not occur to me to move: I was sleepy. 'It *is* unpleasant,'
grunted the uncle. 'He has asked the Administration to be sent
there,' said the other, 'with the idea of showing what he could
do; and I was instructed accordingly. Look at the influence that
man must have. Is it not frightful?' They both agreed it was
frightful, then made several bizarre remarks: 'Make rain and
fine weather—one man—the Council—by the nose'—bits of absurd sentences that got the better of my drowsiness, so that I
had pretty near the whole of my wits about me when the uncle
said, 'The climate may do away with this difficulty for you. Is
he alone there?' 'Yes,' answered the manager; 'he sent his assistant down the river with a note to me in these terms: "Clear
this poor devil out of the country, and don't bother sending more
of that sort. I had rather be alone than have the kind of men
you can dispose of with me." It was more than a year ago. Can
you imagine such impudence!' 'Anything since then?' asked
the other, hoarsely. 'Ivory,' jerked the nephew; 'lots of it—
prime sort—lots—most annoying, from him.' 'And with that?'
questioned the heavy rumble. 'Invoice,' was the reply fired out,
so to speak. Then silence. They had been talking about Kurtz.

"I was broad awake by this time, but, lying perfectly at ease,
remained still, having no inducement to change my position.
'How did that ivory come all this way?' growled the elder man,
who seemed very vexed. The other explained that it had come
with a fleet of canoes in charge of an English half-caste clerk
Kurtz had with him; that Kurtz had apparently intended to return himself, the station being by that time bare of goods and
stores, but after coming three hundred miles, had suddenly decided to go back, which he started to do alone in a small dugout
with four paddlers, leaving the half-caste to continue down the

river with the ivory. The two fellows there seemed astounded at anybody attempting such a thing. They were at a loss for an adequate motive. As to me, I seemed to see Kurtz for the first time. It was a distinct glimpse: the dugout, four paddling savages, and the lone white man turning his back suddenly on the headquarters, on relief, on thoughts of home—perhaps; setting his face towards the depths of the wilderness, towards his empty and desolate station. I did not know the motive. Perhaps he was just simply a fine fellow who stuck to his work for its own sake. His name, you understand, had not been pronounced once. He was 'that man.' The half-caste, who, as far as I could see, had conducted a difficult trip with great prudence and pluck, was invariably alluded to as 'that scoundrel.' The 'scoundrel' had reported that the 'man' had been very ill—had recovered imperfectly. . . . The two below me moved away then a few paces, and strolled back and forth at some little distance. I heard: 'Military post—doctor—two hundred miles—quite alone now—unavoidable delays—nine months—no news—strange rumors.' They approached again, just as the manager was saying, 'No one, as far as I know, unless a species of wandering trader—a pestilential fellow, snapping ivory from the natives.' Who was it they were talking about now? I gathered in snatches that this was some man supposed to be in Kurtz's district, and of whom the manager did not approve. 'We will not be free from unfair competition till one of these fellows is hanged for an example,' he said. 'Certainly,' grunted the other; 'get him hanged! Why not? Anything—anything can be done in this country. That's what I say; nobody here, you understand, *here,* can endanger your position. And why? You stand the climate—you outlast them all. The danger is in Europe; but there before I left I took care to—' They moved off and whispered, then their voices rose again. 'The extraordinary series of delays is not my fault. I did my best.' The fat man sighed. 'Very sad.' 'And the

pestiferous absurdity of his talk,' continued the other; 'he bothered me enough when he was here. "Each station should be
like a beacon on the road towards better things, a center for
trade, of course, but also for humanizing, improving, instructing." Conceive you—that ass! And he wants to be manager!
No, it's—' Here he got choked by excessive indignation, and I
lifted my head the least bit. I was surprised to see how near
they were—right under me. I could have spat upon their hats.
They were looking on the ground, absorbed in thought. The
manager was switching his leg with a slender twig: his sagacious
relative lifted his head. 'You have been well since you came out
this time?' he asked. The other gave a start. 'Who? I? Oh!
Like a charm—like a charm. But the rest—oh, my goodness!
All sick. They die so quick, too, that I haven't the time to
send them out of the country—it's incredible!' 'H'm. Just so,'
grunted the uncle. 'Ah! my boy, trust to this—I say, trust to
this.' I saw him extend his short flipper of an arm for a gesture
that took in the forest, the creek, the mud, the river,—seemed
to beckon with a dishonoring flourish before the sunlit face of
the land a treacherous appeal to the lurking death, to the hidden
evil, to the profound darkness of its heart. It was so startling
that I leaped to my feet and looked back at the edge of the forest, as though I had expected an answer of some sort to that
black display of confidence. You know the foolish notions that
come to one sometimes. The high stillness confronted these
two figures with its ominous patience, waiting for the passing
away of a fantastic invasion.

"They swore aloud together—out of sheer fright, I believe—
then pretending not to know anything of my existence, turned
back to the station. The sun was low; and leaning forward side
by side, they seemed to be tugging painfully uphill their two
ridiculous shadows of unequal length, that trailed behind them
slowly over the tall grass without bending a single blade.

"In a few days the Eldorado Expedition went into the patient wilderness, that closed upon it as the sea closes over a diver. Long afterwards the news came that all the donkeys were dead. I know nothing as to the fate of the less valuable animals. They, no doubt, like the rest of us, found what they deserved. I did not inquire. I was then rather excited at the prospect of meeting Kurtz very soon. When I say very soon I mean it comparatively. It was just two months from the day we left the creek when we came to the bank below Kurtz's station.

"Going up that river was like traveling back to the earliest beginnings of the world, when vegetation rioted on the earth and the big trees were kings. An empty stream, a great silence, an impenetrable forest. The air was warm, thick, heavy, sluggish. There was no joy in the brilliance of sunshine. The long stretches of the waterway ran on, deserted, into the gloom of overshadowed distances. On silvery sandbanks hippos and alligators sunned themselves side by side. The broadening waters flowed through a mob of wooded islands; you lost your way on that river as you would in a desert, and butted all day long against shoals, trying to find the channel, till you thought yourself bewitched and cut off forever from everything you had known once—somewhere—far away—in another existence perhaps. There were moments when one's past came back to one, as it will sometimes when you have not a moment to spare to yourself; but it came in the shape of an unrestful and noisy dream, remembered with wonder amongst the overwhelming realities of this strange world of plants, and water, and silence. And this stillness of life did not in the least resemble a peace. It was the stillness of an implacable force brooding over an inscrutable intention. It looked at you with a vengeful aspect. I got used to it afterwards; I did not see it any more; I had no time. I had to keep guessing at the channel; I had to discern, mostly by inspiration, the signs of hidden banks; I watched for

sunken stones; I was learning to clap my teeth smartly before
my heart flew out, when I shaved by a fluke some infernal sly
old snag that would have ripped the life out of the tin-pot
steamboat and drowned all the pilgrims; I had to keep a look-
out for the signs of dead wood we could cut up in the night for
next day's steaming. When you have to attend to things of that
sort, to the mere incidents of the surface, the reality—the reality,
I tell you—fades. The inner truth is hidden—luckily, luckily.
But I felt it all the same; I felt often its mysterious stillness
watching me at my monkey tricks, just as it watches you fellows
performing on your respective tight-ropes for—what is it? half-
a-crown a tumble—"

"Try to be civil, Marlow," growled a voice, and I knew there
was at least one listener awake besides myself.

"I beg your pardon. I forgot the heartache which makes up
the rest of the price. And indeed what does the price matter,
if the trick be well done? You do your tricks very well. And
I didn't do badly either, since I managed not to sink that steamboat on my first trip. It's a wonder to me yet. Imagine a blindfolded man set to drive a van over a bad road. I sweated and
shivered over that business considerably, I can tell you. After
all, for a seaman, to scrape the bottom of the thing that's supposed to float all the time under his care is the unpardonable sin.
No one may know of it, but you never forget the thump—eh?
A blow on the very heart. You remember it, you dream of it,
you wake up at night and think of it—years after—and go hot
and cold all over. I don't pretend to say that steamboat floated
all the time. More than once she had to wade for a bit, with
twenty cannibals splashing around and pushing. We had enlisted some of these chaps on the way for a crew. Fine fellows—
cannibals—in their place. They were men one could work with,
and I am grateful to them. And, after all, they did not eat each
other before my face: they had brought along a provision of

hippo-meat which went rotten, and made the mystery of the wilderness stink in my nostrils. Phoo! I can sniff it now. I had the manager on board and three or four pilgrims with their staves—all complete. Sometimes we came upon a station close by the bank, clinging to the skirts of the unknown, and the white men rushing out of a tumble-down hovel, with great gestures of joy and surprise and welcome, seemed very strange—had the appearance of being held there captive by a spell. The word ivory would ring in the air for a while—and on we went again into the silence, along empty reaches, round the still bends, between the high walls of our winding way, reverberating in hollow claps the ponderous beat of the stern-wheel. Trees, trees, millions of trees, massive, immense, running up high; and at their foot, hugging the bank against the stream, crept the little begrimed steamboat, like a sluggish beetle crawling on the floor of a lofty portico. It made you feel very small, very lost, and yet it was not altogether depressing, that feeling. After all, if you were small, the grimy beetle crawled on—which was just what you wanted it to do. Where the pilgrims imagined it crawled to I don't know. To some place where they expected to get something, I bet! For me it crawled towards Kurtz—exclusively; but when the steam-pipes started leaking we crawled very slow. The reaches opened before us and closed behind, as if the forest had stepped leisurely across the water to bar the way for our return. We penetrated deeper and deeper into the heart of darkness. It was very quiet there. At night sometimes the roll of drums behind the curtain of trees would run up the river and remain sustained faintly, as if hovering in the air high over our heads, till the first break of day. Whether it meant war, peace, or prayer we could not tell. The dawns were heralded by the descent of a chill stillness; the wood-cutters slept, their fires burned low; the snapping of a twig would make you start. We were wanderers on a prehistoric earth, on an earth that wore the aspect of an unknown planet. We could have fancied our-selves the first of men taking possession of an accursed inherit-ance, to be subdued at the cost of profound anguish and of excessive toil. But suddenly, as we struggled round a bend, there would be a glimpse of rush walls, of peaked grass-roofs, a burst of yells, a whirl of black limbs, a mass of hands clapping, of feet stamping, of bodies swaying, of eyes rolling, under the droop of heavy and motionless foliage. The steamer toiled along slowly on the edge of a black and incomprehensible frenzy. The prehistoric man was cursing us, praying to us, welcoming us—who could tell? We were cut off from the comprehension of our surroundings; we glided past like phantoms, wondering and secretly appalled, as sane men would be before an enthusiastic outbreak in a madhouse. We could not understand because we were too far and could not remember, because we were traveling in the night of first ages, of those ages that are gone, leaving hardly a sign—and no memories.

"The earth seemed unearthly. We are accustomed to look upon the shackled form of a conquered monster, but there—there you could look at a thing monstrous and free. It was unearthly, and the men were— No, they were not inhuman. Well, you know, that was the worst of it—this suspicion of their not being inhuman. It would come slowly to one. They howled and leaped, and spun, and made horrid faces; but what thrilled you was just the thought of their humanity—like yours—the thought of your remote kinship with this wild and passionate uproar. Ugly. Yes, it was ugly enough; but if you were man enough you would admit to yourself that there was in you just the faintest trace of a response to the terrible frankness of that noise, a dim suspicion of there being a meaning in it which you—you so remote from the night of first ages—could compre-hend. And why not? The mind of man is capable of anything —because everything is in it, all the past as well as all the future.

What was there after all? Joy, fear, sorrow, devotion, valor, rage—who can tell?—but truth—truth stripped of its cloak of time. Let the fool gape and shudder—the man knows, and can look on without a wink. But he must at least be as much of a man as these on the shore. He must meet that truth with his own true stuff—with his own inborn strength. Principles won't do. Acquisitions, clothes, pretty rags—rags that would fly off at the first good shake. No; you want a deliberate belief. An appeal to me in this fiendish row—is there? Very well; I hear; I admit, but I have a voice, too, and for good or evil mine is the speech that cannot be silenced. Of course, a fool, what with sheer fright and fine sentiments, is always safe. Who's that grunting? You wonder I didn't go ashore for a howl and a dance? Well, no—I didn't. Fine sentiments, you say? Fine sentiments, be hanged! I had no time. I had to mess about with white-lead and strips of woolen blanket helping to put bandages on those leaky steam-pipes—I tell you. I had to watch the steering, and circumvent those snags, and get the tin-pot along by hook or by crook. There was surface-truth enough in these things to save a wiser man. And between whiles I had to look after the savage who was fireman. He was an improved specimen; he could fire up a vertical boiler. He was there below me, and, upon my word, to look at him was as edifying as seeing a dog in a parody of breeches and a feather hat, walking on his hind-legs. A few months of training had done for that really fine chap. He squinted at the steam-gauge and at the water-gauge with an evident effort of intrepidity—and he had filed teeth, too, the poor devil, and the wool of his pate shaved into queer patterns, and three ornamental scars on each of his cheeks. He ought to have been clapping his hands and stamping his feet on the bank, instead of which he was hard at work, a thrall to strange witchcraft, full of improving knowledge. He was useful because he had been instructed; and what he knew was this—that should the water in that transparent thing disappear, the evil spirit inside the boiler would get angry through the greatness of his thirst, and take a terrible vengeance. So he sweated and fired up and watched the glass fearfully (with an impromptu charm, made of rags, tied to his arm, and a piece of polished bone, as big as a watch, stuck flatways through his lower lip), while the wooden banks slipped past us slowly, the short noise was left behind, the interminable miles of silence—and we crept on, towards Kurtz. But the snags were thick, the water was treacherous and shallow, the boiler seemed indeed to have a sulky devil in it, and thus neither that fireman nor I had any time to peer into our creepy thoughts.

"Some fifty miles below the Inner Station we came upon a hut of reeds, an inclined and melancholy pole, with the unrecognizable tatters of what had been a flag of some sort flying from it, and a neatly stacked woodpile. This was unexpected. We came to the bank, and on the stack of firewood found a flat piece of board with some faded pencil-writing on it. When deciphered it said: 'Wood for you. Hurry up. Approach cautiously.' There was a signature, but it was illegible—not Kurtz—a much longer word. 'Hurry up.' Where? Up the river? 'Approach cautiously.' We had not done so. But the warning could not have been meant for the place where it could be only found after approach. Something was wrong above. But what—and how much? That was the question. We commented adversely upon the imbecility of that telegraphic style. The bush around said nothing, and would not let us look very far, either. A torn curtain of red twill hung in the doorway of the hut, and flapped sadly in our faces. The dwelling was dismantled; but we could see a white man had lived there not very long ago. There remained a rude table—a plank on two posts; a heap of rubbish reposed in a dark corner, and by the door I picked up a book. It had lost its covers, and the pages had been thumbed into a state of extremely dirty softness; but the back had been lovingly stitched afresh with white cotton thread, which looked clean yet. It was an extraordinary find. Its title was, *An Inquiry into some Points of Seamanship,* by a man Towser, Towson—some such name—Master in his Majesty's Navy. The matter looked dreary reading enough, with illustrative diagrams and repulsive tables of figures, and the copy was sixty years old. I handled this amazing antiquity with the greatest possible tenderness, lest it should dissolve in my hands. Within, Towson or Towser was inquiring earnestly into the breaking strain of ships' chains and tackle, and other such matters. Not a very enthralling book; but at the first glance you could see there a singleness of intention, an honest concern for the right way of going to work, which made these humble pages, thought out so many years ago, luminous with another than a professional light. The simple old sailor, with his talk of chains and purchases, made me forget the jungle and the pilgrims in a delicious sensation of having come upon something unmistakably real. Such a book being there was wonderful enough; but still more astounding were the notes penciled in the margin, and plainly referring to the text. I couldn't believe my eyes! They were in cipher! Yes, it looked like cipher. Fancy a man lugging with him a book of that description into this nowhere and studying it—and making notes—in cipher at that! It was an extravagant mystery.

"I had been dimly aware for some time of a worrying noise, and when I lifted my eyes I saw the woodpile was gone, and the manager, aided by all the pilgrims, was shouting at me from the river-side. I slipped the book into my pocket. I assure you to leave off reading was like tearing myself away from the shelter of an old and solid friendship.

"I started the lame engine ahead. 'It must be this miserable trader—this intruder,' exclaimed the manager, looking back malevolently at the place we had left. 'He must be English,' I said. 'It will not save him from getting into trouble if he is not careful,' muttered the manager darkly. I observed with assumed innocence that no man was safe from trouble in this world.

"The current was more rapid now, the steamer seemed at her last gasp, the stern-wheel flopped languidly, and I caught myself listening on tiptoe for the next beat of the boat, for in sober truth I expected the wretched thing to give up every moment. It was like watching the last flickers of a life. But still we crawled. Sometimes I would pick out a tree a little way ahead to measure our progress towards Kurtz by, but I lost it invariably before we got abreast. To keep the eyes so long on one thing was too much for human patience. The manager displayed a beautiful resignation. I fretted and fumed and took to arguing with myself whether or no I would talk openly with Kurtz; but before I could come to any conclusion it occurred to me that my speech or my silence, indeed any action of mine, would be a mere futility. What did it matter what anyone knew or ignored? What did it matter who was manager? One gets sometimes such a flash of insight. The essentials of this affair lay deep under the surface, beyond my reach, and beyond my power of meddling.

"Towards the evening of the second day we judged ourselves about eight miles from Kurtz's station. I wanted to push on; but the manager looked grave, and told me the navigation up there was so dangerous that it would be advisable, the sun being very low already, to wait where we were till next morning. Moreover, he pointed out that if the warning to approach cautiously were to be followed, we must approach in daylight— not at dusk, or in the dark. This was sensible enough. Eight miles meant nearly three hours' steaming for us, and I could also see suspicious ripples at the upper end of the reach. Nevertheless, I was annoyed beyond expression at the delay, and most

unreasonably, too, since one night more could not matter much
after so many months. As we had plenty of wood, and caution
was the word, I brought up in the middle of the stream. The
reach was narrow, straight, with high sides like a railway
cutting. The dusk came gliding into it long before the sun
had set. The current ran smooth and swift, but a dumb immobility sat on the banks. The living trees, lashed together
by the creepers and every living bush of the undergrowth,
might have been changed into stone, even to the slenderest
twig, to the lightest leaf. It was not sleep—it seemed unnatural,
like a state of trance. Not the faintest sound of any kind could
be heard. You looked on amazed, and began to suspect yourself of being deaf—then the night came suddenly, and struck
you blind as well. About three in the morning some large fish
leaped, and the loud splash made me jump as though a gun
had been fired. When the sun rose there was a white fog, very
warm and clammy, and more blinding than the night. It did
not shift or drive; it was just there, standing all round you
like something solid. At eight or nine, perhaps, it lifted as a
shutter lifts. We had a glimpse of the towering multitude of
trees, of the immense matted jungle, with the blazing little ball
of the sun hanging over it—all perfectly still—and then the white
shutter came down again, smoothly, as if sliding in greased
grooves. I ordered the chain, which we had begun to heave
in, to be paid out again. Before it stopped running with a
muffled rattle, a cry, a very loud cry, as of infinite desolation,
soared slowly in the opaque air. It ceased. A complaining
clamor, modulated in savage discords, filled our ears. The sheer
unexpectedness of it made my hair stir under my cap. I don't
know how it struck the others: to me it seemed as though the
mist itself had screamed, so suddenly, and apparently from all
sides at once, did this tumultuous and mournful uproar arise. It
culminated in a hurried outbreak of almost intolerably excessive

shrieking, which stopped short, leaving us stiffened in a variety
of silly attitudes, and obstinately listening to the nearly as appalling and excessive silence. 'Good God! What is the meaning—' stammered at my elbow one of the pilgrims,—a little fat
man, with sandy hair and red whiskers, who wore side-spring
boots, and pink pajamas tucked into his socks. Two others remained open-mouthed a whole minute, then dashed into the
little cabin, to rush out incontinently and stand darting scared
glances, with Winchesters at 'ready' in their hands. What we
could see was just the steamer we were on, her outlines blurred
as though she had been on the point of dissolving, and a misty
strip of water, perhaps two feet broad, around her—and that was
all. The rest of the world was nowhere, as far as our eyes and
ears were concerned. Just nowhere. Gone, disappeared; swept
off without leaving a whisper or a shadow behind.

"I went forward, and ordered the chain to be hauled in short,
so as to be ready to trip the anchor and move the steamboat
at once if necessary. 'Will they attack?' whispered an awed
voice. 'We will be all butchered in this fog,' murmured another.
The faces twitched with the strain, the hands trembled slightly,
the eyes forgot to wink. It was very curious to see the contrast
of expressions of the white men and of the black fellows of our
crew, who were as much strangers to that part of the river as
we, though their homes were only eight hundred miles away.
The whites, of course, greatly discomposed, had besides a curious look of being painfully shocked by such an outrageous row.
The others had an alert, naturally interested expression; but
their faces were essentially quiet, even those of the one or two
who grinned as they hauled at the chain. Several exchanged
short, grunting phrases, which seemed to settle the matter to
their satisfaction. Their headman, a young, broad-chested black,
severely draped in dark-blue fringed cloths, with fierce nostrils
and his hair all done up artfully in oily ringlets, stood near me.

'Aha!' I said, just for good fellowship's sake. 'Catch 'im,' he snapped, with a bloodshot widening of his eyes and a flash of sharp teeth—'catch 'im. Give 'im to us.' 'To you, eh?' I asked; 'what would you do with them?' 'Eat 'im!' he said, curtly, and, leaning his elbow on the rail, looked out into the fog in a dignified and profoundly pensive attitude. I would no doubt have been properly horrified, had it not occurred to me that he and his chaps must be very hungry: that they must have been growing increasingly hungry for at. least this month past. They had been engaged for six months (I don't think a single one of them had any clear idea of time, as we at the end of countless ages have. They still belonged to the beginnings of time—had no inherited experience to teach them as it were), and of course, as long as there was a piece of paper written over in accordance with some farcical law or other made down the river, it didn't enter anybody's head to trouble how they would live. Certainly they had brought with them some rotten hippo-meat, which couldn't have lasted very long, anyway, even if the pilgrims hadn't, in the midst of a shocking hullabaloo, thrown a considerable quantity of it overboard. It look like a high-handed proceeding; but it was really a case of legitimate self-defense. You can't breathe dead hippo waking, sleeping, and eating, and at the same time keep your precarious grip on existence. Besides that, they had given them every week three pieces of brass wire, each about nine inches long; and the theory was they were to buy their provisions with that currency in riverside villages. You can see how *that* worked. There were either no villages, or the people were hostile, or the director, who like the rest of us fed out of tins, with an occasional old he-goat thrown in, didn't want to stop the steamer for some more or less recondite reason. So, unless they swallowed the wire itself, or made loops of it to snare the fishes with, I don't see what good their extravagant salary could be to them. I must say it was paid with a regularity worthy of a large and honorable trading company. For the rest, the only thing to eat—though it didn't look eatable in the least—I saw in their possession was a few lumps of some stuff like half-cooked dough, of a dirty lavender color, they kept wrapped in leaves, and now and then swallowed a piece of, but so small that it seemed done more for the looks of the thing than for any serious purpose of sustenance. Why in the name of all the gnawing devils of hunger they didn't go for us—they were thirty to five—and have a good tuck-in for once, amazes me now when I think of it. They were big powerful men, with not much capacity to weigh the consequences, with courage, with strength, even yet, though their skins were no longer glossy and their muscles no longer hard. And I saw that something restraining, one of those human secrets that baffle probability, had come into play there. I looked at them with a swift quickening of interest—not because it occurred to me I might be eaten by them before very long, though I own to you that just then I perceived—in a new light, as it were—how unwholesome the pilgrims looked, and I hoped, yes, I positively hoped, that my aspect was not so—what shall I say?—so—unappetizing: a touch of fantastic vanity which fitted well with the dream-sensation that pervaded all my days at that time. Perhaps I had a little fever, too. One can't live with one's finger everlastingly on one's pulse. I had often 'a little fever,' or a little touch of other things—the playful paw-strokes of the wilderness, the preliminary trifling before the more serious on-slaught which came in due course. Yes; I looked at them as you would on any human being, with a curiosity of their im-pulses, motives, capacities, weaknesses, when brought to the test of an inexorable physical necessity. Restraint! What possible restraint? Was it superstition, disgust, patience, fear—or some kind of primitive honor? No fear can stand up to hunger, no patience can wear it out, disgust simply does not exist where hunger is; and as to superstition, beliefs, and what you may call principles, they are less than chaff in a breeze. Don't you know the devilry of lingering starvation, its exasperating torment, its black thoughts, its somber and brooding ferocity? Well, I do. It takes a man all his inborn strength to fight hunger properly. It's really easier to face bereavement, dishonor, and the perdition of one's soul—than this kind of prolonged hunger. Sad, but true. And these chaps, too, had no earthly reason for any kind of scruple. Restraint! I would just as soon have expected restraint from a hyena prowling amongst the corpses of a battle-field. But there was the fact facing me—the fact dazzling, to be seen, like the foam on the depths of the sea, like a ripple on an unfathomable enigma, a mystery greater—when I thought of it—than the curious, inexplicable note of desperate grief in this savage clamor that had swept by us on the river-bank, be-hind the blind whiteness of the fog.

"Two pilgrims were quarreling in hurried whispers as to which bank. 'Left.' 'No, no; how can you? Right, right, of course.' 'It is very serious,' said the manager's voice behind me; 'I would be desolated if anything should happen to Mr. Kurtz before we came up.' I looked at him, and had not the slightest doubt he was sincere. He was just the kind of man who would wish to preserve appearances. That was his re-straint. But when he muttered something about going on at once, I did not even take the trouble to answer him. I knew, and he knew, that it was impossible. Were we to let go our hold of the bottom, we would be absolutely in the air—in space. We wouldn't be able to tell where we were going to—whether up or down stream, or across—till we fetched against one bank or the other,—and then we wouldn't know at first which it was. Of course I made no move. I had no mind for a smash-up. You couldn't imagine a more deadly place for a shipwreck. Whether drowned at once or not, we were sure to perish speedily in one way or another. 'I authorize you to take all the risks,' he said, after a short silence. 'I refuse to take any,' I said, shortly; which was just the answer he expected, though its tone might have surprised him. 'Well, I must defer to your judgment. You are captain,' he said, with marked civility. I turned my shoulder to him in sign of my appreciation, and looked into the fog. How long would it last? It was the most hopeless lookout. The approach to this Kurtz grubbing for ivory in the wretched bush was beset by as many dangers as though he had been an enchanted princess sleeping in a fabulous castle. 'Will they attack, do you think?' asked the manager, in a confidential tone.

"I did not think they would attack, for several obvious reasons. The thick fog was one. If they left the bank in their canoes they would get lost in it, as we would be if we attempted to move. Still, I had also judged the jungle of both banks quite impenetrable—and yet eyes were in it, eyes that had seen us. The river-side bushes were certainly very thick; but the undergrowth behind was evidently penetrable. However, during the short lift I had seen no canoes anywhere in the reach—certainly not abreast of the steamer. But what made the idea of attack inconceivable to me was the nature of the noise—of the cries we had heard. They had not the fierce character boding immediate hostile intention. Unexpected, wild, and violent as they had been, they had given me an irresistible impression of sorrow. The glimpse of the steamboat had for some reason filled those savages with unrestrained grief. The danger, if any, I expounded, was from our proximity to a great human passion let loose. Even extreme grief may ultimately vent itself in violence —but more generally takes the form of apathy. . . .

"You should have seen the pilgrims stare! They had no heart to grin, or even to revile me: but I believe they thought me gone mad—with fright, maybe. I delivered a regular lecture.

My dear boys, it was no good bothering. Keep a look-out? Well, you may guess I watched the fog for the signs of lifting as a cat watches a mouse; but for anything else our eyes were of no more use to us than if we had been buried miles deep in a heap of cotton-wool. It felt like it, too—choking, warm, stifling. Besides, all I said, though it sounded extravagant, was absolutely true to fact. What we afterwards alluded to as an attack was really an attempt at repulse. The action was very far from being aggressive—it was not even defensive, in the usual sense: it was undertaken under the stress of desperation, and in its essence was purely protective.

"It developed itself, I should say, two hours after the fog lifted, and its commencement was at a spot, roughly speaking, about a mile and a half below Kurtz's station. We had just floundered and flopped round a bend, when I saw an islet, a mere grassy hummock of bright green, in the middle of the stream. It was the only thing of the kind; but as we opened the reach more, I perceived it was the head of a long sandbank, or rather of a chain of shallow patches stretching down the middle of the river. They were discolored, just awash, and the whole lot was seen just under the water, exactly as a man's backbone is seen running down the middle of his back under the skin. Now, as far as I did see, I could go to the right or to the left of this. I didn't know either channel, of course. The banks looked pretty well alike, the depth appeared the same; but as I had been informed the station was on the west side, I naturally headed for the western passage.

"No sooner had we fairly entered it than I became aware it was much narrower than I had supposed. To the left of us there was the long uninterrupted shoal, and to the right a high, steep bank heavily overgrown with bushes. Above the bush the trees stood in serried ranks. The twigs overhung the current thickly, and from distance to distance a large limb of some tree projected rigidly over the stream. It was then well on in the afternoon, the face of the forest was gloomy, and a broad strip of shadow had already fallen on the water. In this shadow we steamed up—very slowly, as you may imagine. I sheered her well inshore—the water being deepest near the bank, as the sounding-pole informed me.

"One of my hungry and forbearing friends was sounding in the bows just below me. This steamboat was exactly like a decked scow. On the deck, there were two little teak-wood houses, with doors and windows. The boiler was in the fore-end, and the machinery right astern. Over the whole there was a light roof, supported on stanchions. The funnel projected through that roof, and in front of the funnel a small cabin built of light planks served for a pilot-house. It contained a couch, two campstools, a loaded Martini-Henry leaning in one corner, a tiny table, and the steering-wheel. It had a wide door in front and a broad shutter at each side. All these were always thrown open, of course. I spent my days perched up there on the extreme fore-end of that roof, before the door. At night I slept, or tried to, on the couch. An athletic black belonging to some coast tribe, and educated by my poor predecessor, was the helmsman. He sported a pair of brass earrings, wore a blue cloth wrapper from the waist to the ankles, and thought all the world of himself. He was the most unstable kind of fool I had ever seen. He steered with no end of a swagger while you were by; but if he lost sight of you, he became instantly the prey of an abject funk, and would let that cripple of a steamboat get the upper hand of him in a minute.

"I was looking down at the sounding-pole, and feeling much annoyed to see at each try a little more of it stick out of that river, when I saw my poleman give up the business suddenly, and stretch himself flat on the deck, without even taking the trouble to haul his pole in. He kept hold on it though, and it trailed in the water. At the same time the fireman, whom I could also see below me, sat down abruptly before his furnace and ducked his head. I was amazed. Then I had to look at the river mighty quick, because there was a snag in the fairway. Sticks, little sticks, were flying about—thick: they were whizzing before my nose, dropping below me, striking behind me against my pilot-house. All this time the river, the shore, the woods, were very quiet—perfectly quiet. I could only hear the heavy splashing thump of the stern-wheel and the patter of these things. We cleared the snag clumsily. Arrows, by Jove! We were being shot at! I stepped in quickly to close the shutter on the land-side. That fool-helmsman, his hands on the spokes, was lifting his knees high, stamping his feet, champing his mouth, like a reined-in horse. Confound him! And we were staggering within ten feet of the bank. I had to lean right out to swing the heavy shutter, and I saw a face amongst the leaves on the level with my own, looking at me very fierce and steady; and then suddenly, as though a veil had been removed from my eyes, I made out, deep in the tangled gloom, naked breasts, arms, legs, glaring eyes,—the bush was swarming with human limbs in movement, glistening, of bronze color. The twigs shook, swayed, and rustled, the arrows flew out of them, and then the shutter came to. 'Steer her straight,' I said to the helmsman. He held his head rigid, face forward; but his eyes rolled, he kept on lifting and setting down his feet gently, his mouth foamed a little. 'Keep quiet!' I said in a fury. I might just as well have ordered a tree not to sway in the wind. I darted out. Below me there was a great scuffle of feet on the iron deck; confused exclamations; a voice screamed, 'Can you turn back?' I caught sight of a V-shaped ripple on the water ahead. What? Another snag! A fusillade burst out under my feet. The pilgrims had opened with their Winchesters, and were simply squirting lead into that bush. A deuce of a lot of smoke came up and drove slowly forward. I swore at it. Now I couldn't see the ripple or the snag either. I stood in the doorway, peering, and the arrows came in swarms. They might have been poisoned, but they looked as though they wouldn't kill a cat. The bush began to howl. Our wood-cutters raised a warlike whoop; the report of a rifle just at my back deafened me. I glanced over my shoulder, and the pilot-house was yet full of noise and smoke when I made a dash at the wheel. The fool-nigger had dropped everything to throw the shutter open and let off that Martini-Henry. He stood before the wide opening, glaring, and I yelled at him to come back, while I straightened the sudden twist out of that steamboat. There was no room to turn even if I had wanted to, the snag was somewhere very near ahead in that confounded smoke, there was no time to lose, so I just crowded her into the bank—right into the bank, where I knew the water was deep.

"We tore slowly along the overhanging bushes in a whirl of broken twigs and flying leaves. The fusillade below stopped short, as I had foreseen it would when the squirts got empty. I threw my head back to a glinting whizz that traversed the pilot-house, in at one shutter-hole and out at the other. Looking past that mad helmsman, who was shaking the empty rifle and yelling at the shore, I saw vague forms of men running bent double, leaping, gliding, distinct, incomplete, evanescent. Something big appeared in the air before the shutter, the rifle went overboard, and the man stepped back swiftly, looked at me over his shoulder in an extraordinary, profound, familiar manner, and fell upon my feet. The side of his head hit the wheel twice, and the end of what appeared a long cane clattered round and knocked over a little campstool. It looked as though after wrenching that thing from somebody ashore he had lost his balance in the effort. The thin smoke had blown away, we were clear of the snag, and looking ahead I could see that in another hundred yards or so I would be free to sheer off, away from the bank; but my feet felt so very warm and wet that I had to look down. The man had rolled on his back and stared straight up at me; both his hands clutched that cane. It was the shaft of a spear that, either thrown or lunged through the opening, had caught him in the side just below the ribs; the blade had gone in out of sight, after making a frightful gash; my shoes were full; a pool of blood lay very still, gleaming dark-red under the wheel; his eyes shone with an amazing luster. The fusillade burst out again. He looked at me anxiously, gripping the spear like something precious, with an air of being afraid I would try to take it away from him. I had to make an effort to free my eyes from his gaze and attend to steering. With one hand I felt above my head for the line of the steam-whistle, and jerked out screech after screech hurriedly. The tumult of angry and warlike yells was checked instantly, and then from the depths of the woods went out such a tremulous and prolonged wail of mournful fear and utter despair as may be imagined to follow the flight of the last hope from the earth. There was a great commotion in the bush; the shower of arrows stopped, a few dropping shots rang out sharply—then silence, in which the languid beat of the stern-wheel came plainly to my ears. I put the helm hard a-starboard at the moment when the pilgrim in pink pajamas, very hot and agitated, appeared in the doorway. 'The manager sends me—' he began in an official tone, and stopped short. 'Good God!' he said, glaring at the wounded man.

"We two whites stood over him, and his lustrous and inquiring glance enveloped us both. I declare it looked as though he would presently put to us some question in an understandable language; but he died without uttering a sound, without moving a limb, without twitching a muscle. Only in the very last moment, as though in response to some sign we could not see, to some whisper we could not hear, he frowned heavily, and that frown gave to his black death-mask an inconceivably somber, brooding, and menacing expression. The luster of inquiring glance faded swiftly into vacant glassiness. 'Can you steer?' I asked the agent eagerly. He looked very dubious; but I made a grab at his arm, and he understood at once I meant him to steer whether or no. To tell you the truth, I was morbidly anxious to change my shoes and socks. 'He is dead,' murmured the fellow, immensely impressed. 'No doubt about it,' said I tugging like mad at the shoe-laces. 'And by the way, I suppose Mr. Kurtz is dead as well by this time.'

"For the moment that was the dominant thought. There was a sense of extreme disappointment, as though I had found out I had been striving after something altogether without a substance. I couldn't have been more disgusted if I had traveled all this way for the sole purpose of talking with Mr. Kurtz. Talking with . . . I flung one shoe overboard, and became aware that that was exactly what I had been looking forward to—a talk with Kurtz. I made the strange discovery that I had never imagined him as doing, you know, but as discoursing. I didn't say to myself, 'Now I will never see him,' or 'Now I will never shake him by the hand,' but, 'Now I will never hear him.' The man presented himself as a voice. Not of course that I did not connect him with some sort of action. Hadn't I been told in all the tones of jealousy and admiration that he had collected, bartered, swindled, or stolen more ivory than all the other agents together? That was not the point. The point was in his being a gifted creature, and that of all his gifts the one that stood out pre-eminently, that carried with it a sense of real presence, was his ability to talk, his words—the gift of expression, the bewildering, the illuminating, the most exalted and the most contemptible, the pulsating stream of light, or the deceitful flow from the heart of an impenetrable darkness.

"The other shoe went flying unto the devil-god of that river. I thought, by Jove! it's all over. We are too late; he has vanished —the gift has vanished, by means of some spear, arrow, or club. I will never hear that chap speak after all,—and my sorrow had a startling extravagance of emotion, even such as I had noticed in the howling sorrow of these savages in the bush. I couldn't have felt more lonely desolation somehow, had I been robbed of a belief or had missed my destiny in life. . . . Why do you sigh in this beastly way, somebody? Absurd? Well, absurd. Good Lord! mustn't a man ever— Here, give me some tobacco." . . .

There was a pause of profound stillness, then a match flared, and Marlow's lean face appeared, worn, hollow, with downward folds and drooped eyelids, with an aspect of concentrated attention; and as he took vigorous draws at his pipe, it seemed to retreat and advance out of the night in the regular flicker of the tiny flame. The match went out.

"Absurd!" he cried. "This is the worst of trying to tell. . . . Here you all are, each moored with two good addresses, like a hulk with two anchors, a butcher round one corner, a policeman round another, excellent appetites, and temperature normal —you hear—normal from year's end to year's end. And you say, Absurd! Absurd be—exploded! Absurd! My dear boys, what can you expect from a man who out of sheer nervousness had just flung overboard a pair of new shoes! Now I think of it, it is amazing I did not shed tears. I am, upon the whole, proud of my fortitude. I was cut to the quick at the idea of having lost the inestimable privilege of listening to the gifted Kurtz. Of course I was wrong. The privilege was waiting for me. Oh, yes, I heard more than enough. And I was right, too. A voice. He was very little more than a voice. And I heard—him—it—this voice—other voices—all of them were so little more than voices—and the memory of that time itself lingers around me, impalpable, like a dying vibration of one immense jabber, silly, atrocious, sordid, savage, or simply mean, without any kind of sense. Voices, voices—even the girl herself—now—"

He was silent for a long time.

"I laid the ghost of his gifts at last with a lie," he began, suddenly. "Girl! What? Did I mention a girl? Oh, she is out of it—completely. They—the women I mean—are out of it—should be out of it. We must help them to stay in that beautiful world of their own, lest ours gets worse. Oh, she had to be out of it. You should have heard the disinterred body of Mr. Kurtz saying, 'My Intended.' You would have perceived directly then how completely she was out of it. And the lofty frontal bone of Mr. Kurtz! They say the hair goes on growing sometimes, but this—ah—specimen, was impressively bald. The wilderness had patted him on the head, and, behold, it was like a ball—an ivory ball; it had caressed him, and—lo!—he had withered; it had taken him, loved him, embraced him, got into his veins, consumed his flesh, and sealed his soul to its own by the inconceivable ceremonies of some devilish initiation. He was its spoiled and pampered favorite. Ivory? I should think so. Heaps of it, stacks of it. The old mud shanty was bursting with it. You would think there was not a single tusk left either above or below the ground in the whole country. 'Mostly fossil,' the manager had remarked, disparagingly. It was no more fossil than I am; but they call it fossil when it is dug up. It appears these niggers do bury the tusks sometimes—but evidently they couldn't bury this parcel deep enough to save the gifted Mr. Kurtz from his fate. We filled the steamboat with it, and had to pile a lot on the deck. Thus he could see and enjoy as long as he could see, because the appreciation of this favor had remained with him to the last. You should have heard him say, 'My ivory.' Oh, yes, I heard him. 'My Intended,

my ivory, my station, my river, my—' everything belonged to
him. It made me hold my breath in expectation of hearing the
wilderness burst into a prodigious peal of laughter that would
shake the fixed stars in their places. Everything belonged to
him—but that was a trifle. The thing was to know what he
belonged to, how many powers of darkness claimed him for
their own. That was the reflection that made you creepy all
over. It was impossible—it was not good for one either—trying
to imagine. He had taken a high seat amongst the devils of the
land—I mean literally. You can't understand. How could you?
—with solid pavement under your feet, surrounded by kind
neighbors ready to cheer you or to fall on you, stepping delicately between the butcher and the policeman, in the holy terror
of scandal and gallows and lunatic asylums—how can you
imagine what particular region of the first ages a man's un-
trammeled feet may take him into by the way of solitude—utter
solitude without a policeman—by the way of silence—utter
silence, where no warning voice of a kind neighbor can be heard
whispering of public opinion? These little things make all the
great difference. When they are gone you must fall back upon
your own innate strength, upon your own capacity for faithful-
ness. Of course you may be too much of a fool to go wrong—
too dull even to know you are being assaulted by the powers of
darkness. I take it, no fool ever made a bargain for his soul
with the devil: the fool is too much of a fool, or the devil too
much of a devil—I don't know which. Or you may be such a
thunderingly exalted creature as to be altogether deaf and blind
to anything but heavenly sights and sounds. Then the earth
for you is only a standing place—and whether to be like this is
your loss or your gain I won't pretend to say. But most of us are
neither one nor the other. The earth for us is a place to live
in, where we must put up with sights, with sounds, with smells,
too, by Jove!—breathe dead hippo, so to speak, and not be con-

taminated. And there, don't you see? your strength comes in, the faith in your ability for the digging of unostentatious holes to bury the stuff in—your power of devotion, not to yourself, but to an obscure, back-breaking business. And that's difficult enough. Mind, I am not trying to excuse or even explain—I am trying to account to myself for—for—Mr. Kurtz—for the shade of Mr. Kurtz. This initiated wraith from the back of Nowhere honored me with its amazing confidence before it vanished altogether. This was because it could speak English to me. The original Kurtz had been educated partly in England, and—as he was good enough to say himself—his sympathies were in the right place. His mother was half-English, his father was half-French. All Europe contributed to the making of Kurtz; and by and by I learned that, most appropriately, the International Society for the Suppression of Savage Customs had intrusted him with the making of a report, for its future guidance. And he had written it, too. I've seen it. I've read it. It was eloquent, vibrating with eloquence, but too high-strung, I think. Seventeen pages of close writing he had found time for! But this must have been before his—let us say—nerves, went wrong, and caused him to preside at certain midnight dances ending with unspeakable rites, which—as far as I reluctantly gathered from what I heard at various times—were offered up to him—do you understand?—to Mr. Kurtz himself. But it was a beautiful piece of writing. The opening paragraph, however, in the light of later information, strikes me now as ominous. He began with the argument that we whites, from the point of development we had arrived at, 'must necessarily appear to them [savages] in the nature of supernatural beings—we approach them with the might as of a deity,' and so on, and so on. 'By the simple exercise of our will we can exert a power for good practically unbounded,' etc., etc. From that point he soared and took me with him. The peroration was magnificent, though difficult to remember, you know. It gave me the notion of an exotic Immensity ruled by an august Benevolence. It made me tingle with enthusiasm. This was the unbounded power of eloquence—of words—of burning noble words. There were no practical hints to interrupt the magic current of phrases, unless a kind of note at the foot of the last page, scrawled evidently much later, in an unsteady hand, may be regarded as the exposition of a method. It was very simple, and at the end of that moving appeal to every altruistic sentiment it blazed at you, luminous and terrifying, like a flash of lightning in a serene sky: 'Exterminate all the brutes!' The curious part was that he had apparently forgotten all about that valuable postscriptum, because, later on, when he in a sense came to himself, he repeatedly entreated me to take good care of 'my pamphlet' (he called it), as it was sure to have in the future a good influence upon his career. I had full information about all these things, and, besides, as it turned out, I was to have the care of his memory. I've done enough for it to give me the indisputable right to lay it, if I choose, for an everlasting rest in the dustbin of progress, amongst all the sweepings and, figuratively speaking, all the dead cats of civilization. But then, you see, I can't choose. He won't be forgotten. Whatever he was, he was not common. He had the power to charm or frighten rudimentary souls into an aggravated witch-dance in his honor; he could also fill the small souls of the pilgrims with bitter misgivings: he had one devoted friend at least, and he had conquered one soul in the world that was neither rudimentary nor tainted with self-seeking. No; I can't forget him, though I am not prepared to affirm the fellow was exactly worth the life we lost in getting to him. I missed my late helmsman awfully,—I missed him even while his body was still lying in the pilot-house. Perhaps you will think it passing strange this regret for a savage who was no more account than a grain of sand in a black

Sahara. Well, don't you see, he had done something, he had
steered; for months I had him at my back—a help—an instrument. It was a kind of partnership. He steered for me—I had
to look after him, I worried about his deficiencies, and thus a
subtle bond had been created, of which I only became aware
when it was suddenly broken. And the intimate profundity of
that look he gave me when he received his hurt remains to this
day in my memory—like a claim of distant kinship affirmed in
a supreme moment.

"Poor fool! If he had only left that shutter alone. He had
no restraint, no restraint—just like Kurtz—a tree swayed by the
wind. As soon as I had put on a dry pair of slippers, I dragged
him out, after first jerking the spear out of his side, which opera-
tion I confess I performed with my eyes shut tight. His heels
leaped together over the little door-step; his shoulders were
pressed to my breast; I hugged him from behind desperately.
Oh! he was heavy, heavy; heavier than any man on earth, I
should imagine. Then without more ado I tipped him overboard. The current snatched him as though he had been a
wisp of grass, and I saw the body roll over twice before I lost
sight of it forever. All the pilgrims and the manager were then
congregated on the awning-deck about the pilot-house, chattering at each other like a flock of excited magpies, and there was
a scandalized murmur at my heartless promptitude. What they
wanted to keep that body hanging about for I can't guess. Em-
balm it, maybe. But I had also heard another, and a very ominous, murmur on the deck below. My friends the wood-cutters
were likewise scandalized, and with a better show of reason—
though I admit that the reason itself was quite inadmissible.
Oh, quite! I had made up my mind that if my late helmsman
was to be eaten, the fishes alone should have him. He had been
a very second-rate helmsman while alive, but now he was dead
he might have become a first-class temptation, and possibly

cause some startling trouble. Besides, I was anxious to take the wheel, the man in pink pajamas showing himself a hopeless duffer at the business.

"This I did directly the simple funeral was over. We were going half-speed, keeping right in the middle of the stream, and I listened to the talk about me. They had given up Kurtz, they had given up the station; Kurtz was dead, and the station had been burnt—and so on—and so on. The red-haired pilgrim was beside himself with the thought that at least this poor Kurtz had been properly avenged. 'Say! We must have made a glorious slaughter of them in the bush. Eh? What do you think? Say?' He positively danced, the bloodthirsty little gingery beggar. And he had nearly fainted when he saw the wounded man! I could not help saying, 'You made a glorious lot of smoke, anyhow.' I had seen, from the way the tops of the bushes rustled and flew, that almost all the shots had gone too high. You can't hit anything unless you take aim and fire from the shoulder; but these chaps fired from the hip with their eyes shut. The retreat, I maintained—and I was right—was caused by the screeching of the steam-whistle. Upon this they forgot Kurtz, and began to howl at me with indignant protests.

"The manager stood by the wheel murmuring confidentially about the necessity of getting well away down the river before dark at all events, when I saw in the distance a clearing on the river-side and the outlines of some sort of building. 'What's this?' I asked. He clapped his hands in wonder. 'The station!' he cried. I edged in at once, still going half-speed.

"Through my glasses I saw the slope of a hill interspersed with rare trees and perfectly free from undergrowth. A long decaying building on the summit was half buried in the high grass; the large holes in the peaked roof gaped black from afar; the jungle and the woods made a background. There was no enclosure or fence of any kind; but there had been one appar-

ently, for near the house half-a-dozen slim posts remained in a
row, roughly trimmed, and with their upper ends ornamented
with round carved balls. The rails, or whatever there had been
between, had disappeared. Of course the forest surrounded all
that. The river-bank was clear, and on the water-side I saw a
white man under a hat like a cart-wheel beckoning persistently
with his whole arm. Examining the edge of the forest above
and below, I was almost certain I could see movements—human
forms gliding here and there. I steamed past prudently, then
stopped the engines and let her drift down. The man on the
shore began to shout, urging us to land. 'We have been
attacked,' screamed the manager. 'I know—I know. It's all
right,' yelled back the other, as cheerful as you please. 'Come
along. It's all right. I am glad.'

"His aspect reminded me of something I had seen—something funny I had seen somewhere. As I maneuvered to get
alongside, I was asking myself, 'What does this fellow look like?'
Suddenly I got it. He looked like a harlequin. His clothes had
been made of some stuff that was brown holland probably, but
it was covered with patches all over, with bright patches, blue,
red, and yellow,—patches on the back, patches on the front,
patches on elbows, on knees; colored binding around his jacket,
scarlet edging at the bottom of his trousers; and the sunshine
made him look extremely gay and wonderfully neat withal,
because you could see how beautifully all this patching had been
done. A beardless, boyish face, very fair, no features to speak of,
nose peeling, little blue eyes, smiles and frowns chasing each
other over that open countenance like sunshine and shadow on a
wind-swept plain. 'Look out, captain!' he cried; 'there's a snag
lodged in here last night.' What! Another snag? I confess I
swore shamefully. I had nearly holed my cripple, to finish off
that charming trip. The harlequin on the bank turned his little
pug-nose up to me. 'You English?' he asked, all smiles. 'Are

you?' I shouted from the wheel. The smiles vanished, and he shook his head as if sorry for my disappointment. Then he brightened up. 'Never mind!' he cried, encouragingly. 'Are we in time?' I asked. 'He is up there,' he replied, with a toss of the head up the hill, and becoming gloomy all of a sudden. His face was like the autumn sky, overcast one moment and bright the next.

"When the manager, escorted by the pilgrims, all of them armed to the teeth, had gone to the house this chap came on board. 'I say, I don't like this. These natives are in the bush,' I said. He assured me earnestly it was all right. 'They are simple people,' he added; 'well, I am glad you came. It took me all my time to keep them off.' 'But you said it was all right,' I cried. 'Oh, they meant no harm,' he said; and as I stared he corrected himself, 'Not exactly.' Then vivaciously, 'My faith, your pilot-house wants a clean-up!' In the next breath he advised me to keep enough steam on the boiler to blow the whistle in case of any trouble. 'One good screech will do more for you than all your rifles. They are simple people,' he repeated. He rattled away at such a rate he quite overwhelmed me. He seemed to be trying to make up for lots of silence, and actually hinted, laughing, that such was the case. 'Don't you talk with Mr. Kurtz?' I said. 'You don't talk with that man—you listen to him,' he exclaimed with severe exaltation. 'But now—' He waved his arm, and in the twinkling of an eye was in the uttermost depths of despondency. In a moment he came up again with a jump, possessed himself of both my hands, shook them continuously, while he gabbled: 'Brother sailor . . . honor . . . pleasure . . . delight . . . introduce myself . . . Russian . . . son of an arch-priest . . . Government of Tambov. . . . What? Tobacco! English tobacco; the excellent English tobacco! Now, that's brotherly. Smoke? Where's a sailor that does not smoke?'

"The pipe soothed him, and gradually I made out he had run away from school, had gone to sea in a Russian ship; ran away again; served some time in English ships; was now reconciled with the arch-priest. He made a point of that. 'But when one is young one must see things, gather experience, ideas; enlarge the mind.' 'Here!' I interrupted. 'You can never tell! Here I met Mr. Kurtz,' he said, youthfully solemn and reproachful. I held my tongue after that. It appears he had persuaded a Dutch trading-house on the coast to fit him out with stores and goods, and had started for the interior with a light heart, and no more idea of what would happen to him than a baby. He had been wandering about that river for nearly two years alone, cut off from everybody and everything. 'I am not so young as I look. I am twenty-five,' he said. 'At first old Van Shuyten would tell me to go to the devil,' he narrated with keen enjoyment; 'but I stuck to him, and talked and talked, till at last he got afraid I would talk the hind-leg off his favorite dog, so he gave me some cheap things and a few guns, and told me he hoped he would never see my face again. Good old Dutchman, Van Shuyten. I've sent him one small lot of ivory a year ago, so that he can't call me a little thief when I get back. I hope he got it. And for the rest I don't care. I had some wood stacked for you. That was my old house. Did you see?'

"I gave him Towson's book. He made as though he would kiss me, but restrained himself. 'The only book I had left, and I thought I had lost it,' he said, looking at it ecstatically. 'So many accidents happen to a man going about alone, you know. Canoes get upset sometimes—and sometimes you've got to clear out so quick when the people get angry.' He thumbed the pages. 'You made notes in Russian?' I asked. He nodded. 'I thought they were written in cipher,' I said. He laughed, then became serious. 'I had lots of trouble to keep these people off,' he said. 'Did they want to kill you?' I asked. 'Oh, no!' he cried, and checked himself. 'Why did they attack us?' I pursued. He hesitated, then said shamefacedly, 'They don't want him to go.' 'Don't they?' I said, curiously. He nodded a nod full of mystery and wisdom. 'I tell you,' he cried, 'this man has enlarged my mind.' He opened his arms wide, staring at me with his little blue eyes that were perfectly round."

III

"I looked at him, lost in astonishment. There he was before me, in motley, as though he had absconded from a troupe of mimes, enthusiastic, fabulous. His very existence was improbable, inexplicable, and altogether bewildering. He was an insoluble problem. It was inconceivable how he had existed, how he had succeeded in getting so far, how he had managed to remain—why he did not instantly disappear. 'I went a little farther,' he said, 'then still a little farther—till I had gone so far that I don't know how I'll ever get back. Never mind. Plenty time. I can manage. You take Kurtz away quick—quick—I tell you.' The glamour of youth enveloped his parti-colored rags, his destitution, his loneliness, the essential desolation of his futile wanderings. For months—for years—his life hadn't been worth a day's purchase; and there he was gallantly, thoughtlessly alive, to all appearance indestructible solely by the virtue of his few years and of his unreflecting audacity. I was seduced into something like admiration—like envy. Glamour urged him on, glamour kept him unscathed. He surely wanted nothing from the wilderness but space to breathe in and to push on through. His need was to exist, and to move onwards at the greatest possible risk, and with a maximum of privation. If the absolutely pure, uncalculating, unpractical spirit of adventure had ever ruled a human being, it ruled this be-patched youth. I almost envied him the possession of this modest and clear flame.

It seemed to have consumed all thought of self so completely, that even while he was talking to you, you forgot that it was he—the man before your eyes—who had gone through these things. I did not envy him his devotion to Kurtz, though. He had not meditated over it. It came to him and he accepted it with a sort of eager fatalism. I must say that to me it appeared about the most dangerous thing in every way he had come upon so far.

"They had come together unavoidably, like two ships becalmed near each other, and lay rubbing sides at last. I suppose Kurtz wanted an audience, because on a certain occasion, when encamped in the forest, they had talked all night, or more probably Kurtz had talked. 'We talked of everything,' he said, quite transported at the recollection. 'I forgot there was such a thing as sleep. The night did not seem to last an hour. Everything! Everything! . . . Of love, too.' 'Ah, he talked to you of love!' I said, much amused. 'It isn't what you think,' he cried, almost passionately. 'It was in general. He made me see things—things.'

"He threw his arms up. We were on deck at the time, and the headman of my wood-cutters, lounging near by, turned upon him his heavy and glittering eyes. I looked around, and I don't know why, but I assure you that never, never before, did this land, this river, this jungle, the very arch of this blazing sky, appear to me so hopeless and so dark, so impenetrable to human thought, so pitiless to human weakness. 'And, ever since, you have been with him, of course?' I said.

"On the contrary. It appears their intercourse had been very much broken by various causes. He had, as he informed me proudly, managed to nurse Kurtz through two illnesses (he alluded to it as you would to some risky feat), but as a rule Kurtz wandered alone far in the depths of the forest. 'Very often coming to this station, I had to wait days and days before

he would turn up,' he said. 'Ah, it was worth waiting for!—
sometimes.' 'What was he doing? exploring or what?' I asked.
'Oh, yes, of course'; he had discovered lots of villages, a lake,
too—he did not know exactly in what direction; it was dangerous to inquire too much—but mostly his expeditions had been
for ivory. 'But he had no goods to trade with by that time,' I
objected. 'There's a good lot of cartridges left even yet,' he answered, looking away. 'To speak plainly, he raided the country,' I said. He nodded. 'Not alone, surely!' He muttered
something about the villages round that lake. 'Kurtz got the
tribe to follow him, did he?' I suggested. He fidgeted a little.
'They adored him,' he said. The tone of these words was so
extraordinary that I looked at him searchingly. It was curious
to see his mingled eagerness and reluctance to speak of Kurtz.
The man filled his life, occupied his thoughts, swayed his emotions. 'What can you expect?' he burst out; 'he came to them
with thunder and lightning, you know—and they had never
seen anything like it—and very terrible. He could be very terrible. You can't judge Mr. Kurtz as you would an ordinary man.
No, no, no! Now—just to give you an idea—I don't mind
telling you, he wanted to shoot me, too, one day—but I don't
judge him.' 'Shoot you!' I cried. 'What for?' 'Well, I had a
small lot of ivory the chief of that village near my house gave
me. You see I used to shoot game for them. Well, he wanted
it, and wouldn't hear reason. He declared he would shoot me
unless I gave him the ivory and then cleared out of the country,
because he could do so, and had a fancy for it, and there was
nothing on earth to prevent him killing whom he jolly well
pleased. And it was true, too. I gave him the ivory. What did
I care! But I didn't clear out. No, no. I couldn't leave him.
I had to be careful, of course, till we got friendly again for a
time. He had his second illness then. Afterwards I had to
keep out of the way; but I didn't mind. He was living for

the most part in those villages on the lake. When he came down
to the river, sometimes he would take to me, and sometimes it
was better for me to be careful. This man suffered too much.
He hated all this, and somehow he couldn't get away. When
I had a chance I begged him to try and leave while there was
time; I offered to go back with him. And he would say yes,
and then he would remain; go off on another ivory hunt; disappear for weeks; forget himself amongst these people—forget
himself—you know.' 'Why! he's mad,' I said. He protested
indignantly. Mr. Kurtz couldn't be mad. If I had heard him
talk, only two days ago, I wouldn't dare hint at such a thing.
. . . I had taken up my binoculars while we talked, and was
looking at the shore, sweeping the limit of the forest at each
side and at the back of the house. The consciousness of there
being people in that bush, so silent, so quiet—as silent and quiet
as the ruined house on the hill—made me uneasy. There was no
sign on the face of nature of this amazing tale that was not so
much told as suggested to me in desolate exclamations, completed by shrugs, in interrupted phrases, in hints ending in deep
sighs. The woods were unmoved, like a mask—heavy, like the
closed door of a prison—they looked with their air of hidden
knowledge, of patient expectation, of unapproachable silence.
The Russian was explaining to me that it was only lately that
Mr. Kurtz had come down to the river, bringing along with
him all the fighting men of that lake tribe. He had been absent
for several months—getting himself adored, I suppose—and had
come down unexpectedly, with the intention to all appearance
of making a raid either across the river or down stream. Evidently the appetite for more ivory had got the better of the—
what shall I say?—less material aspirations. However he had
got much worse suddenly. 'I heard he was lying helpless, and
so I came up—took my chance,' said the Russian. 'Oh, he is
bad, very bad.' I directed my glass to the house. There were

no signs of life, but there was the ruined roof, the long mud wall peeping above the grass, with three little square window-holes, no two of the same size; all this brought within reach of my hand, as it were. And then I made a brusque movement, and one of the remaining posts of that vanished fence leaped up in the field of my glass. You remember I told you I had been struck at the distance by certain attempts at ornamentation, rather remarkable in the ruinous aspect of the place. Now I had suddenly a nearer view, and its first result was to make me throw my head back as if before a blow. Then I went carefully from post to post with my glass, and I saw my mistake. These round knobs were not ornamental but symbolic; they were expressive and puzzling, striking and disturbing—food for thought and also for vultures if there had been any looking down from the sky; but at all events for such ants as were industrious enough to ascend the pole. They would have been even more impressive, those heads on the stakes, if their faces had not been turned to the house. Only one, the first I had made out, was facing my way. I was not so shocked as you may think. The start back I had given was really nothing but a movement of surprise. I had expected to see a knob of wood there, you know. I returned deliberately to the first I had seen—and there it was, black, dried, sunken, with closed eyelids,—a head that seemed to sleep at the top of that pole, and with the shrunken dry lips showing a narrow white line of the teeth, was smiling, too, smiling continuously at some endless and jocose dream of that eternal slumber.

"I am not disclosing any trade secrets. In fact, the manager said afterwards that Mr. Kurtz's methods had ruined the district. I have no opinion on that point, but I want you clearly to understand that there was nothing exactly profitable in these heads being there. They only showed that Mr. Kurtz lacked restraint in the gratification of his various lusts, that there was

something wanting in him—some small matter which, when
the pressing need arose, could not be found under his magnificent eloquence. Whether he knew of this deficiency himself I
can't say. I think the knowledge came to him at last—only at
the very last. But the wilderness had found him out early, and
had taken on him a terrible vengeance for the fantastic invasion.
I think it had whispered to him things about himself which
he did not know, things of which he had no conception till
he took counsel with this great solitude—and the whisper had
proved irresistibly fascinating. It echoed loudly within him
because he was hollow at the core. . . . I put down the glass,
and the head that had appeared near enough to be spoken to
seemed at once to have leaped away from me into inaccessible
distance.

"The admirer of Mr. Kurtz was a bit crestfallen. In a hurried
indistinct voice he began to assure me he had not dared to take
these—say, symbols—down. He was not afraid of the natives;
they would not stir till Mr. Kurtz gave the word. His ascendancy was extraordinary. The camps of these people surrounded
the place, and the chiefs came every day to see him. They
would crawl. . . . 'I don't want to know anything of the ceremonies used when approaching Mr. Kurtz,' I shouted. Curious,
this feeling that came over me that such details would be more
intolerable than those heads drying on the stakes under Mr.
Kurtz's windows. After all, that was only a savage sight, while
I seemed at one bound to have been transported into some light-
less region of subtle horrors, where pure, uncomplicated savagery
was a positive relief, being something that had a right to exist—
obviously—in the sunshine. The young man looked at me with
surprise. I suppose it did not occur to him that Mr. Kurtz was
no idol of mine. He forgot I hadn't heard any of these splendid
monologues on, what was it? on love, justice, conduct of life—
or what not. If it had come to crawling before Mr. Kurtz, he

crawled as much as the veriest savage of them all. I had no idea
of the conditions, he said: these heads were the heads of rebels.
I shocked him excessively by laughing. Rebels! What would
be the next definition I was to hear? There had been enemies,
criminals, workers—and these were rebels. Those rebellious
heads looked very subdued to me on their sticks. 'You don't
know how such a life tries a man like Kurtz,' cried Kurtz's last
disciple. 'Well, and you?' I said. 'I! I! I am a simple man. I
have no great thoughts. I want nothing from anybody. How
can you compare me to . . . ?' His feelings were too much for
speech, and suddenly he broke down. 'I don't understand,' he
groaned. 'I've been doing my best to keep him alive, and that's
enough. I had no hand in all this. I have no abilities. There
hasn't been a drop of medicine or a mouthful of invalid food
for months here. He was shamefully abandoned. A man like
this, with such ideas. Shamefully! Shamefully! I—I—haven't
slept for the last ten nights. . . .'

"His voice lost itself in the calm of the evening. The long
shadows of the forest had slipped downhill while we talked,
had gone far beyond the ruined hovel, beyond the symbolic
row of stakes. All this was in the gloom, while we down there
were yet in the sunshine, and the stretch of the river abreast
of the clearing glittered in a still and dazzling splendor, with a
murky and overshadowed bend above and below. Not a living
soul was seen on the shore. The bushes did not rustle.

"Suddenly round the corner of the house a group of men
appeared, as though they had come up from the ground. They
waded waist-deep in the grass, in a compact body, bearing an
improvised stretcher in their midst. Instantly, in the emptiness
of the landscape, a cry arose whose shrillness pierced the still
air like a sharp arrow flying straight to the very heart of the
land; and, as if by enchantment, streams of human beings—of
naked human beings—with spears in their hands, with bows,

with shields, with wild glances and savage movements, were poured into the clearing by the dark-faced and pensive forest. The bushes shook, the grass swayed for a time, and then everything stood still in attentive immobility.

"'Now, if he does not say the right thing to them we are all done for,' said the Russian at my elbow. The knot of men with the stretcher had stopped, too, halfway to the steamer, as if petrified. I saw the man on the stretcher sit up, lank and with an uplifted arm, above the shoulders of the bearers. 'Let us hope that the man who can talk so well of love in general will find some particular reason to spare us this time,' I said. I resented bitterly the absurd danger of our situation, as if to be at the mercy of that atrocious phantom had been a dishonoring necessity. I could not hear a sound, but through my glasses I saw the thin arm extended commandingly, the lower jaw moving, the eyes of that apparition shining darkly far in its bony head that nodded with grotesque jerks. Kurtz—Kurtz—that means short in German—don't it? Well, the name was as true as everything else in his life—and death. He looked at least seven feet long. His covering had fallen off, and his body emerged from it pitiful and appalling as from a winding-sheet. I could see the cage of his ribs all astir, the bones of his arm waving. It was as though an animated image of death carved out of old ivory had been shaking its hand with menaces at a motionless crowd of men made of dark and glittering bronze. I saw him open his mouth wide—it gave him a weirdly voracious aspect, as though he had wanted to swallow all the air, all the earth, all the men before him. A deep voice reached me faintly. He must have been shouting. He fell back suddenly. The stretcher shook as the bearers staggered forward again, and almost at the same time I noticed that the crowd of savages was vanishing without any perceptible movement of retreat, as if the forest that had ejected these beings so suddenly had drawn them in again as the breath is drawn in a long aspiration.

"Some of the pilgrims behind the stretcher carried his arms— two shotguns, a heavy rifle, and a light revolver-carbine—the thunderbolts of that pitiful Jupiter. The manager bent over him murmuring as he walked beside his head. They laid him down in one of the little cabins—just a room for a bedplace and a camp-stool or two, you know. We had brought his belated correspondence, and a lot of torn envelopes and open letters littered his bed. His hand roamed feebly amongst these papers. I was struck by the fire of his eyes and the composed languor of his expression. It was not so much the exhaustion of disease. He did not seem in pain. This shadow looked satiated and calm, as though for the moment it had had its fill of all the emotions.

"He rustled one of the letters, and looking straight in my face said, 'I am glad.' Somebody had been writing to him about me. These special recommendations were turning up again. The volume of tone he emitted without effort, almost without the trouble of moving his lips, amazed me. A voice! a voice! It was grave, profound, vibrating, while the man did not seem capable of a whisper. However, he had enough strength in him —factitious no doubt—to very nearly make an end of us, as you shall hear directly.

"The manager appeared silently in the doorway; I stepped out at once and he drew the curtain after me. The Russian, eyed curiously by the pilgrims, was staring at the shore. I followed the direction of his glance.

"Dark human shapes could be made out in the distance, flitting indistinctly against the gloomy border of the forest, and near the river two bronze figures, leaning on tall spears, stood in the sunlight under fantastic headdresses of spotted skins, war-like and still in statuesque repose. And from right to left along the lighted shore moved a wild and gorgeous apparition of a woman.

"She walked with measured steps, draped in striped and fringed cloths, treading the earth proudly, with a slight jingle and flash of barbarous ornaments. She carried her head high; her hair was done in the shape of a helmet; she had brass leggings to the knee, brass wire gauntlets to the elbow, a crimson spot on her tawny cheek, innumerable necklaces of glass beads on her neck; bizarre things, charms, gifts of witch-men, that hung about her, glittered and trembled at every step. She must have had the value of several elephant tusks upon her. She was savage and superb, wild-eyed and magnificent; there was something ominous and stately in her deliberate progress. And in the hush that had fallen suddenly upon the whole sorrowful land, the immense wilderness, the colossal body of the fecund and mysterious life seemed to look at her, pensive, as though it had been looking at the image of its own tenebrous and passionate soul.

"She came abreast of the steamer, stood still, and faced us. Her long shadow fell to the water's edge. Her face had a tragic and fierce aspect of wild sorrow and of dumb pain mingled with the fear of some struggling, half-shaped resolve. She stood looking at us without a stir, and like the wilderness itself, with an air of brooding over an inscrutable purpose. A whole minute passed, and then she made a step forward. There was a low jingle, a glint of yellow metal, a sway of fringed draperies, and she stopped as if her heart had failed her. The young fellow by my side growled. The pilgrims murmured at my back. She looked at us all as if her life had depended upon the unswerving steadiness of her glance. Suddenly she opened her bared arms and threw them up rigid above her head, as though in an uncontrollable desire to touch the sky, and at the same time the swift shadows darted out on the earth, swept around on the river, gathering the steamer into a shadowy embrace. A formidable silence hung over the scene.

"She turned away slowly, walked on, following the bank, and passed into the bushes to the left. Once only her eyes gleamed back at us in the dusk of the thickets before she disappeared.

"'If she had offered to come aboard I really think I would have tried to shoot her,' said the man of patches, nervously. 'I have been risking my life every day for the last fortnight to keep her out of the house. She got in one day and kicked up a row about those miserable rags I picked up in the storeroom to mend my clothes with. I wasn't decent. At least it must have been that, for she talked like a fury to Kurtz for an hour, pointing at me now and then. I don't understand the dialect of this tribe. Luckily for me, I fancy Kurtz felt too ill that day to care, or there would have been mischief. I don't understand. . . . No—it's too much for me. Ah, well, it's all over now.'

"At this moment I heard Kurtz's deep voice behind the curtain: 'Save me!—save the ivory, you mean. Don't tell me. Save *me!* Why, I've had to save you. You are interrupting my plans now. Sick! Sick! Not so sick as you would like to believe. Never mind. I'll carry my ideas out yet—I will return. I'll show you what can be done. You with your little peddling notions—you are interfering with me. I will return. I . . .'

"The manager came out. He did me the honor to take me under the arm and lead me aside. 'He is very low, very low,' he said. He considered it necessary to sigh, but neglected to be consistently sorrowful. 'We have done all we could for him—haven't we? But there is no disguising the fact, Mr. Kurtz has done more harm than good to the Company. He did not see the time was not ripe for vigorous action. Cautiously, cautiously —that's my principle. We must be cautious yet. The district is closed to us for a time. Deplorable! Upon the whole, the trade will suffer. I don't deny there is a remarkable quantity of ivory

—mostly fossil. We must save it, at all events—but look how precarious the position is—and why? Because the method is unsound.' 'Do you,' said I, looking at the shore, 'call it "unsound method"?' 'Without doubt,' he exclaimed, hotly. 'Don't you?' . . . 'No method at all,' I murmured after a while. 'Exactly,' he exulted. 'I anticipated this. Shows a complete want of judgment. It is my duty to point it out in the proper quarter.' 'Oh,' said I, 'that fellow—what's his name?—the brickmaker, will make a readable report for you.' He appeared confounded for a moment. It seemed to me I had never breathed an atmosphere so vile, and I turned mentally to Kurtz for relief —positively for relief. 'Nevertheless I think Mr. Kurtz is a remarkable man,' I said with emphasis. He started, dropped on me a cold heavy glance, said very quietly, 'he *was*,' and turned his back on me. My hour of favor was over; I found myself lumped along with Kurtz as a partisan of methods for which the time was not ripe: I was unsound! Ah! but it was something to have at least a choice of nightmares.

"I had turned to the wilderness really, not to Mr. Kurtz, who, I was ready to admit, was as good as buried. And for a moment it seemed to me as if I also were buried in a vast grave full of unspeakable secrets. I felt an intolerable weight oppressing my breast, the smell of the damp earth, the unseen presence of victorious corruption, the darkness of an impenetrable night. . . . The Russian tapped me on the shoulder. I heard him mumbling and stammering something about 'brother seaman—couldn't conceal—knowledge of matters that would affect Mr. Kurtz's reputation.' I waited. For him evidently Mr. Kurtz was not in his grave; I suspect that for him Mr. Kurtz was one of the immortals. 'Well!' said I at last, 'speak out. As it happens, I am Mr. Kurtz's friend—in a way.'

"He stated with a good deal of formality that had we not been 'of the same profession,' he would have kept the matter to himself without regard to consequences. 'He suspected there was an active ill will towards him on the part of these white men that—' 'You are right,' I said, remembering a certain conversation I had overheard. 'The manager thinks you ought to be hanged.' He showed a concern at this intelligence which amused me at first. 'I had better get out of the way quietly,' he said, earnestly. 'I can do no more for Kurtz now, and they would soon find some excuse. What's to stop them? There's a military post three hundred miles from here.' 'Well, upon my word,' said I, 'perhaps you had better go if you have any friends amongst the savages near by.' 'Plenty,' he said. 'They are simple people—and I want nothing, you know.' He stood biting his lip, then: 'I don't want any harm to happen to these whites here, but of course I was thinking of Mr. Kurtz's reputation—but you are a brother seaman and—' 'All right,' said I, after a time. 'Mr. Kurtz's reputation is safe with me.' I did not know how truly I spoke.

"He informed me, lowering his voice, that it was Kurtz who had ordered the attack to be made on the steamer. 'He hated sometimes the idea of being taken away—and then again . . . But I don't understand these matters. I am a simple man. He thought it would scare you away—that you would give it up, thinking him dead. I could not stop him. Oh, I had an awful time of it this last month.' 'Very well,' I said. 'He is all right now.' 'Ye-e-es,' he muttered, not very convinced apparently. 'Thanks,' said I; 'I shall keep my eyes open.' 'But quiet—eh?' he urged, anxiously. 'It would be awful for his reputation if anybody here—' I promised a complete discretion with great gravity. 'I have a canoe and three black fellows waiting not very far. I am off. Could you give me a few Martini-Henry cartridges?' I could, and did, with proper secrecy. He helped himself, with a wink at me, to a handful of my tobacco. 'Between sailors—you know—good English tobacco.' At the door of the pilot-house he turned round—'I say, haven't you a pair of shoes you could spare?' He raised one leg. 'Look.' The soles were tied with knotted strings sandal-wise under his bare feet. I rooted out an old pair, at which he looked with admiration before tucking them under his left arm. One of his pockets (bright red) was bulging with cartridges, from the other (dark blue) peeped 'Towson's Inquiry,' etc., etc. He seemed to think himself excellently well equipped for a renewed encounter with the wilderness. 'Ah! I'll never, never meet such a man again. You ought to have heard him recite poetry—his own, too, it was, he told me. Poetry!' He rolled his eyes at the recollection of these delights. 'Oh, he enlarged my mind!' 'Good-by,' said I. He shook hands and vanished in the night. Sometimes I ask myself whether I had ever really seen him—whether it was possible to meet such a phenomenon! . . .

"When I woke up shortly after midnight his warning came to my mind with its hint of danger that seemed, in the starred darkness, real enough to make me get up for the purpose of having a look round. On the hill a big fire burned, illuminating fitfully a crooked corner of the station-house. One of the agents with a picket of a few of our blacks, armed for the purpose, was keeping guard over the ivory; but deep within the forest, red gleams that wavered, that seemed to sink and rise from the ground amongst confused columnar shapes of intense blackness, showed the exact position of the camp where Mr. Kurtz's adorers were keeping their uneasy vigil. The monotonous beating of a big drum filled the air with muffled shocks and a lingering vibration. A steady droning sound of many men chanting each to himself some weird incantation came out from the black, flat wall of the woods as the humming of bees comes out of a hive, and had a strange narcotic effect upon my half-awake senses. I believe I dozed off leaning over the rail, till an abrupt burst of yells, an overwhelming outbreak of a pent-up and mysterious frenzy, woke me up in a bewildered wonder. It was cut short all at once, and the low droning went on with an effect of audible and soothing silence. I glanced casually into the little cabin. A light was burning within, but Mr. Kurtz was not there.

"I think I would have raised an outcry if I had believed my eyes. But I didn't believe them at first—the thing seemed so impossible. The fact is I was completely unnerved by a sheer blank fright, pure abstract terror, unconnected with any distinct shape of physical danger. What made this emotion so overpowering was—how shall I define it?—the moral shock I received, as if something altogether monstrous, intolerable to thought and odious to the soul, had been thrust upon me unexpectedly. This lasted of course the merest fraction of a second, and then the usual sense of commonplace, deadly danger, the possibility of a sudden onslaught and massacre, or something of the kind, which I saw impending, was positively welcome and composing. It pacified me, in fact, so much, that I did not raise an alarm.

"There was an agent buttoned up inside an ulster and sleeping on a chair on deck within three feet of me. The yells had not awakened him; he snored very slightly; I left him to his slumbers and leaped ashore. I did not betray Mr. Kurtz—it was ordered I should never betray him—it was written I should be loyal to the nightmare of my choice. I was anxious to deal with this shadow by myself alone,—and to this day I don't know why I was so jealous of sharing with anyone the peculiar blackness of that experience.

"As soon as I got on the bank I saw a trail—a broad trail through the grass. I remember the exultation with which I said to myself, 'He can't walk—he is crawling on all-fours—I've got him.' The grass was wet with dew. I strode rapidly with clenched fists. I fancy I had some vague notion of falling upon him and giving him a drubbing. I don't know. I had some imbecile thoughts. The knitting old woman with the cat obtruded herself upon my memory as a most improper person to be sitting at the other end of such an affair. I saw a row of pilgrims squirting lead in the air out of Winchesters held to the hip. I thought I would never get back to the steamer, and imagined myself living alone and unarmed in the woods to an advanced age. Such silly things—you know. And I remember I confounded the beat of the drum with the beating of my heart, and was pleased at its calm regularity.

"I kept to the track though—then stopped to listen. The night was very clear; a dark blue space, sparkling with dew and starlight, in which black things stood very still. I thought I could see a kind of motion ahead of me. I was strangely cocksure of everything that night. I actually left the track and ran in a wide semicircle (I verily believe chuckling to myself) so as to get in front of that stir, of that motion I had seen—if indeed I had seen anything. I was circumventing Kurtz as though it had been a boyish game.

"I came upon him, and, if he had not heard me coming, I would have fallen over him, too, but he got up in time. He rose, unsteady, long, pale, indistinct, like a vapor exhaled by the earth, and swayed slightly, misty and silent before me; while at my back the fires loomed between the trees, and the murmur of many voices issued from the forest. I had cut him off cleverly; but when actually confronting him I seemed to come to my senses, I saw the danger in its right proportion. It was by no means over yet. Suppose he began to shout? Though he could hardly stand, there was still plenty of vigor in his voice. 'Go away—hide yourself,' he said, in that profound tone. It was very awful. I glanced back. We were within thirty yards from the nearest fire. A black figure stood up, strode on long black legs, waving long black arms, across the glow. It had horns—antelope horns, I think—on its head. Some sorcerer, some witch-man, no doubt: it looked fiend-like enough. 'Do you know what you are doing?' I whispered. 'Perfectly,' he answered, raising his voice for that single word: it sounded to me far off and yet loud, like a hail through a speaking-trumpet. If he makes a row we are lost, I thought to myself. This clearly was not a case for fisticuffs, even apart from the very natural aversion I had to beat that Shadow—this wandering and tormented thing. 'You will be lost,' I said—'utterly lost.' One gets sometimes such a flash of inspiration, you know. I did say the right thing, though indeed he could not have been more irretrievably lost than he was at this very moment, when the foundations of our intimacy were being laid—to endure—to endure—even to the end—even beyond.

" 'I had immense plans,' he muttered irresolutely. 'Yes,' said I; 'but if you try to shout I'll smash your head with—' There was not a stick or a stone near. 'I will throttle you for good,' I corrected myself. 'I was on the threshold of great things,' he pleaded, in a voice of longing, with a wistfulness of tone that made my blood run cold. 'And now for this stupid scoundrel—' 'Your success in Europe is assured in any case,' I affirmed, steadily. I did not want to have the throttling of him, you understand—and indeed it would have been very little use for any practical purpose. I tried to break the spell—the heavy, mute spell of the wilderness—that seemed to draw him to its pitiless breast by the awakening of forgotten and brutal instincts, by the memory of gratified and monstrous passions. This alone, I was convinced, had driven him out to the edge of the forest, to the bush, towards the gleam of fires, the throb of drums, the drone of weird incantations; this alone had beguiled his unlawful soul beyond the bounds of permitted aspirations. And, don't you see, the terror of the position was not in being knocked on the head—though I had a very lively sense of that danger, too—but in this, that I had to deal with a being to whom I could not

appeal in the name of anything high or low. I had, even like
the niggers, to invoke him—himself—his own exalted and incredible degradation. There was nothing either above or below
him, and I knew it. He had kicked himself loose of the earth.
Confound the man! he had kicked the very earth to pieces. He
was alone, and I before him did not know whether I stood on
the ground or floated in the air. I've been telling you what we
said—repeating the phrases we pronounced—but what's the
good? They were common everyday words—the familiar, vague
sounds exchanged on every waking day of life. But what of
that? They had behind them, to my mind, the terrific sugges-
tiveness of words heard in dreams, of phrases spoken in nightmares. Soul! If anybody had ever struggled with a soul, I am
the man. And I wasn't arguing with a lunatic either. Believe
me or not, his intelligence was perfectly clear—concentrated, it is
true, upon himself with horrible intensity, yet clear; and therein
was my only chance—barring, of course, the killing him there
and then, which wasn't so good, on account of unavoidable
noise. But his soul was mad. Being alone in the wilderness, it
had looked within itself, and, by heavens! I tell you, it had gone
mad. I had—for my sins, I suppose—to go through the ordeal
of looking into it myself. No eloquence could have been so
withering to one's belief in mankind as his final burst of sincerity. He struggled with himself, too. I saw it,—I heard it. I
saw the inconceivable mystery of a soul that knew no restraint,
no faith, and no fear, yet struggling blindly with itself. I kept
my head pretty well; but when I had him at last stretched on
the couch, I wiped my forehead, while my legs shook under me
as though I had carried half a ton on my back down that hill.
And yet I had only supported him, his bony arm clasped round
my neck—and he was not much heavier than a child.

"When next day we left at noon, the crowd, of whose presence
behind the curtain of trees I had been acutely conscious all the

time, flowed out of the woods again, filled the clearing, covered the slope with a mass of naked, breathing, quivering, bronze bodies. I steamed up a bit, then swung downstream, and two thousand eyes followed the evolutions of the splashing, thumping, fierce river-demon beating the water with its terrible tail and breathing black smoke into the air. In front of the first rank, along the river, three men, plastered with bright red earth from head to foot, strutted to and fro restlessly. When we came abreast again, they faced the river, stamped their feet, nodded their horned heads, swayed their scarlet bodies; they shook towards the fierce river-demon a bunch of black feathers, a mangy skin with a pendent tail—something that looked like a dried gourd; they shouted periodically together strings of amazing words that resembled no sounds of human language; and the deep murmurs of the crowd, interrupted suddenly, were like the responses of some satanic litany.

"We had carried Kurtz into the pilot-house: there was more air there. Lying on the couch, he stared through the open shutter. There was an eddy in the mass of human bodies, and the woman with helmeted head and tawny cheeks rushed out to the very brink of the stream. She put out her hands, shouted something, and all that wild mob took up the shout in a roaring chorus of articulated, rapid, breathless utterance.

" 'Do you understand this?' I asked.

"He kept on looking out past me with fiery, longing eyes, with a mingled expression of wistfulness and hate. He made no answer, but I saw a smile, a smile of indefinable meaning, appear on his colorless lips that a moment after twitched convulsively. 'Do I not?' he said slowly, gasping, as if the words had been torn out of him by a supernatural power.

"I pulled the string of the whistle, and I did this because I saw the pilgrims on deck getting out their rifles with an air of anticipating a jolly lark. At the sudden screech there was a movement of abject terror through that wedged mass of bodies. 'Don't! don't you frighten them away,' cried someone on deck disconsolately. I pulled the string time after time. They broke and ran, they leaped, they crouched, they swerved, they dodged the flying terror of the sound. The three red chaps had fallen flat, face down on the shore, as though they had been shot dead. Only the barbarous and superb woman did not so much as flinch, and stretched tragically her bare arms after us over the somber and glittering river.

"And then that imbecile crowd down on the deck started their little fun, and I could see nothing more for smoke.

"The brown current ran swiftly out of the heart of darkness, bearing us down towards the sea with twice the speed of our upward progress; and Kurtz's life was running swiftly, too, ebbing, ebbing out of his heart into the sea of inexorable time. The manager was very placid, he had no vital anxieties now, he took us both in with a comprehensive and satisfied glance: the 'affair' had come off as well as could be wished. I saw the time approaching when I would be left alone of the party of 'unsound method.' The pilgrims looked upon me with disfavor. I was, so to speak, numbered with the dead. It is strange how I accepted this unforeseen partnership, this choice of nightmares forced upon me in the tenebrous land invaded by these mean and greedy phantoms.

"Kurtz discoursed. A voice! a voice! It rang deep to the very last. It survived his strength to hide in the magnificent folds of eloquence the barren darkness of his heart. Oh, he struggled! he struggled! The wastes of his weary brain were haunted by shadowy images now—images of wealth and fame revolving obsequiously round his unextinguishable gift of noble and lofty expression. My Intended, my station, my career, my ideas—these were the subjects for the occasional utterances of elevated sentiments. The shade of the original Kurtz frequented the bedside of the hollow sham, whose fate it was to be buried presently in the mold of primeval earth. But both the diabolic love and the unearthly hate of the mysteries it had penetrated fought for the possession of that soul satiated with primitive emotions, avid of lying fame, of sham distinction, of all the appearances of success and power.

"Sometimes he was contemptibly childish. He desired to have kings meet him at railway stations on his return from some ghastly Nowhere, where he intended to accomplish great things. 'You show them you have in you something that is really profit-able, and then there will be no limits to the recognition of your ability,' he would say. 'Of course you must take care of the motives—right motives—always.' The long reaches that were like one and the same reach, monotonous bends that were ex-actly alike, slipped past the steamer with their multitude of secular trees looking patiently after this grimy fragment of an-other world, the forerunner of change, of conquest, of trade, of massacres, of blessings. I looked ahead—piloting. 'Close the shutter,' said Kurtz suddenly one day; 'I can't bear to look at this.' I did so. There was a silence. 'Oh, but I will wring your heart yet!' he cried at the invisible wilderness.

"We broke down—as I had expected—and had to lie up for repairs at the head of an island. This delay was the first thing that shook Kurtz's confidence. One morning he gave me a packet of papers and a photograph—the lot tied together with a shoestring. 'Keep this for me,' he said. 'This noxious fool' (meaning the manager) 'is capable of prying into my boxes when I am not looking.' In the afternoon I saw him. He was lying on his back with closed eyes, and I withdrew quietly, but I heard him mutter, 'Live rightly, die, die. . . .' I listened. There was nothing more. Was he rehearsing some speech in his sleep, or was it a fragment of a phrase from some newspaper article? He had been writing for the papers and meant to do so again, 'for the furthering of my ideas. It's a duty.'

"His was an impenetrable darkness. I looked at him as you peer down at a man who is lying at the bottom of a precipice where the sun never shines. But I had not much time to give him, because I was helping the engine-driver to take to pieces the leaky cylinders, to straighten a bent connecting-rod, and in other such matters. I lived in an infernal mess of rust, filings, nuts, bolts, spanners, hammers, ratchet-drills—things I abominate, because I don't get on with them. I tended the little forge we fortunately had aboard; I toiled wearily in a wretched scrap-heap—unless I had the shakes too bad to stand.

"One evening coming in with a candle I was startled to hear him say a little tremulously, 'I am lying here in the dark waiting for death.' The light was within a foot of his eyes. I forced myself to murmur, 'Oh, nonsense!' and stood over him as if transfixed.

"Anything approaching the change that came over his features I have never seen before, and hope never to see again. Oh, I wasn't touched. I was fascinated. It was as though a veil had been rent. I saw on that ivory face the expression of somber pride, of ruthless power, of craven terror—of an intense and hopeless despair. Did he live his life again in every detail of desire, temptation, and surrender during that supreme moment of complete knowledge? He cried in a whisper at some image, at some vision—he cried out twice, a cry that was no more than a breath—

"'The horror! The horror!'

"I blew the candle out and left the cabin. The pilgrims were dining in the mess-room, and I took my place opposite the manager, who lifted his eyes to give me a questioning glance, which I successfully ignored. He leaned back, serene, with that peculiar smile of his sealing the unexpressed depths of his meanness.

A continuous shower of small flies streamed upon the lamp, upon the cloth, upon our hands and faces. Suddenly the manager's boy put his insolent black head in the doorway, and said in a tone of scathing contempt—

"'Mistah Kurtz—he dead.'

"All the pilgrims rushed out to see. I remained, and went on with my dinner. I believe I was considered brutally callous. However, I did not eat much. There was a lamp in there—light, don't you know—and outside it was so beastly, beastly dark. I went no more near the remarkable man who had pronounced a judgment upon the adventures of his soul on this earth. The voice was gone. What else had been there? But I am of course aware that next day the pilgrims buried something in a muddy hole.

"And then they very nearly buried me.

"However, as you see, I did not go to join Kurtz there and then. I did not. I remained to dream the nightmare out to the end, and to show my loyalty to Kurtz once more. Destiny. My destiny! Droll thing life is—that mysterious arrangement of merciless logic for a futile purpose. The most you can hope from it is some knowledge of yourself—that comes too late—a crop of unextinguishable regrets. I have wrestled with death. It is the most unexciting contest you can imagine. It takes place in an impalpable grayness, with nothing underfoot, with nothing around, without spectators, without clamor, without glory, without the great desire of victory, without the great fear of defeat, in a sickly atmosphere of tepid skepticism, without much belief in your own right, and still less in that of your adversary. If such is the form of ultimate wisdom, then life is a greater riddle than some of us think it to be. I was within a hair's breadth of the last opportunity for pronouncement, and I found with humiliation that probably I would have nothing to say. This is the reason why I affirm that Kurtz was a remarkable man. He

had something to say. He said it. Since I had peeped over the
edge myself, I understand better the meaning of his stare, that
could not see the flame of the candle, but was wide enough to
embrace the whole universe, piercing enough to penetrate all
the hearts that beat in the darkness. He had summed up—he
had judged. 'The horror!' He was a remarkable man. After
all, this was the expression of some sort of belief; it had candor,
it had conviction, it had a vibrating note of revolt in its whisper,
it had the appalling face of a glimpsed truth—the strange commingling of desire and hate. And it is not my own extremity
I remember best—a vision of grayness without form filled with
physical pain, and a careless contempt for the evanescence of all
things—even of this pain itself. No! It is his extremity that
I seem to have lived through. True, he had made that last
stride, he had stepped over the edge, while I had been permitted
to draw back my hesitating foot. And perhaps in this is the
whole difference; perhaps all the wisdom, and all truth, and
all sincerity, are just compressed into that inappreciable moment
of time in which we step over the threshold of the invisible.
Perhaps! I like to think my summing-up would not have been
a word of careless contempt. Better his cry—much better. It
was an affirmation, a moral victory paid for by innumerable de-
feats, by abominable terrors, by abominable satisfactions. But
it was a victory! That is why I have remained loyal to Kurtz
to the last, and even beyond, when a long time after I heard
once more, not his own voice, but the echo of his magnificent
eloquence thrown to me from a soul as translucently pure as a
cliff of crystal.

"No, they did not bury me, though there is a period of time
which I remember mistily, with a shuddering wonder, like a
passage through some inconceivable world that had no hope in
it and no desire. I found myself back in the sepulchral city
resenting the sight of people hurrying through the streets to

filch a little money from each other, to devour their infamous cookery, to gulp their unwholesome beer, to dream their insignificant and silly dreams. They trespassed upon my thoughts. They were intruders whose knowledge of life was to me an irritating pretense, because I felt so sure they could not possibly know the things I knew. Their bearing, which was simply the bearing of commonplace individuals going about their business in the assurance of perfect safety, was offensive to me like the outrageous flauntings of folly in the face of a danger it is unable to comprehend. I had no particular desire to enlighten them, but I had some difficulty in restraining myself from laughing in their faces, so full of stupid importance. I daresay I was not very well at that time. I tottered about the streets—there were various affairs to settle—grinning bitterly at perfectly respectable persons. I admit my behavior was inexcusable, but then my temperature was seldom normal in these days. My dear aunt's endeavors to 'nurse up my strength' seemed altogether beside the mark. It was not my strength that wanted nursing, it was my imagination that wanted soothing. I kept the bundle of papers given me by Kurtz, not knowing exactly what to do with it. His mother had died lately, watched over, as I was told, by his Intended. A clean-shaved man, with an official manner and wearing gold-rimmed spectacles, called on me one day and made inquiries, at first circuitous, afterwards suavely pressing, about what he was pleased to denominate certain 'documents.' I was not surprised, because I had had two rows with the manager on the subject out there. I had refused to give up the smallest scrap out of that package, and I took the same attitude with the spectacled man. He became darkly menacing at last, and with much heat argued that the Company had the right to every bit of information about its 'territories.' And said he, 'Mr. Kurtz's knowledge of unexplored regions must have been necessarily extensive and peculiar—owing to his great abilities and to the deplorable circumstances in which he had been placed: therefore—' I assured him Mr. Kurtz's knowledge, however extensive, did not bear upon the problems of commerce or administration. He invoked then the name of science. 'It would be an incalculable loss if,' etc., etc. I offered him the report on the 'Supression of Savage Customs,' with the postscriptum torn off. He took it up eagerly, but ended by sniffing at it with an air of contempt. 'This is not what we had a right to expect,' he remarked. 'Expect nothing else,' I said. 'There are only private letters.' He withdrew upon some threat of legal proceedings, and I saw him no more; but another fellow, calling himself Kurtz's cousin, appeared two days later, and was anxious to hear all the details about his dear relative's last moments. Incidentally he gave me to understand that Kurtz had been essentially a great musician. 'There was the making of an immense success,' said the man, who was an organist, I believe, with lank gray hair flowing over a greasy coat-collar. I had no reason to doubt his statement; and to this day I am unable to say what was Kurtz's profession, whether he ever had any—which was the greatest of his talents. I had taken him for a painter who wrote for the papers, or else for a journalist who could paint—but even the cousin (who took snuff during the interview) could not tell me what he had been—exactly. He was a universal genius—on that point I agreed with the old chap, who thereupon blew his nose noisily into a large cotton handkerchief and withdrew in senile agitation, bearing off some family letters and memoranda without importance. Ultimately a journalist anxious to know something of the fate of his 'dear colleague' turned up. This visitor informed me Kurtz's proper sphere ought to have been politics 'on the popular side.' He had furry straight eyebrows, bristly hair cropped short, an eye-glass on a broad ribbon, and, becoming expansive, confessed his opinion that Kurtz really couldn't write a bit—'but heavens! how that man could talk.

He electrified large meetings. He had faith—don't you see?—he had the faith. He could get himself to believe anything—anything. He would have been a splendid leader of an extreme party.' 'What party?' I asked. 'Any party,' answered the other. 'He was an—an—extremist.' Did I not think so? I assented. Did I know, he asked, with a sudden flash of curiosity, 'what it was that had induced him to go out there?' 'Yes,' said I, and forthwith handed him the famous Report for publication, if he thought fit. He glanced through it hurriedly, mumbling all the time, judged 'it would do,' and took himself off with this plunder.

"Thus I was left at last with a slim packet of letters and the girl's portrait. She struck me as beautiful—I mean she had a beautiful expression. I know that the sunlight can be made to lie, too, yet one felt that no manipulation of light and pose could have conveyed the delicate shade of truthfulness upon those features. She seemed ready to listen without mental reservation, without suspicion, without a thought for herself. I concluded I would go and give her back her portrait and those letters myself. Curiosity? Yes; and also some other feeling perhaps. All that had been Kurtz's had passed out of my hands: his soul, his body, his station, his plans, his ivory, his career. There remained only his memory and his Intended—and I wanted to give that up, too, to the past, in a way—to surrender personally all that remained of him with me to that oblivion which is the last word of our common fate. I don't defend myself. I had no clear perception of what it was I really wanted. Perhaps it was an impulse of unconscious loyalty, or the fulfillment of one of those ironic necessities that lurk in the facts of human existence. I don't know. I can't tell. But I went.

"I thought his memory was like the other memories of the dead that accumulate in every man's life—a vague impress on the brain of shadows that had fallen on it in their swift and final passage; but before the high and ponderous door, between the tall houses of a street as still and decorous as a well-kept alley in a cemetery, I had a vision of him on the stretcher, opening his mouth voraciously, as if to devour all the earth with all its mankind. He lived then before me; he lived as much as he had ever lived—a shadow insatiable of splendid appearances, of frightful realities; a shadow darker than the shadow of the night, and draped nobly in the folds of a gorgeous eloquence. The vision seemed to enter the house with me—the stretcher, the phantom-bearers, the wild crowd of obedient worshipers, the gloom of the forests, the glitter of the reach between the murky bends, the beat of the drum, regular and muffled like the beating of a heart—the heart of a conquering darkness. It was a moment of triumph for the wilderness, an invading and vengeful rush which, it seemed to me, I would have to keep back alone for the salvation of another soul. And the memory of what I had heard him say afar there, with the horned shapes stirring at my back, in the glow of fires, within the patient woods, those broken phrases came back to me, were heard again in their ominous and terrifying simplicity. I remembered his abject pleading, his abject threats, the colossal scale of his vile desires, the meanness, the torment, the tempestuous anguish of his soul. And later on I seemed to see his collected languid manner, when he said one day, 'This lot of ivory now is really mine. The Company did not pay for it. I collected it myself at a very great personal risk. I am afraid they will try to claim it as theirs though. H'm. It is a difficult case. What do you think I ought to do—resist? Eh? I want no more than justice.' . . . He wanted no more than justice—no more than justice. I rang the bell before a mahogany door on the first floor, and while I waited he seemed to stare at me out of the glassy panel—stare with that wide and immense stare embracing, condemning, loathing all the universe. I seemed to hear the whispered cry, 'The horror! The horror!'

"The dusk was falling. I had to wait in a lofty drawing-room with three long windows from floor to ceiling that were like three luminous and bedraped columns. The bent gilt legs and backs of the furniture shone in indistinct curves. The tall marble fireplace had a cold and monumental whiteness. A grand piano stood massively in a corner; with dark gleams on the flat surfaces like a somber and polished sarcophagus. A high door opened—closed. I rose.

"She came forward, all in black, with a pale head, floating towards me in the dusk. She was in mourning. It was more than a year since his death, more than a year since the news came; she seemed as though she would remember and mourn forever. She took both my hands in hers and murmured, 'I had heard you were coming.' I noticed she was not very young —I mean not girlish. She had a mature capacity for fidelity, for belief, for suffering. The room seemed to have grown darker, as if all the sad light of the cloudy evening had taken refuge on her forehead. This fair hair, this pale visage, this pure brow, seemed surrounded by an ashy halo from which the dark eyes looked out at me. Their glance was guileless, profound, confident, and trustful. She carried her sorrowful head as though she were proud of that sorrow, as though she would say, I—I alone know how to mourn him as he deserves. But while we were still shaking hands, such a look of awful desolation came upon her face that I perceived she was one of those creatures that are not the playthings of Time. For her he had died only yesterday. And, by Jove! the impression was so powerful that for me, too, he seemed to have died only yesterday—nay, this very minute. I saw her and him in the same instant of time— his death and her sorrow—I saw her sorrow in the very moment of his death. Do you understand? I saw them together—I heard them together. She had said, with a deep catch of the breath, 'I have survived' while my strained ears seemed to hear distinctly, mingled with her tone of despairing regret, the summing up whisper of his eternal condemnation. I asked myself what I was doing there, with a sensation of panic in my heart as though I had blundered into a place of cruel and absurd mysteries not fit for a human being to behold. She motioned me to a chair. We sat down. I laid the packet gently on the little table, and she put her hand over it. . . . 'You knew him well,' she murmured, after a moment of mourning silence.

"'Intimacy grows quickly out there,' I said. 'I knew him as well as it is possible for one man to know another.'

"'And you admired him,' she said. 'It was impossible to know him and not to admire him. Was it?'

"'He was a remarkable man,' I said, unsteadily. Then before the appealing fixity of her gaze, that seemed to watch for more words on my lips, I went on, 'It was impossible not to—'

"'Love him,' she finished eagerly, silencing me into an appalled dumbness. 'How true! how true! But when you think that no one knew him so well as I! I had all his noble confidence. I knew him best.'

"'You knew him best,' I repeated. And perhaps she did. But with every word spoken the room was growing darker, and only her forehead, smooth and white, remained illumined by the unextinguishable light of belief and love.

"'You were his friend,' she went on. 'His friend,' she repeated, a little louder. 'You must have been, if he had given you this, and sent you to me. I feel I can speak to you—and oh! I must speak. I want you—you have heard his last words—to know I have been worthy of him. . . . It is not pride. . . . Yes! I am proud to know I understood him better than anyone on earth—he told me so himself. And since his mother died I have had no one—no one—to—to—'

"I listened. The darkness deepened. I was not even sure he had given me the right bundle. I rather suspect he wanted me to take care of another batch of his papers which, after his death, I saw the manager examining under the lamp. And the girl talked, easing her pain in the certitude of my sympathy; she talked as thirsty men drink. I had heard that her engagement with Kurtz had been disapproved by her people. He wasn't rich enough or something. And indeed I don't know whether he had not been a pauper all his life. He had given me some reason to infer that it was his impatience of comparative poverty that drove him out there.

" '. . . Who was not his friend who had heard him speak once?' she was saying. 'He drew men towards him by what was best in them.' She looked at me with intensity. 'It is the gift of the great,' she went on, and the sound of her low voice seemed to have the accompaniment of all the other sounds, full of mystery, desolation, and sorrow, I had ever heard—the ripple of the river, the soughing of the trees swayed by the wind, the murmurs of the crowds, the faint ring of incomprehensible words cried from afar, the whisper of a voice speaking from beyond the threshold of an eternal darkness. 'But you have heard him! You know!' she cried.

" 'Yes, I know,' I said with something like despair in my heart, but bowing my head before the faith that was in her, before that great and saving illusion that shone with an unearthly glow in the darkness, in the triumphant darkness from which I could not have defended her—from which I could not even defend myself.

" 'What a loss to me—to us!'—she corrected herself with beautiful generosity; then added in a murmur, 'To the world.' By the last gleams of twilight I could see the glitter of her eyes, full of tears—of tears that would not fall.

" 'I have been very happy—very fortunate—very proud,' she

went on. 'Too fortunate. Too happy for a little while. And now I am unhappy for—for life.'

"She stood up; her fair hair seemed to catch all the remaining light in a glimmer of gold. I rose, too.

" 'And of all this,' she went on, mournfully, 'of all his promise, and of all his greatness, of his generous mind, of his noble heart, nothing remains—nothing but a memory. You and I—'

" 'We shall always remember him,' I said, hastily.

" 'No!' she cried. 'It is impossible that all this should be lost —that such a life should be sacrificed to leave nothing—but sorrow. You know what vast plans he had. I knew of them, too —I could not perhaps understand—but others knew of them. Something must remain. His words, at least, have not died.'

" 'His words will remain,' I said.

" 'And his example,' she whispered to herself. 'Men looked up to him—his goodness shone in every act. His example—'

" 'True,' I said; 'his example, too. Yes, his example. I forgot that.'

" 'But I do not. I cannot—I cannot believe—not yet. I cannot believe that I shall never see him again, that nobody will see him again, never, never, never.'

"She put out her arms as if after a retreating figure, stretching them black and with clasped pale hands across the fading and narrow sheen of the window. Never see him! I saw him clearly enough then. I shall see this eloquent phantom as long as I live, and I shall see her, too, a tragic and familiar Shade, resembling in this gesture another one, tragic also, and bedecked with powerless charms, stretching bare brown arms over the glitter of the infernal stream, the stream of darkness. She said suddenly very low, 'He died as he lived.'

" 'His end,' said I, with dull anger stirring in me, 'was in every way worthy of his life.'

"'And I was not with him,' she murmured. My anger subsided before a feeling of infinite pity.

"'Everything that could be done—' I mumbled.

"'Ah, but I believed in him more than anyone on earth—more
than his own mother, more than—himself. He needed me! Me!
I would have treasured every sigh, every word, every sign, every
glance.'

"I felt like a chill grip on my chest. 'Don't,' I said, in a
muffled voice.

"'Forgive me. I—I have mourned so long in silence—in
silence. . . . You were with him—to the last? I think of his
loneliness. Nobody near to understand him as I would have
understood. Perhaps no one to hear. . . .'

"'To the very end,' I said, shakily. 'I heard his very last
words. . . .' I stopped in a fright.

"'Repeat them,' she murmured in a heart-broken tone. 'I
want—I want—something—something—to—live with.'

"I was on the point of crying at her, 'Don't you hear them?'
The dusk was repeating them in a persistent whisper all around
us, in a whisper that seemed to swell menacingly like the first
whisper of a rising wind. 'The horror! The horror!'

"'His last word—to live with,' she insisted. 'Don't you understand I loved him—I loved him—I loved him!'

"I pulled myself together and spoke slowly.

"'The last word he pronounced was—your name.'

"I heard a light sigh and then my heart stood still, stopped
dead short by an exulting and terrible cry, by the cry of inconceivable triumph and of unspeakable pain. 'I knew it—I was
sure!' . . . She knew. She was sure. I heard her weeping; she
had hidden her face in her hands. It seemed to me that the
house would collapse before I could escape, that the heavens
would fall upon my head. But nothing happened. The heavens
do not fall for such a trifle. Would they have fallen, I wonder,

if I had rendered Kurtz that justice which was his due? Hadn't he said he wanted only justice? But I couldn't. I could not tell her. It would have been too dark—too dark altogether. . . ."

Marlow ceased, and sat apart, indistinct and silent, in the pose of a meditating Buddha. Nobody moved for a time. "We have lost the first of the ebb," said the Director, suddenly. I raised my head. The offing was barred by a black bank of clouds, and the tranquil waterway leading to the uttermost ends of the earth flowed somber under an overcast sky—seemed to lead into the heart of an immense darkness.

NOTES ON AUTHORS

STELLA BENSON (1892-1933)
("Story Coldly Told")

Stella Benson was born in Shropshire, had no formal education, and spent much of her girlhood on the Continent, chiefly in France, Germany, and Switzerland. Before World War I, she was active as a social worker in the East End of London and became an ardent suffragette. After 1918, she traveled extensively in America and the Far East, recording her experiences in two books of essays, *The Little World* (1925) and *Worlds within Worlds* (1929). For some years she lived in Manchuria, where her husband was an officer in the Chinese Customs Service. She wrote novels (among them are *I Pose,* 1915; *This Is the End,* 1917; *Living Alone,* 1919; and *The Faraway Bride,* 1930), poetry, and many short stories, the best of which appear in her *Collected Short Stories* (1936).

ERSKINE CALDWELL (1903-   )
("Daughter")

Erskine Caldwell was born near White Oak, Coweta County, Georgia. His father was a Presbyterian minister; and the family's frequent moving about, together with the experience he later gained in such jobs as farm-hand, cotton-picker, and mill-worker, gave him a first-hand knowledge of the condition of the impoverished southern tenant farmers. In recent years, his concern for these people has led him to wide travel and investigation throughout the South; and in *Tenant Farmer,* a pamphlet published in 1935, and *You Have Seen Their Faces* (1937), he attacked the problem directly. In 1938 he gave a series of lectures on southern tenant farmers at the New School for Social Research, and most of his fiction (*God's Little Acre,* 1933; *Tobacco Road,* 1934; and many short stories, now collected in *Jackpot,* 1940) is devoted to revealing the hopelessness and degradation of their lot. In 1942 he interrupted the sequence by two books on Russia, but since then has published some seven volumes of stories and novels mainly on southern themes.

Anton Pavlovitch Chekhov (1860-1904)

("Gooseberries")

Born in Taganrog, Chekhov was educated as a doctor but retired from his practice after a single year in order to spend the rest of his life writing. His works, except for several novels and a small number of excellent plays, consist mainly of short stories—the form over which he presides as master.

The Chekhovian short story may be described as a completely economical, highly integrated symbolical situation which reveals the "inwardness" of a personality or experience. It lends itself to character analysis—especially to analysis of character in action—a sphere in which Chekhov's ability was very great.

SAMUEL LANGHORNE CLEMENS (MARK TWAIN) (1835-1910)

("The Man That Corrupted Hadleyburg")

Samuel Langhorne Clemens (Mark Twain) was born in Florida, Missouri, and spent most of his boyhood in the river town of Hannibal. His career as business-venturer, river pilot, newspaper reporter, traveler, lecturer, and (lastly and permanently) story-writer and novelist brought him into direct contact with the life of foreign communities and of parts of America as widely separate as New Orleans, San Francisco, and Hartford, Connecticut. "The Man That Corrupted Hadleyburg" is one of his later stories, not forming part of the "regional" tradition of the Mississippi sketches and novels, but pointing toward the more generalized, skeptical approach to human problems that informs his latest (and bitter) works, *What Is Man* and *The Mysterious Stranger*.

———

JOSEPH CONRAD (1857-1924)

("Heart of Darkness")

Joseph Conrad (Józef Teodor Konrad Korzeniowski) was a Pole who became a British subject in 1886. From 1874 to 1894 he followed the sea, and in 1890, two years after obtaining his first command, he spent about six months in the Belgian Congo and made the long inland voyage that provided most of the material for "Heart of Darkness" (1899). Several of his letters from the Congo have survived, among them being one written soon after this voyage. (See *Letters of Joseph Conrad to Marguerite Poradowska*, 1940, edited by J. A. Gee and P. J. Sturm, pp. 15-18.) G. Jean-Aubry, in his *Joseph Conrad in the Congo* (1926), has revealed the extent to which Conrad based this narrative upon actual experience. Conrad later called the development of the Belgian Congo "the vilest scramble for loot that ever disfigured the history of human conscience and geographical exploration."

FYODOR DOSTOEVSKY (1821-1881)

("The Peasant Marey")

When he was twenty-eight and a rising young author, Dostoevsky, together with a number of other young radical intellectuals, was sentenced to four years of hard labor in Siberia. This experience, which we see reflected in "The Peasant Marey," deepened his insight into the nature and problems of those whom he calls in his great novel, *Crime and Punishment,* "suffering humanity," the outcast and the injured. He returned from Siberia more than ever confirmed in the populist, or Slavophile, cause. A recurrent theme in much of his greatest work is that the salvation of mankind lies in the hands of the meek and pure in heart, of whom perhaps his most notable prototypes are Alyosha in *The Brothers Karamazov* and Sonia in *Crime and Punishment.* The peasant Marey is a minor but unforgettable member of this company.

WILLIAM FAIN (1917-   )
("Harmony")

William Fain was born in New York and graduated from
Harvard after going to many schools, some of them in Europe,
where he has lived a good deal of his life. He served in the
Air Force during World War II, before and after which he
worked for newspapers and magazines, notably for the New
York *World-Telegram and Sun* and for the *New Yorker* magazine. His first novel, *The Lizard's Tail,* was published in
1954 by Alfred A. Knopf, and at this writing he has another
one nearly finished.

WILLIAM FAULKNER (1897-   )
("The Bear")

William Faulkner is a native of Mississippi, and his most
notable books (among them are *The Sound and the Fury;
Light in August; Absalom, Absalom;* and *As I Lay Dying*)
have to do with the South. "The Bear," as it appears in the
present volume, was first published in *The Saturday Evening
Post* for May 9, 1942. A much enlarged version of the story
appeared in Faulkner's *Go Down Moses,* also published in 1942.
The story presents to us in brief compass many of the qualities
which distinguish Faulkner's work: the complex almost florid
style, his liberation from accepted models of composition, and
his use of the South as a source of symbols to express his moral
concern over many aspects of modern life.

JEAN GIONO (1895-   )

("The Corn Dies")

Giono is a cobbler's son, born in the Basses Alpes, south-eastern France. In World War I he fought as an ordinary soldier at Verdun and elsewhere, an experience which perhaps formed the grounds of his subsequent hostility, not only to war, but to politics as well. During the past war he was imprisoned by the French for inciting his neighboring peasants to make a stand against military service; he was released during the Occupation.

Among those of his writings which have been translated into English, the novels *Harvest* (1930) and *Song of the World,* (1934) have excited most enthusiasm. In these novels, as in the short story "The Corn Dies," Giono displays a possibly unique talent for simple, luminous revelations of peasant life. He comes as close as anybody has to the kind of writing Tolstoy dreamed of in *What Is Art?,* except that his scope is not merely the peasant's faith, but his whole existence.

Although his novels have had considerable success in this country, he is perhaps best known to the American public through his movie, "The Baker's Wife."

———————

THOMAS HARDY (1840-1928)

("The Three Strangers")

Thomas Hardy incorporated into many of his novels and stories the atmosphere of the Wessex country (the name he used to designate the south-west counties of England, chiefly

Dorset), which pervades "The Three Strangers." He grouped
Wessex Tales (1888), from which this story is taken, with what
he called his "novels of character and environment," the most
famous of them being *The Return of the Native* (1878), *The
Mayor of Casterbridge* (1886), *Tess of the D'Urbervilles* (1891),
and *Jude the Obscure* (1896).

NATHANIEL HAWTHORNE (1804-1864)
("Mr. Higginbotham's Catastrophe")

Nathaniel Hawthorne was deeply rooted in New England by
heritage, birth, upbringing, and (except for travels abroad and
a four-year tenure as consul in Liverpool, 1853-1857) lifelong
residence. He was born in Salem, Massachusetts, went to Bow-
doin College in Brunswick, Maine, and then returned to his
native state to live for many years in Concord. "Mr. Higginbotham's Catastrophe" is one of his early stories and appeared
in his first published collection, *Twice-Told Tales,* in 1837. Together with his other sketches and stories of New England life
done in a light vein, it provides a good counterpoint to the
somber mood and deeper penetration of his great novel, *The
Scarlet Letter* (1850).

ERNEST HEMINGWAY (1898-   )
("In Another Country")

The terse conversation, the ironic humor, the understatement,
and the careful patterning of "In Another Country" are charac-

teristic of much of Hemingway's work (see *The Fifth Column, and the First Forty-nine Stories,* 1938, for his collected short stories). In general, his writing reflects directly his own wide and intense experience. His service with an American ambulance unit in the Italian army during World War I furnished much of the material for *A Farewell to Arms* (1929); and his experience in Spain during the Civil War led to the writing of *The Fifth Column* (1939), a play, and *For Whom the Bell Tolls* (1940), his most recent novel. His firsthand knowledge of post-World War I Paris, bull-fighting, big game hunting, and life on the Florida Keys has all been incorporated, from time to time, in his fiction.

WASHINGTON IRVING (1783-1859)

("The Legend of Sleepy Hollow")

One of the brightest lights in American literature of the early nineteenth century, Washington Irving gave Europe almost its first favorable impression of American culture, especially that of Irving's native state, New York. His writings began to circulate largely in 1807; in 1809 he published *A History of New York,* under the name of Diedrich Knickerbocker; in 1819-1820 he published serially *The Sketch Book of Geoffrey Crayon, Gent.,* from which "The Legend of Sleepy Hollow" has been taken. Irving served as diplomat on various occasions, especially as Minister to Madrid from 1842 to 1846, but he is principally remembered as the author of "The Legend of Sleepy Hollow" and "Rip Van Winkle."

HENRY JAMES (1843-1916)

("The Pupil")

Henry James was born in New York and educated in this country and abroad. In 1875 he settled permanently in England, living in London for some twenty years before he moved to Rye, in Sussex; a year before his death he became a British subject. He retained his interest in America, at least to the point of studying his countrymen in various foreign environments, a theme which is central to many of his best-known novels (*The American,* 1877; *Daisy Miller,* 1879; *Portrait of a Lady,* 1881; *The Golden Bowl,* 1904). The delicate psychological analysis of "The Pupil" (published in *Longman's Magazine,* 1891, and revised for the New York Edition of James's works in 1908) is characteristic of his work. He wrote nearly a hundred short stories, of which perhaps the most famous is the ghost story, *The Turn of the Screw.*

JAMES JOYCE (1882-1941)

broken relations with family ("Clay") *against old nationalism*

James Joyce, a native of Dublin, knew at first-hand the environment which forms the setting of the story, "Clay," and of the other stories in the volume from which it is taken, *Dubliners* (1914). The sharp, objective clarity of *Dubliners* gives way in *A Portrait of the Artist as a Young Man* (1916) to a subjective, psychological treatment of the author's early environment and his revolt from it. Joyce's other novels, *Ulysses* (1920) and *Finnegans Wake* (1939), depart more widely from the conventional form of the early stories, exploring with increasing thoroughness the realm of the subconscious and the possibilities of linguistic invention.

Franz Kafka (1883-1924)
("The Great Wall of China")

Born in Prague and educated for upper middle-class life, Kafka spent his life under the oppressive shadows of a domineering father, psychological insecurity, and tuberculosis. Writing was for him partly an escape and partly an additional compulsion. A few of his works were published during his life; he did not destroy the rest, but requested his friend and eventual editor-biographer, Max Brod, to destroy them after his death, a request which Brod ignored after much pondering. His works consist of novels (among which *The Trial* and *The Castle* are notable), short stories, and various gnomic observations. *The Great Wall of China and Other Pieces* was published in 1931 and translated by Edwin and Willa Muir in 1933. Through these works, Kafka has exerted a somber fascination upon the intellectuals of America and of all Europe.

Thomas Mann (1875-1955)
("Mario and the Magician")

Thomas Mann, whose importance both as an artist and as a force in world opinion was equaled by few contemporary men of letters, was born in Lübeck, Germany. He achieved gradually increasing fame by a series of novels and stories published during the last forty years (*Buddenbrooks,* 1901; *Death in Venice,* 1912; *The Magic Mountain,* 1924; *Mario and the Magician,* 1930; *Young Joseph,* 1935; *Joseph in Egypt,* 1938; *The Beloved Returns,* 1940; *Joseph the Provider,* 1944; and *Doctor Faustus,* 1948). Exiled by the Nazi régime from Germany, he lived for some years in this country and became an American citizen. "Mario and the Magician" expresses the attitude toward human freedom, more fully developed by Mann in the essays and lectures, which resulted in his estrangement from his country. For his other works in the short story form, see his *Stories of Three Decades* (1936), which also includes the longer piece, "Death in Venice."

KATHERINE MANSFIELD (1888-1923)
("A Dill Pickle")

Katherine Mansfield (Katherine Middleton Murry, *née* Katherine Beauchamp) was born in Wellington, New Zealand, and in 1909 went to live in London, where she had attended Queen's College from 1902 to 1906. She published over seventy stories in her brief career and left some fifteen others unfinished at her death. "A Dill Pickle" is characteristic of her interest in psychological situations and of her sharp attention to the significant minute detail. A collected edition of her stories was edited by her husband, J. Middleton Murry, the English critic, in 1937.

HERMAN MELVILLE (1819-1891)

("Bartleby the Scrivener")

"Bartleby the Scrivener" is rare among Melville's stories and novels for its setting in New York City, where he was born and where he worked as customs inspector from 1866 to 1885. He had ample opportunity to observe the city's legal and financial life. "Bartleby" was written during his residence at Pittsfield, Massachusetts, in the years directly following the publication of *Moby Dick* in 1851. In spite of its obvious differences in tone and method from this masterwork, it has unmistakable affinities with it in its unremitting concern for the ambiguities of moral and practical life.

———

FRANK O'CONNOR (1903-   )

("Mac's Masterpiece")

Frank O'Connor is one of a group of Irish writers interested in exploring the Irish character. Educated by the Christian Brothers of Cork, he was encouraged to develop his literary talents by Æ (George Russell, the famous Irish poet and artist) and has long been a member of the Irish Academy of Letters. He has published *Guests of the Nation; Death in Dublin* (1937), the story of Michael Collins and the Irish rebellion; *Dutch Interior* (1940); and about twenty-five other volumes, mainly novels and stories with an Irish setting. His reputation has grown steadily; many now consider him one of the most interesting, as well as most substantial, writers of our time.

———

ALLAN SEAGER (1906-   )

("This Town and Salamanca")

Allan Seager was born in Adrian, Michigan, and educated at the University of Michigan and at Oxford as a Rhodes Scholar. He has done editorial work and is now teaching English at the University of Michigan. "This Town and Salamanca," which was first published in 1934 in *Story Magazine,* was chosen by Edward J. O'Brien for inclusion in *Fifty Best American Stories, 1915-1939* (1939). His other stories include "Pommery 1921," "Fugue for Harmonica," and "Berkshire Comedy." He has also published *They Worked for a Better World* (1939); *Equinox* (1943); and *Inheritance* (1948); his collected stories, *The Old Man of the Mountain* (1950); and *Amos Berry* (1953).

JOHN STEINBECK (1902-   )

("The Leader of the People")

John Steinbeck was born in Salinas, California, went to local schools as a boy, and to Stanford University from 1919 to 1925. He had many odd jobs, mostly on the farm, during his boy-hood; and after he left Stanford, he worked for a while in New York as a reporter. He soon returned to California, was vari-ously employed, and began his career as a writer of fiction. His reputation has steadily increased with *Tortilla Flat* (1935); *Of Mice and Men* (1937); and *The Grapes of Wrath* (1939). In 1938, his short stories were collected in the volume called *The Long Valley,* from which "The Leader of the People" was taken. His principal subsequent publications have been *Cannery*

Row (1944); *The Wayward Bus* and *Pearl* (1947); and *Russian Journal* (1948).

———————

DYLAN THOMAS (1914-1953)

("A Story")

Dylan Thomas was born in South Wales, the son of a schoolmaster, and was educated at Swansea Grammar School. His published poems, stories, and sketches reflect his love for the human and natural richness of his Welsh background. After some earlier, rather mannered sketches, in volumes mainly poetical, he published a book of excellent prose pieces, *Portrait of the Artist as a Young Dog* (1940), followed by the posthumously published *Quite Early One Morning* (1955), from which "A Story" has been taken as a typical example of his extraordinary linguistic virtuosity. By the time of his death, at the age of thirty-nine, he had already established himself as one of the leading poets in the English-speaking world.